The Geology of Europe

The Geology of Europe

Derek V. Ager

University College, Swansea

McGRAW-HILL Book Company (UK) Limited

London · New York · St Louis · San Francisco · Auckland · Bogotá · Guatemala · Hamburg · Johannesburg · Lisbon · Madrid · Mexico · Montreal · New Delhi · Panama · Paris · San Juan · São Paulo · Singapore · Sydney · Tokyo · Toronto

Published by
McGRAW-HILL Book Company (UK) Limited
MAIDENHEAD . BERKSHIRE . ENGLAND

British Library Cataloguing in Publication Data

Ager, Derek Victor
 The geology of Europe.
 1. Geology—Europe
 I. Title
 554   QE260   80-40318

 ISBN 0-07-084115-2

12345 MPMP 83210

Typeset by Santype International Limited and
printed and bound in the United States by Maple Press Company, Pennsylvania.

For my many geological friends who live between the Atlantic Ocean and the Urals, between the Arctic Ocean and the Sahara.

Contents

Preface

I wrote this book for anyone who is interested in the geological history of this wonderful continent. All they need is a little basic knowledge of the subject and a lot of enthusiasm. The book can be used for advanced courses in geology (or geography); it can be used by any European going to a new area who wants the basic facts; it can be used by our friends from other continents (and I have drawn parallels with North America in particular); and I hope it can just be read for itself.

It is Europe as seen by a stratigrapher–palaeontologist. I do not pretend to dig deep into the geometry of fold belts or into the wealth of geophysical data. I am concerned primarily with geology as it can be seen and as I have seen it myself.

The discoveries of residual magnetism in rocks sent the continents scuttling about the earth's surface in past geological time, and dismembered Palaeozoic and pre-Palaeozoic Europe so that it is hardly recognizable. The revolution of plate tectonics set people theorizing about plate margins at various moments in European history with hypothetical oceans that have since disappeared and sutures where one plate allegedly drove under another. I regard some of these ideas with scepticism; some of the reconstructions make absolute nonsense of my kind of evidence.

I do not decry the hurricane of fresh air that these new geophysical thoughts breathed into our subject. Some of us were enthusiastic about continental drift when the geophysicists said it was impossible! But the pendulum has swung too far and I think it is time to look again at some of the basic geological facts.

In this book I have dealt with Europe systematically, in the way that I see it, region by region. I would draw attention particularly to the summaries—Chapters 4, 7, 12, and 17, plus perhaps 15(f)—in which I try to draw the threads together. No continent is more complex geologically, politically, and culturally than Europe. For the Carpathian chain alone there is geological literature in ten languages and the structure passes through six different countries. My generalizations may be outrageous at times, my ignorance may show through in places, and there is, I am well aware, the risk of superficiality. But I did not want to produce three massive volumes that no one would read. I believe it a good thing for students and geologists to see the geological wood as well as the specialist trees.

Nothing could be easier for the reader than to tear apart my version of those little pieces of our continent which he happens to know best. All I ask is that he should consider what I have tried to do and the limitations within which I have worked. *First*, I have tackled the whole of Europe as a natural entity, not just those parts of it that happen to be geographically convenient. *Second*, I have tried to present a balanced picture of the history of the different parts of Europe, which is not just a bundle of fold belts as some would have us believe. Even without the East European Platform, the continent is just about evenly divided between mountain chains and sedimentary basins. *Third*, to keep the book within readable proportions and to a reasonable price, the publishers and I agreed a strict length limitation. Anything omitted could only have been put in at the expense of something else. *Fourth*, there are limitations on what it is possible for one man to do (especially one who is basically a stratigrapher-palaeontologist). No doubt there is a bias towards the later part of the story and perhaps the resolution of my spy-glass diminishes the farther away I point it from the offshore islands on which I live.

I have tried to see everything for myself. Until you have agonized over half-a-dozen passes in the Pindus, you do not really comprehend the immense thicknesses of flysch and radiolarites in that trough. Until you have spent days looking for non-existent exposures in Aquitaine, you do not fully appreciate the complete dependence on bore-holes in that region.

It would be presumptuous of me to pretend that I know more about a particular part of our continent than specialists who have devoted their lives to its study. I cannot resist commenting on things which seem obvious to me, or which have particularly caught my fancy, but as a rule I have relied heavily on the latest synthesis when available. If you disagree with me, you may be disagreeing with my summaries of summaries: disagreeing with the 'received' opinion of an outsider—from impressions gained from the literature or from a persuasive director in the field.

I have for the most part omitted the brief complexities of the Quarternary glaciations of Europe. These, along with human history, are but the latest moments in the long record of our continent and are best dealt with elsewhere. I have played down the geophysics, partly through ignorance but largely because the evidence is capable of so many different interpretations. I am concerned basically with what I can and have seen. I have tried to tell the reader where he can easily see the same. I try to concentrate on the evidence rather than summarize the theories.

If there are blatant errors, please let me know gently; I am a sensitive soul. Better still, invite me over to see the truth for myself!

In reading the literature I am constantly demoralized by jargon, only to find that the ideas hidden behind it are basically quite simple. There are very few things in geology that cannot be expressed in simple English. A handful of terms and the stratigraphical table which is provided seem enough to me.

I have used what seem to be the lastest standard spellings of place-names, whether they be Welsh or Georgian, and I have mostly used English versions of the names of regions. I felt, however, that it would be an inverted affectation to call the Massif Central the 'Central Massif' or the Rheinisches Schiefergebirge the 'Rhine Slate Mountains'. I have tried to use the names most familiar to English readers. I hesitated over the Schwarzwald, but had no doubts whatever over the Góry Swiętokrzyskie! Where in our troubled continent the present official name is different from that by which a place is better known, I have given both versions the first time it occurs.

References are given to works in languages other than English only when they are of outstanding importance or no relevant English work is available. This is not insularity but is a compromise between usefulness and length. No attempt is made to provide more than a few recent references for each chapter.

So much confusion has been caused by American and British billions and by abbreviations such as m.y., my, m.a., and Ma that I make no apology for using 'million years' every time. My basic aim throughout has been to avoid confusion and to be readable.

I often find myself apologizing for light-heartedness in my scientific writing. I don't know why I should! As Oscar Wilde might have said: geology is too important a matter to take it seriously. I enjoy geology and I enjoy Europe. To wrap it all up in solemnity and to ignore all the other wonderful (and tragic) things that have happened in our continent takes away from me half the fun and glory. If I slip in the odd adjective, or the odd aside, it is because they make it all 'come alive' to me and, in many years' teaching, to my students. If I call the Valle d'Aosta 'noisy', it is because I once spent a sleepless night camping there, listening to the roar of the traffic and the torrent, the barking of dogs, and the voluble vivacity of the Italians. If I associate Salzburg with Mozart it is because he is to me one of the two greatest Europeans and I think he deserves mention.

Acknowledgements

A large section of the third part of this book was originally written, in a much more thorough way, by my former colleague, Peigi Wallace of Imperial College. As our styles and approaches were very different, we eventually decided that I should rewrite these parts in my own way, although inevitably I depended very much on what she had summarized so ably. I am extremely grateful to Dr Wallace for allowing me to use her work and for the many useful discussions we have had on various aspects of this book. She very kindly read and criticized the whole text, but I would not wish to blame my sins of omission, over-simplification, and plain ignorance on her or anyone else.

I offer my sincere thanks to Jose Nuttall, Viv Jenkins, and Diana Viggers who typed the text, and to John Edwards and Alan Smith who produced the originals of the text figures, often from most inadequate originals. Jane Fletcher helped with many of the final stages of the work.

My travels in every European country (with the one regrettable exception of Albania) have extended over several decades and I would like to record the many enjoyable and instructive days I have spent on the fields, cliffs, and mountains with scores of geological friends. In many regions I have wandered with the literature and my own ignorance, but I must mention Anton Ruttner and Benno Plöchinger in Austria; Ivo Sapunov and Platon Tchoumatchenko in Bulgaria; Eva Hanzlíková and Miloš Siblik in Czechoslovakia; Tove Birkelund and Wienberg Rasmussen in Denmark; Daniel Laurentiaux and Georges Lienhardt in France; Josef Fulop and Gustav Vigh in Hungary; Augusto Azzaroli and Maurizio Gaetani in Italy; Marian Książkiewicz and Krzysztof Birkenmajer in Poland; Dan Patrulius in Romania; Vladimir Menner and Achil Tzagareli in the Soviet Union; Kemal Erguvanli in Turkey; and many others, including fine geologists and friends who, alas, have now followed their structures up to heaven.

I also pay tribute to many colleagues and students who explored with me various parts of this fascinating continent, and all the airline and railway officials, garage mechanics, hotel and camping site staff, policemen, and passers-by who helped me travel around the thirty or so countries of Europe with an inadequate knowledge of its babel of languages.

Most of all, I thank that wonderful fraternity and sorority of geologists, only very few of whom I can mention here, but who are always hospitable and always willing to demonstrate their favourite rocks and to discuss them (and everything else) over a good meal and excellent wine.

Geologists are the best of ambassadors. They are not restricted to diplomatic circles, like a country's official representatives, or to the bars of a capital, like journalists. They go where they go because of the chances of uncovering geological history, not because the localities are show-places. They meet normal people (in so far as geologists are normal). They see men at work in mines and quarries, forests and farms, and can judge the realities of life for themselves.

I despise narrow nationalism and all the religious and political bigotry that has brought so much suffering to Europe, but I am proud of a supernationalism that glories in all that Europe has given to the world in music, art, literature and, of course, in geology.

Derek Ager

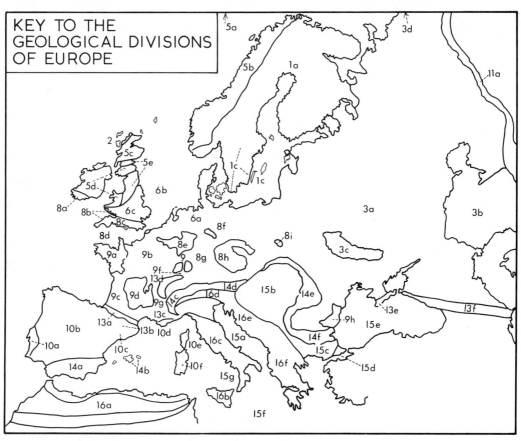

KEY TO THE
GEOLOGICAL DIVISIONS
OF EUROPE

Geological divisions of Europe used in this book. For key see contents list. (After Ager, 1975, by kind permission of the Council of Geologists' Association.)

Stratigraphical table

Stratigraphical divisions used in this book. It is well understood that there are many other names and usages, and that nothing arouses more controversy in geology than stratigraphical nomenclature, but I have included *what seem to me* to be the 'standard' usages and *what seem to me* to be the most commonly used alternatives. The Precambrian names are so different in content and meaning from the others that it is almost pointless to include them here.

Systems	Series and/or stages		*Approximate equivalence of other terms in regular use*	
	Holocene	Versilian		
QUATERNARY (Anthropogene)	Pleistocene	Tyrrhenian U. Milazzian Sicilian		
		L. Emilian Calabrian		
1.8 million years			Villafranchian Astian	Pontian
	Pliocene	Piacenzian Zanclean	Pannonian	
NEOGENE	Miocene	U. Messinian Tortonian	Helvetian	Sarmatian
		M. Serravallian Langhian	Vindobonian	
22.5 million years		L. Burdigalian Aquitanian		
	Oligocene	U. Chattian L. Rupelian	Stampian	Sannoisian
		U. Bartonian (Priabonian)	Ludian Marinesian Auversian	Lattorfian
PALAEOGENE	Eocene	M. Lutetian	Wemmelian Ledian Bruxellian	Biarritzian
		L. Ypresian	Cuisian Sparnacian	
		U. Thanetian	Landenian	
65 million years	Paleocene	L. Montian Danian		

Left margin labels: CAINOZOIC, TERTIARY

Systems	Series and/or stages		Approximate equivalence of other terms in regular use		

MESOZOIC

Systems		Series and/or stages	Approximate equivalence

CRETACEOUS

U.
- Maastrichtian
- Campanian
- Santonian
- Coniacian
- Turonian
- Cenomanian

Senonian } Emscherian

——— Vraconian

L.
- Albian
- Aptian
- Barremian
- Hauterivian
- Valanginian
- Berriasian

Urgonian

Neocomian
  Ryazanian

141 million years   Purbeckian

JURASSIC

U. (Malm)
- Volgian — Tithonian / Virgulian / Pterocerian — Portlandian
- Kimmeridgian — Sequanian
- Oxfordian — Rauracian — Corallian / Lusitanian
  Argovian

M. (Dogger)
- Callovian
- Bathonian — Vesulian
- Bajocian
- Aalenian

L. (Lias)
- Toarcian
- Pliensbachian — Charmouthian
- Sinemurian — Lotharingian
- Hettangian

195 million years

TRIASSIC

U.
- Rhaetian
- Norian — (Keuper)
- Carnian

M.
- Ladinian — (Muschelkalk)
- Anisian

L.
- Scythian (Werfenian) — Olenekian / Induan — (Bunter)

230 million years

	Systems		Series and/or stages	*Approximate equivalence of other terms in regular use*		
PALAEOZOIC / UPPER	PERMIAN		U. Tartarian / Kazanian	Thuringian	(Zechstein)	
	280 million years		L. Kungurian / Artinskian / Sakmarian / Asselian	Saxonian / Baigendzinian	(Rotliegendes)	
	CARBONIFEROUS	U. (Silesian)	Stephanian	Uralian	Orenburgian / Gzhelian / Kasimovian	'U'
			Westphalian / Namurian	Moscovian / Bashkirian		'M'
	345 million years	L. (Dinantian)	Visean / Tournaisian	Serpukhovian		
	DEVONIAN		U. Famennian / Frasnian	Strunian		
			M. Givetian / Couvinian	Eifelian		
	395 million years		L. Emsian / Siegenian / Gedinnian	Lochkovian	Coblencian	
PALAEOZOIC / LOWER	SILURIAN (GOTHLANDIAN)		U. Ludlow / Wenlock	Přidolian / Downtonian / (Middle Silurian)		
	435 million years		L. Llandovery	Valentian		
	ORDOVICIAN		U. Ashgill / Caradoc		(Middle Ordovician)	
	500 million years		L. Llandeilo / Llanvirn / Arenig / Tremadocian	Canadian		
	CAMBRIAN		U.	Potsdamian		
			M.	Acadian		
	570 million years		L. Elankian / Botomian / Atdabanian / Tommotian	Georgian		

	Systems	Series and/or stages		Approximate equivalence of other terms in regular use	
PRECAMBRIAN		U. { Varegian	Eocambrian	Torridonian	Vendian
		{ Jotnian	Riphean 1100 million years		Brioverian
	PROTEROZOIC	M. Gothian	Laxfordian 1800 million years		
		L. Svecofennian Inverian (Karelian)		Lewisian	Pentevrian
	260 million years				
	ARCHAEAN	Belomorian	Scourian		
		Saamian			

Introduction

The General Structure of Europe

Europe was the birthplace of geology and the continent where the main features of the geological record were first worked out. This happened because of the accident of human history that brought together the right level of civilization and the right men at the right time, and because of the accident of geological history that brought about the great diversity of rocks in Europe which gave those men their opportunity. Like so many other features of recent human history, geology grew out of the industrial revolution which, in itself, was fundamentally a geological matter.

Geographically, Europe is no more than a peninsula projecting from the continent of Asia, but there is a fantastic variety of rocks and structures exposed at the surface within this comparatively small area. We may contrast it with the geological monotony of great areas of the Canadian Shield or the Central Stable Region of North America. Only in the extreme east of Europe—on the Russian plains—do we find a comparable situation in Europe.

Although but an appendage of Asia, Europe is in fact a very real and separate geological entity and always seems to have been so, in spite of the palaeomagnetists. It will be argued that parts of the extreme north-west are more American than European in geological character and history. Some would slice off a fair chunk of the 'soft underbelly of Europe' and make it part of the African plate. Others would argue that the extreme north-west corner of Africa is, geologically, Europe. It would be misleading to omit anything that is Europe in the strictly political sense (with the exception of Iceland and the other Atlantic islands which are part of the ocean rather than the continent). In addition the Atlas ranges of Morocco, Algeria, and Tunisia and all that lies north of them are briefly included since they connect directly with the structures of southern Spain and Italy. We are therefore left with the natural boundaries of the European continent as the Atlantic in the west, the Urals and the Caspian Depression in the east, the Arctic Ocean in the north, and the Sahara in the south. That should be enough for a book of this size.

The complexity of Europe makes it particularly necessary to divide it into manageable units. This can be done in several different ways, none of them completely satisfactory. Clearly, political divisions are of no use to us, even though these human fictions are more commonly related to geological realities in Europe than anywhere else in the world. Thus

Italy and Hungary have some geological meaning, but most of the borders of Yugoslavia and East Germany have none.

One could use a purely historical approach, but that would relate to continuous time rather than the distinct regions in which I am interested. What is more, even in well-studied Europe there is still much that is inadequately dated, so a purely historical approach can only produce a confused picture or a spuriously accurate one. One still cannot, for example, produce a meaningful synthesis of the European Cambrian.

Physiographical units are somewhat better. These are the natural regions which represent the surface expression of the geological record. But these too are misleading since they place undue emphasis on the latest events. For example, the south-west peninsula of England (Cornubia) and southern England generally (Wessex and the Weald) are quite different physiographically: the former ruggedly composed of ancient rocks, the latter gently covered with geologically modern sediments. But from deep borings and geophysical evidence we know that the two areas are quite comparable. Similarly, one of the most startling facts to the beginner in English geology is that Devonian rocks can be found *in situ* less than 300 metres from central London—straight down—whereas one has to go about 100 miles to see them at the surface. This relates to the fact that one of the major geological boundaries of Europe passes through the apparently dull geology of the Thames Basin.

Nevertheless, we clearly cannot ignore the obvious physiographical features of Europe—the modern mountains, the ancient massifs, and so on—and they must form an essential part of our framework.

In the simplest possible physiographical terms, Europe may be divided into four regions (Fig. 0.1):

1. The North-west Highlands, comprising most of Scandinavia and the north-west part of the British Isles. This region is composed mainly of rugged country formed of complexly folded and faulted Precambrian and Palaeozoic rocks.
2. The Great North European Plain, extending from the Aquitaine Basin and eastern England right across Europe to the Russian steppes. The whole area between Wales and the Urals is geologically monotonous at the surface, since it is smothered by great thicknesses of Mesozoic and Cainozoic sediments.
3. The Old Massifs, which are isolated, uplifted blocks such as the Massif Central of France, the Black Forest in Germany, and the Bohemian Massif in Czechoslovakia. They are composed predominantly of Precambrian and Palaeozoic rocks showing complex structures.
4. The Alpine Mountains, those great arcs of geologically modern (mostly Tertiary) mountain ranges in southern Europe extending from southern Spain and north-west Africa to the Caucasus. Their structures are extremely complex and involve major thrusts.

The above four divisions, together with the modern seas and river systems, are the most obvious physiographic features of Europe. But such a classification is obviously very naive geologically.

Alternatively, and much more satisfactorily, one can divide Europe on the basis of the orogenic events which have affected it through geological time (Fig. 0.2). This was the classic approach of Stille, who claimed the progressive building-up of the continent as a

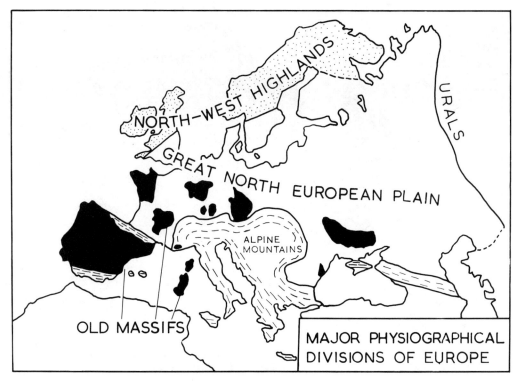

Fig. 0.1 Major physiological divisions of Europe.

series of orogenic belts. The approach is not quite as simplistic as it sounds, for no one was more aware than Stille of the multiplicity of phases within each orogeny. It has been updated in the light of later thought, but Stille's four basic divisions are still usable today. Each is defined by its last phase of major tectonism. It does not imply a progressive accretion of our continent, but merely the stages at which stability was achieved.

Stille's divisions were called Eo-Europa,* Palaeo-Europa, Meso-Europa, and Neo-Europa. *These refer to the age of the last major orogenic event affecting the rocks of the region concerned.* This has been misunderstood by several committees (but committees are often stupid), it has been misunderstood by an anonymous reviewer of this book, and it was misunderstood by some of the most eminent continental geologists when we organized a meeting on this theme at Reading in 1975.

Thus Palaeo-Europa, for example, refers to those parts of Europe which were not affected by major orogenesis after the end of the early Palaeozoic. It does *not* refer to all those areas of Europe afflicted by real or imagined Caledonian orogenies. Similarly Meso-Europa does not refer to the Mesozoic rocks of Europe, beautiful though they are. It refers to those areas that have not been affected by severe tectonism since the beginning of the Mesozoic Era.

---

*He called it 'Ur-Europa', but I find this aesthetically unpleasant, besides being at variance with the Greek prefixes of the others. I have therefore followed the more common later usage.

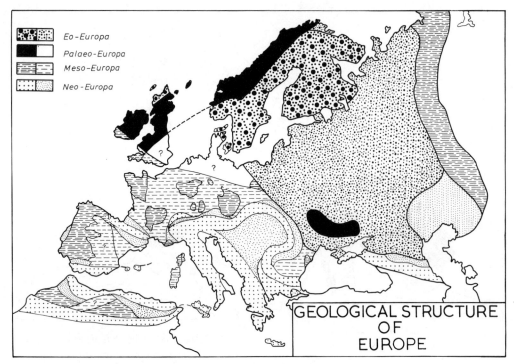

Fig. 0.2 Tectonic divisions of Europe (modified after Stille, 1924).

This approach has two great advantages: first, it fits the facts, whatever explanation you may later put on them; secondly, in spite of the misunderstandings, it is simple and straightforward. We may argue for generations whether some of those nasty messed-up Palaeozoic rocks of southern Europe were or were not affected by a 'Caledonian orogeny'. No one, so far as I know, has ever suggested that the 'Old Red Sandstone' basins of Scotland or the Tertiary sediments of the Paris Basin were ever affected by major movements.

What theories you like to include with these observations is another matter. Stille thought in terms of simultaneous orogenic phases and the progressive accretion of the continent. By using his factual classification I am not necessarily accepting his highly hypothetical deductions. In fact, I do not, nor do I accept a lot of other theories either, such as the one that makes every threadbare patch in the carpet a micro-continent. So these ideas, which are beyond even my unscientific imagination, should not be attributed to me.

Let us consider each of the four great divisions in turn.

Eo-Europa. This is the old Precambrian complex of northern Europe—the Fenno-Scandian Shield with its platform extension under Russia and Poland, together with the small separate region on the west coast of Scotland and in the Hebrides. It was affected by many orogenic episodes during the Precambrian and its earliest rocks may have no particular relationships to any entity we now call Europe. It records by far the greater part of European history, but is proportionately the least well known. The essential

4

feature of this region is that it has not been affected by orogenic movements since the end of Precambrian times. It does *not* mean that there are not Precambrian rocks or orogenies recorded anywhere else, but only that elsewhere they were also involved in later mountain-building episodes.

Palaeo-Europa. This is the mainly mountainous region of north-west Europe, where Precambrian and Lower Palaeozoic rocks were affected by the Caledonian orogeny, but late Palaeozoic rocks are either flat-lying or only gently folded. The north-east trending folds and thrusts of Norway, Scotland, north-west England, most of Wales, and much of Ireland were produced at this time. There have been lengthy arguments about the age of the movements and metamorphism. The orogeny is usually thought of as reaching its maximum at the end of the Silurian, but there were movements as early as the Cambrian with a major spasm in mid to late Ordovician times. It lingered on into the Devonian to merge with the early phases of the Variscan orogeny which followed.

Meso-Europa. This division occupies much of the 'middle' part of Europe and is characterized by flat-lying Mesozoic and Tertiary sediments resting on strongly folded rocks up to and including late Palaeozoic systems. The dividing line between this and Palaeo-Europa is quite clearly defined. It passes through southern Ireland, cutting off the old south-western province of Munster, and it passes north of Pembrokeshire in South Wales and then via the University College of Swansea, south of Bristol and under London to enter the continent along the south side of the Brabant Massif. South of the continuation of that line lie most of the massifs and the lowlands in between, extending from the Iberian Massif round the outside of the Alps and Carpathians as far as Dobrogea at the mouth of the Danube. The Ural Mountains of the Soviet Union and their extension in Novaya Zemlya may also be included here, although they are strictly a separate structural province on the other side of the East European Platform. The dominant folding in Meso-Europa is Variscan in age; this started during the early Carboniferous and reached a crescendo in the late Carboniferous and early Permian. Thereafter the diminuendo of the later Permian and Triassic periods led directly into the next orogeny.

Neo-Europa. This constitutes the Alpine fold belts of southern Europe with the main folding and thrusting in Cretaceous to mid Tertiary times. Only Neogene and later sediments are comparatively undisturbed, as in the great Pannonian Basin of Hungary and adjacent countries. The dividing line between this and Meso-Europa may be defined as the front edge of intense Alpine movements. This is usually very obvious topographically, for the Alpine mountains are the dominating feature of the European landscape, from the Betic Cordillera in southern Spain to the Caucasus in southern Russia. The Alpine movements began in the Triassic, but reached their climax first in mid Cretaceous times and then in the mid Tertiary. Miocene sediments were locally involved in the later phases of the orogeny and the last push usually carried the frontal ranges over Neogene deposits. Further movements, especially isostatic uplift, continued into the Quaternary.

A large part of Europe is classified herein as Neo-Europa; this includes a number of different mountain chains with rather different tectonic and sedimentary histories. Also included in this region are the troughs in front of the Alpine mountains, the ancient massifs in their cores, and the intermontane basins filled with thick Neogene sediments.

The above major divisions, and the smaller divisions within them, are by no means perfect, and include obvious anomalies, but it seems to be the most workable method by which a regional approach (which was the original intention of this book) can be combined with an evolutionary approach for the continent as a whole. It is but a classification and like all classifications it is an artificial, pragmatic thing, intended mainly for the convenience of the reader.

It is tempting to erect further divisions beyond those of Stille—'Actuo-Europa' perhaps—for the areas where the plates are still grinding together, but unless we think the Alpine orogeny has ended and a new one started, these are logically still part of Neo-Europa. Certainly the long history of Europe has not yet ended. Sedimentation and volcanism continue, even in some of the most ancient parts of our continent, and one can envisage yet another division—'Parona-Europa'—concerning the Europe of the future, even further from America and closer to Africa, with new mountain ranges in the Mediterranean, with major marine transgressions covering the worn-down stumps of the Alps, and with our beautiful continent as active and exciting as ever.

General References

Ager, D. V. (1975), 'The geological evolution of Europe', *Proc. Geol. Assoc.*, **86**, 127–154.

Ager, D. V. and M. Brooks, eds. (1976), *Europe from Crust to Core*, Wiley, London, 202 pp.

Anderson, J. G. C. (1978), *The Structure of Western Europe*, Pergamon, Oxford, 250 pp.

Brinkmann, R. (1960), *Geologic Evolution of Europe*, Enke, Stuttgart, 161 pp. (translated from German).

Gignoux, M. (1955), *Stratigraphic Geology*, Freeman, San Francisco, 659 pp. (and five earlier editions in French).

Lemoine, M., ed. (1978), *Geological Atlas of Alpine Europe and Adjoining Alpine Areas*, Elsevier, Amsterdam, 584 pp.

Lobeck, A. K. (1951), 'Physiographic diagram of Europe', Geographical Press, New York, 1 sheet.

Rutten, M. G. (1969), *The Geology of Western Europe*, Elsevier, Amsterdam, 520 pp.

Stille, H. (1924), *Grundfragen der vergleichenden Tektonik*, Borntraeger, Berlin, 443 pp.

Von Bubnof, S. (1926–36), *Geologie von Europa*, 4 vols, Borntraeger, Berlin, 1922 pp.

Ziegler, P. A. (1978), 'North-western Europe: tectonics and basin development', *Geol. Mijnb.* **57**, 589–626.

Zwart, H. J. and U. F. Dornsiepen (1978), 'The tectonic framework of central and western Europe', *Geol. Mijnb.*, **57**, 627–654.

Part One

Eo-Europa

That part of Europe which has not suffered major tectonism since the end of Precambrian times

Chapter One

Fenno-Scandian Shield

The Fenno-Scandian Shield is defined here as that region of ancient, mostly Precambrian rocks between the front of the Scandinavian Caledonides in the west and the continuous cover of the East European Platform in the east. The term is preferred to 'Baltic Shield' since most of the southern Baltic is, in fact, Platform, while westwards the shield extends through southern Norway to the Atlantic.

1(a) Precambrian Basement

This section concerns all those Precambrian rocks in the shield area which are at the surface at the present time and which have been virtually undisturbed since the end of Precambrian times. The shield occupies the whole of Finland, most of Sweden, a large part of southern Norway (including a strip in the north), and the north-west corner of the Soviet Union. It is not implied that the rocks here are fundamentally different from those hidden under younger sediments of the East European Platform or from those that appear at the surface again in the Ukraine, but it is by far the largest and best known area of Precambrian rocks in the continent.

One can say that this is the core of Europe, although this does not mean accepting the concept of a continent growing by accretion. That idea is hardly acceptable in view of the general pattern of Precambrian rocks throughout the continent, but it is only here that they have remained stable and untectonized since the beginning of Palaeozoic times.

It is a bleak, unfriendly land for most of the year, to those of us from softer latitudes, and presents a paradoxical combination of the oldest and the youngest geological phenomena—the Precambrian orogenies and the Pleistocene glaciations. From the air (especially over Finland) it seems to consist mostly of water—just innumerable lakes scattered through the unending fir and birch forests of a monotonous plain. It is a region of immense problems for the specialist geologist and one in which I have no real scientific right to set foot. In this chapter my generalizations are likely to be even more outrageous than those elsewhere in this book, and to my critics I can only use Dr Johnson's most disarming response to correction: 'Ignorance, madam, pure ignorance!'

These complexly metamorphosed rocks are only now being sorted out into a coherent story, thanks to modern ideas about metamorphism and tectonics, and to radiometric dating. That is not to say that this region is not well known geologically in so far as the poor degree of exposure will allow; it has some of the greatest mineral wealth and mineral exploitation in the continent.

The divisions that have been proposed for the Fenno-Scandian Shield are many and contradictory, but the following seem to be the ones most commonly used today:

	minimum age in millions of years
Lower Palaeozoic	
Jotnian	600
Dalslandian	1000
Gothides	1300
Svecofennides (including Karelides)	1800
Belomorides	2000
Saamides (including Pregothides)	2500
? Katarchaean	3000

The very generalized distribution of these is shown in Fig. 1.1.

We are clearly dealing with a time-scale inconceivably longer than the comparatively petty detail that concerns most of the rest of this book, but the degree of knowledge is inversely proportional to the time-span. Real advances were only made in the understanding of the Fenno-Scandian Shield when geologists broke away from the naive idea that increasing metamorphism went with increasing age. This was replaced by the approach of recognizing successive orogenic episodes, often superimposed one on another. Later this was helped and largely confirmed by radiometric dating. The above table indicates the orogenic 'cycles' now recognized. The '-ides' endings, however, also indicate that we are dealing with areas of ground where the rocks concerned actually appear at the surface. Many of the rocks were probably formed at the bottom of the crust or in the upper mantle and at a time when our normal uniformitarian principles, based on the crust as we know it today, did not apply. The older rocks here show a style of plastic folding unknown in younger orogenic cycles.

Saamides

These are the truly Archaean rocks of Europe. The main Saamides belt extends from the south side of Varanger fjord in the north-east corner of Norway into the Kola Peninsula of Russia, which projects eastwards from the north end of Scandinavia, and to an area around Lake Onega (Onezhskoye) in southern Karelia, north-east of Leningrad. It should be emphasized, however, that rocks of several cycles are exposed in this belt and the truly Saamide rocks are only seen locally.

The metamorphic rocks of the cycle include possible gneissose and granitic relicts of yet older cycles, probably more than 3000 million years old, which are sometimes referred to as the 'Katarchaean'. Dates as old as 3500 million years have been recorded

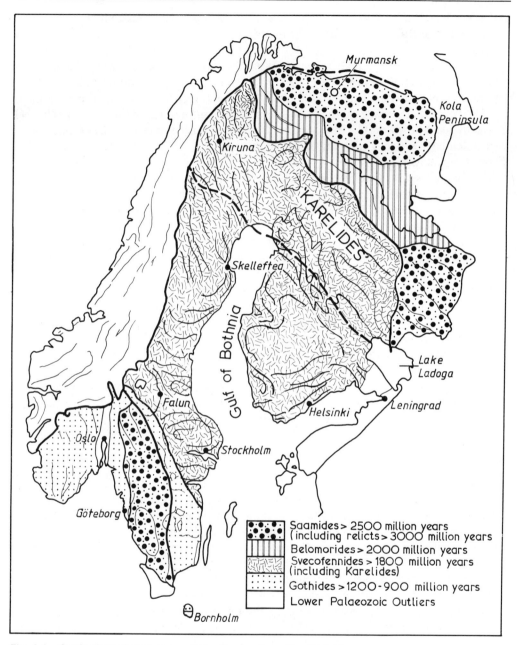

Fig. 1.1   Geological sketch-map of the Fenno-Scandian Shield.

and there have been two distinct episodes of granitic emplacement. Much greater ages recorded by the Russians on particular minerals have now been corrected by whole-rock analyses.

There is another belt of high-grade gneisses in the south of Sweden which have yielded dates of about 2500 million years. These form the north and south shores of Lake Vänern and reach the west coast south of Göteborg (Gothenburg). They finally disappear under the Palaeozoic and Mesozoic rocks of Skåne at the southern tip of the country. This belt is usually just known as the 'Pregothides', but that is misleading since the Gothian was a very much later orogeny. Besides the usual gneisses, they include charnockites and intrusions of olivine gabbro.

The Saamides are, in effect, a series of ovoid masses of Archaean rocks which are scattered through Eo-Europa generally, like plums in a Proterozoic pudding. They appear again at the surface in the Ukrainian Massif and more than twenty have been recognized altogether, mostly hidden beneath the Phanerozoic sediments of the East European Platform. They all exceed 2500 or 2600 million years in age and are mainly composed of granites, gneisses, and low-pressure granulites. Associated metamorphosed sediments, however, imply a yet older crust from which they were derived. There are also volcanic rocks (now amphibolites) and the first of many famous Precambrian iron-ores at Olenegorsk in the Kola Peninsula and north of Lane Vänern in the 'Pregothide' belt. Although it falls within the main Saamide belt in Fig. 1.1, the banded iron-ore mined around much-bombed Kirkenes, at the easternmost extremity of Norway, is later in age. It belongs to a succession resting unconformably upon the oldest suite.

All the Saamide rocks are in a medium or high metamorphic grade and there is a noteworthy lack of greenstone belts and of anorthosites such as are well known in other Archaean terrains. Anorthosites and higher pressure granulites do occur, for example, in the Lewisian of the Hebridean Province described below.

Belomorides

The Belomorides (or Byelomorides or Marealbides) outcrop along the south-west coast of the White Sea, to which their various names refer.* Their north-west trend sets a pattern to be followed by later belts as does their position on the south-west flank of their predecessor. It is hardly surprising that such a distribution made some geologists think of lateral accretion in the build-up of the core of the European continent, although from the scatter of such 'cores' across the East European Platform generally (as on a much bigger scale on the Canadian Shield) this simplistic interpretation is clearly not adequate.

Radiometric ages of about 2000 million years suggest that the Belomorides belong either to the very late Archaean or to the early Proterozoic. However, other dates of 2600 to 2800 million years suggest that they might be much older and the lateral equivalents of the Saamides, just as the later Karelides are interpreted as the lateral equivalents of the Svecofennides. In general terms they are similar, but the Belomorides include very important granulites—the Lapland granulites—which have been interpreted as representing a major suture that has been compared with the Limpopo Belt of southern Africa

---

* In south-east Europe 'White Sea'—again in various languages—refers to the Aegean, in contradistinction to the Black Sea.

(which also cuts across an Archaean shield). These pale garnetiferous rocks are by far the most distinctive and characteristic elements within the cycle. They pass right through the country of the multinational Lapps, trending in a clearly north-westerly direction. They are last seen in the poorly exposed river terrace country along the Tana river where it forms the frontier between Finland and Norway and disappears under the Caledonian front, almost exactly at right angles, near the Lapp village of Levajok (Laevvajok).

The Belomoride belt just invades the southern edge of the Kola Peninsula. Also in this region there are representatives of some of the later units which are better discussed below.

Svecofennides

Rocks of this cycle occupy the greater part of Sweden and Finland, as their name implies. They extend into the old province of Karelia, beloved of Sibelius but now in the Soviet Union, before disappearing beneath the Palaeozoic sediments of the platform. This vast area includes the Lapland plateau in the north, the Swedish highlands to the west, and the Finnish plain. It also includes the main mineral wealth of those two countries.

We are now definitely in the Proterozoic. Radiometric ages for Svecofennide rocks range from about 1640 to 1870 million years, but the main metamorphism seems to date around 1800. There now seems to be general agreement that there was a major event in the world tectonism about 1800 million years ago (comparable with the one at the end of the Archaean at about 2600 million years). In the Baltic region this would be when the craton was first stabilized as a single entity. This was the beginning, perhaps, of true continental crust as we understand it today and therefore the date when Europe can be said to have been born as a continent.

Certainly from Svecofennide times onwards we seem to have a geological situation comparable in generalities with what was to be the pattern thereafter, even to the extent of recognizing a 'geosynclinal couple' of eugeosyncline in the Svecofennides *sensu stricto* (in the south-west) and miogeosyncline in what used to be called the Karelides (in the north-east).

The Karelides, long regarded as a separate tectonic belt, extend from the Norwegian–Swedish frontier north of Narvik to the north shores of Lake Ladoga (Ladozhskoye), north of Leningrad. They consist of great thicknesses of pure quartzites and dolomitic marbles, in keeping with their miogeosynclinal image, but there is also a considerable development of metamorphosed basic volcanics which do not belong so well in that picture. There are breaks within the succession followed by basal conglomerates full of pebbles of Archaean rocks. Stromatolites are fairly common. These and the problematical fossil *Collenia* enable a very approximate correlation with Lower Proterozoic successions elsewhere in the Soviet Union. The dolomites are well seen, in so far as anything is well seen in this conifer-, water-, and snow-covered country, around the southern shores of rambling Lake Inari (Inarin-Järv) in northernmost Finland. The quartzites and associated basic volcanics, on the other hand, are better seen around Rovaniemi, the capital of Finnish Lapland, just south of the Arctic Circle. The Karelian is commonly separated by Finnish geologists into two divisions, each beginning with a basal conglomerate followed by thick quartzites. The basic volcanism appears to be largely confined to the lower division.

15

The Russians speak of 'several kilometres' of such rocks and distinguish several 'suites' within them. Many of them contain staurolite and kyanite, sometimes of economic importance. There are also nickeliferous intrusions, copper mineralization, and some banded iron-ore. Silver occurs fairly widely in both Finland and Sweden, leading to a notable local craft, and Finland had its own little gold rush in 1868 in northern Lapland (following the rule that gold usually occurs in the most uncomfortable places.). Tankavaaran and Lemmenjoki are said to be the last places on earth where gold is still regularly produced by panning sediment from the streams.

The Lapponian volcanics within the Karelide succession are always basic in composition and well-preserved pillow lavas are said to be typical, but there are also tuffs and agglomerates. Higher up the succession there are extensive andesitic porphyries, with minor amounts of pyroclastic rocks. The whole region is cut by several generations of granites, for example the great area north of Rovaniemi where the granite produces rounded bracken-covered hills emerging from the monotonous forest. In the past, windows of Svecofennide rocks within the Karelides belt have been claimed as evidence of a separate and younger age for the enclosing rocks. The fact that the main metamorphism affects both successions, together with the comparable radiometric dates, has brought most geologists round to the view, long held in Finland, that the Karelides are mainly epicontinental deposits on the edge of a Svecofennide trough filled with deeper water deposits.

The Svecofennides, in the older more restricted sense, occupy the greater part of central Sweden and southern Finland. They are not seen at the surface in the Soviet Union, where the Karelides are overlain unconformably by later Precambrian rocks. The junction between the Karelides and the Svecofennides s.s. strikes north-west across Finland to hit the Swedish coast near the busy little town of Pitea. The Svecofennides in general seem to have originated from a much more argillaceous succession than the Karelides. They consist mainly of thick and monotonous sequences of greywackes and slates, altered to quartz-felspar and mica schists and gneisses, together with great quantities of phyllite. Near the top of the succession graphitic rocks are common, suggesting the presence of organic material, but the rocks generally are not such as to encourage the palaeontologist, although sedimentary structures are often visible (as on the camping site at Skellefteå). The fact that the Svecofennide rocks appeared to be more highly metamorphosed than the Karelides explains the long-held view that they were older, but this is probably mainly a function of their original composition and situation in a vulnerable trough.

The Finns nowadays recognize three divisions within the Svecofennides s.s. known by a variety of names. In Finland the lowest division characteristically includes considerable developments of volcanics as well as intercalated sediments, while the top division is typically argillaceous in origin. All these are now mainly seen as mica schists, mica-gneisses, and 'leptite gneisses' (probably originally arkosic). In the south of Sweden the volcanic rocks appear to be near the bottom of the succession. Cutting through the succession generally and most obvious in its upper part, are many intrusive dolerites, now amphibolites, that appear to post-date the Svecofennian folding.

Where these surface rocks sank deepest into the crust, notably in the syncline west of Stockholm, granitization and alteration into veined gneisses was most intense. Elsewhere there are roughly circular masses of diapiric granite with associated aplitic and pegmatitic dikes (e.g., around Täby, just north of the Swedish capital), but vast areas of similar pale granites occupy much of the rocky, elk-filled forests of Central Sweden. In fact, the greater part of this belt is composed of various white and pink granites, cut by or cutting black amphibolites. There is very little to be seen throughout this vast area of even remotely recognizable sedimentary rocks. To a certain extent this may be a misleading impression, since the granites tend to form the low hills and such few natural exposures as there are. However, modern roads have provided a wealth of almost random sections and these seem to confirm the above impression (as does the general geological map). Thus the new motorways radiating from Stockholm provide many magnificent, but untouchable, cuttings through granites and basic rocks that are aesthetically pleasing if scientifically confusing. Similarly, around Helsinki (Helsingfors), the Finnish capital, acid plutonic rocks dominate the picture in what is thought to be the root zone of the Svecofennian chain.

Intensive mineralization is concentrated in various places, notably in the form of sulphides of iron, nickel, copper, zinc, and lead, for example in the Ammerberg region. Most remarkable is the narrow zone of mineralization that runs north-west from Lake Ladoga across the 'main sulphide zone' of Finland and the north end of the Gulf of Bothnia. It continues as the ore-field along the Skellefte River of northern Sweden, notably the Boliden mines, west of the sportive cum industrial town of Skellefteå, which produce (among other things) some 4000 kg of gold every year, together with the lead that goes into the marvellous Swedish glass.* This belt has been interpreted as a continental margin type of mineralization, possibly associated with an island arc. Its palaeogeographical position, only some 80 km south of the boundary between the Karelides and the Svecofennides s.s. may be significant.

Another belt of mineralization farther south passes through the town of Falun in central Sweden, which had the distinction for a short time in the seventeenth century of being the world's biggest producer of copper. A by-product of this copper mining was the dark red paint seen on wooden buildings all over Scandinavia.

Before leaving mining matters, special mention must be made of the iron-ores which have been of such economic importance to Sweden and of such strategic importance to Europe as a whole. The banded apatite iron-ores are best known at Kiruna, south-east of its Norwegian port of Narvik, and said to be the largest town on earth (i.e., in areal extent). The ores are remarkable as being magmatic in origin, both as dikes and lava flows, and apparently formed as a differentiate of a syenite porphyry. They are quite different from the banded iron-ores known in so many parts of the world (including nearby Norway) in the Precambrian, which were sedimentary in origin.

Considering the Svecofennides as a whole, it must be said that they do not seem to qualify as ocean crust. The only faint sign of ophiolites is in the Karelides, which paradoxically are the most continental part of the belt. Without that part we have here a trough some 350 km wide containing a variety of sediments, including a fair proportion of land-derived material, together with various volcanic rocks, none of them ophiolitic. There are basal conglomerates and at least one major break in the middle (above the acid volcanics), followed by further conglomerates.

---

*The paucity of exposures in this forested, glaciated country make it unsurprising that Finns have trained dogs to sniff out the sulphide ores.

There is evidence of Archaean continental crust to the north, to the west (along the Caledonian front), and to the south (in a reworked condition) so the trough, although wide, was limited in extent. There is the possibility, although it has been denied, of Archaean continental crust showing through in places from below. The associated granites are of various ages and types, both synorogenic and post-orogenic, and clearly reflect a complex history of continental crust formation.

Looked at from an astronaut's eye-view, the general trend of all these rocks is from north-west to south-east. This is also the trend within the Karelides and of the junction between them and the rest of the Svecofennides. This line has in fact been traced all the way to the Ukrainian Massif. The fact that the mineralized zone of central Finland and northern Sweden also exactly parallels this line implies that it is a deep-seated phenomenon. Nevertheless, it must be pointed out that the detailed structures in the main part of the Svecofennides s.s. are not so cooperative. They show many and complex trends, partly related to later intrusions, but on the whole are more north–south oriented than the Karelides and oblique to the junction between them. A suggested explanation for this has been a major transform movement. The Svecofennides s.s. may represent a small ocean basin involved in such a structure along the edge of a large moving continent.

After the orogenesis and metamorphism of the Svecofennides, there was an important event throughout Eo-Europa (and even in Greenland), but one that was particularly obvious here. This was the emplacement of the Rapakivi-type granites, with their characteristic zoned felspar phenocrysts which have radiometric ages of between 1800 and 1650 million years. These and certain associated igneous rocks occur in a broad east-south-east trending zone from northern Scandinavia down to the Ukraine. Some of the largest masses occur on the comparatively well-exposed south coast of Finland, east of Helsinki and along the south-west margin of the Svecofennides in southern Sweden. This apparently completed the solidification of the Baltic basement and the mobile belt again moved to the south-west.

Gothides and Dalslandian

The Gothides were a much younger fold belt, separated by four or five hundred million years from their predecessors and only found in southern Norway and Sweden running roughly north–south on either side of the 'Pregothide' belt referred to earlier. The ages usually attributed to these rocks seem nowadays to range around 1300 million years and there is everywhere a very marked break below them.

In general terms they are very reminiscent of the Karelides and were presumably formed under similar conditions. There are conglomerates, quartzites (showing well-preserved cross-bedding and ripple-marks), limestones, and low-grade bedded ironstones. This sedimentary sequence is most fully preserved on the Baltic coast around the port of Vastervik.

There are also basic lavas, tuffs, and agglomerates. All these are altered into gneisses, up to sillimanite grade, and invaded by a series of 'Dalslandian' granites (accompanied by pegmatites and migmatites) such as the one on the west coast of Sweden which crosses the frontier to reach the Oslo graben.

The name Gothides is particularly associated with the low, ice-smoothed country of islands and inlets around Göteborg in south-west Sweden (and presumably with the Goths who left this part of the world to drive through the Roman Empire to the Black Sea and beyond). But it is also used in a much wider sense to cover the whole of southern Norway as well. Sometimes the term 'Sveconorwegides' is used instead, but we already have enough polysyllabic names in this chapter.

In the broader sense the Gothides include what is probably a separate, later orogenic cycle dating from about 1100 to 900 million years ago. This episode is often called the Dalslandian. It has been equated with yet another term, the 'Ripheid', which is sometimes applied to a narrow fold belt at the other end of Scandinavia cutting across the northern tip of Norway and just taking in one peninsula (Rybachiy, the Fisherman's Peninsula) to the north-west of Murmansk in the USSR. This is the belt that includes the 'Eocambrian' rocks on the north side of Varanger fjord in north-east Norway. These are moderately folded and cleaved, but it is not clear (at least to me) why they should not be regarded as part of the Caledonide story (Chapter 5). It has therefore been postulated that, late in Proterozoic times, fold belts were formed on both sides of the newly consolidated Baltic craton. The whole complex seems to represent a grand cycle of increasing and decreasing orogenesis. Sediments such as greywackes in the lower part and quartzites higher up are lost in floods of volcanic rocks and even more so in a profusion of granitic and other intrusions. The final orogenic phase, about 1000 million years ago, coincided with the third of the major world-wide events (such as the Grenvillean) that have been claimed for Precambrian times. It has also been said that, at about this time, rigid plates were first established. Deformation took on a different form thereafter and only occurred in marginal areas. Many would dispute this, however, on the evidence of much later episodes in earth history.

The general trend of the Gothide structures is north–south and is probably seen in the basement under Denmark and perhaps controlling the orientation of salt diapirs under the southern part of the North Sea. These rocks and this orogenic cycle have not been recognized elsewhere in Europe.

Jotnian

For the past few hundred million years of Precambrian time, the only record on the Baltic Shield is in the form of red sandstones and conglomerates known as the Jotnian. They appear to be fluviatile, similar to deposits dated by spores as late Proterozoic, and comparable with the Torridonian of the Hebridean Province. Like the latter they are completely unmetamorphosed and bear witness to the stability of this area since way back in Precambrian times. They cover a very large area of west central Sweden, mainly in the Kopparberg Län ('Copper Mountain Province').* Here they are sometimes associated with basal ignimbrites and extensive basic igneous rocks. Red Jotnian sandstones also occur as scattered, poorly exposed outliers farther east in Sweden, under the Baltic, and in some patches on the south-west corner of Finland. They occur even more extensively as glacial erratics, and it was one such in Germany that yielded one of the most remarkable Precambrian fossils in Europe—the curious segmented and appendaged structure known as *Xenusion*.

*Confusingly this has nothing to do with the place called Kopparberg or with Falun and the famous copper deposits.

The relationship between the Jotnian and the 'Eocambrian' sandstones of the Scandinavian Caledonides is not clear, but the latter are evidently later. Arkosic sandstones on the Danish island of Bornholm, south-east of Skåne (and certainly part of the Fenno-Scandian Shield) are commonly attributed to the 'Eocambrian'.

Finally, very late in Precambrian history, there came into position a variety of intrusive bodies, punched through the central and southern part of the shield, but this is all there is that can be called a terminal Precambrian event. There was no equivalent of the Cadomian orogeny known farther south.

After that, the dominant process on the shield was one of erosion. Apart from the evidence of the Phanerozoic outliers in the south, discussed below, these old rocks were being gently uplifted and eroded during the time that the other exciting events of geological history were happening in the rest of Europe.

So now we have a landscape worn down to its roots, for the most part a monotonously beautiful, endlessly flat landscape of birch, fir, moss, and reindeer, with almost uncountable lakes. It was scraped clean by the ice and scattered with its products. Hardly any of the rocks you see belong where you see them. Then as it heaved up with relief after the melting of the ice, it has been bequeathed the finest series of river terraces and raised beaches known to me anywhere in the world.

1(b)   Phanerozoic Outliers

Palaeozoic outliers

Sprinkled across the ancient rocks of the southern part of the Fenno-Scandian Shield are blobs of Palaeozoic sediment, studies of which have made Norwegian and Swedish stratigraphers and palaeontologists some of the best in the world. There are several of these outliers in Sweden, as well as the Oslo Graben in Norway. They are complemented by the rocks of the Baltic syncline which are discussed in Section (c) below.

Clearly here, as on the East European Platform (and for that matter on the Canadian Shield), shallow epicontinental seas swashed briefly to and fro leaving a succession of thin smears of sediment, most of which were eroded away in the subsequent long history of emergence. For the most part the remaining sediments are thin, flat-lying, shallow-water deposits, resting with marked unconformity on the Precambrian metamorphics and hardly disturbed since they were deposited. They range from early Cambrian to late Silurian in age and include some 'Old Red Sandstone' type sediments that may belong to the early Devonian. The largest outcrop lies along the south-east front of the Caledonides in northern Sweden and southern Norway, but this is so much linked with the story of the Scandinavian Caledonides that it is best dealt with in Part Two of this book.

The generally flat-lying nature of these outliers is locally disturbed, notably in the Oslo Graben and in Dalarna (Fig. 1.2), for reasons that will be discussed later. In the extreme south of Sweden, in Skåne (Scania) and on Bornholm, the Palaeozoic sediments are associated with Mesozoic rocks. They are slightly more complicated here, presumably because they are near the edge of the shield. Recent gravity measurements have shown

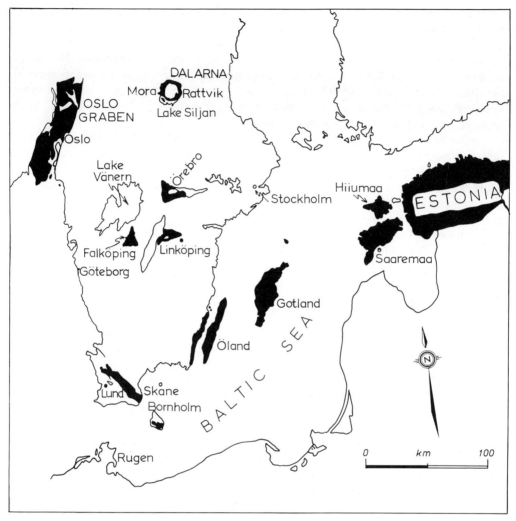

Fig. 1.2 Sketch-map of the Baltic area showing Palaeozoic outcrops in black.

that this border zone is underlain by basement rocks that are block-faulted along north-westerly trends and cut by Permian dikes. This is also the pattern of the younger rocks seen at the surface.

Generally speaking the Palaeozoics of the shield contrast markedly with those of the Caledonides in tectonic style and in facies. From the abundance of their carbonates and the absence of volcanics (other than bentonitic layers) they have been called miogeosynclinal, but this makes the term almost meaningless.

The Cambrian is much more uniform in character than the other systems. It almost always ranges from sandy at the base to shaly at the top, with a notable development of kerogenous alum shale. It is thickest in Skåne, with a succession reminiscent of the Welsh Borderland. Basal ripple-marked quartzites, lacking fossils other than burrows, pass up

21

through glauconitic sandstones into fossiliferous shales. These shales include thin bituminous limestones or 'stinkstones' which seem to imply frequently repeated euxenic conditions over large areas. The Upper Cambrian part of the shale succession is particularly fossiliferous and has been very finely divided by means of trilobites. The shales continue into the Ordovician with thin limestones and many graptolite zones; most of the Silurian is the same. At the top of the latter, however, more varied, shallow-water sediments come in, leading to what looks like continental 'Old Red Sandstone', thus completing a megacycle of transgression and regression.

Farther north, limestones are very much a feature of the Ordovician succession. The most characteristic are red and grey, highly bioturbated, flaggy limestones containing large orthocone nautiloids. These were probably the only ornamental stones the locals could use before they found a method for cutting their beautiful granites and gneisses. So they are seen everywhere in Sweden as paving and facing stones, and '*Orthoceras*' is a fossil known to every Swedish schoolboy.*

North-east of Göteborg, Sweden's second city, is the almost perfectly triangular outlier of the Falköping district and nearby Mount Kinnekulle on Lake Vänern. These have a mainly Cambrian and Ordovician succession, preserved under a Permian dolerite, and survive as table mountains of flat-lying strata. This area was studied particularly by Linnaeus, the eighteenth-century founder of the binomial system of taxonomy. In fact much of the early work on all the outliers and islands was done by this great man, who named many of the most familiar Lower Palaeozoic fossils. These particular outliers are also notable for oil in the Upper Cambrian which was cooked by the intrusions into an asphaltite and is used as fuel. Oil is also extracted near Orebo, in the little outlier farther north in Närke Lan, but Sweden is not likely to be invited to join OPEC.

North from here the Cambrian disappears and the early Palaeozoic transgression began with the Tremadocian, which rests with a basal conglomerate on the Precambrian metamorphics or on the Jotnian sandstones. This is seen in the northernmost outlier of Dalarna (Dalecarlia), for example near Djupgrav on the north side of the structure. The outlier shows up clearly on even the biggest scale maps, since it is an almost perfect ring of Lower Palaeozoic sediments, more than 40 km across, with the Precambrian basement showing through in the middle. The outcrop of the softer sediments is ornamented with a ring of lakes, including famous Lake Siljan which often gives its name to the whole structure.

Following the recent fashion for 'astroblemes', this has been interpreted as a meteoritic impact structure. Sure enough, the telltale shatter cones have been found in the basement rocks and such an origin would also explain the steep dips, faulting, and local brecciation of the Lower Palaeozoic rocks which generally are not features of the shield outliers. It is tempting, in passing, to note a number of other circular structures in the Fenno-Scandian Shield hereabouts.

Another feature of the Dalarna outlier are the mid and late Ordovician reefs. The visitor from the south does not expect such things in rocks of this age, and one would think these were tropical parts in Ordovician times, while the Sahara was in the grip of an

---

*A story is told of the new director of a geological institute who, following the Swedish custom, was a lawyer rather than a geologist. On arrival for the first time at the institute and seeing a core from a deep borehole, he was anxious to show off his one little snippet of geological knowledge and commented: 'What a splendid *Orthoceras*!'

ice sheet. Unfortunately the palaeomagnetists want to put them near the South Pole. The reefs are of particular interest because they contain hydrocarbons in the form of asphalt (e.g., at Boda). They complement the Silurian reefs of Gotland, to be discussed later. Here the Silurian is mostly shaly. In fact, in places Silurian graptolitic shales fill fissures in the Ordovician reefs (well seen in the big quarry at Kallholm, north-east of Mora). The shales and thin limestones of the Silurian are poorly exposed and much hidden under water. At the very top they become reddened and pass into fine red sandstones, frequently ripple-marked, remarkably like the 'ORS' ('Old Red Sandstone') and coincidentally called the 'ORSA sandstone'. They are best seen near the town of that name and are well displayed in paving slabs around the old bell-tower in Mora.

Like the earlier divisions, the Silurian thickens southwards and the uppermost Silurian in particular is exceptionally thick in Skåne, implying differential subsidence at the end of early Palaeozoic times along the south-west margin of Eo-Europa. All the Lower Palaeozoic rocks of this region are comparable with those of the Anglo-Welsh Caledonides, both in facies and faunas. In other words they are very much part of Europe and were laid down on our side of an earlier Atlantic Ocean. They differ from the Lower Palaeozoics of the Caledonides generally, however, in their tectonic calm. The only exception to this (if one excludes the extraterrestrial encounter at Dalarna) is in the Oslo Graben.

The Oslo Graben is included here because its classic Lower Palaeozoic succession is completely contained within the Fenno-Scandian Shield. It is a slice of the cover that has been faulted down and preserved for us beneath Permian volcanics (Fig. 1.3). However, unlike the other cover rocks on the shield, the Cambrian to Silurian rocks around the Norwegian capital have undoubtedly been affected by the Caledonian orogeny. Some of the folding can be related to the later faulting, but it is by no means always so. Thus in the splendid section above Tyrifjord, west of Oslo, quite strongly folded Silurian sediments, with white bentonite marker bands, can be seen beneath a cliff-top capping of undisturbed Permian lava.

The situation is perhaps comparable with that of the Jura in the Alpine orogeny. We are in an intermediate position between the highly disturbed rocks of the Caledonian front and the undisturbed cover of the main Fenno-Scandian Shield. The Lower Palaeozoic sediments, although moderately folded, are in a much healthier condition than they are not very far to the north-west, near Fagernes in the Caledonides, but are more disturbed than in the Swedish outliers around Falköping, a short distance to the southeast. As in the Jura, there was probably *décollement* here, with the Lower Palaeozoic sediments coming unstuck and crumpling on a rigid Precambrian basement.

The lower Palaeozoic succession of the Oslo Graben fits in with that of the other Phanerozoic outliers. The Cambrian is thin and shaly, and the lower part is missing. The Ordovician is much thicker, with shales and limestones representing a shallowing sequence with a break at the top before a Silurian transgression with basal conglomerate. The Silurian, although the least of the Lower Palaeozoic systems, is thicker again and passes up eventually into what are generally referred to as Downtonian rocks, by analogy with the Welsh Borderland. The marine sequence is tantalizingly well exposed along the new motorways out of the Norwegian capital, with the black shales and thin limestones undulating in the cuttings, notably around Slemmerstad, on the west side of the graben. It has been divided in almost excruciating detail by means of trilobites and other organisms.

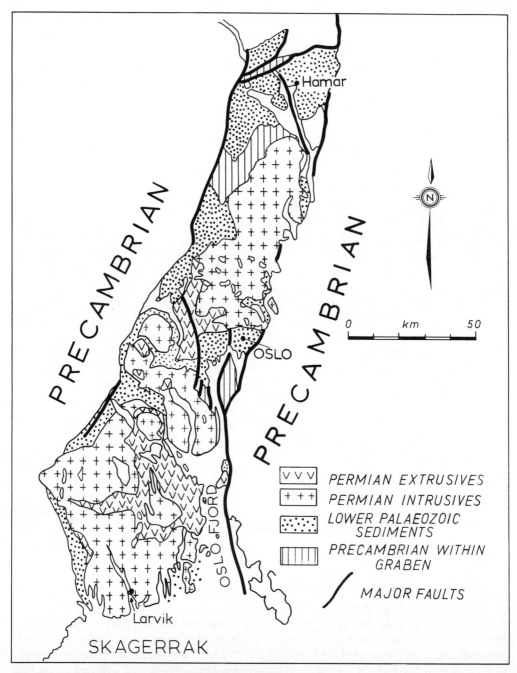

Fig. 1.3   Geological sketch-map of the Oslo Graben.

The 'Downtonian', now officially back in the Silurian (if correctly dated), is very much of an 'Old Red Sandstone' facies, with red sandstones and mudstones, cross-bedded, ripple-marked, green reduction spots, etc. As the 'Ringerike Sandstone' it is the best seen around the town of that name (now usually under the alias of Hønefoss), north-west of Oslo. This too has been moderately disturbed, mainly along fault lines.

The Oslo Graben is unique on the Fenno-Scandian Shield in preserving rocks of late Palaeozoic age. These are mainly Permian intrusive and extrusive rocks, but include non-marine, mainly clastic sediments which have yielded enough plant and animal remains to suggest a Rotliegendes age. The intrusives, associated with major Permian faulting, occupy a large part of the graben. Their most famous representative is larvikite (with its glittering labradorite crystals) named—with various spellings—after Larvik on the south coast. This was extensively exported around northern Europe as an easily recognizable erratic in the Pleistocene glaciations (ranging from the huge block on the quayside at Frederikshaven, just across the Skagerak in northern Jutland, to small pebbles that reached as far as north London). Later it was even more widely exported as a facing stone to give an air of opulence to banks and the more pretentious kind of shops.

Besides the massive intrusions, which range from gabbroic to granitic in composition via the syenitic larvikites, there are several cauldron subsidences with ring-dikes and cone-sheets, producing almost perfect circular outlines on the geological map. Among the extensive Permian extrusives, certainly the most famous are the rhomb porphyries, in various forms and colours, also easily recognized in glacial deposits.* One of the odd coincidences of European geology (if it does not have a deeper significance) is the general resemblance of these acidic volcanic rocks to those of a similar age around Bolzano in the southern Alps. Both are associated with a system of faults of continent-wide importance.

The Oslo Gaben is a north–south trending bundle of faults within the Fenno-Scandian Shield which contains within itself smaller horsts and graben. Nowhere is this structure better displayed than in Oslofjord itself, just south of the capital, with the dark gneissose horst of the Nesodden peninsula on the east side, islands of Lower Palaeozoic sediments in the middle, and a further horst of a different colour on the western shore, made of pale pink granite.

In modern terminology, the Oslo Graben is a 'failed arm' of a rift system that nearly tore Europe apart at the end of Palaeozoic times. Some would extend it to the Rhine and Rhône graben and down through the Campidano rift of Sardinia to lose itself somewhere in Africa. Perhaps so. But so far as the Fenno-Scandian Shield is concerned the wound did not go very far and was soon healed. By analogy with other comparable dotted lines in Western Europe, one would have expected it to have continued tearing apart in Triassic times, but there is no evidence of this.

Post-Palaeozoic outliers

In southernmost Sweden, or Skåne, the ancient rocks of the Fenno-Scandian Shield begin to dip down under the Mesozoic and Cainozoic rocks of the Great Northern Plain

---

*They were also strangely recognized in a Carboniferous conglomerate in the north of England when the lava was thought to be Devonian in age!

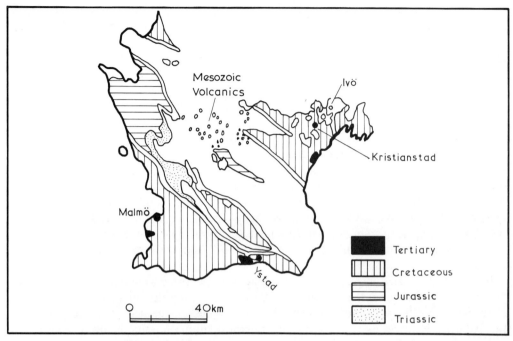

Fig. 1.4 *Sketch-map of the Mesozoic rocks of Skåne (after Brotzen, 1960, by kind permission of the Sveriges Geologiska Undersökning).*

of Europe (Fig. 1.4). Much more is known from boreholes than is seen at the surface and an almost complete, but thin, Mesozoic succession is present. The rocks outcrop along north–west lines, conforming with the trend of the Precambrian rocks below. Horsts and graben are similarly oriented.

The oldest Mesozoic rocks seen at the surface are late Triassic ('Keuper') red sandstones, conglomerates, and mudstones in a graben north-east of Malmö, where they rest unconformably on early Palaeozoic sediments. At the very top of the Trias are deltaic sediments with coal seams that range in age through from the Rhaetian into the earliest Jurassic. The coal was once mined fairly intensively around Höganäs, in what must be the cleanest mine in the world, complete with its own underground cinema. The accompanying shales are used for brick-making, since such materials are rare in hard-rock Sweden.

Not much higher up in the Lower Jurassic, brick-pits just south of Hälsinborg have a sparse marine fauna and other poor exposures of marine sediments have even yielded ammonites and brachiopods. Higher again are unfossiliferous sandstones which may be mid Jurassic in age and remind one of the North Sea and underground Denmark. Later coal-bearing strata with a fairly good flora may belong to the late Jurassic.

One of the most interesting recent developments in Swedish geology concerns the scatter of volcanic necks and basalts in Skåne that used to be regarded as Tertiary in age. I had always thought of them as the probable source of the many ash-bands in the Eocene of Denmark. Now radiometric dating has shown them to fall into two groups, one Jurassic and the other Cretaceous. This fits in with the recently discovered Jurassic volcanics in the North Sea and the presumed volcanic origin of Jurassic and Cretaceous bentonitic 'fuller's earths' in Britain.

The Jurassic–Cretaceous boundary is probably hidden within coal-bearing sands and clays which are also important sources of glass-sand and kaolin. This must represent deep subaerial weathering of the ancient rocks before a late Cretaceous marine transgression. A few brackish water bivalves and ostracods appear to indicate an early Cretaceous age.

On the island of Ivö, in the lake north-east of Kristianstad, one can see the actual rocky islands and beach boulders of the first transgressive late Cretaceous (Campanian) sea up against the edge of the exposed Fenno-Scandian Shield. Blocks of adjacent Precambrian metamorphic rocks are encrusted with oysters and other organisms that have been studied with as much care and precision as those of a modern beach. Drifted land plants are found in a sandy layer.

Higher up in the chalky limestones are lenses of metamorphic pebbles, well seen between Hässleholm and Kristianstad in the north-east of Skåne. These look quite out of place to those of us who are familiar with the pure white chalk of most of northern Europe, but testify to the proximity of an ancient land-mass in the adjacent horst. A neighboring fault-line probably moved repeatedly during sedimentation to provide the blocks.

In general the uppermost Cretaceous is like that of Denmark, with abundant belemnites for correlative purposes and bryozoan reefs seen in incredibly clean and tidy quarries such as Limhamn on the outskirts of Malmö. The Danian continues the facies of the Maastrichtian along the south coast, as in Denmark, with the reefs oriented along familiar west-north-west lines. The facies change comes above the Danian, thus producing generations of fatuous arguments about the Cretaceous–Tertiary boundary. 'Tertiary-type' sediments start with a basal conglomerate and glauconitic clays, only preserved in a very small area and best seen in the flooded Klagshamn quarry, south-west of Malmö. But by this level all trace of the basement seems to have disappeared and this little patch of Paleocene sediments, as well as a larger one just west of Ystad, are best thought of as part of the Baltic Plain.

Further mention should be made of the Danish island of Bornholm, which lies about 40 km south-east from the Skåne coast. The main northern part of this island consists of Precambrian metamorphic rocks and granites faulted like Skåne, along west-north-west/east-south-east lines. Such faults also affect slices of Palaeozoic sediments in the south of the island and small patches of Mesozoic rocks along the south coast. But the most important outcrop of Mesozoic lies along the west coast, where both the coast itself and a fault about a kilometre inland delimit the outcrop along north–south lines, cutting across the earlier faults and reminding one of the North Sea, the two sides of Scotland, and the opening of the North Atlantic.

1(c) Baltic Sea

The Baltic, like so many other features of Europe, is a very ancient structure. It is most obviously so from the syncline and seaway of Lower Palaeozoic rocks that lie between Sweden and the Soviet Union. But it may be much older than this. Late Precambrian Jotnian sediments outcrop (albeit poorly exposed) along the Swedish coast, notably at the busy port of Gävle. 'Eocambrian' and other late Precambrian sediments continue the line of the Gulf of Finland up to and beyond Lake Ladoga. Characteristic red sandstones of the Jotnian are commonly seen as glacial boulders on Baltic beaches, transported from where they form the floor of that sea to the north. It may not be too far-fetched to mention the much earlier Gothide sediments which are only recognizably preserved on the coast around Västervik, west of Gotland.

The marine succession, however, only starts with the Cambrian. Soft, low-lying, and poorly exposed Cambrian sediments outcrop along a narrow coastal strip between Oskarshamn and Karlskrona on the south-east corner of Sweden and on the west side of the long, narrow island of Öland, which parallels the coast. Near Kolmar, with its remarkable old castle and its equally remarkable new bridge (to Öland), the Cambrian rests on an irregular surface of Precambrian metamorphics. On the west coast of Öland, a break is seen at the bottom of the Middle Cambrian (as in the Welsh Borderland), with a basal conglomerate and glauconitic sediments containing *Paradoxides*. Similar Cambrian sediments also outcrop along the south coast of the Gulf of Finland, in Estonia, and on to the south coast of Lake Ladoga, via the beautiful city of Leningrad. Here the Middle Cambrian appears to open the Palaeozoic story.

The Ordovician is particularly well seen on Öland, since it forms most of that island and is seen in low, highly fossiliferous cliffs, for example in the nature reserve once studied by Linnaeus, along the coast from Byxelkrok at the north end of the island. The main north–south road down the west side runs on the top of an escarpment formed by Ordovician limestones overlooking the low ground of the Cambrian. Late Arenig limestones provide abundant large orthocene nautiloids, as elsewhere in Sweden.

From here the Ordovician dips eastwards under the Baltic and is known in oil-searching boreholes on Gotland and north of there on the tiny island of Gotska Sandon. It reaches the surface again in Estonia, where it passes under the capital Tallin and is still well exposed, notably at the famous locality of Kukruse, with its wonderful fossils, and on the offshore island of Hiiumaa. The Lower Palaeozoic of these three little countries of my youth—Estonia, Latvia, and Lithuania—will be discussed again as part of the East European Platform, but must be mentioned here as the complementary eastern limb of the syncline that passes under the Baltic. It is now evident that much of the floor of that sea, at least in the south, is formed of Lower Palaeozoic rocks, so that there is a continuous outcrop which attaches to the East European Platform rather than to the scattered outliers on the shield.

The Silurian, similarly, outcrops in the southern part of the mainland Estonia, dipping south under the 'Old Red Sandstone'. It is known in boreholes in Latvia and Lithuania. In the Baltic itself, the Silurian is only seen at the surface in the much-visited island of Gotland, on the Swedish side, and on the unvisited island of Saaremaa (Oesel) off Estonia. Gotland, of course, gave its name to a major division of geological time—the Gotlandian—although nowadays this is generally accepted as a junior synonym of the Silurian.* Gotland is a Baltic counterpart of Malta, but here the flat-lying limestones of the cliffs are all of Silurian age, not Tertiary, illustrating the difference, between Eo-Europa and Neo-Europa.

Especially well known are its splendid reef complexes which, with their inter-reef

*A pity, since its sunny cliffs give a much better picture than the wooded ridges and placid fields of the Silures, but my anti-chauvinism is countered by my hatred of 'stratotypes'.

sediments, have been intensively studied by both Swedes and foreign geologists, especially in recent years from the hospitable University of Uppsala research centre at Allekvia. They have also been studied by the oil prospectors, for whom Gotland now has a considerable petroleum potential. The reefs are well seen in the fairly high cliffs on the west and north-west side of the island, especially north of the walled town of Visby, standing out as buttresses. The reefs are at three levels and are probably diachronous (as reefs commonly are), becoming progressively younger to the south-east, through Wenlock and Ludlow divisions. In the centre of the island there is a complete lateral transition from lagoon to reef to fore-reef deposits, and this is repeated upwards. The broad contemporaneity of these reefs with those (generally smaller) in the Wenlock Limestone of England and those (of course much larger) in the Niagaran limestones of the American Mid-West is noteworthy. They are mostly formed of stromatoporoids and tabulate corals and take on conical, mushroom, or other strange shapes by the erosion of the softer, fragmental limestones in between. They form sea-stacks and natural arches offshore, and circular structures along the coasts have been interpreted as massive reefs that have sunk into the softer sediments.

It is worth noting that the highest reefs of all (about Middle Ludlow in age), seen on the east of the island, show a very low faunal diversity suggesting a changing salinity reminiscent of changes that were to happen very much later in the history of the Baltic. This is also suggested by late Silurian salt deposits just across in Estonia and reminds one of the situation above the Niagaran reefs in the Michigan Basin.

Facies changes in the Lower Palaeozoic, especially in the Silurian, seem roughly to parallel the Baltic trend, indicating that this was already a seaway. Certainly it was a feature from the end of early Palaeozoic times. It is reasonable to postulate that the Baltic syncline was formed in Caledonian times, since the uppermost Silurian is missing, there is no sign of marine Devonian, and the continental 'Old Red Sandstone' rests unconformably on the gently folded strata.

Of the rest of the Palaeozoic story of the Baltic I know nothing. There are the marginal lappings of Mesozoic and Tertiary seas in the south (discussed for convenience elsewhere) and then the catastrophe of the Pleistocene glaciations smothering, scouring, and scraping out the basin.

The post-glacial history of the Baltic is well known, but so classic that it deserves breaking my usual rule about ignoring these things. It illustrates beautifully the interplay of isostatic and eustatic forces, operating in opposite directions. Whereas the sheer weight of the ice on Scandinavia depressed the land surface, the stealing of water to form ice led to isostatic recovery and uplift of the land surface. The eustatic processes were clearly the more rapid of the two.

The last forward-pushing moraines of the Scandinavian glaciations are those of Pomerania, on the southern shores of the Baltic. As the ice retreated so the great depressed basin it left filled with water to form the 'Baltic Ice Lake', cut off from the Atlantic but having about the same form as the present sea. The moraines had now retreated to a line between the Norwegian and the Swedish capitals, and up into southern Finland. The continued melting led to a rapid rise in sea-level and the North Sea came flooding in across southern Sweden to form the 'Yoldia' Sea', characterized by the small Arctic bivalve of that name. This left deposits up to 150 m up and seasonal varved clays which have been patiently counted by the Swedes.

However, this sea was cut off again by the recoil from glacial loading. Dry land broke the surface where Denmark is today and the '*Ancylus* Lake' was formed, named after the so-called 'fresh-water limpet'. This lasted some 3000 years, but its record is fragmentary. It forms, for example, the highest features on Gotland.

The continued rise in sea-level and the see-saw effect of isostatic recovery led to relative depression in the south and the sea came in again to form the '*Littorina* Sea', more extensive and more saline than the present Baltic. The raised beaches of this sea are very widespread in Sweden, Finland, and the Baltic states of the Soviet Union. On Gotland, for example, it formed a convenient shelf for shy nudists. The continuing and slower isostatic rise of the areas that had carried the heaviest ice load progressively restricted the Baltic to its present size and again almost converted it to a fresh-water lake.

The later stages of uplift are well documented by magnificent raised beaches from the sharply defined surfaces around the top end of the Gulf of Bothnia to Linnaeus's 'Neptuni Åkrar' (Neptune's ploughland) on the island of Öland. The Gulf of Bothnia is still rising at about 11 mm a year, and is producing the melancholy swamps around its head waters.

The narrow straits of the Skagerrak and the Kattegat, together with the plentiful supply of fresh water from melting snow and rivers, give the Baltic a biology all of its own. Anyone can see how the cockles and mussels get progressively smaller northwards along the beaches of this inland sea. The freshness of the water excluded *Teredo*, the 'ship-worm', and so ensured the almost perfect preservation of the disastrous early seventeenth century man-o'-war 'Wasa' in the mud of Stockholm harbour. At the top end of the Gulf of Bothnia, the fauna and flora are those of a northern lake. But geological change never stops and the marine molluscs are slowly creeping in again.

Selected references to Chapter 1

Section 1(a) Precambrian Basement

Holtedahl, O. (1960), *Geology of Norway*, Norges Geol. Undersølkelse No. 208, Oslo, 540 pp. + atlas.

Magnusson, N. H. (1965), 'The Pre-Cambrian history of Sweden', *Quart. Jl. Geol. Soc., Lond.*, **121**, 1–30.

Nalivkin, D. V. (1973), *Geology of the U.S.S.R.* (English transl. by N. Rast), Univ. Toronto Press, 855 pp.

Polkanov, A. A. and E. K. Gerling (1960), 'The Precambrian geochronology of the Baltic Shield', *21st Internat. Geol. Congr., Copenhagen*, Sess. 9, pp. 183–191.

Rankama, K., ed. (1963), *The Precambrian. I. Fennoscandian Shield*, Interscience, New York, 279 pp.

Simonen, A. (1960), 'Precambrian stratigraphy of Finland', *21st Internat. Geol. Congr., Copenhagen*, Sess. 9, pp. 141–153.

Watson, J. (1976), 'Eo-Europa: the evolution of a craton', in D. V. Ager and M. Brooks (eds.), *Europe from Crust to Core*, Wiley, London, pp. 59–78.

Section 1(b) Phanerozoic Outliers

Bromley, R. G. (1979), 'Field meeting in southern Scandinavia', 18–28 September 1975, *Proc. Geol. Ass. Lond.*, **90**, 181–191.

Brotzen F. (1960), 'The Mesozoic of Scania, southern Sweden', in *Guide to Excursions Nos. A21 and C16*, Internat. Geol. Congr., Surv. Sweden, Norden, XXI Sess, 15 pp.

Henningsmoen, G. and N. Spjeldnaes (1960), 'Palaeozoic stratigraphy and palaeontology of the Oslo region, Eocambrian stratigraphy of the Sparagmite region, Southern Norway', in *Guide to Excursions Nos. A14 and C11*, Internat. Geol Congr., Surv. Sweden, Norden, XXI Sess., Norges Geol. Undersøk No. 212, 30 pp.

Regnell, G. and J. E. Hede (1960), 'The Lower Palaeozoic of Scania', in *Guide to Excursions Nos. A22 and C17*, Internat. Geol. Congr., Surv. Sweden, Norden, XXI Sess., 89 pp.

Thorslund, P. and V. Janussion (1960), 'The Cambrian, Ordovician and Silurian in Västergötland, Närke, Dalarna, and Jämtland, central Sweden', in *Guide to Excursions Nos. A23 and C18*, Internat. Geol. Congr., Surv. Sweden, Norden, XXI Sess., 51 pp.

Section 1(c) Baltic Sea

Grigelis, A. A., ed. (1975), *The Fauna and Stratigraphy of Paleozoic and Mesozoic of Baltic and Byelorussia*, Lithuanian Sci. Res., Geol. Surv. Inst., 'Mintis', Vilnius, 249 pp. (in Russian with English abstracts).

Kaljo, D. L. (1970), *Silurian of Estonia*, Inst. Geol. Akad. Nauk Estonian SSR, 343 pp. (in Russian with English summary).

Kaljo, D. L. (1977), *Facies and Fauna of the Baltic Silurian*, Inst. Geol. Akad. Nauk Estonian SSR, 286 pp. (in Russian with English summary).

Manten, A. (1971), 'Silurian reefs of Gotland', in *Developments in Sedimentology*, No. 13, Elsevier, Amsterdam, 539 pp.

Martinsson, A. (1962), 'The concealed Silurian of the Baltic area', *Geol. Foren. Stockholm Forhand.*, **84**, 539–541.

Regnell, G. and J. E. Hede (1960), 'The Silurian of Gotland', in *Guide to Excursions Nos. A22 and C17*. Internat. Geol. Congr., Surv. Sweden, Norden, XXI Sess., 89 pp.

Sviridov, N. I. and V. M. Litvin (1979), 'Structure of the southwestern Baltic Sea floor', *Internat. Geol. Rev.*, **21**, 497–508.

Chapter Two

Hebridean Province

This is the remotest, wettest and—some would say—most difficult corner of Europe. It could be said that it is not part of Europe at all, but a slice of North America left behind by chance in the shuffling of the continents. It is treated here with Eo-Europa because it has clearly not suffered any major disturbance since way back in Precambrian times. Nevertheless it has a remarkably complete story and forms an essential part of any jigsaw puzzle type of game with the continents. It will be considered under three headings, more for convenience that geological logic: first, the ancient fragment of Precambrian shield and its sedimentary cover; second, the Tertiary volcanic rocks which spill over on to a lot of Palaeo-Europa as well; and third, the continental shelf west of Scotland which is separated chiefly because we know so little about it.

2(a) Precambrian Basement and sedimentary cover

We are concerned here with a long, narrow strip of wet and windswept coastline in north-west Scotland and the even wetter and more windswept islands that lie to the west. The older rocks are seen chiefly on the mainland and on the farthest belt of islands (the Outer Hebrides). The belt in between (the Inner Hebrides) displays much of the sedimentary cover, but is chiefly occupied with the Tertiary volcanic rocks that are described in Section (b) below.

Lewisian floor

An undulating floor of grim, grey gneisses everywhere underlies the rest of the succession on the mainland and forms almost the whole of the long watery islands of the Outer Hebrides. It was from the northernmost of these that the Lewisian Complex took its name. These rocks extend along the Atlantic margin at least as far as the little island of Inishtrahull off the north coast of Ireland, in one direction, and in the other direction to the edge of the continental shelf west of the Shetlands (nearly 300 km north-east of the mainland outcrops).

There is no doubt that the Lewisian rocks are comparable in general terms with the rocks of the Fenno-Scandian Shield, but in many ways they have closer affinities with the basement rocks of Greenland and with those of the Canadian Shield. They evidently suffered a series of orogenic cycles, each in itself longer than the rest of the geological record. The complexity of the Lewisian long defeated detailed elucidation, but some thirty years ago it was shown that they could be divided into an older (Scourian) and a younger (Laxfordian) cycle, each representing a vast period of sedimentation, extrusion, intrusion, orogenesis, and metamorphism. These are not stratigraphical divisions in the usual sense, but fragments of orogenic belts which have suffered in different ways and at different times. Radiometric dating later provided a splendid confirmation of this work. Later an intermediate Inverian orogenic phase was recognized, but the apparent absence of a late Precambrian orogenic cycle comparable to that of the Gothides in the Fenno-Scandian Shield is an obvious important difference from that region.

Scourian. Rocks wholly attributable to this cycle occur in two main areas. In the Outer Hebrides they form the islands of North Uist and Benbecula, together with the northern part of South Uist and a small part of Harris (Fig. 2.1). On the mainland they are found in the wild country some 50–60 km south of Cape Wrath. They are also found in patches along the Moine Thrust, which delimits the Hebridean Province to the east.

They are high-grade metamorphic rocks of which it is difficult to determine the original nature and composition. A superficial simplicity of structure certainly conceals a complex history of plastic deformation. In age they are usually placed between about 2900 and 2400 million years. The main metamorphism, however, seems to have occurred fairly early in this period, between about 2700 and 2600 million years. The Scourian therefore compares in age with the Saamides, the oldest orogenic cycle in the Fenno-Scandian Shield, but it may also be equivalent to the Belomorides, and like the latter includes quantities of deep-seated granulites. The most common rock type is a granular pyroxene gneiss, much or most of it migmatitic in origin. It is difficult to be dogmatic in view of the state of the resultant rocks, but there does not seem to be anything undoubtedly sedimentary in origin, although the probability must be there.

Besides the all-enveloping, monotonous banded gneiss, there are also numerous ultrabasic bodies and there is even a belt of these at the southern end of Lewis (the part known as Harris, where the tweed jackets come from) that has been interpreted as a slice of oceanic crust thrust up on to an Archaean continent. This is perhaps pushing things too far in every sense, but it is an interesting thought. Also here is a large anorthosite body that may be part of a massive layered intrusion.

A special feature of the Scourian orogenic cycle, and its most distinctive character, was the emplacement of a great series of basic dikes after the main metamorphism. These distinguish the Scourian in two ways: they do not penetrate rocks formed in later times, and they are virtually unmetamorphosed in the 'Scourian' areas but *are* metamorphosed in the Laxfordian areas to the north and south, where the older rocks were reworked. These dikes therefore provided the critical evidence in unravelling the complex history of the Lewisian.

Inverian. In recent years a further orogenic phase has been recognized between the main Scourian and Laxfordian events, although this does not seem to have been accepted as of equivalent rank by all Highland geologists. It is named after Lochinver in the centre of the largest mainland Scourian outcrop and has been dated as around 2200 million years. This would include the dike emplacement referred to above, but also involved localized isoclinal folding and amphibolite grade metamorphism. In Precambrian terms

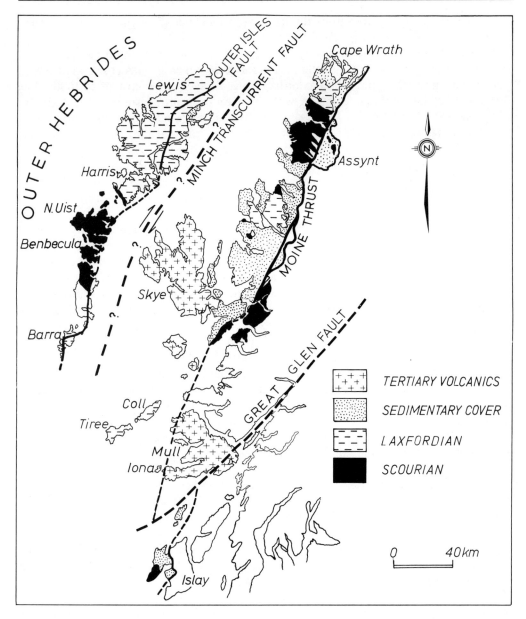

Fig. 2.1 Geological sketch-map of the Precambrian and sedimentary cover of the Hebridean Province

it seems difficult to separate from the main orogenies, but through Phanerozoic spectacles they look like very separate affairs indeed.

Laxfordian. The Laxfordian metamorphism was superimposed on all previous metamorphic rocks throughout the greater part of this area. All earlier structures were usually obliterated. In terms of time the Laxfordian orogenic cycle may have lasted from about 2000 to about 1500 million years ago, with the main orogenic spasm near the beginning of that period (about 1975 to 1850), although it must be realized that these things have only been dated in a few places and it is by no means clear that they were contemporaneous everywhere, even within a small area such as this. Such dates would, of course, make the Laxfordian event the equivalent—at least in general terms—of the main Svecofennian orogeny of the Fenno-Scandian Shield. It also equates with major happenings in Greenland and in the Canadian Shield and was obviously a very important episode in earth history.

The main areas which can be regarded as Laxfordian lie north and south of the main Scourian areas, both on the Scottish mainland and in the Outer Hebrides. The name comes from Loch Laxford, about 25 km south of Cape Wrath (the village of Scourie, incidentally, is just a few kilometres south again). Most of the Laxfordian gneisses are, in fact, Scourian gneisses that have been subjected to further ill-treatment, and it is only the presence of the 2200 million year old dike swarms in a metamorphosed condition that gives the game away. There are, however, some entirely new rocks of which perhaps the most interesting are some that are clearly of sedimentary origin.

The largest area of these is around Loch Maree (on the mainland opposite the northern tip of Skye) where there is a sequence of quartzitic, pelitic, and calcsilicate gneisses, with recognizable crystalline limestone and dolomites and—most significantly—graphite schists. Some would refer these to the Inverian, but they post-date the earlier phases of metamorphism and are not cut by the swarm of basic dikes. There are several other areas of metasediments in the Lewisian, of which the most famous are the attractive marbles of the little islands of Tiree and saintly Iona, but these may be much older and have even been called 'pre-Scourian'.

Late in Laxfordian times, about 1200 million years ago, there was considerable emplacement of granites and pegmatites, both on the mainland and in the Hebrides. However, it seems probable that most of the Laxfordian record has been lost in the vast periods of erosion that followed the orogeny and uplift.

There was no later orogeny in Precambrian times here, in spite of the fact that the term 'Assyntian' is used in some parts of Europe for such an orogeny and is taken from the classic Assynt region in the east of this area.

General trends of the Lewisian rocks. It is clearly dangerous to generalize about rocks as complex as these; nevertheless it can be said that the dominant trend acquired by the Lewisian rocks by the end of their long and painful history was a north-westerly one like that of the Fenno-Scandian Shield and that of Greenland. There are complications, especially in the older Scourian central area, where a more north-easterly trend is commonly seen. However, the north-westerly line is the general pattern and is emphasized by the distribution of the Scourian and Laxfordian as a whole. The central belt of Scourian can be traced all the way to Greenland. The fact that the Scourian in the Outer Hebrides seems to be offset relative to that on the mainland has led to the suggestion of a major transcurrent fault—the Minch Fault—running through that troubled belt of water known as the Minches between the Inner and Outer Hebrides. Parallel to this and actually seen, rather than imagined, is a belt of shattered flinty rock and mylonite which runs through the Outer Hebrides close to the eastern shores. This is the Outer Isles Thrust which reminds us of other later thrusts along similar north-easterly trends. This must have happened late in the history of the Lewisian at about the same time as these rocks acquired their general north-westerly trend. Apart from the general foliation and other structures along these lines, there were also the dike swarms and a series of separated belts of intense shearing, right across the Lewisian outcrops from north-west to south-east.

Torridonian. Above the Lewisian comes one of the finest unconformities in Europe. After the intense metamorphism of the Laxfordian (for which up to six distinct phases have been postulated) there was an immensely long period of uplift, cooling, and erosion, before the next rocks came to stay in this region. Completely unmetamorphosed and for the most part hardly disturbed sediments of late Precambrian age rest on and fill up an irregular buried landscape of ancient gneisses. They are in no way related to either of the Lewisian orogenies, but perhaps to a much later Grenville orogeny.

These sediments are the 'Torridon Sandstone' or Torridonian, named after Loch Torridon near the south end of the Lewisian mainland outcrop. They are typically red, well-bedded sandstones that contrast markedly with the grey metamorphic rocks below. They form high, spectacular mountains (at least by non-Alpine standards) such as the great ridge of Suilven.

They have been dated between 1000 and 800 million years and are obviously comparable with the Jotnian of the Fenno-Scandian Shield. They too are thought to be fluviatile in origin and are of great thickness, up to well over 4000 m. Although best known and seen on the mainland, they are also present in the Inner Hebrides. The thickness of these deposits and their general sedimentary features, notably the coarse conglomerates and felspathic sandstones, suggest that they are fairly near their source area. It is generally thought that they were derived from mountains to the north-west which sat over the Outer Hebrides and eastern Greenland, when the latter was back in its proper place. Over the greater part of the Torridonian outcrop (which is most of the stippled area in Fig. 2.1) the sediments are flat-lying or only gently inclined and completely unmetamorphosed. Locally, however, they are involved in the Caledonian structures with thrusts and slight metamorphism.

Phanerozoic. Resting on the Torridonian in its turn, mainly in a long narrow outcrop along the eastern edge of the region, are Lower Palaeozoic sediments of a particularly interesting kind. A basal conglomerate and unfossiliferous quartzites are followed by further quartzites and shales with early Cambrian fossils of North American affinities. These pass up into the lower part of a thick carbonate sequence—the Durness Limestone—which is unfossiliferous in its middle part but yields early Ordovician fossils (again of a North American type) at the top. The sequence as a whole is very similar, both in its sediments and its fossils, to that of eastern Canada and, even more so, to that of eastern Greenland. That a single formation (in a broad sense) should have Lower Cambrian fossils at the bottom and Lower Ordovician ones at the top is clearly a problem. One distinguished Danish geologist, on a fleeting visit to Britain, did find an unconformity in the middle like one he knew in Greenland, but no one else seems to have seen it, and the situation is very comparable with that in other fragments of a dismembered early North American continent. The contrast between the early Palaeozoic faunas here and those in the Anglo-Welsh area is described in every textbook and blamed, presumably correctly, on continental wanderings, but it should not be forgotten that there is also a considerable contrast in sedimentary environments.

Higher Palaeozoic rocks were lost, if they were ever there, in the forward thrusting of the Caledonian front which, as the Moine Thrust, is always there to the east. There is a patch of about 3000 m of red sandstones and conglomerates near Stornoway the 'capital' of the Outer Hebrides, which it would be easy to call Torridonian but which is currently regarded as Permo-Triassic in age. After that the next sediments in the Hebridean Province are the Mesozoic successions of the Inner Hebrides (with some small patches on the mainland). Triassic conglomerates and sandstones pass up into marine Lower Jurassic beds that are particularly well seen on the island of Skye and the smaller island of Raasay that lies to its east. This is thicker than elsewhere and with unusual developments such as an ironstone in the Upper Lias of Raasay that was worked during the First World War. It also includes fossils that show closer affinities with Greenland than with other parts of Britain.

Marine deposition in early mid Jurassic times was followed by deltaic sedimentation as on the opposite side of Scotland, and then by a further marine transgression in the Callovian (as in many other parts of Europe) which continued into the Kimmeridgian. But these later Jurassic beds and thin late Cretaceous sandstones are only preserved in tiny patches, mostly on Skye. Lower Cretaceous and Tertiary also occur offshore. All was then smothered along the coast in Tertiary extrusives.

2(b) Thulean Volcanic Region

If you ask a non-geologist what he knows of the rocks of the Hebrides, the feature he is most likely to remember (thanks partly but not wholly to Mendelssohn) is the columnar basalt of Fingal's Cave in the island of Staffa. Ask the same question about Northern Ireland and the answer would be the Giant's Causeway. Both of these tourist spectacles relate to the first phase of a period of intense volcanic activity in the western part of the British Isles, early in Tertiary times.

It is a geological paradox in north-west Europe that the most placid and urbanized sediments (e.g., in the London and Paris Basins) are contemporaneous with the volcanic rocks of some of the wildest scenery in the continent. The area under consideration (Fig. 2.2) is most of the Inner Hebrides (notably the islands of Skye, Mull, Rum, and Eigg), the peninsulas of Ardnamurchan and Morvern, part of the Isle of Arran to the south, and most of Northern Ireland. The term 'Thulean' is often applied here (sometimes in a much broader sense) following the concept of Thule, a semi-mythical land at the extreme north-westerly end of Europe beyond which there was nothing. If you go there you appreciate how well the name fits.

The rocks through which most of these volcanics punch, at least in Scotland, are those of the Hebridean Province, that is to say Lewisian gneisses overlain by flat-lying Torridonian sandstones and a scarcely disturbed succession of Palaeozoic and Mesozoic sediments. In the east, some of the intrusions come through metamorphic rocks of the

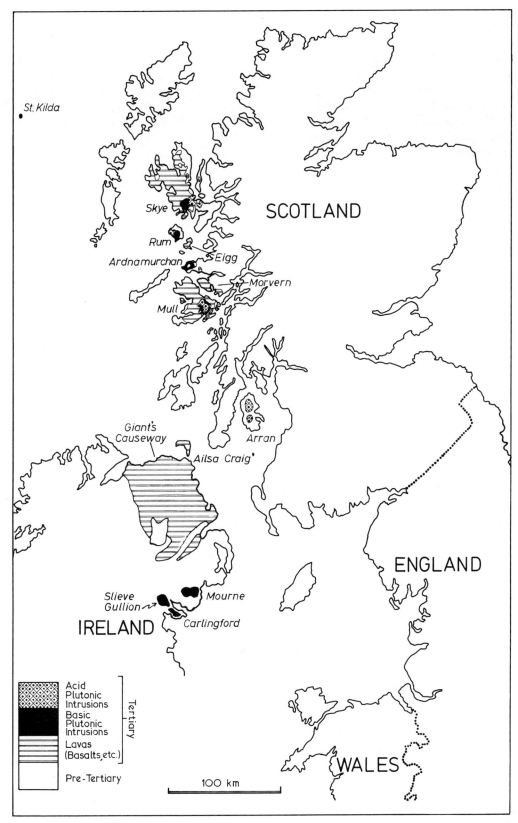

St. Kilda

Skye

Rum

Ardnamurchan

Eigg

Morvern

Mull

SCOTLAND

Giant's
Causeway

Ailsa Craig

Arran

Slieve
Gullion

Mourne

Carlingford

IRELAND

ENGLAND

WALES

Acid
Plutonic
Intrusions

Basic
Plutonic
Intrusions

Lavas
(Basalts, etc.)

Pre-Tertiary

Tertiary

100 km

Fig. 2.2 Sketch-map showing the distribution of Tertiary plateau basalts, intrusive centres, and dike swarms, in the British area (based on Richey, 1961).

Scottish Caledonides, and in Ireland they are wholly within Palaeo-Europa. Some of the late phase dikes go very much farther. However, since so many of them lie west of the Moine Thrust and because they are clearly part of the history of the Atlantic, it seems most reasonable to include them here.

The volcanism is usually assumed to have started very early in Palaeogene times, although there is some evidence that it may have begun even earlier. This is more acceptable now that Mesozoic volcanicity in the British area is not such an unthinkable idea as it would have been a few years ago. There are problems over the dating partly, I suspect, because the floras present have variously been compared with those of Green-land to the north and those of south-east England to the south, mixing latitude with age. It has also been suggested recently, with the increasing evidence from radiometric dates, that the volcanicity was concentrated into a very short time indeed.

The first phase of activity was great outpourings of plateau basalts. These may have come from volcanic centres or from fissures, but they did so very gently, with little evidence of any explosive violence. They are inevitably associated in geologists' minds with the ripping open at this time of the northern part of the North Atlantic. It is also logical to connect them with those other volcanic islands of the North Atlantic, the Faroes, and Iceland which, although similar in nature, are much later in age. It has been suggested that the sort of elongated mantle 'hot spot' that underlies Iceland at the present day extended, in early Tertiary times, along the western coastline of Britain. Connecting links are provided by tiny St. Kilda, the loneliest of the British Isles, out on the edge of the continental shelf and by dredgings from the Porcupine and Rockall Banks, which may be regarded as detached fragments of the continent.

The largest area of these basalts is in Ulster, where a succession of flows covers some 3800 km², forming the Antrim Plateau with sheer black cliffs along the coast. The lavas rest on faulted and eroded Mesozoic and older rocks which have been cooked to most unfamiliar forms and colours by the heat. The finding here of roasted Jurassic ammonites in what looked like an igneous rock was a strong argument for the 'plutonists', who favoured fiery birth-pangs for the rocks in the days of the great battles between them and the 'neptunists' who preferred a more placid, watery origin.

The Giant's Causeway near Portrush, on the north coast, was an alleged attempt by an Irish giant to build a link to Scotland, long before the Unionist Party. Its columnar weathering (like that of Fingal's Cave) is, of course, just a splendid example of a cooling effect that is widespread in these basalts, although unusual in that here it fills a pre-existing valley, with the columns tilted as they sweep down its sides. A special feature of the Giant's Causeway is a bright red horizon between the basalts, which represents a long period of lateritic weathering in tropical conditions. Iron and bauxite were both formerly worked extensively in Northern Ireland at this level. Lignite also occurs here, as well as abundant plant remains of a strikingly modern appearance.

In Scotland, the continuation of what must have been a vast black blanket of basalt covers the greater part of Mull and the northern half of Skye. It is also seen in many smaller islands (such as Staffa) and on the mainland peninsula of Morvern. Here it shows a series of nearly 500 m of persistent lava flows which spread gently over a vast land surface and which characteristically weather into staircases. Soils formed between the basalts, including stratigraphically useful plant horizons with exotic plants such as the lotus, magnolia, and *Ginkgo*, seem out of place under these grey northern skies.

40

In Mull there is a central caldera from which some of the basalts may have flowed. An interesting feature is the presence of thick pillow lavas which must have formed by flowing into periodic crater lakes. This is a clear warning to those who automatically associate such things with ocean floors for, although probably related to the opening of the Atlantic, there is no hint here of the sea.

In Skye the succession is thicker and more varied, with rhyolites as well as the inevitable basalts, and—unusual in this general setting—some tuffs indicating at least a little explosive activity. This was symptomatic of what was to follow in the way of much more violent volcanism. Explosive vents appeared in both Scotland and Northern Ireland. All that is seen now are the roots of rotted volcanoes, which are the great complex intrusions. Basic sills were first injected, such as those that form the spectacular cliffs of Fair Head in Antrim and north of Portree in Skye. Then, in Ireland, came the complex stories of Carlingford, Slieve Gullion, and the Mountains of Mourne rolling down to the sea south of Belfast. These three upland areas are granitic masses with complicated histories. Thus in the Mournes there were no fewer than five successive emplacements which resulted from a 'cauldron subsidence' of Silurian rocks. The granites represent repeated intrusion at depth as the country rock of Silurian age foundered into the underworld. They have been worked extensively for building stone. The ships that took Cambrian slate to Ireland brought back Mourne granite to pave Lancashire and build the Albert Memorial in Kensington Gardens.

Similar repeated intrusions occurred in the Cuillin Hills of Skye, Ardnamurchan, south-central Mull, and Arran. In Skye, for example, there are the Red Hills of granite in the east and the Black Hills (or Cuillins *sensu stricto*) of gabbro in the west. Nevertheless, geologists have managed to observe that there are as many as twelve successive phases in this very complex intrusion, with the main basic intrusions preceding the acid ones, but with a long series of minor basic and ultra-basic intrusions taking place thereafter.

Cone-sheets and ring-dikes are particular features of the intrusive masses. The former were probably the result of a diapirically rising body of magma, while the latter were the effect of the subsidence at the end of an intrusive episode. The centres of activity moved with time, so that there are two distinct centres on Mull and three on Ardnamurchan. Each centre is characterized by great masses of granophyre and granite although geophysical studies indicate gravity 'highs', suggesting columns of basic material below each centre.

This is not the place to go into the bewildering complexity of these igneous centres which are classic for their variety of intrusive and extrusive characters. There are some really magnificent structures, such as the huge, although degraded, caldera forming the central complex on Ardnamurchan. There are vents containing fragments of sedimentary rocks that are not known anywhere *in situ*. There are unbelievable concentrations of dikes, so that in places there are more dikes than country rock. And there are repeated changes in rock composition, ringing the changes from the most basic to the most acid and back again, to satisfy the most dedicated geochemist. But it is the concentration of these phenomena, both in area and time, that is their most fascinating feature.

Apart from the main centres, there are also a number of smaller intrusive bodies scattered over a larger area. These range down through those of Arran and Rum to tiny Ailsa Craig, well on the way from Scotland to Ireland, which is famous for its evil-smelling gannetry and for its riebeckite microgranite which is easily recognized as glacial erratics and was formerly worked to make the stone discs used in the curious Scottish sport of 'curling'.

The final episode in this spasm of volcanic activity was the emplacement of vast dike swarms on north-west–south-east lines. These extend far beyond this area. They cross Northern Ireland into the Republic in one direction and via the Isle of Man to Wales and central England in the other. The Scottish ones spread up to the Outer Hebrides and down across southern Scotland into northern England, where they swing eastwards and even reach the North Sea. They concentrate on the centres and become scarcer as one moves away from them. The far-travelled ones, such as the Cleveland Dike of Yorkshire, are all basic in composition, but more acid types are found near the centres. Most distant of all is the tiny granite island of Lundy in the Bristol Channel, which is now known to be part of a Tertiary intrusive centre.

2(c)   Scottish continental shelf

The continental shelf to the west of Scotland is obviously part of Eo-Europa, although the level of knowledge is quite different from that of the land areas. We are always contrasting the continents and the oceans in structure and geological history, but I am always struck by the abrupt changes that so often accompany the step from the seashore on to the continental shelf. This is particularly well shown in the Hebridean region, where we now know that the masses of very ancient rocks on land are separated by basins of very young sediment offshore.

The most obvious feature that has emerged from oil exploration in this region in recent years has been the presence of long normal faults parallel to the edge of the shelf which have let down and controlled sedimentation in long narrow troughs (Fig. 2.3). One of these—the Minch Fault—has already been mentioned because it was deduced as a transcurrent movement to account for the relative displacement of the Lewisian outcrops. However, it clearly also has a considerable vertical throw and delimits a deep basin of Mesozoic and Tertiary sediments between the Scottish mainland and the Outer Hebrides (Fig. 2.4).

These graben structures start from the Firth of Clyde running up to Glasgow (well into Palaeo-Europa) and extend to beyond St. Kilda. The Great Glen Fault (Chapter 5), which has several times torn Scotland apart, is included in this story and runs parallel to the other main features. It may be that all the major faults had a considerable lateral component early in their history, as we know to be the case with the Great Glen Fault and perhaps the Minch Fault. From Permo-Triassic times onwards, however, vertical movements seem to have dominated, producing asymmetrical basins in which up to about 5000 m of Mesozoic and Tertiary sediments accumulated. These are always thicker and coarser on the western sides. This followed a long period of continental emergence, with arid desert conditions all over the Scottish region. The two main basins are on either side of the Outer Hebrides. That to the east, often called the Sea of the Hebrides, is in effect divided up into a series of smaller basins, separated by pre-Mesozoic rocks or by areas where much less sediment accumulated. The supposedly Permo-Triassic deposits of the Stornoway district of Lewis, are, in fact, just a marginal lobe of the sediments that accumulated throughout this trough below the present sea-level.

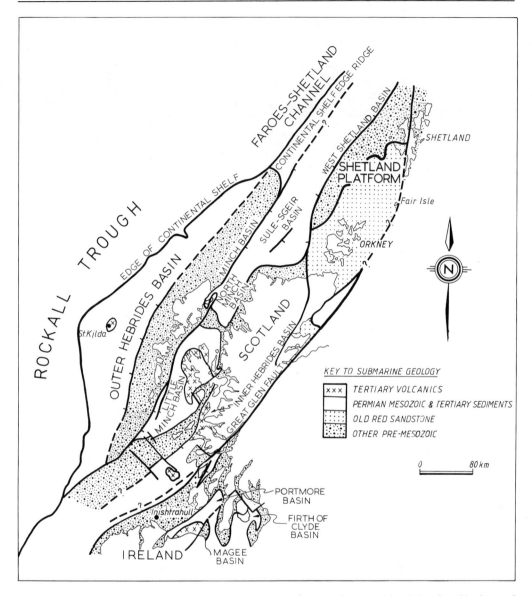

Fig. 2.3 *Sketch-map of the continental shelf to the west of Scotland (mainly after Naylor and Mounteney, 1975, by kind permission of Messrs Graham and Trotman Ltd).*

Much of our understanding of the continental shelf comes from gravity and seismic studies. The former show up clearly features such as the Minch Fault, but for the most part they only tell us about great thicknesses of sediment of uncertain age resting on the metamorphic basement. However, more evidence is being collected in oil exploration, and some of it is being published. The Permian and Triassic rocks (if they are really both there) are dominantly sandstones and conglomerates and would make good hydrocarbon

43

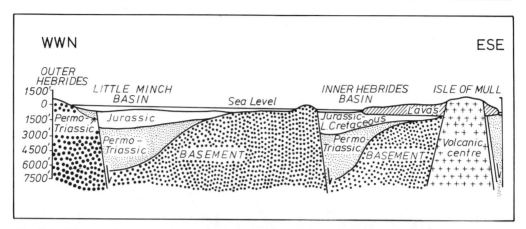

Fig. 2.4 *Diagrammatic cross-section of the continental shelf west of Scotland (after Naylor and Mounteney, 1975, by kind permission of Graham and Trotman Ltd).*

reservoirs were there any source rocks. They reach about 3000 m in thickness at Stornoway.

The Jurassic is about 300 m thick in Skye and thereabouts, but it is not thought to contribute a great deal to the infill of the shelf basins, since the record is so thin and scattered on islands such as Mull and Arran. The same could be said of the Cretaceous, which is known mainly by a few scattered remnants of late Cretaceous desert sands and chalk of no great thickness. More may be preserved in the north, west of the Orkneys and Shetlands.

So far as the Tertiary is concerned, most of what we know on dry land in this region consists of huge quantities of extrusives. We know that there is a certain amount more of this below the waves, notably west of Skye and around the Blackstones rocks (Dubh Artach) south-west of Mull. We must also never forget St. Kilda and its neighbouring rocks, way out beyond the Outer Hebrides. But the most surprising feature of the west Scottish continental shelf is the presence of great thicknesses of Tertiary sediments. These are not in all the basins. In fact there is probably little or none in the Inner Hebrides and Minch basins. But farther north, in the Sule-Sgeir and West Shetland basins, the Tertiary is probably nearly as thick as the whole Mesozoic and we know now that there is at least one important oil-field to be developed here.

Although not strictly relating to this chapter, it is noteworthy that the Shetland Platform east of a metamorphosed backbone of very ancient rocks, is largely formed of a considerable thickness of 'Old Red Sandstone'. This is continuous with the Devonian post-orogenic basins of north-east Scotland, but indicates that at least part of the shelf here (as in the North Sea) was subsiding way back in Palaeozoic times.

Westwards the Tertiary thickens markedly into what are truly oceanic deposits. Little is known about the Outer Hebrides Basin, but the sea-floor drops steeply down the continental slope beyond our reach and concern. In the north, the Faroes–Shetland Channel is quite a narrow passage between Europe and the volcanic Faroes Shelf. Farther south the much larger feature of the Rockall Trough separates the British Isles from that remarkable feature known as the Rockall Bank. The tiny island of Rockall, the last conquest of the British Empire, is clearly part of a continental fragment of Precambrian metamorphic rocks, from which Grenville dates have been obtained. It is cut by Tertiary igneous extrusives and intrusives such as the granite which forms the tiny island itself. A major fracture across the Rockall Bank matches up with the Great Glen Fault if one first closes up the Rockall Trough.

The inescapable conclusion would seem to be that these graben, and the edge of the continental shelf itself, were all formed during a major tensional episode at about the beginning of Mesozoic times. Faulting produced and preserved the sedimentation in the troughs. It is then but a step to relate this faulting to the various graben that formed in Triassic times onshore in western Europe and north-west Africa and along the eastern seaboard of the United States. One more step takes us then to the first stages in the opening of the modern Atlantic.

In the north it may be said that the attempted separation failed; at least it only went far enough to produce the narrow Faroes–Shetland Channel. In the south, it went much farther, but the Rockall Bank may be regarded as a torn-off piece of Europe that did not make the crossing. Probably we had no true ocean here for a very long time after the initial splitting, but the western Scottish continental shelf preserves an almost unique record of this crucial moment in the history of Europe.

Selected references to Chapter 2

Section 2(a) Precambrian Basement and sedimentary cover

Craig, G. Y., ed. (1965), *The Geology of Scotland*, Oliver and Boyd, Edinburgh and London, 556 pp.

Park, R. G. and J. Tarney, eds (1973), *The Early Precambrian of Scotland and Related Rocks of Greenland*, Univ. Keele, 200 pp.

Phemister, J. (1960), *British Regional Geology. Scotland: The Northern Highlands*, 3rd edn, Geol. Surv. and Mus., London, 104 pp.

Sutton, J. and J. Watson (1951), 'The pre-Torridonian metamorphic history of the Loch Torridon and Scourie areas in the North-West highlands, and its bearing on the chronological classification of the Lewisian', *Quart. Jl. Geol. Soc., Lond.*, **106**, 241–307.

Watson, J. (1975), 'The Lewisian Complex', Geol. Soc., Lond., Spec. Rep. No. 6, 15–29.

Section 2(b) Thulean volcanic region

Brooks, M. (1973), 'Some aspects of the Palaeogene evolution of western Britain in the context of an underlying mantle hot spot', *J. Geol.*, **81**, 81–88.

Charlesworth, J. K. (1963), *Historical Geology of Ireland*, Oliver and Boyd, Edinburgh and London, 565 pp.

Richey, J. E. (1961), *Scotland: The Tertiary Volcanic Districts*, 3rd edn, Inst. Geol. Sci., British Regional Geology, 120 pp. (and many detailed memoirs produced by the Institute of Geological Sciences).

Walker, G. P. L. (1975), 'A new concept of the evolution of the British Tertiary intrusive centres', *Jl. Geol. Soc. Lond.*, **131**, 121–41.

Whittow, J. B. (1974), *Geology and Scenery in Ireland*, Penguin Books, Harmondsworth, 301 pp.

Section 2(c) Scottish continental shelf

Binns, P. E., R. McQuillin, and N. Kenolty (1974), 'The geology of the Sea of the Hebrides', Inst. Geol. Sci., London, Rep. No. 73/14, 44 pp.

Naylor, D. and S. N. Mounteney (1975), *Geology of the North-west European Continental Shelf*, vol. 1, Graham Trotman Dudley, London, 162 pp.

Chapter Three

East European Platform

South and east of the Fenno-Scandian Shield is the vast area of the East European Platform which is directly linked to it in fundamental geology, notably in its exceptionally thick crust (more than 40 km) which is considerably thicker than the rest of the continent. The platform may be considered in four parts, as follows:

1. The Russo-Polish Plain, where the shield rocks are hidden under later sediments.
2. The Caspian Depression, where the floor drops steeply at the south-east corner of Europe.
3. The Ukrainian Massif, where the ancient rocks of the Shield emerge again at the surface.
4. Timan, that curious belt in the Arctic north, which appears to be related to the Caledonides, the Urals, and to the platform; to this must be added the Pechora Depression beyond, and remote Franz Josef Land.

3(a) Russo-Polish Plain

The endless monotony of the Russo-Polish Plain is the largest single natural division of Europe, although due to its uniformity there is comparatively little to say about it geologically. It is delimited to the east by the Urals, to the south by the Alpine fold belts, to the north-west by the Fenno-Scandian Shield, and to the west by the Tornquist/Danish–Polish Line separating it from the Baltic Plain, which continues the monotony to the North Sea (Fig. 3.1).

The Russo-Polish Plain is comparable to the Stable Interior of the USA (between the Appalachians and the Rockies) in topography, in tectonic position, and in stratigraphical history. Geographers divide it into the harsh Tundra Belt of the Arctic north, the densely forested Central Russian Tableland in the centre, and the Black Earth region of the Steppes in the south. Although the major part of it lies in European Russia, it also includes the Baltic States, Belorussia ('White Russia'), part of the Ukraine, and a large part of Poland.

Throughout the greater part of this immense region there is a comparatively thin, flat-lying cover of Palaeozoic and later sediments on the Precambrian metamorphic

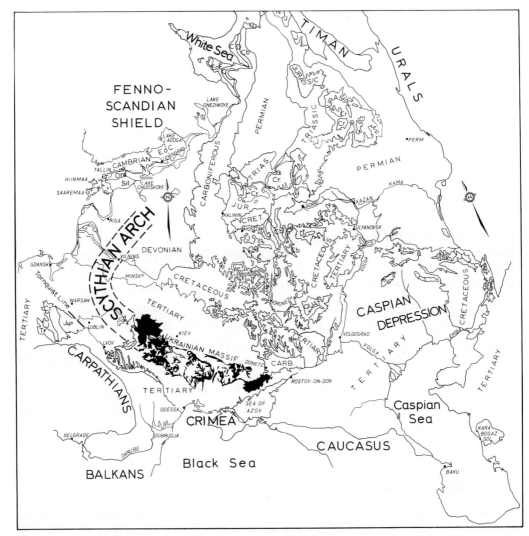

Fig. 3.1 *Geological sketch-map of the East European Platform (founded on the International Geological Map of Europe).*

basement. This cover thickens in places into broad, flat-bottomed basins, approaching 4000 m deep, such as the Moscow Basin, which may be compared with structures such as the Illinois Basin in the Stable Interior. These are what Russians like to call 'synclises' and some Americans call 'auto-' and 'zeugo-' geosynclines; I shall stick to 'basins'. The corresponding rises between the basins are 'anteclises'.

Because of their flat-lying nature, the same strata outcrop over considerable distances, although they are rarely seen under a thick glacial cover in the north and a thick loess cover in the south. At the same time, because of their thin development, the outcrops are often deeply dissected, producing extremely complex outcrop patterns on the geological map, especially around the great river systems between Moscow and the Black Sea.

In the simplest terms the basement is similar to what is seen at the surface in the Fenno-Scandian Shield. The general north-westerly trend of most of the Fenno-Scandian Shield appears to continue under the northern part of the Russian Plain and then to swing round in a north-easterly direction under Moscow and on towards the Tornquist Line. South of Moscow and Warsaw, however, it turns sharply north-west again, paralleling the Ukrainian Massif and other major features in the basement. Archaean rocks have been detected in many places within a general 'matrix' of Proterozoic, notably a large mass in the 'knee-bend' north-east of Moscow, in northern Estonia, northern Poland, and in two areas west of Volgograd (Stalingrad). Others have postulated much more (even in the same book) so that most of the East European Platform would, according to them, be directly underlain by very ancient rocks like the Saamides of the Shield.

It is presumably significant that the faulted troughs or 'aulacogens' that cut across the ancient surface trend predominantly towards the north-west and north-east. There is convincing evidence that most of the major structures in the cover are reflections of structures within the basement itself. Thus the Moscow Basin, which is elongated north-east–south-west, corresponds with a mobile zone in the Riphean (late Precambrian) and with the general trend of the basement. South-east of Moscow the Pachel'ma structure trends north-west as does the White Sea.

But the chief interest on the Russo-Polish Plain must attach to the Phanerozoic systems which are all represented and which are so perfectly preserved. If you take the train or road from Leningrad to Moscow, you pass in turn over late Precambrian, Cambrian, Ordovician, Devonian, Carboniferous, Jurassic, and Cretaceous rocks. A slight detour would take in the Permian and a bigger detour the overstepped Silurian and Triassic as well, all in the correct order. It is comparable to the somewhat shorter, classic traverse from Anglesey to London, except that all the strata (and not just the later ones) are almost flat and untroubled by deformation or alteration.

Immediately adjacent to the Fenno-Scandian Shield are undisturbed 'Eocambrian' deposits. Leningrad stands on them where they cross the Karelian isthmus between the Gulf of Finland and Lake Ladoga (an isthmus much in the news during the winter of 1939–40). From there the outcrop passes on to Lake Onega where it disappears, to reappear again in the broad peninsula that projects into the White Sea.

These rocks have usually been referred to as the 'Vendian' (named in traditional fashion after a local tribe) but, in the absence of good evidence, the arguments about correlation have been intense. Soviet geologists have done marvels in extracting spores and simple organisms from Precambrian rocks, but the matter is still far from settled. Generally a whole group of such contrasting formations around the platform is placed in the 'Sinian', but as this was founded on sections near Pekin, the term 'Riphean' of local connotation seems preferable.

The 'Vendian' rocks are essentially a conglomerate–sandstone–clay succession, with a fair amount of organic material, including jelly-fish in the White Sea area. They have been correlated by some workers with the 'Eocambrian' of Scandinavia, which seems to be acceptable, but the diverse developments known in various places under the cover of the Russo-Polish Plain probably range down lower in the Proterozoic and up into the Cambrian. Such sediments, together with volcanic material, can be traced all the way down to Saratov (on the Volga north of Volgograd) in one direction, and to the front of the Carpathians in the other, but they are absent from a large part of the platform in the south. In places, late Precambrian sediments are difficult to distinguish from the Palaeozoic above (e.g., from Devonian sandstones) and they are impossible to distinguish when only geophysical data are available.

Cambrian rocks provide a fringe along the south coast of the Gulf of Finland in Estonia, and from there all the way up to the Barents Sea. Again there is a classic succession of sands passing up into clays—the famous ' blue clays' which are particularly well known around Leningrad. It is symptomatic of these clays and of the deposits on the East European Platform generally, that the standard Russian textbook comments that 'the blue Cambrian clays of the Baltic countries are almost indistinguishable from the blue Quaternary clays'. The latter also inconveniently fringe this coast as a record of the wider extension of the Baltic during late post-glacial times. Subsurface, Cambrian and Ordovician rocks are known to extend beyond the longitude of Moscow eastwards and south-westwards into Poland. Similarly, the Ordovician and Silurian outcrop in turn across Estonia, forming the south-east limb of the Baltic syncline. The Ordovician is particularly noteworthy on the island of Hiiumaa and at Kukruse on the mainland, where oil shale or kukersite was quarried and is now mined on a big scale. It is an accumulation of unicellular algae and lights with a match; it is also best known to palaeontologists for the fabulous preservation of its larger fossils such as trilobites. The oil reminds one of concentrations in the Ordovician of Sweden and, generally speaking, the succession is very similar, with a notable development of carbonates (like the Palaeozoic in general all over the Russian Plain). Fossils are so abundant and well preserved that at one place in Estonia they quarry Ordovician inarticulate brachiopods for phosphate. Most of the deposits are clearly of shallow-water origin, including glauconitic sandstones and phosphorites, and the whole system forms a sedimentary cycle with a transgression at the bottom and a regression at the top. The latter removed the Ordovician sea from the greater part of the Russo-Polish Plain, back to its Baltic source.

The Silurian too matches the Swedish story. It outcrops on Saaremaa, as has already been mentioned, and then across the centre of Estonia to Lake Chudskoye (Peipis). After that it is overstepped by the Devonian, although it is known in boreholes to the south, in Lithuania and Latvia. It is the usual story of limestones and shales, all very shallow water, passing up into lagoonal deposits and evaporites. It is a Baltic story and hardly part of the Russian Plain at all. Unlike the Ordovician, the Silurian does not extend southwards (except possibly as terrestrial deposits) and the sea soon withdrew. South-westwards, however, it is known in many borings in eastern Poland, where it passes into deeper water muddy deposits with graptolites.

The Devonian rocks of the plain present quite a different story. They outcrop over a very large area and show the classic passage from terrestrial 'Old Red Sandstone' facies in the north to marine Devonian in the south. From southern Estonia, the main Devonian outcrop extends nearly to Minsk and to beyond Smolensk in the south, and then as complex valley inliers to Voronezh (all familiar wartime names) and way down the Volga. Underground Devonian strata extend almost everywhere, except where older rocks show through, and are known in considerable detail because of their economic importance.

Although there was nothing that could be called a Caledonian orogeny in this region, the effects of happenings elsewhere produced major geographical changes at the end of early Palaeozoic times. The sea withdrew almost completely from the plain and much of the thin cover on the basement rocks must have been eroded away at this time. The only sediments that are regarded as Lower Devonian are some sandstones and clays in bore-holes near Sovetsk in Lithuania (best known to those of us who remember their history as Tilsit) and the lower part of the 'Old Red Sandstone' in the Baltic States and over towards the Urals. The latter facies has enough fish and plants for dating purposes, although it could be that part of it represents the missing uppermost Silurian.

Higher up in the 'Old Red Sandstone' there is a classic story of lateral change in sediments, in faunas, and in floras as it is traced from the Baltic into the limestone country of central Russia. The main transgression was at the beginning of mid Devonian times, when the sea that had lingered on in the Urals trough burst its banks north of Perm and flooded across the deeply eroded platform. The transgression reached its maximum in the Frasnian and then withdrew again to the south.

At the time of the maximum extent of the sea there accumulated the bituminous limestones and shales (with their oil migrating into associated sands) that make the country between the Volga and the Urals one of the great oil-producing regions of the Soviet Union. As in many other parts of the world, the Frasnian here marked a climax in limestone deposition. In the Famennian, the limestones were replaced by dolomites and then, with the withdrawal of the sea at the end of the period, gypsum, anhydrite, and halite. Some of these are also of considerable economic importance, especially in the north-east.

In the north-west of the Soviet Union, the Devonian progressively oversteps the Lower Palaeozoic systems right down to the Precambrian as one traces the outcrop northwards, before it is overstepped, in turn, by the Carboniferous.

Under the Polish part of the Russo-Polish Plain, Devonian rocks are almost unknown. Evidently the Ukrainian Massif and its continuation formed a barrier and/or was later uplifted so that all evidence was eroded away. Younger sediments rest directly on the Lower Palaeozoic. However, the persistence of similar facies belts of 'Old Red Sandstone' and marine Devonian west of the Tornquist Line implies that, in part at least, the period did not pass unnoticed at the western end of the platform.

Carboniferous rocks also outcrop over a broad belt of the Russo-Polish Plain, coming down from the Barents Sea in a broad sweep to beyond Ryazan, south-east of Moscow. There is also a large separate outcrop in the Donetzk* Basin in the south. After the 'Old Red Sandstone' and the Frasnian limestones, the Carboniferous succession too sounds familiar to the western European, with a dominance of limestones in the lower part and of clays and sands in the upper. But it is much more complicated than this, especially in terminology. Russian geologists still recognize a division known as the 'Middle Palaeo-zoic', not accepted internationally, but comprising the Silurian, Devonian, and Lower Carboniferous. This puts a major boundary somewhere in the middle of the Russian Carboniferous. Also it must be pointed out that here most of the coal occurs in the lower part of the system (as in Scotland). It is mined on a big scale in the Moscow Basin and thereabouts, but over large areas the whole system consists of an unbroken limestone succession.

---

* The familiar usage of Russian place names in their anglicized forms commonly differs from standard transliteration and even from simple logic. I have tried to be consistent on the basis of the Russian spelling, so it is Donetzk rather than Donetz or Donets.

The sea spread from the Urals in Tournaisian times to a complex shoreline in the west. The so-called Scythian Arch prevented it spreading farther into central Europe, although it broke through at times into a Podolian basin around Lvov. This just extended into modern Poland. Carbonates were deposited and were then eroded again below the first Visean deposits. Over much of the plain at this time continental conditions prevailed with the local formation of coal measures. In Podolia such conditions persisted (with marine incursions) throughout Visean times. In the Donetzk Basin, on the other hand, and in the south generally, the whole succession is marine. But over the greater part of the Russo-Polish Plain, the Visean was dominantly a period of pure limestone deposition. Many of the low hills such as the Valdaiian Uplands, north-west of Moscow, are formed of these limestones, with the Upper Carboniferous sediments forming the valleys in between. One remembers that, at the other end of Europe and even in the USA, this used to be called the 'Mountain Limestone' because of its topographical prominence. The traditional white building stone of Moscow comes from this part of the succession.

The complexities of early Carboniferous palaeogeography are impossible to summarize, although they make a fascinating story of faunal and floral distribution. There are coals and bauxites and plant beds where there was emergence, gradations in salinity with abundant shallow-water invertebrates of all kinds and away to the east, the source of it all, the Uralian trough.

The Upper Carboniferous here, including what the Russians call Namurian, Bashkirian, and Moscovian (placed by them in the 'Middle' Carboniferous) is equally extensive and calcareous. There are now large fusulinid foraminifera for correlation and many small divisions can be recognized. There was still land in the west and again the sea was shallow and the facies complex. In the south there was another shoreline and thousands of metres of sands and clays accumulated in the Donetzk Basin. Land floras interdigitate with the marine invertebrates. This southern development has been compared with flysch. Within this are the very important coals of the Donetzk Basin which range through the Upper Carboniferous and Lower Permian. They form the end point of a long belt of Coal Measure deposition that extended all the way to the American Mid-West.

The Permian was, in many ways, the climax of the Russo-Polish Plain's history. It was, of course, here that Murchison named the system, after the city and province of Perm,* east of Moscow. The outcrops are immense. The Perm one is a huge triangle with its base on the Urals and its apex almost at Moscow. It dips down under the north-easterly trending Moscow Basin to appear again in a broad belt running up to the Arctic. This is one of the classic regions of the earth for the passage of thin platform carbonates into thick geosynclinal deposits. The whole story is clearly displayed if one sails down the Kama River from Kazan into the Urals. The standard stage divisions of the Permian were all named hereabouts. But obviously the story is most complete in the thick Ural development, which is discussed in Chapter 11.

On the platform, uplift was beginning to get the better of subsidence, so that there are many gaps and lateral passages into continental deposits. In the Lower Permian south of

---

* Also known as Molotov, perhaps an even better name for a geological system (molot = hammer), but political vicissitudes caused it to revert to its old name.

Perm, for example, there is a remarkable development of reefs, up to 600 m thick, which have formed important oil-traps, while westwards into the Moscow Basin equivalent strata are down to 15 m. Northwards towards the Arctic the Lower Permian takes the form of red beds with gypsum and anhydrite. A similar situation, with complications, persisted all through the Permian, with continental deposits slowly getting the upper hand over the limestones and dolomites full of brachiopods, bivalves, goniatites, and schwagerinid forams. At times—as at the beginning of the late Permian—continental conditions with red beds or erosion, spread right across the Russo-Polish Plain. At other times—as in the later Kazanian—a shallow, carbonate, low-salinity sea, which has been compared with the contemporaneous Zechstein Sea of western Europe (although the faunas are quite different), spread westwards. However, the Zechstein Sea did invade the Polish end of the plain, being seen under the little Triassic outlier at Łeba on the north coast, north-west of Gdansk (the ominous Danzig of 1939). It also reached Latvia, where it outcrops south-west of Riga and is known in many boreholes in between, and down to the south of Warsaw. The earlier Stassfurt-type salts are known throughout the same area.

Throughout its vast outcrop, the Permian is for the most part hidden by Quaternary rubbish. The only exposures usually to be seen are splendid long river cliffs and, curiously enough, hills and ridges formed by the frequent masses of gypsum.

The last stage of the Permian, and of the Palaeozoic, was marked by a general withdrawal of the two seas, the main one back to the Urals and the Zechstein Sea back to the Alps. They were replaced by extensive fresh-water and saline lakes, lying in an arid desert of blowing dust and ephemeral streams. The vital boundary is, as so often, lost in the red beds and there is no perceptible break between the Palaeozoic and the Mesozoic.

The main outcrop of Triassic rocks on the Russo-Polish Plain is a large, roughly triangular area in the north-east, coming down from the Arctic almost to Gorkii. Little more is seen of rocks of this age apart from a small strip on the Latvian–Lithuanian frontier and the tiny outlier on the north Polish coast. The uplift continued and almost the whole platform was subject to erosion and continental deposition. Only way down in the Caspian Depression is there a thin record of early Triassic marine strata, while only the arrival of dinosaurs and new floras indicates that the era boundary has been passed. The red sandstones, mudstones, and conglomerates are almost entirely referred to as the Lower Triassic. Only locally, north of Gorkii, are there conglomerates and other deposits that may be later in age. Vast thicknesses of detrital material from the plain were accumulating around the Volga and Emba rivers to the south.

In Poland, the German-type Trias spread in from the south-west, including a widespread Muschelkalk, right up to the Baltic, but only the Lower Trias reached as far as Lithuania and Latvia, thinning rapidly northwards.

The main break on the plain occurs not between the Permian and the Triassic, but between the Lower Triassic and the Middle Jurassic. This makes the volume of Russian literature thankfully small for those of us that concentrate of the Lias! Early Jurassic seas were confined to the extreme north and south of the Soviet Union. Over the plain, erosion continued and continental sediments, including coals, accumulated in the Donetzk region. The sea began to invade again, both from the north and the south during mid Jurassic times, spreading down towards Perm and up towards Gorkii. Another sea from the west crossed the Tornquist Line into northern Poland. For the most part the deposits were dark clays and sands, as are all the Jurassic deposits of the Russo-Polish Plain (contrasting markedly with the bright limestones of Mediterranean Europe).

The main transgression came in the Callovian, which is why Russian geologists have been so keen to make this the bottom of the Upper Jurassic rather than the top of the Middle. Right through to the end of the period, clays and sands were laid down, albeit thinly, over a large part of the Russian Plain. Outcrops are seen chiefly in the north-east and centre. Moscow is, surprisingly, the only capital in Europe standing on Jurassic rocks. Unconsolidated sands and highly fossiliferous clays are seen in scattered exposures around the city. Farther east on the Volga, north of Lenin's birthplace of Ulyanovsk (Simbirsk), is the 'stratotype' of the Volgian Stage at the top of the system. This is typical of the Jurassic on the East European Platform generally, since it consists mainly of dark shales with a very abundant Boreal fauna of bivalves, belemites, and ammonites and shows evidence of frequent breaks in deposition with layers of bored phosphatic nodules.

In Poland, the mid Jurassic sea continued to spread north and east, reaching its maximum extent in the Callovian and seen in an outcrop running in from the Baltic across central Lithuania. Before the end of the period it had retreated again west of the Tornquist Line. One of the most remarkable deposits of Poland is a mass of Callovian clay at Łukow, south-east of Warsaw, which is literally packed with beautifully preserved, iridescent ammonites. This appears to have been carried there by ice (like other masses in north-west Poland). Some came from outcrops under the southern part of the Baltic. They show that the late Jurassic sea probably at times extended to a shoreline near Skåne and Bornholm. Farther south there are the limestones and sponge reefs of central Europe, standing up as sudden hills from the flat landscape, for example at Ogrodzieniec.

The early Cretaceous story continued that of the late Jurassic, with a fresh-water development in eastern Poland being followed by a break. In central Russia, the marine Volgian was followed by marine early Cretaceous deposits and some specialists want Ryazan, south-east of Moscow, to be chosen as the 'stratotype' of the basal stage of the Cretaceous. This again is a Boreal facies and would compete with the Berriasian of the Tethyan facies, but might help with the problem of Boreal Volgian competing with Tethyan (and mythical) Tithonian and Anglo-Saxon Portlandian. Personally I do not mind which of these we choose, so long as we all speak the same language.

Cretaceous rocks underlie most of the southern part of the Russo-Polish Plain, including virtually the whole of eastern Poland. They also occur in the axis of the Moscow Basin running up towards Timan. In the south they are mostly uppermost Cretaceous, whereas farther north they are nearly all pre-Cenomanian. The north was rising and the Aptian deposits there are near-shore sands and clays with abundant plant remains. By Cenomanian times the sea did not extend beyond Moscow, except in one small embayment. Southwards there were extensive spreads of sands (often glauconitic) passing southwards into deeper water deposits. At the west end of the plain, the transgression was more on the west European pattern with widespread Cenomanian deposits, extending up to Lithuania, being the culmination of an extension that began in the Albian. In fact it was probably during Albian times that the Scythian Arch was first crossed (just when the London–Brabant ridge was being flooded, over in my corner of Europe).

The glauconitic sands slowly passed up into sandy clays and marls, becoming progressively whiter until a great part of Europe was united under the warm, pure sea of the chalk. From the seas off south-west Ireland, via the white cliffs of Dover and the wheat-growing uplands of northern France, the white chalk extended across southern Scandinavia and the two Germanies to Poland and the southern part of Russia to the Urals. It also extended south to the Crimea and Georgia, and beyond the Black Sea to northern Turkey. The chalk is so familiar to northern Europeans that it seems almost superfluous to describe it. Throughout this vast belt it is remarkably uniform. The purity of its calcium carbonate is difficult to explain although it passes into sandy and clayey deposits near the shoreline and around the few remaining islands. It reaches some 750 m in thickness near Kharkov and in a famous borehole at Lublin, in south-east Poland, it reaches what is probably its greatest thickness (nearly 1200 m) and deepest facies. Old ideas about abyssal depths have now been abandoned and it is generally accepted as an outer shelf or upper slope deposit.

Movements during Cretaceous times in the fold belts to the south had their effects on the East European Platform, but generally speaking all that is seen is the subsidence of large troughs in which the greatest thicknesses accumulated. The platform continued its up-and-down existence, but was still basically stable. Elevation at the end of Cretaceous times led to the withdrawal of the sea again to the south.

Tertiary deposits are not widespread on the Russo-Polish Plain. Apart from a small incursion in the Arctic, they are confined to the south and are mostly in scattered patches, tens rather than hundreds of metres thick. The biggest patches in the Soviet Union are south of Ulyanovsk on the Volga, around the Ukrainian Massif and under the vast and gloomy Pripyat (Pripet) marshes on the borders of the western Ukraine and Belorussia. They extend up through north-east Poland to the Baltic. Many bits and pieces of the Tertiary succession have been recognized in boreholes in the Soviet Union and Poland, and the general story seems to be of repeated comings and goings of the sea from the south. Continental deposits tend to predominate, of which the most famous are the Oligocene beds containing lumps of coniferous resin that has become amber (with occasional trapped insects). This was worked on a big scale in that part of the Soviet Union and Poland that used to be called East Prussia.

In Neogene times a gradual rise led to the complete exclusion of the sea. Things were happening to the south, including intensive volcanism near the Sea of Azov that scattered ash into the Neogene sediments, but there is little to show of it in this region. Then followed the more startling events of the Quaternary (which the Russians like to call Anthropogene). The glaciations spread great thicknesses of till, outwash deposits, etc., over the northern plain. Russian friends of the Pleistocene get excited about the merest shadow of a morainic ridge in the endless flatness, just as do their opposite numbers in the American Mid-West. A more important east–west line of moraines south of Leningrad separates the Baltic drainage from that flowing ultimately into the Black Sea or Caspian Sea. The ice also provided almost the only tectonics on the Russian Plain by scuffing up the sediments in places into little thrusts and overturned folds, again reminiscent of things I have seen in the Stable Interior of North America, for example in southern Saskatchewan.

In Post-glacial times the sea broke right through again from the Gulf of Finland via Lakes Ladoga and Onega to the White Sea and the Arctic. Recent marine deposits are widespread along that sunless sea in the far north. Meanwhile in the south there accumulated vast and extensive thicknesses of loess and alluvial deposits along the Volga and other great rivers. These gave rise to the Black Earth of one of the most fertile regions of the world (again rivalled by the equivalent situation in the Mississippi basin of the American Mid-West).

Now the Russian people themselves are becoming important geological agents with their huge engineering schemes, such as the vast inland sea that now stretches out below the cliff on which stands Lenin's home town of Ulyanovsk.

3(b) Caspian Depression

As one traces the East European Platform down to the south-east, the floor suddenly drops away and we are in the Caspian Basin. The south of it is filled with the Caspian Sea. The north is the vast monotonous lowland (the Caspian Depression) that extends south-westwards from the southern end of the Urals to reach the Caspian Sea roughly between the Volga and the Emba rivers (see Fig. 3.1). It is hardly separable from the plain that stretches on westwards to Rostov-on-Don, the Sea of Azov, and beyond that via the Prichornomorsk Plain across north of the Crimea to Odessa and the mouths of the Danube. However, this latter hollow, sometimes called the Manitch Depression, is the frontal trough of the Greater Caucasus and the mountains of the Crimea, so is best considered in Neo-Europa.

The Caspian Depression may best be regarded as a great downwarp of the south-east corner of the Russian Platform. It is dominated in the north and west by the mighty Volga and presents a remarkable analogy with the Mississippi Embayment of North America, with the Volga playing the part of the Mississippi and the Caspian Sea/Black Sea the part of the Gulf of Mexico. Northwards stretches the East European Platform (Stable Interior of the USA), north-eastwards are the Urals (Appalachians), westwards are the Carpatho-Balkans (Rockies–Mexican Sierras), and southwards are the Crimean–Caucasus (Tertiary fold belts of the West Indies). This is hardly the place to pursue this analogy further but it is worth mentioning that both the Caspian Depression and the Mississippi Embayment are now known to have long histories as negative areas going back into Palaeozoic or even Precambrian times and may be regarded as 'failed arms' of triple junctions.

Below Volgograd, the Volga and a wide belt of the Transcaspian Plain is below sea-level, as is the Caspian Sea itself. The bleak steppe-land of the depression is thinly covered with alluvium, dusty loess, and drifting sand. Below is a considerable thickness of Tertiary deposits that reveal a continuously subsiding story. This is a part of the earth's crust that 'got that sinking feeling' a long time ago and has not yet got out of its depressive mood.

Geophysical work has shown that the northern part of the depression is more complicated than the rest, with two long but gentle elevations that rise as much as 3 km above the general floor of the structure. Recent deeper seismic work has revealed that the base of the crust may sink as low as 50 km below the surface. Two reference horizons have been traced all over the depression and have been identified as the boundaries between gabbros and eclogites and between eclogites and dunite-peridotites. The crust in the central part of the depression has been called sub-oceanic and identified as a relict structure of a very early Tethyan Ocean that may go back to Precambrian times. No boreholes have even reached the Lower Palaeozoic in the Caspian Depression but late Palaeozoic rocks are known.

Just as many of the rivers of this region terminate in highly saline lakes, so considerable salt deposits have accumulated here in the past, especially in the west. These punch up from Devonian and Lower Permian as much as 10 km down. They are commonly seen reaching the surface through Lower Cretaceous, Triassic, or Permian outcrops. Besides rock-salt there are domes of potash salts and they are both associated with thick gypsum developments, often forming cap-rocks.

Devonian and Carboniferous rocks are mainly known as fragments brought up in the diapirs, although they have been reached in at least one borehole. They are thick, marine, and somewhat metamorphosed. Permian rocks, on the other hand, do outcrop at the surface in the low Mugodzhar Range which forms the eastern edge of the depression, just beyond the Emba. They include a variety of sediments, but the most important are the thick Kungurian salts.

Generally speaking the Permian and early Triassic rocks are in their usual unfossiliferous red bed facies, (as much as 2500 m thick), although spores have helped. There is evidence of a marine transgression from the south in early Triassic times and this reminds one of the suggestion that the Caspian itself is a remnant of Triassic Tethyan oceanic crust.

Continental conditions returned, however, for the rest of the Triassic and the early and mid Jurassic. The latter rocks include workable coals and bituminous horizons which are probably the source of the oil associated with the salt-domes, especially in the often brecciated cap-rocks. It is not always clear from the Russian literature whether the oil mainly originated in the Middle Jurassic or (as in the North Sea) mainly accumulated there, but certainly rocks of this age are very important to the petroleum industry, and not only in the Caspian Depression. Oscillating marine and continental conditions continued through the rest of the Jurassic and the Cretaceous, with further oil-bearing horizons and true chalk, as in the Crimea, at the top of the Mesozoic.

The Cainozoic of the Caspian Depression is generally similar to the Pannonian, Dacian, and the other Neogene post-orogenic basins of Europe, with the gradual exclusion of the sea. Unlike them, however, its main northern continental part was largely beyond the influence of the Alpine movements, and the only surface structures worthy of the name are the upthrusting salt-domes which (as in the bayou country along the coast of the Gulf of Mexico) form the only topographic features in a monotonous landscape.

The present Caspian Sea can be regarded as a remnant, albeit a very large one, of the Caspian Depression as a whole, just as the Black Sea fills a much larger proportion of the Dacian Basin and Lake Balaton a much smaller proportion of the Pannonian Basin. Although it is comparable with the Black Sea in size, it is more comparable with Lake Balaton in history, since the outward marine connection was finally cut in Neogene times. The present remarkable fauna of the Caspian is derived from the fauna of the great brackish Pliocene lake that the sea proper left behind. The Caspian extended very widely to the north in late Pleistocene times, presumably with the melt waters of the ice coming off the Russo-Polish Plain and the Urals by way of the early Volga and several other large rivers. It is still highly saline, most notably in the large embayment of Kara Bogaz

Gol, halfway up its eastern coast, which is much cited in sedimentary texts for its modern evaporites.

At its southern end it rises steeply into the Elburz Mountains of northern Iran, but eastwards the plain seems to go on for ever, past the Aral Sea and far beyond the limits of our continent, there to rise to the 'Roof of the World' in Kirgizstan and Tadzhikstan.

3(c) Ukrainian Massif

If you ask someone which is the second largest country in Europe after Russia (and you have to word the question carefully) they never get it right. The answer is that very distinctive republic within the Soviet Union—the Ukraine. A large part of that country is occupied by an ancient massif—the Ukrainian or Podolian Massif—which is a sort of miniature Fenno-Scandian Shield. It is in fact a direct continuation of that shield, appearing again from beneath its cover of younger rocks at the very edge of Eo-Europa. To continue the analogy with North America, it may be compared with the Ozarks in southern Missouri and Arkansas which give us another glimpse of the Canadian Shield at the southern edge of the 'Stable Interior'.

The Ukrainian Massif is of no great height—little more than low hills in fact—and is deeply dissected by the major rivers of the region. It is also very much concealed, especially at its southern end, by thin Tertiary sediments. With it, for convenience, may be included the Voronezh Massif, west of that city and centred on Kursk. This is only seen at the surface in a few small hills and is almost entirely concealed beneath Palaeozoic and Mesozoic sediments, so that it does not appear on Fig. 3.1. It lies some 350 km north-east of the main massif, but is comparable in generalities.

The Ukrainian Massif exerted a considerable influence on geological history long after its ancient rocks had lithified. It appears to have been an upstanding feature in palaeogeography through a great part of Phanerozoic time. It formed part, with the White Russian Uplift (south-west of Minsk) and the Masurian Uplift (north-east of Warsaw) of the 'Scythian Arch'. This was a westward-facing, bow-shaped, positive feature with its apex near the Polish capital, that formed a barrier between seas and lakes extending from the east across the Soviet Union and from the west across Poland. The other parts of the arch are now completely buried, but the Ukrainian Massif has continued to persist as an obvious feature. The metamorphic rocks of the Ukrainian (and Voronezh) Massif seem, to an outsider, to match those of the Fenno-Scandian Shield. Lower Archaean or Katarchaean gneissose masses, more than 2700 million years old, are known among the migmatites of the region and may be compared with the Saamian and Belomorian cycles of the Shield. Archaean ophiolites have been recorded. The main part of the massif, however, would seem to be younger. There seem to have been three metamorphic cycles within the time interval 2700–1900 million years, the earliest one being the above migmatites, all more than 2300 million years old. There is then a set of granites emplaced between 2300 and 2100 and finally more granites, charnockites and migmatites dated as between 2100 and 1900 million years. All these are presumably the equivalent of the Svecofennides which make up so much of Sweden and Finland. The geosynclinal 'couple' of Karelide miogeosyncline and Svecofennide *sensu stricto* eugeosyncline may be traceable all the way from the Fenno-Scandian Shield to the Ukrainian Massif. The equivalent of the Karelides would be at the eastern end of the massif, in the neighbour-hood of Dnepropetrovsk. This would be a direct continuation of the south-south-easterly trend seen in the north.

In the early Proterozoic, the massif again allegedly went through three paroxysms, two tidily of 300 million years' duration and the last of 200, between 1900 and 1100 million years ago. They must be compared with the Gothides of Fenno-Scandia. Apart from the inevitable granites (and gabbros) at the end of the story, most of the rocks involved are recognizably sedimentary and volcanic in origin. The most valuable are the Krivoli Rog iron-ores which are worked on a big scale in the central part of the massif. These are seen again in the Voronezh Massif and can in fact be traced for a considerable distance as the Kursk Magnetic Anomaly. Their correlation with Scandinavia is a matter of some dispute, but they seem to be equivalent to Lower Proterozoic iron-ores elsewhere.

Above the metamorphic rocks come the usual late Proterozoic sandstones (some very like the Jotnian), together with argillaceous deposits and some volcanics. They are commonly rhythmically banded like flysch and could be called geosynclinal except that they do not reach great thicknesses, probably no more than 600 m.

Along the River Dnestr on the south-west side of the massif, not very far from the Romanian border and the frontal trough of the Carpathians, there are some very good sections in Lower Palaeozoic sediments. These are seen in river cliffs (up to 120 m high) near Kamanetz-Podolsk and Chernovitzy, both along the main river and some of its tributaries. The basement is not seen here, but late Precambrian sediments like those on the Baltic are overlain by Cambrian to Devonian sediments. It is a typical platform situation. Lower Cambrian glauconitic sandstones dipping at five or six degrees are overlain by Upper Ordovician sandstones and sandy limestones (only 0.4–6 m thick) dipping at one or two degrees. Then there is another break, without discordance, below the Silurian.

The Silurian, however, is somewhat different. It is much more widely distributed with a rich 'southern' fauna; it is thick (up to 850 m) and has no important breaks. For this reason it is classic in the Soviet Union and on an international scale. Presumably the unusual thickness relates to the deep trench then developing in front of what were to be the Carpathians. Everything thickens that way. At the bottom it consists mainly of carbonates, but as one passes up the succession more and more terrigenous material appears until at the top it passes into 'Old Red Sandstone' type of sediments of evidently fluvial origin. There is a gradual parallel passage from fully marine to fully fresh-water faunas of early Devonian age, with intriguing mixtures of the two in between. For this reason this area was considered as a possible standard for defining the Silurian–Devonian boundary.

The Lower Palaeozoic and Devonian rocks were very gently folded, so gently indeed as to be hardly worth mentioning. The next thing we know on the south-west side is transgressive Cretaceous (mainly Cenomanian) resting on a planed-off surface all along this part of the Dnestr. Above that again are Neogene deposits at the top of the river cliffs.

Tertiary deposits are very widespread and bury much of the Ukrainian Massif, especially at its southern end. On the north-east side of the massif, there is a much more complete story of these later rocks, which overstep the Palaeozoic and Cretaceous to rest directly on the Precambrian. A map of the lower surface of the sedimentary mantle of the whole East European Platform shows that this is the only place where Tertiary sediments rest directly on the basement, testifying to the positive role played by the massif.

A whole series of plateaux are developed above the great rivers of the region. Above the Don there is a plateau on the Eocene. Above the Donetzk there is a plateau on the overlying Oligocene and above the Dnepr a higher plateau on the same system where it rests on the Precambrian. Granites exposed in river valleys below the Oligocene have been much used as the foundations of dams, such as the one at Dnepropetrovsk which holds up an inland sea that generates immense quantities of hydroelectric power. The highest plateau is the Podolian Plateau above the Bug and Dnestr on Neogene strata. For the most part the plateaux are dull and featureless, although the top one is relieved by the development of many small reefs of Sarmatian age, which show up as little hills and are much quarried for building stone and lime.

3(d) Timan, Pechora Depression, and Franz Josef Land

This is the most forgotten corner of Europe. It consists of the north-east extremity of European Russia, mostly in the Arctic, and it is included here largely (although not entirely) because there seems to be nowhere else to put it (Fig. 3.2).

Timan is the strange fold belt that runs from north-west to south-east to meet the Urals north of Perm at an acute angle. The Pechora Depression is the triangle left between Timan and the northern Urals, and way beyond that is the lonely Franz Josef Land archipelago which, almost incredibly for a part of Europe, was only discovered in 1872.

Timan

Strictly speaking Timan does not belong to the East European Platform because it was strongly affected by the 'Baikalian' orogeny at the end of Proterozoic times (when late Precambrian sediments were being peacefully deposited to the west) and also by later movements that have been doubtfully called 'Caledonian'. It clearly predates the Urals, which are a Variscan structure, although it is obviously attached to that range. Whereas the comparisons tend to centre on the Russo-Polish Plain and the Urals (familiar to local geologists), one is also tempted to relate Timan to the Scandinavian Caledonides, since it seems to form a natural continuation of that chain around the north side of the Kola Peninsula, if one forgets about Spitsbergen or interprets those islands in some other way.*

Pursuing my analogy with the North American continent, Timan may be compared with the 'Paleo-Rockies', which meet the Rockies at a similarly acute angle from the south-east and which predate them in time. Timan suffered both its orogenies and its metamorphism before the Urals came into existence.

---

* In an earlier address on the subject of this book, my brief remarks about Timan were the only passage about which I received (no doubt fully justified) criticism.

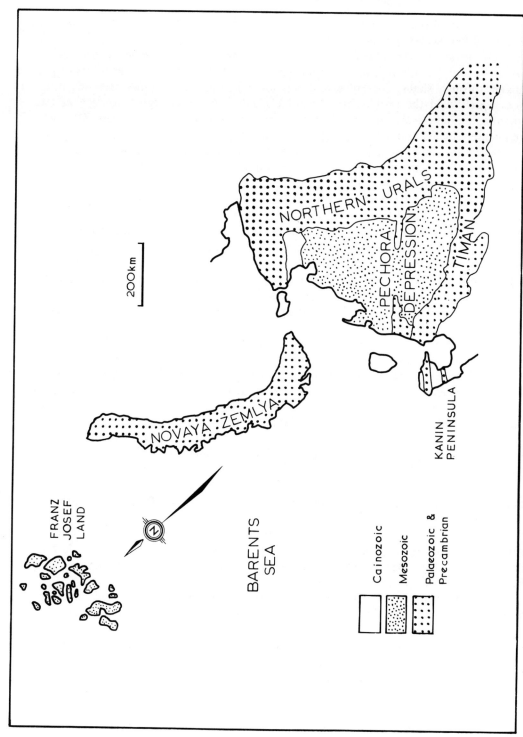

Fig. 3.2 Geological sketch-map of Timan, the Pechora Depression, and Franz Josef Land (founded on the International Geological Map of Europe).

It extends from the Kanin Peninsula, on the east side of the entrance to the White Sea, as a broad belt across northern Russia to merge with the Urals near Troitsko Pechorsk. Nowhere does it exceed about 450 m in height and the most prominent features are formed by late Precambrian metamorphic rocks. These are mainly of sedimentary origin, ranging through slates, quartzites, and conglomerates to altered limestones and dolomites which yield the problematical fossil *Collenia*. This is enough to date it as late Proterozoic. Radiometric ages range from 1100 to as late as 480 million years. The rocks are intensely folded and cut by granites below a widespread erosion surface.

Although the radiometric ages suggest the presence of Cambrian and even Ordovician rocks within the metamorphosed sequence, no fossil evidence has been found to confirm either of those systems. An unmetamorphosed sedimentary sequence rests on the above with marked unconformity. This starts with the Silurian, which consists of a variety of sandstones, shales, and limestones, yielding shallow-water, shelly faunas. The Silurian rocks were gently folded before the Devonian, and in places stand on end, leading to the statement that we have here a manifestation of the Caledonian orogeny. This is very tempting, since the Scandinavian Caledonides seem to be wrapping round the north side of the Fenno-Scandian Shield and heading this way. However, the tectonism is nothing like that in the Caledonides proper and the succession, both Silurian and later, is very much that of the East European Platform and not at all that of either the Caledonides or the Uralides.

The Devonian rocks of Timan are well known because they yield valuable hydrocarbons. The gentle north–west trending folds which affect the Silurian were sharply truncated beneath the Devonian, but movements along the same lines continued until the end of the Palaeozoic, especially in the form of growth faults producing restricted basins of Devonian and Carboniferous sediments. The Devonian is much thicker than on the Russo-Polish Plain and is thicker still in the Pechora Depression. There is a break at the bottom and then sandstones and clays with some volcanics, passing up into the carbonates which so often dominate the Upper Devonian. These are the rocks which accommodate the oil.

After the carbonate climax of the Frasnian, the Famennian as usual records a regression, with dolomites and gypsum. Continental red beds are never far away, even though we are now presumably north of the 'Old Red Sandstone' continent. Thus they replace the Frasnian limestones on the Kanin Peninsula. Presumably the sea came from the trough to the east, as it did again in the early Carboniferous. The whole Lower Carboniferous is well developed in eastern Timan, but marine sedimentation in the west only began again in the Visean.

Petroleum occurs in the Carboniferous as well as in the Devonian as oil shales and asphalt, as well as in liquid form. The later Carboniferous is widely transgressive and dominantly carbonate. In the east, it passes up into similar Permian carbonates, closely related to the succession in the Urals. These are much more limited in extent than the Carboniferous and thin out westwards, with the appearance of evaporites.

Permian rocks only occupy a very small area of Timan and are much better developed in the Pechora Depression. There are enough of them, however, to show that the north–west trending structures continued to form until the end of Palaeozoic times. This applies particularly to faulting, including the faults that delimit the Timan range against the Russian plains. Presumably these later movements are merely a marginal manifestation of what was going on in the Urals at this time, reactivating old lines. Rather than thinking in terms of Caledonian orogenies, however, it seems more appropriate to think of the even older north-westerly trend of the Fenno-Scandian Shield revealing itself again through a not very thick cover.

Pechora Depression

This is the triangle of arctic and sub-arctic land enclosed between Timan, the northern Urals, and the Barents Sea. It presumably extends far out under the Barents Sea, since similar rocks are found as erratics along the coast, and geophysical surveys are extending the picture northwards. It is a low-lying region, thickly forested in the south and rising to bleak tundra in the north, with a low range of hills that are notable as the only one in Europe (unless one counts the Dolomites) that have been named by an ungrateful world after a geologist—the Chernyshev Range.*

Whereas Timan is largely composed of Precambrian and Palaeozoic rocks, the Pechora Depression is largely floored by flat-lying Mesozoic. However, the structural relationship of the two is revealed by a second shorter belt of Palaeozoic rocks that takes off from the Urals near the town of Pechora and runs parallel to Timan towards the centre of the Depression. This is further paralleled northwards by the dog-leg at the arctic end of the Urals where that range swings round north-westwards to run out to Novaya Zemlya. In other words, there is not a narrow 'Caledonide' belt but a broad region, nearly 900 km across, which reflects the north–west trend of the Kola Peninsula and of the Fenno-Scandian Shield generally.

Permian rocks underlie a great deal of the southern part of the Depression. They form a fore-deep in front of Timan. In the east they include the valuable deposits of the Pechora Coal Basin, but this is really part of the Urals story. In the west, there are evaporites near the coast, but they have not been exploited. At the top of the Permian, continental deposition conceals the Palaeozoic–Mesozoic boundary. There are red beds of no great thickness of early Triassic age which extend over a fairly large area due to the absence of dip. They are followed by similarly thin mid Jurassic continental deposits with plant remains.

Only in late Jurassic and early Cretaceous times were there brief further marine incursions from the north. The former are largely restricted to the present river valleys, implying that these features were already established at that time. Early Cretaceous rocks are very widespread in the barren arctic north, but have not yet been studied in detail. They appear to range from Valanginian to Aptian in age, but no later Cretaceous sediments are known. There are, however, widespread basalts in the east of the Depression which have been provisionally dated as late Cretaceous.

Everything is smothered with a varying thickness of Quaternary moraines and other debris from the ice. Along the coast there are the raised beaches of the post-glacial Boreal transgression.

---

* F. N. Chernyshev was director of the Russian geological survey before the First World War and was a pioneer researcher in this region.

Franz Josef Land

The Russian textbook says of Franz Josef Land, 'Glaciation is widespread . . . . The climate is rigorous and arctic. . . . Transport is difficult. . .'. I don't think the wine is very good either! However, the islands of this archipelago are firmly fixed on the European continental shelf, so I cannot ignore them; what is more, Franz Josef Land (Zemlya Frantza-Iosifa) is wholly made of Mesozoic rocks, even if not as beautiful as elsewhere.

The only natural connection on the mainland would seem to be with the Pechora Depression, although many points in their succession link them with the east side of the arctic Urals rather than with the west side. They are contained between Caledonide Spitsbergen to the west and Variscide Novaya Zemlya to the east. The succession is dominated by dark shales and sandstones, alternating between marine and non-marine, and is capped by extensive plateau basalts and sills which are probably the reason for the islands being there at all.

The oldest rocks known are the dark shales and limestones of the Upper Triassic which have yielded a few Carnian ammonites and other fossils. These are followed by a continental sequence of sandstones, siltstones, and coals, which are dated by their spores as ranging through the Norian and Rhaetian up into the early Jurassic. There was a transgression at the beginning of mid Jurassic times with a shallow-water fauna. By Bathonian times Franz Josef Land probably had the deepest facies in the Arctic (its muddy deposits contrasting with the deltaic sands to the west) but even so it was never very deep.

So it is here that the Callovian transgression was probably less marked than elsewhere in the Soviet Union, and there is a gradual passage up through the Upper Jurassic. Although this was the maximum transgression of the Mesozoic in the Arctic region, and all stages are present, it attains no great thickness. The rich faunas of ammonites and belemnites are all Boreal in nature. The thin nature of the succession (less than 200 m) is partly accounted for by frequent breaks which probably represent the tectonism that started at this time in the Arctic generally. It must be emphasized, however, that all the strata and volcanics of these chilly islands are flat-lying and of no interest to the structural geologist.

A further transgression in Valanginian times was followed by a regression in the Barremian with continental deposits, abundant plant remains, and poor coals. It was also at this time that the widespread lava flows were extruded and sills intruded, making the most prominent features of the scenery where it shows under the snow and ice. Finally there are some marine shales with Albian and Cenomanian ammonites, but nothing else until the Boreal transgression after the Pleistocene glaciations (when Franz Josef Land had its own private ice-cap).

The chief interest of this archipelago is what it tells us about the continental shelf off the arctic coast of Russia, which is no doubt being investigated for potential hydrocarbons like similar shelves all around the world. This area would seem to have been a marine basin, albeit a shallow one, through a large part of Mesozoic times. There were often marine deposits here when Spitsbergen was a land-mass and when only small embayments of the sea were invading northern Russia and the north-west corner of Siberia on the other side of the Urals. The news has not yet reached me if anything is known of the older continental rocks of the Barents microplate down below.

Selected references to Chapter 3

All sections

Bukowy, S. *et al.* (1970), *Geology of Poland*, vol. 1, *Stratigraphy*, pt 1, 'Pre-cambrian and Palaeozoic', Wydawn. Geol., Warsaw, 651 pp.

Bulin, N. K., N. G. Beryland, and L. F. Bulavko (1979), Deep structure of Timan-Pechora Province (based on geophysical data), *Internat. Geol. Rev.*, **21**, 1070–1078.

Książkiewicz, M., J. Samsonowicz and E. Rühle (1968), *An Outline of Geology of Poland*, Sci. Publ. Foreign Coop. Center, Central Inst. Sci. Tech. Econ. Inf., Warsaw, 414 pp.

Markov, F. G. and B. V. Tkachenko (1961), 'The Palaeozoic of the Soviet Arctic', in G. O. Raasch (ed.), *Geology of the Arctic*, vol. 1, Univ. Toronto Press, pp. 31–47.

Nalivkin, D. V. (1973), *Geology of the U.S.S.R.* (English transl. by N. Rast), Univ. Toronto Press, 855 pp.

Rabkin, M. I. and M. G. Ravich (1961), 'The Precambrian of the Soviet Arctic', in G. O. Raasch (ed.), *Geology of the Arctic*, vol. 1, Univ. Toronto Press, pp. 18–30.

Sachs, V. N. and S. A. Strelkov (1961), 'Mesozoic and Cenozoic of the Soviet Arctic', in G. O. Raasch (ed.), *Geology of the Arctic*, vol. 1, Univ. Toronto Press, pp. 48–67.

Section 3(b)   Caspian Depression

Garetsky, R. G. *et al.* (1972), 'The Caspian Depression—the deepest depression of old platforms', *24th Internat. Geol. Congr.*, Montreal, Sec. 3, pp. 348–354.

Slepakova, T. L. (1961), 'Sub-salt structures of the Ciscaspian Depression on the basis of geophysical data', *Trudy VNIGRI, Moscow*, **186**, 253–272 (in Russian).

Volozh, Y. A., R. B. Sapozhnikov and V. A. Tsimmer (1975), 'Structure of the crust in the Caspian depression', *Sovetskaya Geologia*, **11**, 93–103 (in Russian). English translation: *Internat. Geol. Rev.*, 1977, **19**, 25–33.

Chapter Four

General conclusions on Eo-Europa

To sum up Eo-Europa in one short chapter, near the beginning of this book, is like those English historians who start off with a paragraph or two dealing with the history of man for his three million years or so before the early eleventh century, which is where the writer really wants to begin. This inexcusable bias is both intentional and inescapable. I was tempted to start 2600 million years ago with the major events at the end of the Archaean, or at 1800 million which might be regarded as Europe's birthday with the stabilization of the craton or better still 1000 million with the last orogeny to affect the Fenno-Scandian Shield. But I am tidy-minded.

For all the marvellous studies that have been made on these difficult rocks in the past few decades, the Precambrian history of our continent is still for the most part lost in the mists of metamorphism. Even the margins of error are greater than whole periods, or even whole eras, later in the record. In Eo-Europa it is very much the Precambrian that dominates the story. The rest is little more than a symbolic sprinkling of dirt on the coffin lid. Only in places on the East European Platform are there really important thicknesses of flat-lying cover rocks. It is increasingly evident that the Archaean rocks of Eo-Europa, or at least all but the youngest part of them, are different in many respects from the later part of the record. Charles Lyell would not have been at home here. It has been estimated that about 85 per cent of the world's Archaean rocks are granite gneiss which, from their chemistry, seem to include much mantle material. There is, for example, a notable lack of potassium and of alkaline rocks generally. The other 15 per cent is formed of the so-called 'greenstone belts' which are rare in later rocks. These include high-temperature pillow lavas, notably ultramafic lavas that we never see again and which must have been extruded at very high temperatures. Following metamorphism these are now amphibolites, but in the metamorphic suites generally there is an absence of 'blue schist' facies, again indicating high temperatures, and no eclogites until very late in the Archaean. All this suggests high-temperature–low-pressure processes and a much higher geothermal gradient than anything today.

It has been estimated that Archaean rocks, such as those of the Scottish Lewisian, formed at depths of 30–50 km, perhaps even more. They are dominantly acidic or intermediate in composition and we are therefore thinking of an exceptionally thick granitic crust. It is obvious from recent geophysical maps of Europe that there is a marked contrast between the thick crust of the Russo-Polish Platform (and most of the Fenno-

Scandian Shield) compared with that of the rest of the continent. But so far as the original crust is concerned, this was probably fundamentally different in character from that with which we are subsequently involved. It was probably built up to its great thickness by a massive addition of mantle material by under-plating rather than by lateral accretion. Many geologists would, however, say that the greenstone belts are major sutures indicative of plate tectonic processes already operating. At the same time, sediments are few and thin, probably less than a kilometre in maximum thickness (and then mostly conglomerates). But all these things are better discussed on a global scale and many of them—such as the greenstone belts—are not easy to consider in a purely European context.

If plate tectonics was already a going concern in Archaean times, then the plates were probably much smaller than the ones we find subsequently. Perhaps we should think of the Archaean plums that are scattered through the Proterozoic pudding of Europe in this light, such as those of the Kola Peninsula in the USSR and the 'Pregothides' of southern Sweden, together with all the others hidden under the younger sediments of the East European Platform.

There seems to have been this major event in earth history (including European history) about 2700–2500 million years ago, at the end of the Archaean. After that there was stability on a continental scale with persistent lineaments and dike swarms over very large areas. As has already been said, Europe may be said to have been born about 1800 million years ago with the Svecofennide orogeny on the Fenno-Scandian Shield. Most of the present features of the continental crust seem to have originated at about that time.

Looking at the shield and the Hebridean Province one cannot help noticing the north-west–south-east trend that was established at this time. In my student days it was called the 'Charnoid trend' after Charnwood Forest in central England, where peaks of younger Precambrian rocks poke out from a Triassic cover and are folded on these lines. 'Charnoid' became almost a dirty word, and certainly if one looks at any of these rocks in detail the complexity of fold phases mocks such generalizations. It is perhaps excessively chauvinistic of the Mercians to think that their little local structure may be applied on a continent-wide scale.

It must also be said that the patterns now recognized under the East European Platform do not conform with such a simple trend. Nevertheless, there are so many general features trending in a north-westerly direction that one cannot just ignore it. There is the trend of the Lapland granulites, the junction of the earliest part of the shield with the 'Karelides' and the 'Karelides' with the Svecofennides *sensu stricto*. There are the great mineralization belts across Finland and Sweden, there are the Rapakivi granites, and there is the edge of the Fenno-Scandian Shield itself (e.g., in Bornholm).

Then there is the trend of Timan and its parallel ridges, including the remarkable 'dog-leg' of the Urals on the Arctic coast. Here we can see clear evidence of the ancient trend controlling sedimentation right up to the end of the Palaeozoic Era. One is tempted to say that other trends are only postulated in the East European Platform where the basement rocks have safely dipped out of sight beneath the cover. And even here there are major features such as the 'aulaçogens' of Ryazan and the Donbass which display the old allegiance to the north-west. Perhaps these were graben where the Proterozoic continent almost split apart on the old lines.

What is more, where the basement appears again in the Ukrainian Massif, here we are back on a north-westerly trend. In this case it clearly persisted not only through the Palaeozoic, but—as a positive feature—through Mesozoic and Cainozoic times as well and, of course, continues to stand out today. From there it is but a step to the north–west trending Tornquist Line, running up to Denmark and west again to the *Randtröge* or marginal troughs of the Danish Triangle, which will be discussed in Chapter 6(a). Perhaps it also has something to do with the north-easterly margin of the Central British Block.

In the Hebridean Province and, for that matter, in Greenland, the north-westerly trend delimits the boundary between Scourian and Laxfordian terrains and shows up particularly in the orientation of the great swarms of Scourian dikes and later structural features.

So there is this undeniable feature which is so very different from the Caledonide–Atlantic and the Variscide–Alpide–Mediterranean trends that were to dominate the rest of European history. I have referred to the last two as the *leitmotivs* of the European symphony. The 'Charnian' was perhaps the overture (albeit a very long one) that preceded the main performance.

Although the influence of the fundamental structures was to be felt for a very long time, the pattern of the Fenno-Scandian Shield and its extensions was really chosen in the Svecofennide movements. Great thicknesses of mature shelf-type sediments had been incorporated in the basement and from then on there was, on the whole, very little sedimentation in Eo-Europa. There is nothing really oceanic within the shield and platform, although there is evidence of marginal troughs which persisted thereafter for a very long time. Thus, on the East European Platform, sedimentation was very thin and impersistent, but around its edges there is evidence of considerable subsidence from way back in Precambrian times, for example in the Urals and the Carpathians. The extreme example is the Caspian Depression, which may be a remnant of a Proterozoic Tethys ocean.

We must also consider the possibility of an east-west trench right across central Europe in the Proterozoic and Palaeozoic, seen for example in the Bohemian Massif. This will be the concern of Part Three of this book (Meso-Europa), but it should be mentioned here as an indication that this other great trend was already under way. It is interesting to note that, on the north side of this east–west trench, the old craton bobbed up again most obviously in Devonian times under the alias of the 'Old Red Sandstone' continent. I will discuss in Part Two whether I should, in fact, have extended the East European Platform to the Severn bridge or even to south-west Wales.

We now have to think, however, of things happening at the north-west end of our continent, on what was to be the Atlantic margin. As has already been indicated, the 'Charnoid' trend links the Fenno-Scandian Shield with that little slice of Eo-Europa along the Atlantic seaboard of Scotland, and links that in turn with Greenland. In fact, in Archaean and early Proterozoic times one must think in terms of a single great craton being formed that included what are now major portions of North America, Greenland, and Europe. Certain contrasts between North America and Europe, such as the apparent absence in the latter of the important Grenvillian events of Canada, are now beginning to disappear with detailed studies and more radiometric dates. It would be dishonest to pretend that there are not still major differences, but these fortunately are not my concern in this context.

In fact this would seem to be the best place to mention the important north–south Gothide and Dalslandian structures of the Baltic Shield which, with an age of about 1000 million years, are roughly contemporaneous with the Grenvillian. This was the last orogeny to affect Eo-Europa. Although its pattern is nothing like as well marked as the others, one can see it surely in the persistent Baltic structure (of early Palaeozoic to Recent times) and in certain features such as the North Sea and the shape of Denmark. One interesting thought is that the extensive coarse clastic sediments of the late Protero-zoic, whether they be called Jotnian or Torridonian or 'Eocambrian' or Brioverian (in Brittany), may be thought of as the molasse of that orogeny, even in areas (such as the Hebrides) where the Grenvillian mountain chains themselves are not preserved. These sediments are too young to be the debris of the earlier orogeny and have not, within the limits of Eo-Europa, been affected by any major later movements.

But now to the Atlantic. Apart from the hint of a greenstone belt in the Scourian of the Outer Hebrides, it was not until the Proterozoic that the Atlantic Line became moderately obvious. From a global viewpoint, one can say that by Proterozoic times onwards there seems to be a clearly recognizable plate tectonic story with drifting and the coincidence of glacial deposits with supposed pole positions. So we may suspect that something was happening in the North Atlantic long before the end of Precambrian times. It seems to take the form of a belt of thick sedimentation and later orogenesis. The Moinian of Scotland (to be discussed under Palaeo-Europa) and the Brioverian of Brit-tany (to be discussed under Meso-Europa) are obvious examples. It may not be entirely coincidental that the 'Assyntian' orogeny was named from north-west Scotland and the 'Cadomian' from north-west France. Subsiding troughs seem to have formed on the western edge of the craton in late Proterozoic times and to have been converted into mountain belts at the end of the era or soon after.

The Atlantic Line has become something of a fixation with me and must be discussed here, even though much of it concerns Palaeo-Europa. The separation of the Hebridean Province itself from the rest of the craton is obviously along a line that is parallel to the Atlantic margin and the split has become the Caledonides.

Whether or not the sudden transition from the Torridonian of the Hebridean Province into the Moinian of the Scottish metamorphic Caledonides is truly a facies change or just a chance juxtaposition, the point remains the same. The line between them is parallel to, and not very far from the Atlantic coastline. It also coincides, of course, with that important Caledonian and Caledonoid feature, the Moine Thrust Belt. But there is far more to it than this.

We have long contrasted the continents and the oceans, but in recent years it has become increasingly apparent that there is also frequently a sharp contrast between land areas and the offshore shelves. Nowhere is this more apparent than down the north-west coasts of Europe where the present shoreline, far from being a passing vagary of geogra-phy, is often the boundary (or very close to the boundary) between two very different geological realms. Stand on the coast south of Harlech in North Wales and you can almost throw a piece of the Lower Cambrian slate at your feet on to one of the thickest Mesozoic successions in Britain. You could (almost) do the same in the Sea of the Hebrides or off the west coast of Norway. Over and over again there is a remarkable parallelism between the line of the North Atlantic (with its attendant lesser seas) and structural or stratigraphical lines throughout the record. Obvious examples are the thrust that runs the length of the Outer Hebrides through Lewisian rocks and the nearby supposed Minch Fault with its repeated movements that determines the inner margin of those islands.

The Caledonides are not the concern of this chapter, but feature after feature in their history parallels this ancient line. Tension leading to the formation of the present Atlantic started in the early Mesozoic and produced the deep parallel troughs full of Mesozoic and Tertiary sediments, having great economic potential, on the Scottish continental shelf. Many exciting discoveries remain to be made in this region with respect to the actual appearance of what may be truly called an ocean.

In Tertiary times the tensions of an opening Atlantic must have been responsible for the intrusions and the extrusions of the Thulean Volcanic Province. It is surely significant that there is no Tertiary volcanism within the Fenno-Scandian Shield or the East European Platform. What little was suspected in southern Sweden is now known to be Mesozoic and related to the earlier splitting of the North Sea. One way of defining the Tornquist Line might be to say that it is the eastern limit of Atlantic influence on Europe. It certainly does not seem to have been as much of a palaeogeographical barrier as the Scythian Arc to its east.

The very latest faulting dropped down Quaternary sediments and slight seismic activity continues along certain of the lines. So it is that structures parallel to the Atlantic Ocean can be recognized controlling sedimentation, volcanicity, and metamorphism, right through from the Proterozoic to the present day.

Selected references to Chapter 4

Sutton, J. (1968), 'Development of the continental framework of the Atlantic', *Proc. Geol. Ass.* **79**, 275–303.

Watson, J. (1976). 'Eo-Europa: the evolution of a craton', in D. V. Ager and M. Brooks (eds.), *Europe from Crust to Core*, Wiley, New York and London, 59–78.

Windley, B. F. (1977), *The Evolving Continents*, Wiley, London, 385 pp.

Part Two

Palaeo-Europa

That part of Europe which was affected by a major orogeny at or near the end of the early Palaeozoic, but has not since been affected by major tectonism

Chapter Five

Caledonides

Palaeo-Europa divides naturally into two parts: the Caledonides (which are here interpreted as the complex series of orogenic belts that runs down the north-west coast of Europe) and what I have called the Danish Triangle (which is considered in Chapter 6).

5(a) Spitsbergen

The logical starting point for the Caledonide ranges of Europe is Spitsbergen (Svalbard) in the far north. This lonely arctic archipelago is closely related to that of the Scandinavian Caledonides, but it has features of its own of which the most interesting is its Tertiary fold belt. This might be said to exclude it from Palaeo-Europa, but the late movements are so different from those of the Alpine chains that it is better to leave Spitsbergen where it has always been, as part of the Caledonide belt.

Pre-Caledonian

The oldest rocks seen at the surface are the schists and granites on the north coast of Nordaustlandet which, as its name implies, is the island in the north-east of the group (Fig. 5.1). Although dominantly schistose, these rocks include a variety of metamorphic and igneous types, notably garnetiferous gneisses, gabbros, and anorthosites, all invaded by grey granites. The rocks strike dominantly north–south or within a limited sector on either side. They are generally interpreted as basement rocks below everything else and are presumably part of the craton of the Barents Sea microplate; dates of around 600 million years have been obtained, although the main metamorphism is Caledonian in age (about 430–390 million years ago).

There then follow the best-known and most extensive rocks of Spitsbergen, the thick sedimentary pile known as the Hecla Hoek Group. This is said to range from Precambrian to Ordovician in age and outcrops over a large area in Nordaustlandet, in the north and west of the main island of Vestspitsbergen and on narrow little Prince Charles Foreland in the west. In Vestspitsbergen the lowest part of the group is always highly tectonized and metamorphosed, but there is no sign of a distinctive basement unconformably below. This is one of the big problems about the age of some of the metamorphism. However, there is no doubt that the lower part of the Hecla Hoek originated as a

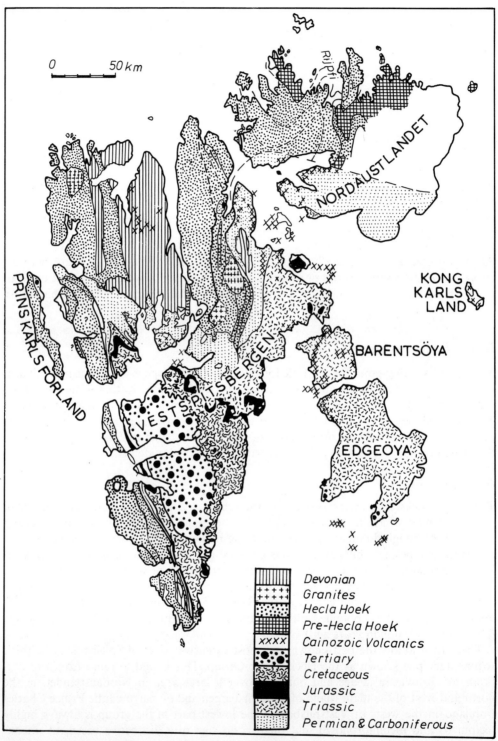

Fig. 5.1 Geological sketch-map of Spitsbergen (founded on maps in Harland, 1961, by kind permission of the author).

succession of dominantly argillaceous sediments, with a fair amount of volcanic material. Inevitably it has been called eugeosynclinal. It seems to thicken into 'turbidites'* towards the north-west.

It is overlain by dominantly quartzitic sediments, with more basic volcanics and a possible glacial horizon. There appears to have been uplift, although no real orogeny is recognized at this time. The eastern and western parts of the trough may have been separated, since they subsequently had rather different histories, and it has been suggested that later transcurrent faults brought together very different provinces.

Clastic sedimentation was then replaced by limestones (including oolites) and dolomites. These were very extensive, going as far as Bear Island (Bjønøya) halfway between Spitsbergen and mainland Norway.† The carbonates are confidently dated as late Proterozoic. Above them, as in many other places around the world, come undoubted glacial deposits. Although tillites of various kinds may occur at several horizons, they are usually accepted as marking the 'Varangian' episode near the end of Precambrian times, by analogy with mainland Norway. Further thick carbonates at the top of the Hecla Hoek Group have now yielded fossils at a number of localities and are undoubtedly of early Palaeozoic age. The same curious situation obtains as in similar carbonates in Greenland to the west and in Scotland to the south. That is to say, there are Lower Cambrian fossils at the bottom and Lower Ordovician fossils near the top, but nothing datable in between and no evidence of a break. The Ordovician fossils (mainly nautiloids and gastropods) make a close comparison possible with the early Ordovician ('Canadian') Beekmantown Limestone of eastern Canada. This fits in well with the evidence in Greenland and Scotland and tempts one to say that this all belongs to North America rather than to Europe.

So ended a long carbonate-dominated succession, without volcanics, which may be regarded as a miogeosyncline coming on top of a eugeosyncline. The long period of stability represented by the Hecla Hoek Group was only disrupted by the Caledonian orogeny. The main spasm cannot be dated precisely. All that can be said is that it was later than early Ordovician and earlier than late Silurian. It imparted a north–south strike to the islands and produced considerable metamorphism, at least in the lower part of the Hecla Hoek succession. The tectonism was most intense in the west where the succession was thickest. Geophysical trends in the floor of the Barents Sea connect Spitsbergen with the Scandinavian Caledonides.

Bright pink, porphyritic granites (contrasting with the grey granites of the Precambrian) were extensively emplaced at a late stage in the orogeny and were followed by uplift and erosion. In northern and central Spitsbergen the eroded surface is buried beneath thick conglomerates, sandstones, and siltstones of an 'Old Red Sandstone' facies. This mainly accumulated within a graben and has been dated by fish as ranging from Downtonian to Givetian in age. It was clearly formed from the debris of the new Caledonian mountains, but a feature of Spitsbergen geology is the post-'Old Red Sandstone' diastrophism (often called the Svalbard folding). The movements at the end of

---

* Throughout this book I put 'turbidites' in inverted commas since it is to me unacceptable as a rock name, assuming as it does an origin that cannot be proved.

† Strictly speaking Bear Island, Hope Island (Hopen), and King Charles Land (Kong Karls Land) to the east are part of Svalbard but not part of Spitsbergen.

Devonian times were mainly concentrated along the eastern edge of the graben and involve overfolding and thrusting towards the west. The block to the east had evidently already become stable.

Late Palaeozoic and later

Carboniferous and Permian rocks outcrop over a large part of central and north-east Vestspitsbergen and in the southern part of Nordaustlandet. Basal sandstones rest with marked unconformity on the rocks below. They yield early Carboniferous plants. There were slight movements after this, including the uplift of the Devonian graben, but there was then a long period, right through to the end of the Palaeozoic, during which gradual subsidence accommodated a mainly marine succession. A transgression was heralded by gypsiferous deposits and then warm, tropical-looking limestones, full of corals, brachiopods, and fusulinids, were laid down in later Carboniferous and Permian times. There may have been slight breaks—suggested by further gypsum—but generally speaking nothing much happened until the Mesozoic.

Thus Spitsbergen has a late Palaeozoic succession that is completely unknown in the Scandinavian Caledonides. As might be expected, it appears that it may be correlated with the succession in east Greenland. The marine Lower and Middle Trias which follow are all the more strange to European eyes. In view of the possibility of very early Triassic faunas being present here (and the presence of faunas of this age in east Greenland) this might be the best place in our continent to study the Palaeozoic–Mesozoic junction, but the assemblages are poor.

Mesozoic and Cainozoic rocks occur chiefly in a broad basin that occupies the greater part of southern Vestspitsbergen and the whole of the eastern islands of Edgeöya and Barentsöya. Jurassic and Cretaceous sediments also occur on the ridge-like island of Hopen, south-east of Edgeöya, and on the King Charles archipelago, south-east of Nordaustlandet. Here again we have a succession that is almost unknown on the mainland of Scandinavia, but close to that of east Greenland.

The Triassic is mainly sandy with marine beds passing up into continental deposits with coal seams. There are ammonites enough for correlation but also reptiles and fish. There are obvious breaks and most of the Upper Triassic is missing, although the Rhaetian is seen as 'Coal Measures' with bone beds. The sea did not return until Toarcian times, and then only briefly, while the main transgression—as in so many places—came at the end of mid Jurassic times in the Callovian. Black shales yield Boreal-type faunas and then the sea withdrew again before the end of the period. A Berriasian transgression brought back comparable sediments and faunas for a while, but before the end of Neocomian times it was 'Coal Measures' again with splendid floras. Yet another short-lived marine invasion laid down Aptian and Albian deposits, but there are no sediments of late Cretaceous age. More 'Coal Measures' and marine intercalations represent the Palaeogene in the middle of the Mesozoic basin and along the strait that separates the Prince Charles Foreland from the main island.

So the whole Mesozoic and early Tertiary story is one of comings and goings of a northern sea, separated by episodes of vigorous plant growth which produced the coals that have been the chief reason for settlements on Spitsbergen (the more so because of the absence of coal on mainland Norway). There are also a number of dolerite sills cutting the Mesozoic rocks which are generally thought to be of late Cretaceous or very early Tertiary age and to be associated with the tensions of an opening Atlantic.

The broad synclinal structure which holds most of the Mesozoic and Palaeogene outcrops trends in the same direction as the Caledonian folds beneath, but the western limb is much steeper than the eastern. It forms part of a belt of intense Tertiary folding up the west coast of Vestspitsbergen, which is most obviously exemplified in the long narrow feature of Prince Charles Foreland. The beds are vertical or overturned and there is major thrusting from the west.

In places it is difficult to distinguish the Tertiary folding and faulting from that of Caledonian age along the same lines, since much of it is within the Hecla Hoek Group. Such intense Tertiary deformation is remarkable for northern Europe and there is nothing else like it north of the Alps. As such, it is surprising that it has not attracted more attention prior to the coming of plate tectonics. Nowadays it seems simple to explain it as the final grinding together of continental plates in the north as the Atlantic swung open from the south. In detail it would be Greenland coming into violent contact with the Barents microplate. Land mammals were still migrating from Europe to North America in Palaeogene times, probably by this route.

Apart from the western fold belt, the post-Devonian rocks are little more than warped and faulted on north–south lines. This was followed by a general uplift and peneplanation that forms one of the most striking features of Spitsbergen scenery. Everything is planed off at a remarkably persistent surface that ranges from about 500 to about 1500 m. There are some very late volcanics on this peneplain, notably in the north central part of Vestspitsbergen. These are mainly subaerial basalts of Quaternary age. There are also puy-like volcanic cones and hot springs. Uplift has resumed since the end of the last glaciation, although in these parts the glaciation is still very much with us.

5(b) Scandinavian Caledonides

The Scandinavian Caledonides are more clearly defined than almost any other unit considered in this book. On their west side is the Atlantic Ocean and on their east side is the front of the overthrusts pushing on to the Fenno-Scandian Shield (Fig. 5.2).

Within this belt, however, the picture is far less clear. The tectonics are complex and the nomenclature is worse. No Scandinavian seems to have been foolhardy enough to attempt a synthesis, so who am I to do so? A quick search of some of the literature provided more than thirty named nappes, of which at least five are multiple, but little or no agreement has been reached as to how they relate to one another, although there do not seem to be more than four in any one place. There are also considerable differences in opinion as to the dating of the various events, and the whole situation has been complicated by attempts to force it into various theoretical models.

This section concerns the greater part of Norway, a strip of the western part of northern Sweden, and a minute corner of Finland. The Scandinavian Caledonides differ from their counterparts in the British Isles in representing a far deeper level of erosion. This has been an upstanding, positive area for the last 400 million years or so. As a result, these mountains have lost most of their post-orogenic cover.

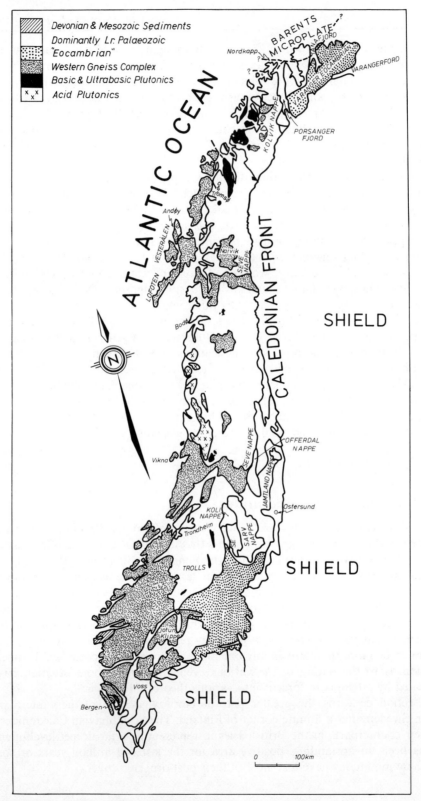

Fig. 5.2 Geological sketch-map of the Scandinavian Caledonides (founded on the 1:1 000 000 geological maps of Norway and Sweden).

It is customary to relate the Scandinavian Caledonides to Greenland, which includes both the foreland for this particular orogen and a belt of dominantly carbonate Lower Palaeozoic rocks which has been called the 'internal miogeosyncline'. Greenland is not part of Europe geographically (although it does have one representative in the European parliament) but it reminds us that the rocks of Palaeo-Europa have as much to do with North America as with Europe.

It will be my custom in this book to deal with fold belts from the 'interior' towards the 'exterior', that is to say in the direction of major thrusting, but this presents problems in Palaeo-Europa since so much of the story is lost in or beyond the Atlantic. This part of our continent has long been associated with the Atlantic Ocean, both in its early Palaeozoic form and in the later phase of development leading to what it is today.

Western Gneiss Complex

Along the west coast of Norway there are two great belts of Precambrian rocks. They are often known as the 'Western Gneiss Complex', the 'Basal Gneiss', or the 'Bunngneiss'. But these terms obviously hide much ignorance and the more that is revealed about these rocks, the more complex they become.

In the north a belt extends from Norfolda, north of Bodø, up to Vannøy, north of Tromsø (the 'capital of the Arctic'). It includes most of the deeply dissected coastline and the offshore islands, notably the Lofotens and Vesterålen, whose charnockitic rocks produce a spectacularly jagged skyline. The rocks concerned are mostly granites and granite gneisses forming a splendidly naked landscape—one of the most attractive in Europe—at least for the summer visitor. Locally there are gabbroic rocks and granulites. They seem to have been little affected by the Caledonian metamorphism and the Lower Palaeozoic can be shown locally to have been thrust over them. This has led to the modern view that they are not Caledonian at all, but an integral part of the Fenno-Scandian Shield, appearing through the nappes.

These rocks are comparable to the Scourian of the western highlands of Scotland and have similar radiometric ages of around 2800 million years. One rock at Vikan i Bö in the Versterålen group has the distinction of being the oldest known rock in Europe, dated as 3460 million years, putting it firmly in the 'Katarchaean'. The deformation that affected these rocks before Cambrian times seems to have been of a high-temperature, plastic nature and to have involved deep crustal or mantle material as in the Fenno-Scandian Shield.

South of Narvik there is a south-easterly trending culmination of these rocks running up from beautiful Tysfjord deep into Sweden, all the way to the Caledonian front south-west of Kiruna. The relationship of these Precambrian rocks to the Lower Palaeozoic successions which form most of the Caledonide belt is not always clear, although there is frequently close parallelism between the two. In places in the west (as on Mesozoic-bearing Andøy) Lower Palaeozoic rocks are involved in the same structures, while in the east they can be seen passing into undoubtedly allochthonous Precambrian rocks that have been thrust eastwards on to the shield.

The southern area of Precambrian rocks is much more extensive. It extends from the island of Vikna, north of Namsos, southwards to Fensfjord, north of Bergen, and to the islands west of that city. These rocks were much more involved in the Caledonian orogeny than those in the north. The main trend of their structures is Caledonoid and many of the fjords of this part of Norway (e.g., Langfjord, Vartdalsfjord, and Storfjord, near Ålesund) display a definitely north-easterly line. In places undoubtedly early Palaeozoic rocks are involved in the same structures. Thus Trondheimfjord, which is within the main Palaeozoic outcrop, continues the line of the fjords just mentioned. North-west of Trondheim at Størnfjord, Lower Palaeozoic rocks come right through to the coast on a parallel line.

The Precambrian rocks of this southern belt (forming the main part of the western 'bulge' of Norway) include a great variety of metamorphic types, mostly gneissose but including granulites and (very locally) ultrabasic masses. On the basis of a limited number of samples it can be said that the rocks are younger than those in the north, up to no more than 1800 million years old, which would make them comparable with the Laxfordian of the Scottish Highlands. Unlike the Laxfordian, however, they have been considerably affected by the Caledonian orogeny, reaching an amphibolitic grade of metamorphism, although this is not wholly Caledonian.

In many areas it is not possible to say to what extent these high-grade Precambrian rocks are allochthonous. Locally, however, as in the north, they have clearly been thrust over the Lower Palaeozoic. Thus inland from Namsos, in central Norway, a klippe of the western gneiss rests on the eastern facies of the Lower Palaeozoic, which is itself allochthonous. There is also a decline in metamorphism from west to east, so that—at the east end of Sunndal for example—there are recognizable flaggy sediments, while at the west end (and in overthrust slices) they are high-grade gneisses.

Special consideration must be given to the classic region of the Bergen Arcs in southern Norway. A 'Western Gneiss Complex', similar to that already described, forms the island of Sotra and projects eastwards as the Lyderhorn peninsula, south-west of the city of Bergen. Round this wraps the 'Minor Arc' of early Palaeozoic schists and gneisses on which Grieg's city is built. This arc swings from a north-westerly trend in the north to a south-westerly trend in the south. It is separated by a belt of anorthositic rocks, of uncertain age, from the 'Major Arc' comprising further metamorphosed early Palaeozoic sediments. The altered sediments include conglomerates and marbles and—following the general pattern—the grade of metamorphism decreases eastwards. Quite reasonable fossils, especially corals and crinoids, are preserved in places in the 'Major Arc', notably along the shore of Samnangerfjord, south-east of Bergen. Much of the succession was argillaceous and includes some volcanic rocks. There is also serpentinite (formerly worked for talc) and a mass of gabbro, implaced within the lower part of the succession. This is one of the few suggestions in the Scandinavian Palaeozoics of ocean-floor material, but some of the sediments and all the fossils imply shallow-water environments, at least at times during the Ordovician and Silurian.

The relationship of the various elements within the Bergen Arcs is still not agreed. It was long thought that the two arcs were synclines in which the Lower Palaeozoic rested unconformably on a Precambrian basement. Others believe, however, that the 'Western Gneiss Complex' (at least here) and the anorthosites between the arcs are also early Palaeozoic in age, all pushed eastwards in the Caledonian movements.

On the north side, the Bergen Arcs adjoin the vast area of supposedly Precambrian gneisses along north-west trending Fensfjord. On their south side, however, they are adjacent and parallel to the long series of nappe fronts that extend across Norway into

Sweden. From here on eastwards, as far as Ostersund, there is a heap of allochthonous masses all pushed in that direction. The nearest rocks are masses of amphibolite (e.g., forming most of the island of Tysnesøy) and large areas of highly deformed metamorphic rocks (e.g., around Voss, east of Bergen) whose relationships are uncertain.

The clearest and largest nappe in this region is that of the Jotunheimen—the Jotun Nappe—which forms high, rugged country over a large part of central southern Norway. Locally, for example up the Hemsedal and Bagndal, north-west of Oslo, the Jotun Nappe is thrust right on to the semi-autochthonous Lower Palaeozoic at the very front of the Caledonides. The nappe is really a huge klippe, closely resembling the rocks between the two Bergen Arcs, notably in the development of large masses of white anorthosite (e.g., around Sogndal, at the head of its fjord) and mangerite (e.g., up the spectacular Flåm railway). The Jotun Nappe may therefore be regarded as part of the 'Western Gneiss Complex'.

Trondheim and Rödingsfjall Nappes

We now come to the great area of rocks in central Norway (together with small parts of north-west Sweden) which are interpreted as belonging to a eugeosynclinal belt of early Palaeozoic age pushed from the west. These include the Trondheim nappe in the south centre and a large part of southern arctic Norway which can only provisionally be attributed to the Rödingsfjall Nappe. The latter was named by the Swedes for the tiny part of the nappe that protrudes into south-west Swedish Lapland.* There are also several other names available, and a typical structure is shown in Fig. 5.3.

The nappes consist for the most part of high-grade schists (up to sillimanite level) and include considerable quantities of altered basic volcanics, which explains their attribution to a eugeosyncline. There are some chaotic olistostromes near the base of the complex—for example south of the old Norwegian capital of Trondheim. There are also thick marbles (e.g., west of Narvik) in lower sheets to the east and the whole seems to represent oceanic material subducted beneath a fore-arc trench. There is little evidence, in the form of fossils, of an early Palaeozoic age, although the marbles just mentioned do appear in places to rest on the so-called 'Eocambrian'.

In addition to the extrusives there are, in both the regions mentioned above, huge gabbroic masses. In the south there are scattered bodies in the dark country south of Trondheim (including a diorite body that forms most of the islands of Smøla and Hitra, off the entrance to Trondheimsfjord). In the arctic north there is the splendid gabbroic peninsula of peaks between Ullsfjord and Lyngsfjord (which I look at from my mobile home as I write). It is tempting to suggest that these were thrust up from great depths.

There are also granitic masses, for example in the great troll-ridden Dovre Massif† and it seems to me that too much effort had been put into forcing these ancient rocks into modern plate tectonic hypotheses. Ophiolite suites are rare and incomplete. Certainly there is no continuous belt and where they exist (as at Sulitjelma, east of Bodø) they were probably back-arc developments rather than truly oceanic. Basic and ultra-basic rocks

---

* The name comes from a mountain that is difficult to find in any map or gazetteer, just over the Swedish border south of Narvik.
† Peer Gynt's 'Hall of the Mountain King'.

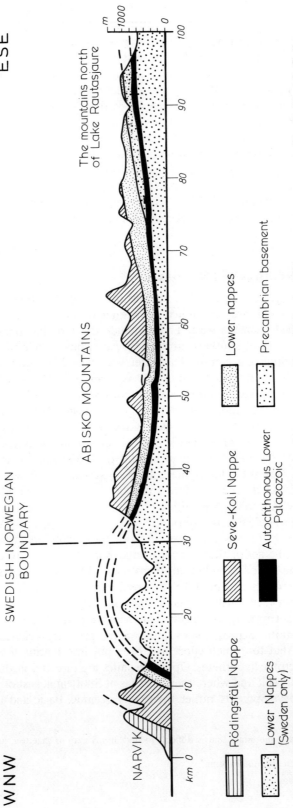

Fig. 5.3 *Geological cross-section of the Scandinavian Caledonides, running approximately 100 km east from Narvik (after Kulling & Geijer, 1960, by kind permission of the Sveriges Geologiska Undersökning).*

are concentrated in the northern Tromsø region and in the southern Trondheim region, while the great mass of the Caledonian granites and most of the marbles occur in the region in between, where basic extrusives and intrusives are very rare.

Between the Tysfjord 'culmination', south of Narvik, and a similar belt of Precambrian running inland from Namsos, is a belt of Lower Palaeozoic rocks where Norway is at its narrowest; these are peppered with granites and granite gneisses, especially in the west. The largest is a vast mass south-west of the aluminium town of Mosjøen. Thick belts of carbonates occur within the schists and gneisses, for example around the marble-quarrying town of Fauske. Marble also forms the peninsula between Fauske and Bodø where the famous whirlpools of Saltstraumen heave menacingly as the tide rises and falls.

The whole of this belt shows very clearly a rising grade of metamorphism westwards, so that along the coast almost everywhere there are granites and 'injection gneisses', while eastwards recognizable sedimentary rocks begin to appear.

The abundance of carbonates in the central belt of Lower Palaeozoic rocks, and the absence of extrusives, might encourage the use of the term 'miogeosynclinal' in contrast with the 'eugeosynclinal' regions to the north and south. The granites also suggest more continental affinities, but the relationship between the three regions is far from clear. It may be that the central belt originally lay east of the other two, but the eugeosynclinal belt to the south is more clearly allochthonous than that to the north. One possibly significant point is that the only truly 'American' (i.e., Appalachian) early Palaeozoic fauna in the Scandinavian Caledonides comes from the Trondheim district.

Eastwards all these rocks are thrust directly on to the stable basement of the Fenno-Scandian Shield. Within the nappes there are, however, windows of basement rocks which are also taken to be autochthonous. The largest of these is the 'Rombak Window' at the head of Ofotfjord, east of Narvik, which consists of granites and mica schists that do not seem to have been affected at all by the Caledonian orogeny.

Seve–Koli Nappes

These two units are commonly taken together and sometimes just referred to as the 'Upper Thrust Unit', but that term is confusing since it only applies in Sweden (and not everywhere there), while in Norway there are other units above them tectonically. They form the most extensive of all the structural units—a great flat, westerly-dipping slab of Precambrian and Lower Palaeozoic rocks. The latter are more typically eugeosynclinal in character than those discussed previously and are often called the 'eastern' as distinct from the 'western' eugeosynclinal facies. The latter is said to have closer affinities with the Greenland succession. It may be that the thick marbles mentioned above belong to a miogeosynclinal belt between the two but these may be the same structure.

The Seve–Koli Nappes are dominantly schists, comparable with the *schistes lustrés* of the Alps, with associated flysch-type sediments, basic volcanics, and some conglomerates. The Seve Nappe is only distinguishable from the Koli Nappe by the presence of masses of amphibolite, for example in the Abisko mountains of Sweden, east of Narvik. There is still, however, very little that could be called ophiolite.

Here at last we have some good fossil evidence giving an Ashgill to Llandovery age to the upper part of the sequence, which is presumed to range down into the Precambrian at the bottom. Further thrust slices beneath the Seve–Koli Nappe with their own names consist of slabs of Archaean granite and syenite.

The Seve Nappe is best known in Sweden as a large klippe west of Ostersund. There it rests on other nappes which are sometimes regarded as part of the same complex and sometimes honoured as distinct units.

Estimates as to how far these upper nappes have travelled vary enormously. It is said that in the south of Norway nappes moved more than 100 km over unmoved Precambrian basement. More commonly figures around 50 km are cited, but some authors postulate vastly more and even 1000 km is in print. Since the whole fold belt is less than 500 km wide at its maximum, it is difficult to justify such figures. Nevertheless, it is often said with confidence that the eastward movements of the Caledonides in Scandinavia were much greater than the northward and westward movement of the Alpides in central Europe.

Also included here for convenience must be the vast area of late Precambrian and early Palaeozoic rocks, in a more or less metamorphosed condition, which cover the greater part of western Finnmark and part of Troms in the extreme north of Norway. These are sometimes called the 'Kolvik Nappe'. Again there is a story of increasing grades of metamorphism to the west, so that—for example—around Hammerfest on the island of Kvaløy* there are really high-grade gneisses. On the other hand, along the splendid new road up the west side of Porsangerfjord, the micaceous sediments are really quite reasonably preserved. Detailed sedimentary sequences have now been worked out in the late Precambrian rocks and with them the structures, which seem to indicate at least three phases of movement. The changing grades of metamorphism are particularly well seen on the island of Magerøy, at the very top of Norway. In the east of this island the sediments are sufficiently well preserved to yield recognizable crinoids and pentamerids indicating a Silurian age. By Nordkapp (the much-visited northernmost point in Europe) the rocks are dull biotite schists, and by the fishing village of Gjesvaer on the west side of the island (with its multitudes of sea-birds) the Lower Palaeozoic sediments have been transformed into high-grade gneisses.

Peeping through these rocks are tectonic windows of the 'Raipas Formation'. This consists of quite reasonable sedimentary rocks—sandstones, slates, and dolomites—with associated 'greenstones' that are all thought to be autochthonous. They are well seen around the town of Alta on the Arctic Highway, in one of the largest of these windows.

Mention should also be made of the great masses of basic and ultra-basic rocks that occur in the western islands here, notably Sørøy, Seiland, and Stjernøy, and in the broad peninsula west of Alta—a gravity anomaly linking these with the Vesterålen and Lofoten islands to the south. These rocks would seem to have been emplaced early in the Caledonian orogeny. Oceanic thoughts are inevitable and these rocks must have originated from large-scale melting in the upper mantle. They have been compared with similar rocks on the opposite side of the Atlantic in Newfoundland. They seem to have been pushed up from the west to rest on some 30 km of crustal material.

A further complication is the presence of a curved fault in the extreme north (east of Magerøy) which has been suggested as a major transcurrent junction separating Europe from a distinct Barents Microplate to the north.

---

* Which claims to be the northernmost town in the world, and where reindeer browse among the marigolds of the suburban gardens.

Sarv–Offerdal Nappes

The Sarv, Sarvas, or Serv Nappe (not to be confused with the Seve Nappe) occupies a large area of central Sweden near the Norwegian frontier west of Östersund. Together with the Offerdal Nappe farther north, and a scatter of bits and pieces, it constitutes what is sometimes called the 'Middle Thrust Unit', coming below the 'Upper Thrust Unit' of the Seve–Koli Nappes. Others would simply regard it as the lower part of that complex. Whatever it is called, it may be regarded as an example of the complexity of the Caledonide structure.

These nappes consist mainly of Lower Palaeozoic rocks, in a fairly good state of preservation, together with large masses of Precambrian metamorphics. The abundance of conglomerates, quartzites, dolomites, and limestones, contrasts markedly with the eugosynclinal nature of the Seve–Koli unit proper and presumably implies a shallower, more marginal development eastwards towards the Fenno-Scandian Shield. The Sarv rocks are low-grade metamorphics, cut by a dike complex. The Offerdal nappe to the north is slightly lower structurally and consists of high-grade basement gneisses, presumably much older, overlain by 'Eocambrian' conglomerates.

Klippen of the Sarv Nappe are scattered as far as the Caledonian front, notably the quartzite masses north of Strömsund in Sweden, which are only separated by a narrow strip of the Jämtland Nappe from the Fenno-Scandian Shield.

Jämtland Nappe

Following the terminology mentioned above, this has been called the 'Lower Thrust Unit', which is a less ambiguous and therefore more acceptable term than the others. It comprises a heap of thrust slices and some would call it a 'nappe complex'; others would say that it has not travelled far enough to be dignified with the name 'nappe' at all.

It consists essentially of flat-lying plates of semi-autochtonous late Precambrian and early Palaeozoic rocks, all of low metamorphic grade. They extend for a considerable distance along the Caledonian front in both Norway and Sweden and rest on the autochthonous sediments of the Glint Line. It takes its name from the Jämtlands Lån (province) of northern Sweden and passes through its capital, Östersund, in the centre of that front. Theoreticians who wish to put major sutures along this line should remember, however, that there are tectonic windows of autochthonous material showing through for a considerable distance to the west.

The Jämtland Nappe (or Nappes) comes clearly below all the other allochthonous units. Sometimes the term is used for all the slices below the 'Great Seve Nappe' and it could be said that all these lower units are of a basically similar nature, including their dominantly shallow-water facies.

The Caledonian front is usually not all that obvious, being lost in undulating, densely forested country or hidden under the waters of the lakes that give the Glint Line its evocative name. It is a feature of Caledonian geology that the most important structures are hidden under long, narrow lakes. At Östersund itself, the most obvious frontal thrust is in fact the second one, where porphyry forms a local feature on the monster-haunted island of Frösö (in the town's lake) where it pushes eastwards over the Silurian of the frontal slice.

Also included here must be two vast areas of 'Eocambrian' sediments. In the south there is the classic Sparagmite area that extends from lovely Lake Kjøsa, north of Oslo, to beyond the Swedish border. This includes a variety of late Precambrian sediments, but mainly arkosic sandstones, together with the important conglomerates that give the group its name.* The sediments suggest rapid deposition, perhaps by floods in a normally dry climate, and there is strong evidence to suggest localized deposition in graben before the main marine transgression of the early Palaeozoic. The fact that they pass up conformably into fossiliferous Cambrian led to their being called 'Eocambrian', but there is no doubt that the bulk of them belong to the Proterozoic. The importance of the conglomerates lies in their supposedly glacial origin, mainly by comparison with much more convincing evidence in similar deposits in the north.

The Sparagmite rocks are folded and thrust, although they have generally been very little altered. Apart from their main outcrop they often form noticeable klippen, like buttes in the wild west. They are certainly the lowest and least travelled of the allochthonous masses.

The other big area of 'Eocambrian' rocks is in the extreme north of Norway, extending in a broad belt from the south end of Porsangerfjord eastwards to form the broad Varanger halvøya (peninsula) on the north side of the cold waters of Varangerfjord. These again are almost unaltered sediments, dominantly sandstones but including dolomites (with stromatolites) in the lower part and the famous Varanger tillites in their upper part.

The tillites are most accessible along the 'Arctic Highway' around Vestertana, at the south-west head of Tanafjord. No geologist could doubt the glacial origin of the scattered angular boulders in a fine silty matrix, but even more convincing is the classic exposure on the peninsula south of Varangerbotn (at the head of Varangerfjord). Here the boulder beds rest on an ice-scratched surface. This very distinctive formation, with other associated glacial phenomena, has been traced in various forms the whole length of the Caledonides through Scotland to the west of Ireland (and to Newfoundland). It represents a climatic event about 660 million years ago which may well correlate with late Precambrian phenomena elsewhere in Europe and in other parts of the world.

At the top of the Varanger succession, some 2000 m of quartzite above the tillites, Cambrian and early Ordovician fossils have been found on the Digermul peninsula on the west side of Tanafjord. Again there is no apparent unconformity below the Palaeozoic.

The Varanger rocks are folded and slightly cleaved. There is evidence of a thrust as their base, at least in the western part of their outcrop where they rest on autochthonous Lower Palaeozoic. Farther east, however, the thrusting is not apparent where they rest on the rocks of the Fenno-Scandian Shield.

Autochthon

Finally there is the narrow strip of autochthonous sediments along the Glint Line which separates the Caledonides from the shield. They are not very different from the successions in the frontal thrust slices and it is therefore convenient to deal with them here, rather than as part of the cover rocks discussed previously.

* It comes from the Greek word *sparagma*, meaning fragment.

There is a regular succession from 'Eocambrian' to Downtonian with a good fossil record. This fits into the general picture of a transition from deeper water to the west (with dominantly shaly sequences and much volcanic material) on to a shelf to the east (with carbonates and repeated transgressions and regressions). The generally soft nature of the frontal outcrop produces low-lying country and much is hidden under lakes, although the *Orthoceras* limestones of the Ordovician stand up as features in places. Where seen, and although quite acceptable to stratigraphers inured to this sort of geology, it is much more chewed up by the overthrusting than the placid outliers not so very far away on the shield.

Right on the other side of the fold belt, Middle Devonian 'Old Red Sandstone' type of sediments are found on the Norwegian coast between Nordfjord and Sognefjord, north of Bergen. These rocks are closely related (as are so many other things) to their equivalents in the Orkneys and Shetlands, north of the Scottish mainland. They differ significantly, however, in having been somewhat folded and thrust to the south-east, although certainly not metamorphosed. This is evidence of a late phase of the Caledonian orogeny as in Spitsbergen, but which is not really seen elsewhere in Palaeo-Europa.

One presumes that such 'Old Red Sandstone' sediments formerly covered much of the Scandinavian Caledonides, but have been removed by erosion. Presumably, as elsewhere, they represent the detritus of newly raised mountains after the main phase of the Caledonian orogeny, but there is evidence for a whole series of movements in early Palaeozoic times. One of the most convincing pieces of evidence for this is the so-called 'Valdres Sparagmite', which has nothing to do with the Sparagmite proper. This outcrops south of Peer Gynt's Gudbrandsdal in southern Norway. It is a felspathic sandstone of late Ordovician or Silurian age and rests unconformably on already folded Ordovician phyllites. It may be regarded as the molasse of a mid-Ordovician orogeny. However, modern views tend to emphasize two main episodes in the Caledonian orogeny in Scandinavia. The earlier ('Finnmarkian') was late Cambrian to early Ordovician in age, while the later ('Scandian') folding was mid to late Silurian. Nothing else is known of the late Palaeozoic in the Scandinavian Caledonides, so there is no clear date for the final ending of the movements. When we come to the next sediments, all is at comparative peace.

A few years ago I was asked to address a Jurassic meeting held by oil geologists at Stavanger. I commented in my opening remarks that a few years earlier a meeting on the Jurassic in Norway would have been as unlikely as a meeting on perma-frost in Zaire. The Jurassic of Norway used to be a joke. With the bulk of their North Sea wealth lying in Jurassic rocks, it is certainly not a joke today. All that is seen *in situ* on shore is a tiny patch of late Jurassic and early Cretaceous sediments down-faulted amidst the Caledonides on the island of Andøy, the northernmost of the Lofoten–Vesterålen group. They are sandstones and shales with some coals at the bottom and a Boreal fauna; they are closely related to what is now known under the North Sea. Scattered erratics of similar rocks are found elsewhere along the Norwegian coast.

While it is not my intention in this book to deal with the complexities of the Pleistocene, it is hard to leave the Scandinavian Caledonides without at least a mention of the events that had such a spectacular effect on the local scenery.

Nowhere in Europe is there better evidence of the great glaciations than in the fjords and lakes of south-west Norway. Every valley is U-shaped, every solid rock is smoothed and scratched by the moving ice, everywhere are the scattered and perched blocks of ice transport. Fjords such as Innviksfjord and Geirangerfjord are supreme textbook examples, while above them Jostedalsbreen is the largest ice-field in Europe, feeding a dozen active glaciers.

The general rise of Scandinavia, following the melting of the main ice-cap, has left staircases of high-level erosion surfaces and raised beaches down the west coast of Norway. The highest is at around 1600 m, well seen on the gabbros of the spectacular Lyngen peninsula. At a lower level (but with several intermediaries) is the famous and much photographed plateau that drops abruptly into the sea at Nordkapp (North Cape). Other splendid surfaces are seen around Porsangerfjord in the north and around Oslo fjord in the south. What is more, the fjords are cut deep below present sea-level (700 m in the case of Tysfjord, south of Narvik) and the uplift has still a long way to go.

Norwegian continental shelf

The narrowness of this shelf excuses me from saying much about it herein (other than in connection with the North Sea), but it is probable that rifting began here in late Palaeozoic times with thick sedimentation and the opening of the first seaway from the Arctic to the north-west European basins.

5(c)   British metamorphic Caledonides

The part of Palaeo-Europa that falls within the British Isles can be divided into a broad belt through northern Scotland and north-west Ireland where Lower Palaeozoic rocks have been metamorphosed, and a broad belt through southern Scotland, north-west England, Wales, and central Ireland, where these rocks have hardly been altered at all. In current jargon these are the orthotectonic and paratectonic Caledonides, respectively.

We are concerned in this section with the former division (see Figs 5.4 and 5.5). The main rock groups here are the ancient Lewisian (as in Eo-Europa), the monotonous Moinan, the diverse Dalradian, and the post-orogenic deposits and igneous rocks. For convenience the Tertiary volcanics and associated rocks, which invade this region from Eo-Europa, have already been dealt with under the Thulean Volcanic Region.

Moine Thrust Zone

One of the best-defined lines in European geology is the Caledonian front in north-west Scotland. The Moine Thrust Zone is a narrow belt at least 250 km long and 18 km wide. It carries nappes of Precambrian and Lower Palaeozoic rocks west-north-westwards over the Lewisian, Torridonian, and Cambro-Ordovician, of the Hebridean basement. The distance of transport is much disputed, but figures such as 'upwards of 20 km' are usually quoted. Several phases of movement are represented, starting after the early Ordovician and probably ending before the Devonian, since pebbles of sheared rock are found in the basal 'Old Red Sandstone' conglomerates. The thrusting is therefore 'Caledonian' in the classic sense, but was probably a late feature in that orogeny.

The Moine Thrust Zone stretches from the north coast of Scotland, east of Cape Wrath, down to the Point of Sleat at the southern tip of Skye, but the zone is probably at least twice as long as this in Scotland alone. It extends down to the west of the Isle of Mull and is perhaps seen again, displaced by the Great Glen Fault, in the island of Islay.

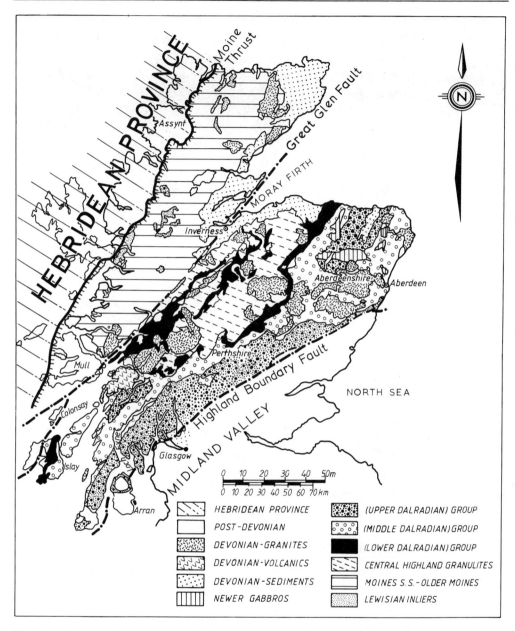

Fig. 5.4 *Geological sketch-map of the metamorphic Caledonides of Scotland (founded on Phemister, 1960 and Johnstone, 1966; by permission of the Director, Institute of Geological Sciences, Crown copyright reserved).*

Then presumably it heads off for Ireland, swinging westwards to separate that green island (and the rest of Europe) from the tiny Lewisian islet of Inishtrahull, whose sheared condition suggests thrusting in the vicinity. In the opposite direction, the thrust belt may well extend up to the west of the Orkneys.

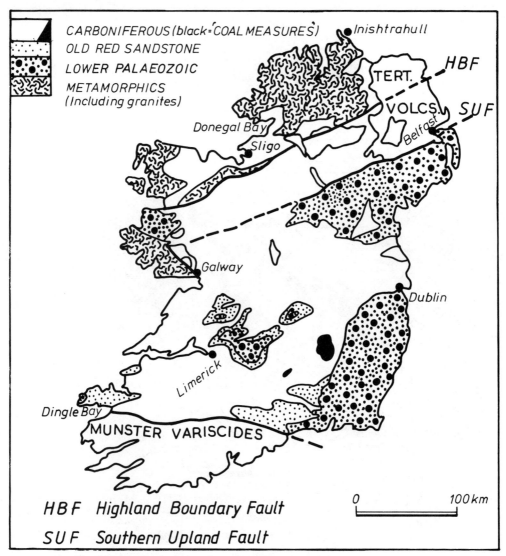

Fig. 5.5 *Geological sketch-map of the Caledonide rocks of Ireland.*

The Moine Thrust in the strict sense was the last and highest of the thrusts, carrying Moine schists over an imbricate jumble of slices, putting everything in the wrong order, and further confusing the issue with effects such as retrograde metamorphism. All this caused years of controversy before Charles Lapworth solved 'the secret of the Highlands' as it was called, in the 1880s. These things are probably best seen in the great bulge of Assynt where a complex anticline splays out the structure over a large area providing one of the classic field laboratories for British geological students. This then is the north-western front of Palaeo-Europa, just as we had the south-eastern front along the Glint Line in Scandinavia.

Lewisian inliers

East of the Moine Thrust there are various areas of high-grade metamorphic rock that contrast markedly with the monotony of the mica schists that form most of the country. Such is the belt of hornblende gneiss that runs south, in an intermittent fashion, from about the centre of the north Scottish coast. These areas were always interpreted as inliers of Lewisian, comparable with that on the foreland to the west. During my early days in geology, the great Highland geologists of the time were busy demolishing the supposed inliers. However, the Lewisian inliers have all been put back again and it is now generally accepted (as in Scandinavia) that they represent cores of older rocks showing through the Moine cover.

The most clearly defined of the Lewisian inliers is probably that at Glenelg, on the mainland opposite Skye, where there is a sharp contrast in metamorphic grade between the Lewisian and the overlying Moinian, and the latter has a fairly obvious basal conglomerate. Distinguishing the two is easiest here because there is a progressive increase in metamorphism eastwards, where the differences tend to be obliterated. Recent work has shown that most of the Lewisian east of the Moine thrust can be referred to the Scourian.

Moinian

The Moinian may be simply defined in Scotland as all those metamorphic rocks (apart from the Lewisian inliers) that lie between the Moine Thrust Zone and the Great Glen Fault. Nowadays, Highland workers would also include the so-called 'younger Moines' (the Central Highland Granulites) east of the Great Glen. But it must be realized that the Moinian is a division of convenience rather than reality and gives a false impression of unity and significance to a very confused and complex group of rocks.

The Moines are mostly of sedimentary origin, and probably started life as alternating sequences of shales and sandy mudstones. They are now mica schists and quartz-felspathic granulites, stretching on monotonously over the crags and peat-bogs of the Northern Highlands. The two basic rock-types alternate in broad belts across the country and many weary wet summers have been spent trying to establish a stratigraphy in these rather uniform and yet very complex rocks. There are now plenty of stratigraphies, in many different areas, but as yet there is no standard succession that can be recognized everywhere.

The other great Highland controversy of my geological youth was where to put the Moinian and the Dalradian as a whole. It was usually assumed that they fitted between the highly metamorphosed Lewisian and the very much younger unmetamorphosed Torridonian, but were mysteriously missing west of the Moine Thrust. It then became customary to regard the Moinian rocks as lateral equivalents of the Torridonian, albeit in a metamorphic grade that ranges up to kyanite and (east of the Great Glen Fault) into granulites. This seemed to make good sense although the Torridonian and the Moinian must have been very different in their original character. The former were continental fluviatile deposits, the latter most probably shallow-marine deltaic sediments and much thicker than the Torridonian. Since they both rest with apparent unconformity on Lewisian gneisses it was logical to regard the Moinian as the offshore equivalent of the Torridonian. A Greenlandian continent would seem to have provided the detritus. Study of sedimentary structures still preserved in places in the Moinian showed a pattern of longitudinal trough filling from the south-west. The only unlikely element in this story was the remarkable coincidence in position of the facies change and the thrust front. This is not all that unlikely, however, if the Moines were in a deeply-subsiding trough and the Torridonian on the edge of the stable platform. There is also the likelihood that the two facies have since been brought much closer together by the thrusting.

The whole story of the Torridonian–Moinian transition makes such very good sense that I feel (like Winston Churchill on some imaginative sidelight of history) that if it did not actually happen, then it should have done! However, facts are facts and some geochemical observations are almost facts. Whereas there are a large group of radiometric dates from the Moinian which straddle Caledonian events (about 320–560 million years ago) there also seems to be a distinct group (around 730–1050) which are well back in the Precambrian. These latter have been compared with the Grenvillian orogeny of the Canadian Shield. This may have been the orogeny that produced the mountains of which the Torridonian is the erosional debris.

If these dates are correct, we can no longer accept the equivalence of the whole of the Moinian with the whole of the Torridonian. However, there are the Central Highland Granulites, east of the Great Glen Fault, which were probably sandier in origin and can be equated with at least the upper part of the Torridon succession. Their very high grade of metamorphism fits in with the general easterly trend in these characters and makes another interesting comparison with the Scandinavian Caledonides where the trend goes in the opposite direction. However, no one has yet found evidence of a major unconformity within the Moinian succession, nor between it and the overlying Dalradian—a transition which is now dated as about 700 million years ago. In Ireland, Moinian rocks have been claimed by various workers in a small area of southern Donegal near Ballyshannon, in the Ox Mountains south of Sligo Bay, and elsewhere. They swim in a sea of Dalradian, but their metamorphism has again been dated as Grenvillian in age. This and the other units of the Irish Caledonides have been correlated with structural zones in the Appalachians.

Dalradian

Dalradian rocks occupy most of the south-east Highlands of Scotland between the Great Glen Fault and the Highland Boundary Fault. Both of these structures, with the Dalradian rocks between them, can be traced across northern Ireland.* The Dalradian followed the Moinian without a perceptible break. Like the latter, it was clearly sedimentary in origin, although of a rather different character with notable developments of carbonates (very rare in the Moines), orthoquartzites, and tillites.

There is in fact a refreshing variety of rock-types after the monotony of the Moines. It is correspondingly easier to work out a stratigraphy and thence to elucidate the major structures. What is more, there are also fossils. Just before the Second World War, when all things metamorphic tended to be automatically Precambrian, there was a startling discovery of Middle Cambrian trilobites in a faulted sliver at Callander, north of Glasgow, near the Highland boundary. Nowadays it is thought that if at least the Upper

---

* Not to be confused with that part of it known as Northern Ireland, the political entity.

Moines are the metamorphic equivalent of the Torridonian, then the Dalradian includes metamorphosed Lower Palaeozoic up to the Lower Ordovician, if not higher. On the evidence of the tillites the Dalradian also presumably includes the continuation of the 'Eocambrian' of Scandinavia.

The Dalradian is divided into three groups, which succeed each other in a broadly southerly and south-easterly direction, to terminate against the Highland Boundary Fault. At the base there are alternating quartzites and pelites. These are followed by the widespread tillites, which can be traced right across the Scottish Highlands and Ireland. They are equated with the Varanger tillites of northern Norway and, although the precision of the correlation might not satisfy a Quaternary specialist, they seem to be a useful indicator of so-called 'Eocambrian' times. The tillites are always associated with algal dolomites, although they seem to be unlikely climatic associates. Hereabouts in the succession one longs for a gap. Overlying limestones and volcanics have been attributed, on spore evidence, to the Lower Cambrian.

In the Upper Dalradian come the sandstones, shales, and further volcanics, that are thought to range up into the Lower Ordovician. It is presumed that they equate with the top of the Durness Limestone of the Hebridean Province, although quite different in character.

There are probably more than 8000 m of Dalradian altogether, much in the form of 'turbidites' and associated pillow lavas. We must be in a sizable trough which contrasted markedly with the geography on either side, even if a lot has been lost down subduction zones. Whether an early Atlantic ocean spread its waters over these abandoned crofts and tree-less deer forests will be discussed in Chapter 7, but the alleged ophiolites are certainly not oceanic and are underlain by granites.

In Ireland very similar rocks extend in a broad belt under the Tertiary basalts and Londonderry to form the greater part of Donegal. Again they have been correlated with a similar structural zone in the western Appalachians. At Killary Harbour they can be dated as pre-Silurian by an overlying Wenlock conglomerate and possibly pre-Arenig on the evidence of included fragments.

Pre-Devonian structures

It is difficult to separate the orogenic movements that affected the Moinian and Dalradian rocks. The Moinian structures generally, like the Moine Thrust Zone, appear to face west-north-west and westerly-moving nappes have been recognized in the south-west, but the major structures have not yet been fully worked out. All that can be said with confidence is that there have been several phases of deformation extending through a vast period of time. As a crude generalization it may be said that whereas the earliest structures tend to be on north–south axes, sometimes swinging to the north-west, the later open folds generally trend north–east in the approved Caledonoid direction. Only some very late small-scale east–west folds along the Moine Thrust are at variance with the general pattern and these probably had a special local cause.

In the Dalradian, the general map (Fig. 5.4) clearly shows the Caledonoid trend, but the folds seem to be closing to the south-east. Detailed stratigraphy has made possible the elucidation of large overturned nappe structures, such as that at Banff on the north side of the Aberdeenshire promontory. Again up to four phases of movements have been recognized, of which the first formed the large recumbent nappes, which have been compared in size with those of the Pennine Alps. One of these has been traced for nearly 300 km along the strike. Huge slide planes pass over the nappes in the same general direction.

The movements that affected these rocks have been called the Grampian Orogeny after the mountains of the south-east Highlands of Scotland which separate the highlanders from the 'Sassenachs' (i.e., supposed Saxons) of the lowlands. It was named for an orogenic phase in the early Ordovician (comparable with the Finnmarkian of Scandinavia) to distinguish it from the Caledonian in the strict sense which was much later in age (although also taking its name from Scotland). Apart from the fossil evidence, several radiometric dates of around 500 million years have been obtained from rocks that were emplaced immediately before the last phase of the Grampian movements.

Besides the major folding, thrusting, and metamorphism which took place at this time, two major structures were initiated: the Highland Boundary Fault and the Great Glen Fault. The former is seen today as a reversed fault separating the Highlands from the Midland Valley of Scotland. It is commonly picked out by serpentinites, for example where it crosses Loch Lomond, north-west of Glasgow. It moved several times and it has recently been suggested that it was initiated as a transform fault during the Ordovician. Although it is used here as a boundary line between the metamorphosed and the non-metamorphosed Caledonides, it must be mentioned that high-grade Dalradian rocks do occur south of the direct extension of this fault in Connemara, western Ireland (famous for its marbles). These seem to have been displaced by a transcurrent fault that connects with the main dislocation.

A major feature of the orogenic movements was the emplacement of large masses of granite and gabbro. Granites in the Moinian have been dated as around 550 million years. The largest are those in the far north-east, bordering the 'Old Red Sandstone' basin. More famous, however, are the later granites in the Dalradian around Aberdeen. Indeed, that was the 'Granite City' when oil was only something used in crofters' lamps. These newer granites were largely post-orogenic, late Silurian to early Devonian in age. In Ireland, similar granites include the Main Donegal Granite which has been shown to include at least four distinct phases of granitic emplacement and to involve both replacement of the country rock and (notably in the case of the little Ardara Pluton at the south-west end) of diapiric intrusion. One of the most fascinating features of the former process is the way different members of the Dalradian succession can be traced in what has been called 'ghost stratigraphy' through the main body of the granite.

The Great Glen Fault has been kept until last because it moved very late, although it probably started early. It is the most spectacular feature of the geology of Scotland, being a dead straight line that cuts that ancient kingdom in two by way of a series of long narrow lakes (or lochs), the best known of which (for monsters rather than for its geology) is Loch Ness. It seems to be a feature of this part of Palaeo-Europa too that all the best structures are hidden under water, but this is obviously not just coincidental.

The Great Glen Fault corresponds with an important junction in Highland geology with the central Highland Granulites and the Dalradian on its south-east side and the Moinian in the strict sense to the north-west. The most exciting new idea in British geology that had just appeared when I was a student was the demonstration that this was a great tear fault. The best evidence was the matching of a granite on the west coast opposite Mull, north of the fault, with a granite on the south side close to the North Sea coast. This implies over 100 km of lateral displacement, with the northern part of Scotland moving down to the south-west. Unfortunately, as with so many good theories, later the iconoclasts arrived and had the fault moving in the opposite direction. Since then it has been moved backwards and forwards by geologists more than by tectonic forces. The original idea seems to be back with us today, but it is obvious that it moved several times and is still a centre for tiny earthquakes.

It was later than the Moine Thrust which it displaces, and it affected the 'Old Red Sandstone' of Devonian age. The fault which later shifted a strip of Jurassic sediments on the east coast of Sutherland was probably a branch of the Great Glen. From there it extends northwards through the remote Shetland Isles. It has been traced in the opposite direction to the north coast of Ireland.

Post-orogenic rocks

The comment was made in the last chapter that the Scandinavian Caledonides represent a much lower level of erosion than those of the British Isles. This is particularly evident from the preservation of post-orogenic rocks, of which there is only the meerest trace in the Norwegian and Swedish parts of Palaeo-Europa.

So far as sediments are concerned, the 'Old Red Sandstone' is preserved over a large area of north-east Scotland around the Moray Firth, and in the steep-cliffed Orkney Islands. This was the Orcadian Cuvette, named after the latter islands and filled with a considerable thickness (over 6000 m) of continental sediments. These are preserved in a broad, very gentle syncline with its axis along the line of the Great Glen Fault, which evidently had a connection with what was going on. In fact this axis can be imagined under the stormy waters of the Pentland Firth all the way to the Shetlands, where great thicknesses are preserved.

The generally low-lying ground around the Moray Firth and its extension in Caithness in the extreme north-east ('the Lowlands beyond the Highlands') are the classic ground of the 'Old Red Sandstone'. Here Hugh Miller, the quarryman turned geologist, found and described the famous fish faunas and here at Rhynie (some 50 km west-north-west of Aberdeen) were found what were, for a long time, the oldest known land plants. The man who found the latter thought that they were rhyolitic lavas and was astonished, when they were sectioned in the laboratory, to see perfectly preserved cellular structures of simple plants silicified where they lived in a dampish bog.

The earliest deposits, as at Rhynie, belong to the Lower Devonian. They represent the first filling in of an eroded landscape of Moinian and Dalradian rocks. They are mostly coarse grained and there are some associated volcanics. The bulk of the sedimentary pile, however, belongs to the Middle 'Old Red Sandstone' and appears to have been laid down in an extensive lake. Thin-bedded flagstones are the rule (so easily split that they are stood on end to make walls round fields). The famous fish occur at limited horizons, notably at Achanarras in Caithness.

It will be noted that the 'Old Red Sandstone' syncline, although very minor compared with the intense folding that went on before, was still on Caledonoid lines. There were evidently very late pulses in Devonian times, for the Upper 'Old Red Sandstone' rests unconformably on the Middle and shows a fresh inrush of coarse material. This is best

97

seen on the island of Hoy in the Orkneys where a high, slender sea-stack (the 'Old Man of Hoy') shows a fine section through the Upper 'Old Red Sandstone', studied intimately by those who climb it. There was also some more volcanicity, although not approaching the scale of south-west Scotland, and things soon quietened down again to fine-grained deposition which may cross the Devonian–Carboniferous boundary.

The only later deposits, if one excludes the Jurassic of the Sutherland coast (which is dealt with in the North Sea Basin) are some patches of red sandstone on the south side of the Moray Firth near Lossiemouth. These were naturally enough taken to be 'Old Red Sandstone' until they yielded the remains and footprints of Permian and Triassic reptiles.

We must now go back to the Caledonian movements in the south-west Highlands. Here on the Lorne Plateau, inland from Fort William, there is a remarkable group of igneous rocks which may date back to the Silurian, but which include lava flows interbedded with Lower and Upper 'Old Red Sandstone'. There are great 'cauldron subsidences' at Ben Nevis (the highest point in the British Isles at a mere 1340 m) and Glen Coe (famous for a massacre in 1691); there are larger masses of granite; there are extensive lava flows (especially around Oban); and there are swarms of north–east trending dikes. Dikes with similar trends occur over a large part of the Dalradian floor, but later dikes in the Moinian terrain trend east–west.

In Ireland, flat-lying Upper Palaeozoic rocks rest on the Caledonides over great areas, but they are mainly confined to the unmetamorphosed Caledonides and are best discussed there. Only in an area round Donegal Bay in the west do they invade the metamorphic terrain. Here they are largely early Carboniferous carbonates, as over so much of central Ireland.

There only remains the Pleistocene glaciations, which had such a considerable effect on the scenery of the Scottish Highlands and at the same time scraped clean the ancient rocks of Ireland. There are a multiplicity of glacial features, both erosional and depositional, and a fine series of post-glacial raised beaches.

5(d)   British non-metamorphic Caledonides

The Precambrian and Lower Palaeozoic rocks of central and western Britain and the greater part of Ireland are the concern of this section. This is the region where Lower Palaeozoic rocks have been folded, often intensely but not significantly metamorphosed. They are seen mainly in the Southern Uplands of Scotland (Fig. 5.6), the Lake District of north-west England (Fig. 5.7), the greater part of Wales (Fig. 5.8), and in eastern and south-east Ireland (Fig. 5.5). There are smaller outcrops (and borehole records) in between, under the thick cover of flat-lying Upper Palaeozoic and Mesozoic rocks that occupy the rest of the belt, dealt with in Section (e) below.

The north-west boundary is clearly defined as the Highland Boundary Fault of central Scotland, which runs from Stonehaven, south of Aberdeen on the east coast, to the Isle of Arran in the west. It continues across Ireland from north of Belfast (under the Antrim basalts) to Clew Bay in Mayo.

The south-east margin is not so easy to define, but is here taken in England and South Wales as the line along which strong folding of the Lower Palaeozoic ends as one moves south-east. Southwards the non-metamorphosed Caledonides end against the Variscan Front, both in South Wales and in southern Ireland.

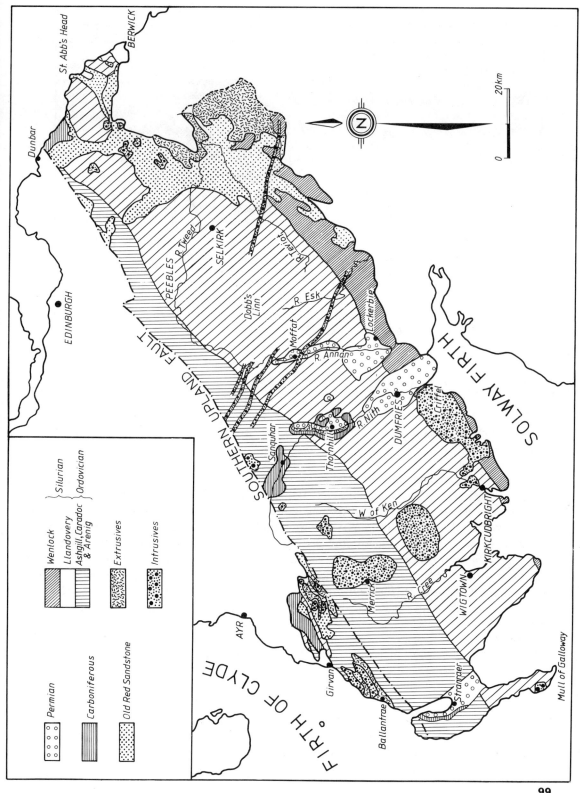

Fig. 5.6 Geological sketch-map of the Southern Uplands of Scotland (after Greig. 1971. by kind permission of the Director of the Institute of Geological Sciences. Crown copyright reserved).

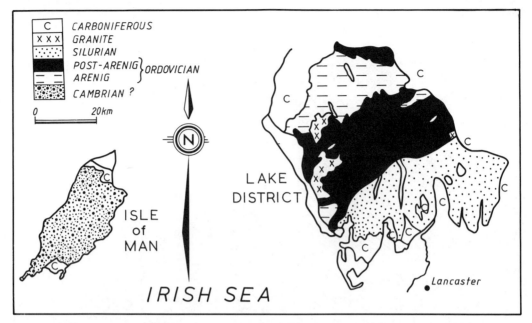

Fig. 5.7   Geological sketch-map of the English Lake District and the Isle of Man.

Southern Uplands and Girvan area

The Scottish non-metamorphic Caledonides are chiefly exposed in the grey, gloomy, glaciated hills of the Southern Uplands (where the English raided the Scots when the Scots were not raiding the English). This is almost holy ground to Lower Palaeozoic stratigraphers, for here Charles Lapworth first showed that graptolites could be used to correlate Ordovician and Silurian strata and so unravel the complex structures of the region. I remember his famous pupil, Gertrude Elles, telling how at the end of a day's field-work he would produce the specimens collected up one stream section from the many pockets on one side of his remarkable waistcoat. He would then proudly show how they matched the specimens from another stream section in the pockets on the other side. He was able to do this because the succession, especially at his classic locality of Dobb's Linn, near Moffat in the centre of the Southern Uplands, is extremely thin and condensed. Some 17 zones of the late Ordovician and early Silurian, each perhaps representing some 3 million years, are packed into 80 m of sediment. But farther north in the Southern Uplands the succession is much thicker and up to 9 km of sediments have been estimated for the Ordovician and Silurian.

Southwards the Lower Palaeozoic rocks disappear under an unconformable cover of Devonian and Carboniferous. Northwards they are thrown down by the Southern Uplands Fault into the great graben of the Midland Valley of Scotland. In the extreme south-west of the Midland Valley, however, there is another classic area of Lower Palaeozoic rocks around the grey little seaside towns of Girvan and Ballantrae.

In the Girvan area there are fragments of one of the best ophiolite suites in the British Isles. Down the coast towards Ballantrae are pillow lavas, serpentinites, radiolarian cherts, and graptolitic shales, with some glaucophane schists and eclogites. These range

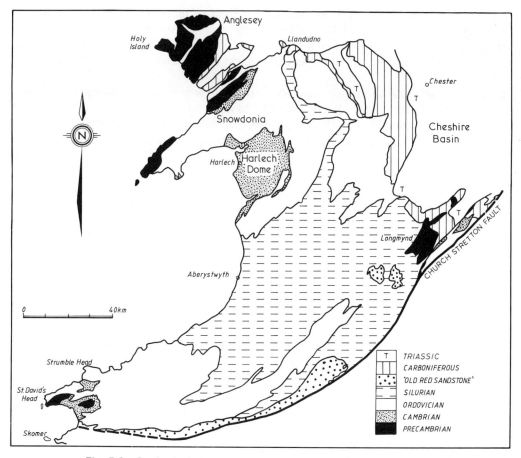

Fig. 5.8 Geological sketch-map of the Anglo-Welsh Caledonides.

from early to late Ordovician in age (although the eclogites and glaucophane schists may be older). Obviously they have been interpreted as ocean-floor material, probably in the region of an island arc.

They are overlain by coarse sediments with numerous breaks and several conglomerates that range from Caradoc up to Wenlock in age. There are marginal deposits with shallow-water faunas of North American affinities, and their correlation by Lapworth with the graptolitic shales of Moffat was a classic demonstration of facies change. Presumably they accumulated after the ocean floor had been subducted against a continental margin. Southwards the sediment pile thickens rapidly as soon as one crosses the Southern Uplands Fault, which seems to be a very fundamental junction between regions of quite different crustal structure, so that in the northern part of the Southern Uplands proper there are immense thicknesses of trench-type deposits. These are 'turbidites' and conglomeratic greywackes of Caradoc and Ashgill age. They are interpreted as submarine fans at the bottom of a south-east facing continental slope. The more distal 'turbidites' show evidence of lateral transport along the trough towards the south-west.

101

In the central and widest belt of the Southern Uplands most of the rocks at the surface are early Silurian shales with inliers of Ordovician, as in the section at Dobb's Linn. Here everything is very thin with vast numbers of graptolites packed together for the benefit of the stratigraphers and interpretable as the thinnest deposition farthest from the sediment source.

There is a generally ascending sequence south-eastwards across the Southern Uplands, although it probably never gets above the Middle Silurian. The structure was long thought to be a complex bundle of tight isoclinal folds, but a recent trench for a gas pipeline across the range suggests that it is basically nothing more than a series of thrust slices, all moving south-eastwards. It has been compared with the structures seen in modern ocean trenches. From stratigraphical evidence it seems that the belt of sedimentation was moving south with time and that earlier sediments were being cannibalized to produce newer ones. Altogether the ocean margin may have moved about 70 km between Llandeilo and Wenlock times.

The final orogeny was near the end of the Silurian Period. This is the classic Caledonian. Three large granite masses were emplaced near the south-west end of the range, dated as around 386 million years old, putting them conveniently in the early Devonian. There were also a large number of minor intrusions.

At the north-east end, flat-lying 'Old Red Sandstone' sediments and lavas spread over the Southern Uplands, followed by early Carboniferous. At Siccar Point, west of St. Abb's Head, is the most famous unconformity in Britain. Here almost horizontal Upper 'Old Red Sandstone' rests directly on nearly vertical Silurian shales. This was James Hutton's classic demonstration of his 'succession of former worlds'. Nowhere is the Caledonian orogeny more obvious.

Later Palaeozoic sediments are represented in the thin little Thornhill and Sanquhar coal basins, which cut across the structure north-west of Robert Burns's Dumfries and by thick 'Permo-Triassic' cross-bedded sandstones, now thought to range down into the Carboniferous. These are seen particularly at Dumfries and at nearby Lockerbie, and in the narrow neck of land at Stranraer which nearly cuts off the pick-head of the Rinns of Galloway from the rest of Scotland.

North-east Ireland

The direct continuation of the Southern Uplands is seen in north-east Ireland in the mainly lowland area south and south-west of Belfast. A broad outcrop of Ordovician and Silurian rocks passes through the counties of Down, Armagh, Monaghan, and Cavan, disregarding the troubled border. The scenery is quite different from that of southern Scotland, being comparatively low, rolling country scattered with drumlins and very few exposures. The rocks, when you can see them, are like those of the Southern Uplands, with a similar structure of thrust slices getting younger to the south. South-westwards these rocks dive under the Carboniferous blanket of central Ireland.

The Lower Palaeozoic here is again cut by Caledonian granites, of which by far the largest is the Newry Granite in the east (overshadowed topographically by the Mourne Mountains granite of Tertiary age, mentioned earlier). The Newry granite has been dated as early Devonian, like those in Scotland.

Throughout this belt, which many geologists want to interpret as ocean-floor material, there is evidence of continental crust beneath. The geophysical evidence is somewhat inconclusive, but there is also solid evidence in the form of clasts of gneiss in Lower Carboniferous agglomerates.

Lake District and the Isle of Man

In the north-west of England is the Lake District, a beautiful dome-like region of Lower Palaeozoic which was popular with nineteenth century poets, and the craggy heights of which are much climbed by mountaineers. Out in the Irish Sea, halfway to Ireland, is the slaty Isle of Man, chiefly known to the outside world by its tailless cats, its three-legged symbol, and its motor-cycle races.

The oldest rocks known at the surface in the area are the slates that make up the greater part of the Isle of Man, which have long been hesitantly attributed to the late Cambrian. If correct, this may be true only in the strictly British sense, since they are allegedly Tremadoc, which the rest of the world puts in the Ordovician. There is a problem here, since no less than 7.5 km of slates and 'turbidites' have been recorded, all practically without macrofossils but all attributed to half a stage or so. Although this appeals to my catastrophist spirit, it does seem rather out of proportion to common experience.

The Manx Slates may well pass up (on the main island) into the Skiddaw Slates of the Lake District, named after England's highest mountain.* These are muddy 'turbidites' of Arenig to Llanvirn age and form a broad belt across the north of the Lake District. They are followed (perhaps after a minor orogenic phase) by the dominantly volcanic series of the Llandeilo and early Caradoc which forms most of the picturesquely dramatic scenery of the region—some 5 km of mostly andesitic rocks that are infernally difficult to map. There is then a marked unconformity below the highest Ordovician rocks, which are more calcareous. They cut right across the earlier divisions with outcrops both to the south and north. These later Caradoc and Ashgill rocks (the latter in their type locality) are very thin but demonstrate clearly that major earth-movements took place in mid to late Ordovician times.

Silurian sediments follow on conformably and extend over a wide belt of country in the south of the Lake District. Their dominantly argillaceous character gives rise to a more placid landscape, such as pleased Wordsworth so much around Lake Windermere; but in the upper part more 'turbidites' coming from the north finally filled up the trough. As in the Southern Uplands, there is a generally ascending succession southwards. Also the general strike of the folding, thrusting and cleavage is to the east-north-east. This was produced in the final intense deformation that occurred at the end of Silurian times. Granites were then emplaced (of which the most famous is that of Shap Fell, with its large pink felspars), together with many smaller intrusions and mineralization.

A miniature, elongated replica of the Lake District is seen to the east on the opposite side of the Vale of Eden graben, which operated in Permian times. Within this valley

* Less than 1000 m in height, but our mountains are very old and worn.

there are preserved the screes that spread out from the faulted margins, desert sands, a Permian flora adapted to aridity, and a whiff of the Zechstein Sea in the form of a thin equivalent of the Upper Permian limestones that are important on the other side of the Pennines.

Caledonian Wales and the Welsh Borderland

The lovely 'Land of Song' in which I presently live is largely composed of early Palaeozoic rocks intensely folded, although not appreciably metamorphosed, in the Caledonian orogeny. There are also some small areas of Precambrian rocks. The Cambrian, Ordovician, and Silurian Periods all take their names from this area and it was here that Sedgwick and Murchison did their great labours and fought their great battles.

The oldest rocks seen at the surface are in Anglesey, that stronghold of the druids off the north coast. The older Precambrian here was evidently a thick sedimentary sequence of flysch-type rocks on Holy Island (beautifully exposed by the lighthouse at South Stack, on an island off an island off an island off an island). There are associated quartzites and other sedimentary rocks, including a giant olistostrome, but the succession is far from clear. Local experts have interpreted it first one way up and then the other, and more recently, sideways (with lateral transition), so I am not getting involved in that one. Also there are elements of what has been called an ophiolite suite with pillow lavas (well seen at Llanddwyn Island), serpentinites (badly seen at Rhos Colyn), and cherts. There is also a development of glaucophane schists (seen near the little village of Llanfairpwllgwyngyllgogerychwyrndrobwllllantysiliogogogoch), so there would seem to be everything that is needed for a subduction zone. This, however, has been strongly disputed as have the general plate tectonic pictures that have been painted of the Welsh Precambrian.

The above sedimentary sequence is commonly metamorphosed, often to quite a high grade and all within a remarkably small area. This whole sequence is commonly called the Mona Complex (after the Welsh name Môn for Anglesey) or Monian (not to be confused with Moinian). It is seen again in the Lleyn peninsula on the Welsh mainland and both there and on Anglesey it is overlain unconformably by a volcanic series of acid lavas and pyroclastics which are late Precambrian in age and comparable with volcanic developments at this level in south-west Wales and on the Central British Block. Everywhere, acidic volcanism seems to have been the rule. The only later Precambrian rocks known in this region are the thick sedimentary sequence of the large flat upland of the Longmynd in Shropshire. This is mainly flysch-like, with some volcanics and some unconformities (and a great number of controversies). They date from very late in the Precambrian. All of these Precambrian successions were strongly folded and eroded before the beginning of Palaeozoic time, although the trends of the folding are commonly Caledonoid in direction.

The Cambrian System takes its name from Wales and the type area would presumably be the slates and 'grits' of the Harlech Dome in the north-west, where the contrasting lithologies produce concentric elliptical amphitheatres between Harlech and Dolgellau. The sediments are typical 'turbidites' and associated sediments of a deep trough, but they are generally lacking in fossils and difficult to correlate. They disappear northwards under the Ordovician of the Snowdon syncline and appear again against the Precambrian ridges of northernmost Wales in the form of the famous purple and green roofing slates that were formerly exported around the world and have left some huge holes in the Welsh countryside, notably at Llanberis.

There are hints of volcanism in the Cambrian but, as in the Southern Uplands and Lake District, it was the Ordovician Period that really exploded in this way. Snowdonia is a great syncline filled with eugeosynclinal Ordovician rocks, including pillow lavas and a variety of other volcanics. They are seen again in the Cader Idris range to the south, near Montgomery, around Builth in the south-east and in Pembrokeshire where there is a magnificent display of pillow lavas on Strumble Head. The volcanism lasted spasmodically all through the Ordovician, but decreased markedly eastwards away from the great trough. Here also the succession is much thinner and has notable gaps. In places (as around the islands of Longmyndian rocks that stood out of the Silurian sea) it is missing altogether. Associated mineralization has been worked on a very small scale, since Roman times and before. Enough gold is extracted to provide wedding rings for British queens; other deposits have a rather larger potential.

The Silurian presents a similar picture of deep-water graptolitic facies in central Wales, passing laterally through a range of supposedly depth-controlled fossil assemblages into what were clearly the shallowest environments at the margin, with breaks and transgressions (most notably in the late Llandovery). The most significant difference from the Ordovician situation is that Silurian carbonate shelf sediments extended over the English Midlands. Volcanism all but ended, continuing only in the south, roughly along the line that was to be the Variscan Front. The interaction between the Caledonoid and Variscoid trends is interesting. The general south-westerly trending Welsh Caledonides swing round to an almost east–west direction as they approach the Variscan front in Pembrokeshire. It has commonly been supposed that the later folding affected the earlier, but this cannot be since the trend also conforms with facies distributions.* Both the Ordovician and the Silurian have passed into shallow-water facies by the time one reaches the edge of the outcrop north and west of the South Wales coal-field. Here the outcrop passes such famous place-names as Llandovery and Llandeilo and we may not be all that far from the edge of the great Anglo-Welsh trough.

This is a well-studied part of the world and the story is far from simple. Many of the important facies changes seem to relate to the Church Stretton Fault, named after the pleasant little Salop town that stands between the Precambrian sediments of the Longmynd and the Precambrian volcanics of Caer Caradoc.† Here runs the fault that operated several times in several different ways and which can be traced all the way down through South Wales to St. Bride's in Pembrokeshire.‡

The Church Stretton Fault can be called the south-east Caledonian Front, for it marks the edge of the intense folding and of the trench. The Caledonian orogeny here, as elsewhere, was a multiphase affair, but reached its climax at the end of the Silurian. In South Wales, for example along the Sawdde gorge at Pontarllechau, east of Llandeilo,

---

* Thus the symbol of the Geology Department at Swansea is a trilobite, not a graptolite!

† One of the many places in the Welsh Borderland laying claim to be where the British chieftain Caradoc or Caractacus made his last stand against the Romans.

‡ In spite of geographers and politicians, British geologists insist on retaining this useful old county name, which is much more meaningful than amorphous Dyfed.

105

the transitional beds at the much-disputed Silurian–Devonian boundary can be seen to have been stood on end. The intensity of the folding was less in the Anglo-Welsh area than, for example, in Scotland. The absence of metamorphism is further emphasized by the absence of major intrusive bodies like the Caledonian granites of the north. There are some sizable basic intrusions, such as the mass that holds up the memorial to Admiral Rodney in the Breidden Hills west of Shrewsbury, and many minor intrusions, but these are all associated with the Ordovician volcanicity and not post-orogenic. It is, however, easy to be distracted by the details around the edges and to overlook the great thicknesses of sediment—perhaps 6 km of Ordovician and Silurian alone—under the rugged and remarkably little mapped sheep farms of central Wales. This was a great trough full of sediment, whatever name we choose to give it.

South-east Ireland

The direct continuation of the Welsh Caledonides can be seen in the Wicklow Mountains south of Dublin and in south-east Ireland generally, down nearly to the Variscan Front. There are many other patches of Lower Palaeozoic sediments showing up as far west as the Dingle Peninsula. Most interesting are the metamorphic rocks of the extreme south-easterly corner, south of Wexford, which have been compared with the Monian of Anglesey. Amphibolite grade gneisses with granitic intrusions are followed by greywackes and quartzites, reminiscent of North Wales. They were finally cut by the granite which forms Carnsore Point and which has been dated around 550 million years old. Also as in Anglesey they are overlain by a transgressive Ordovician conglomerate. It is tempting to see this as the mirror-image of the situation on the opposite side of the Anglo-Welsh trough. Often compared with the 'slates' of the Isle of Man is the thick argillaceous succession that outcrops for long stretches along the coast south of Dublin, most notably at Bray Head and on the headland of Howth, which guards the sea entrance to the Irish capital (and in the tiny island to the north of that, known as Ireland's Eye). Like the Manx Slates, these beds lack fossils apart from the problematical *Oldhamia*, but they are usually called 'Cambrian' with a question mark.

The Ordovician occupies a much wider area and shows signs of a shoreline to the south-east and a trough centre to the north-west. Unlike the situation in Great Britain, it is possible to see the connection between the Anglo-Welsh counterpart and the Southern Uplands counterpart up in the region round the River Boyne, north of Dublin. There is a great deal of basic volcanicity associated with the monotonous greywackes and slates and the volcanism seems to grow later westwards. As in Wales the main eruptions ceased with the Ordovician, but they did continue into the Silurian near the Variscan Front. The western inliers are almost entirely composed of Silurian rocks, notably the outcrop that forms most of the Dingle Peninsula, where volcanicity was as late as Ludlow in age.

The intense deformation of this eugeosynclinal pile came at the end of early Palaeozoic times, although again it is possible in places to see a gentle passage through into the 'Old Red Sandstone' facies. A feature that distinguishes this region from the Anglo-Welsh non-metamorphic Caledonides is the presence of two large granite plutons forming the higher parts of the Wicklow Mountains and other mountains on the borders of Wexford. These granites have been dated as around the Silurian–Devonian boundary.

5(e) Post-Caledonian Basins

Superimposed on the non-metamorphic Caledonides is a series of major sedimentary basins, mostly of great economic importance.

Midland Valleys of Scotland and Ireland

The former is the great graben across the centre of Scotland, delimited to the north by the Highland Boundary Fault and to the south by the Southern Uplands Fault (Fig. 5.9). It is a low-lying area compared with the Highlands on one side and the Southern Uplands on the other; it contains both Edinburgh and Glasgow and most of the industry (and population) of Scotland.

Included within it are inliers of Lower Palaeozoic rocks, notably those around Girvan and Ballantrae in the west which were discussed earlier. There are some other Silurian inliers, however, of a rather different nature, notably at Lesmahagow, south of Glasgow, and in a broad sweep of smaller outcrops round to the outskirts of Edinburgh. These show a somewhat anomalous succession from marine to continental (and highly conglomeratic) beds, with early fish faunas, which are thought to represent the Middle and Upper Silurian. It is quite different from the succession in the Southern Uplands but may be the weathering product of the earliest uplifted slices which were mainly shedding sediment to the south but may also have been filling this new trough to the north.

The 'Old Red Sandstone' rests unconformably on the Silurian and outcrops along both sides of the Midland Valley in the form of fluviatile and lacustrine sandstones and conglomerates. This was when the valley began to form in earnest. There is a particularly wide outcrop along the north side, from Greenock to Stonehaven, past the old Scottish capital of Perth.*

There were also great outpourings of lavas and tuffs, both along the boundary faults and in a broad belt in the north, parallel to the Highland Boundary Fault, from Stirling up past Perth nearly to Dundee. There are approximately 6000 m of Lower 'Old Red Sandstone' alone, and another 1000 m of Upper 'Old Red Sandstone' unconformably above. Both sedimentation and volcanicity were clearly related to the faulting.

Hydrocarbon accumulation began early in the Carboniferous of the Midland Valley, especially in the east, where there are thick oil shales (once extensively mined in Midlothian) and an early Carboniferous Coal Measure development with ironstones on the shores of the Firth of Forth. Contemporaneous volcanicity aided the preservation of delicate plant tissues, in exquisite detail, far better than most botany students can get from living material.

Marine facies are also present, although on nothing like the scale seen in northern England. Limestones and shales are found from one sea to the other, with rich and well-preserved faunas (e.g., on the Fife coast) and mini-reefs. But the outstanding feature of the Lower Carboniferous here is its volcanicity. Great flat spreads of basaltic lava

---

* The Scottish kings used to be crowned at Scone near here, and the 'Stone of Scone', stolen by the English, is now incorporated in the Coronation Chair in Westminster Abbey. Legend has it that it was the stone used as a pillow by the patriarch Jacob, when he dreamed his dream of the ladder to heaven. Sceptical geologists have identified it as a sample of the local 'Old Red Sandstone'.

107

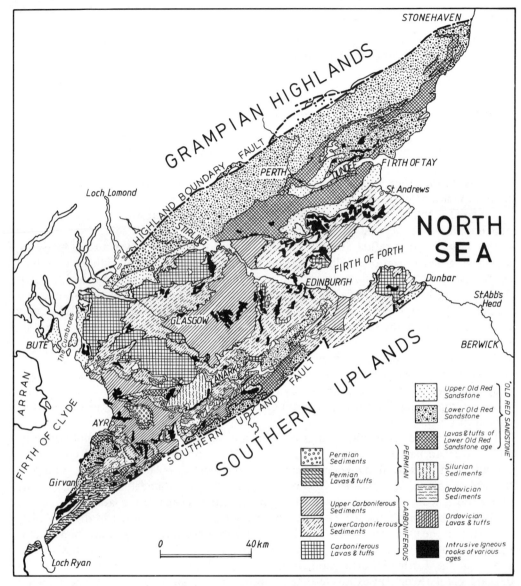

Fig. 5.9 *Geological sketch-map of the Midland Valley of Scotland (after MacGregor and MacGregor, 1948, by permission of the Director, Institute of Geological Sciences, Crown copyright reserved).*

extend north, south, and west of Glasgow weathering into a characteristic staircase topography, for example in the Campsie Fells. Volcanic necks are eroded out as upstanding pillars, such as Dunbarton Rock on the Clyde. At the other end of the valley is some of the most famous volcanic topography in the world, with volcanic necks forming the glowering hill from which Edinburgh Castle guards its capital, while another forms Arthur's Seat above Holyrood Palace.

The deltas and swamps of the late Carboniferous produced the cross-bedded sandstones and Coal Measure cycles which form so much of the confused geology of the Midland Valley. The mainly flat-lying rocks have weathered into complicated outcrops with a scatter of coal-fields that did so much for the heavy industries of the region. Their thickness contrasts markedly with that of the thin coal-fields of the Southern Uplands and with the almost complete absence of such strata north of the Highland Boundary Fault. Marine intercalations disappear well below the top of Carboniferous which passes into barren red beds. Large-scale, cross-bedded dune sandstones, photographs of which appear in many textbooks, were formerly thought to be Permian in age but are now referred to the topmost Carboniferous. There is also a further scatter of volcanic necks and lava flows that presumably reflect the continuing weaknesses of this subsiding trough.

Curiously enough, after the Ordovician, Devonian, Carboniferous, and possibly Permian volcanism in this area, the hard rock record ends with Tertiary dikes, but these derive from the volcanic centres of the Inner Hebrides and have nothing to do with the Midland Valley structure.

The continuation of the graben can be traced by its marginal faults right across the north of Ireland. Most of it is filled with Lower Carboniferous rocks, but Lower Palaeozoic is preserved at its western end, reminiscent of the situation at Girvan. Permian continental sands rest unconformably on the Carboniferous and the eastern end of the Irish version of the Midland Valley is swamped with Tertiary lavas.

Pennine region

The Pennines are the 'backbone' of northern England, which once separated the warring tribes of Yorkshire and Lancashire (a conflict now largely restricted to cricket). They are dominated by the rocks of the Carboniferous System, especially the carbonates of the lower part, which used to be called the 'Mountain Limestone' (Fig. 5.10).

Many British geologists might think it odd to include the Pennines here, but to me it is very logical. Where we can see the Lower Palaeozoic rocks beneath the Carboniferous, as in the famous sections in Ribblesdale and in other inliers, they are strongly folded and planed off below late Palaeozoic strata.

Precambrian sediments are found in places and then Ordovician and Silurian argillaceous and arenaceous deposits, with volcanics in the former. The Cambrian has been recognized in boreholes. At the famous unconformity near Horton-in-Ribblesdale, the 'Carboniferous Limestone' rests horizontally on flaggy Silurian rocks that dip at about 50 degrees. Not only are the Lower Palaeozoic rocks intensely folded, they are also invaded by massive granites, although these are nowhere seen at the surface. Two granites have been deduced under the Pennines by geophysical surveys and one of them proved by a borehole. An interesting sidelight here is that the presence of a granite was also deduced from the mineralization in the Lower Carboniferous. However, when the granite was reached by the boring it turned out to be Caledonian in age, separated from the Carboniferous by an unconformity and therefore not responsible for the later mineralizing fluids. As someone said at the time, they found the right granite for the wrong reason! The contrast between the Lower Palaeozoic under the Pennines and that in the English Midlands (where it is calcareous and flat-lying) is obvious.

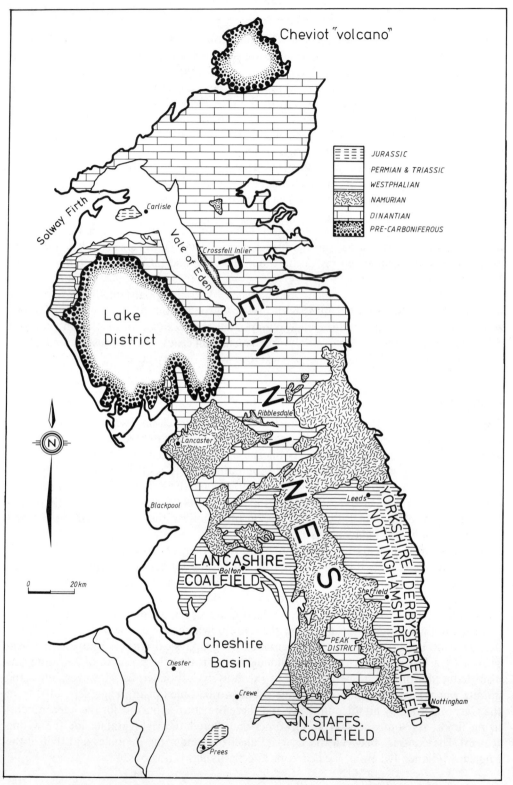

Fig. 5.10   Geological sketch-map of the Pennine region of northern England.

Cheviot "volcano"

JURASSIC
PERMIAN & TRIASSIC
WESTPHALIAN
NAMURIAN
DINANTIAN
PRE-CARBONIFEROUS

Solway Firth

Carlisle

Vale of Eden

Crossfell Inlier

Lake District

P E N N I N E S

Ribblesdale

Lancaster

N

Blackpool

Leeds

YORKSHIRE

NOTTINGHAMSHIRE

DERBYSHIRE COALFIELD

0   20km

LANCASHIRE COALFIELD

Bolton

Sheffield

PEAK DISTRICT

Cheshire Basin

Chester

Crewe

Nottingham

N. STAFFS. COALFIELD

Prees

The Devonian has always been a problem period for Pennine geologists. Once one has left the 'Old Red Sandstone' of southern Scotland and the great volcanic pile of the Cheviot Hills in the northernmost corner of England, there is little that can be attributed to this age until one gets right down to the southern part of the Welsh Borderland. There are some conglomerates around the Lake District which extend eastwards, and it is possible that the very bottom of the carbonate pile belongs to the Devonian, but that is all.

Although carbonate sedimentation dominated the early Carboniferous story, there was in the northernmost Pennines an important development of deltaic sandstones and 'Coal Measures', comparable with those in the Midland Valley of Scotland. Otherwise there is a fascinating picture of facies changes from shallow-water deposition on rigid blocks to basinal sedimentation in between. Along the edge between the two, often related to contemporaneous faulting, there are little reefs which weather out as low hills or 'reef-knolls'. The most famous of these are near Malham in west Yorkshire.

The sea in which these limestones and basinal shales were deposited evidently invaded the region from the west and the upstanding blocks of the Pennines proper were only submerged in late Dinantian times. The Pennines are, above all, an upland region of limestone cliffs, karst surfaces, caves, underground waterways, and peat bogs. In the central part of the region, the Lower Carboniferous disappears under later strata, to appear again southwards in the dome-like structure of the Derbyshire Peak District (Fig. 5.11). This has all the characters of the northern Pennines, with particularly fine cave systems and a notable development of contemporaneous volcanicity and of mineralization including lead and fluorspar. There are also local concentrations of heavy hydrocarbons and Britain's one oil-field for many years, at Eakring in Nottinghamshire, produces from the Carboniferous down dip not very far to the east.

The traditional, if quaint, three-fold division of the British Carboniferous was into 'Carboniferous Limestone', 'Millstone Grit', and 'Coal Measures' in ascending order. Nowhere is this triumvirate better displayed than in the Pennine district. Above the Dinantian carbonates come cyclic deposits, open marine to deltaic, first on a small scale and then in four or five major cycles which are the 'Millstone Grit' proper. That name is derived from the use of its coarse sandstones to make millstones for grinding corn. The major part of this is Namurian in age and detailed studies have revealed a story of distributaries of a large river system coming generally from the north-east.

The general north–south anticlinal structure of the Pennines means that the Westphalian Coal Measures dip off to the east and west. Those on the east may be regarded as part of the Danish Triangle (Chapter 6). Nevertheless correlation across the Pennines is remarkably good with the Cumberland coal-field (which dives down under the Irish Sea) and with the Lancashire coal-field. The story is always cyclic deposition with marine intercalations in the lower part of the Westphalian, and then the complete disappearance of marine bands and the progressive invasion of red bed facies in the upper part.

There is nothing that can be called a Variscan orogeny, although folding is fairly intense locally, mainly related to faults. Indeed faulting had been the theme of several earlier phases of movement which affected contemporaneous sedimentation. At the end of the Carboniferous the principal structure was the gentle up-arching of the Pennine anticline and the Derbyshire dome on a roughly north–south axis. Other folds radiate from this, almost at right angles and more intense to the west, where there was consider-

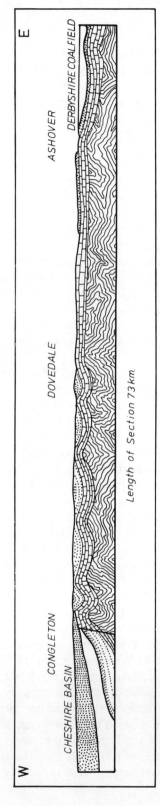

Fig. 5.11 Diagrammatic cross-section of the Derbyshire dome (after Edwards and Trotter, 1954, by permission of the Director, Institute of Geological Sciences. Crown copyright reserved). For interpretation see fig. 5.10.

able normal faulting. By late Permian times the Pennines were an effective barrier to the westward transgressing Zechstein Sea, which only managed to break through briefly in one place (to reach the Isle of Man and Northern Ireland).

The 'Muschelkalk' Sea did not pass at all, so far as we can judge, although it must just have lapped against the eastern slopes. The very thick Trias, to the west of the Pennines, is wholly of the 'Bunter' and 'Keuper' facies. Faulting continued to influence sedimentation, as is particularly well seen in the earliest conglomeratic deposits. Above come the usual terrestrial sandstones and mudstones, almost devoid of life (although there are famous footprints near Liverpool). The thickest development is in the Cheshire Basin, where rock-salt has been mined in the upper part of the Trias since Roman times. Today it is exploited on a large scale and forms the basis of a major chemical industry. Right in the middle of the Cheshire Basin at Prees and in a smaller basin on the north side of the Lake District, are little outliers of Lower Jurassic marine sediments. These are comparable with that now known to the west of Wales and testify to the wide extent of the early Jurassic sea with no evidence of a shoreline.

Apart from some small pockets of late Tertiary continental sands high up in Derbyshire, nothing more is known of the stratigraphical record of this part of Britain before the Pleistocene. It should be emphasized, however, that the story is continuous with that in undoubted 'Caledonide' areas such as North Wales, for Pennine-type rocks appear again on the west side of the Cheshire Basin. They are seen, for example, in the Flintshire coal-field, in the great 'Carboniferous Limestone' escarpment at Eglwyseg near Llangollen, and in the towering promontory of the Great Orme above Llandudno on the north Welsh coast.

Irish Sea

Between the Welsh Caledonides and the Irish Caledonides, which are obviously directly connected, there is a belt of country that is almost completely different in geological character. It also happens to be almost completely covered with water. This is the Irish Sea (Fig. 5.12).

A few years ago there was a remarkable discovery of thick Lower Jurassic sediments at Mochras near Harlech. This followed geophysical surveys which suggested that there was a sedimentary basin just offshore here. Even earlier something of the sort had been suggested from pure geological reasoning, on the grounds of the close comparability of the Irish Sea with the Cheshire Basin.

Thanks to the quest for oil we now know that a series of sedimentary basins extend through the Irish Sea on roughly north–south lines, some of them clearly delimited by normal faults like those of the Trias graben onshore (Fig. 5.13).

The greater part of the northern Irish Sea, as well as a strip along the Irish coast and a large horst in the centre, is formed of Palaeozoic sediments and metamorphic rocks of uncertain age. In the north it is probable that the greater part consists of strongly folded Lower Palaeozoic rocks (the equivalents of the Southern Uplands and Lake District) overlain by gently folded 'Carboniferous Limestone' such as is well displayed on the Isle of Man. An extension of the Carlisle basin extends out to the Isle of Man from the north-east, taking with it the Permian Magnesian Limestone, but probably mainly filled with Triassic red beds. The latter presumably also fill the much larger basin in the space

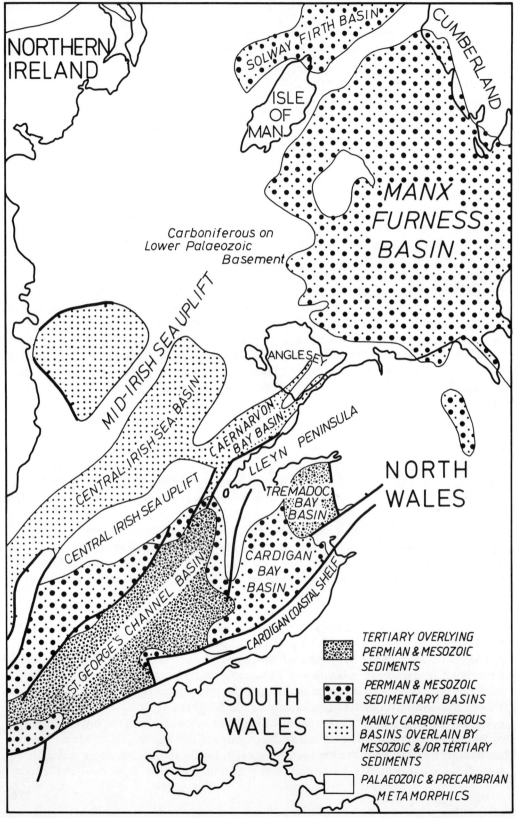

Fig. 5.12 *Structural sketch-map of the Irish Sea (after Naylor and Mounteney, 1975, by kind permission of Graham and Trotman Ltd).*

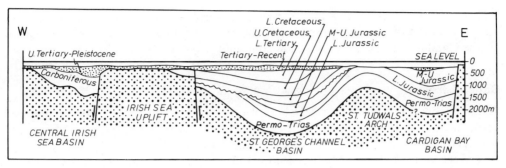

Fig. 5.13 Diagrammatic cross-section of the southern Irish Sea (after Naylor and Mounteney, 1975, by kind permission of Graham and Trotman Ltd).

between Man, Anglesey, and the Cheshire Basin. This just creeps on to the shore on the south-west side of the Lake District.

Farther south the situation seems to be more complicated, perhaps simply because it is better known. There are essentially three uplifted belts, trending east of north, in a distinctly Caledonoid trend, with down-faulted graben in between. The Mid-Irish Sea Uplift of Lower Palaeozoics runs down to the Irish coastline and separates basins filled with Carboniferous and later sediments. Next comes the Central Irish Sea Uplift. Here ancient (probably Lower Palaeozoic) rocks continue south as a clearly defined horst, but with a thick cover of Permian and Mesozoic sediments. On either side of this are graben with thick Tertiary infills; the one to the west is very narrow but that to the east is a broad, down-folded, and partly down-faulted trough in which reflection profiling suggests an infill of some 6000 m of sediment.

The Lleyn Peninsula, which projects from northern North Wales in a Caledonoid direction, is now known to continue, partly cutting off a basin in Cardigan Bay. This is filled with Mesozoic sediments, and right up in the north-east corner up against the Cambrian rocks of the Harlech Dome there is a further cover of Tertiary sediments. The Mochras borehole was put down on a shelly shingle bank south of Harlech, as far as one could get out into Cardigan Bay without getting one's feet wet. It revealed some 370 m of Tertiary clays and lignites, 1300 m of Lower Jurassic mudstones and siltstones, and finished in what were obviously Triassic red beds. It was 'the most important discovery in Welsh geology since the heroic age of Sedgwick and Murchison'. Most significant perhaps is the fact that the Lower Jurassic is of an offshore facies and one therefore suspects that much of the Mesozoic and Tertiary succession in the Irish Sea may once have covered Wales and probably much of Ireland as well. It has long been argued that the concordance of summit levels across Wales reflects a former Chalk cover and although this has been doubted by some, it is supported by the presence of presumed late Cretaceous rocks in St. George's Channel and their known presence farther south.

The Cardigan Bay Basin is delimited on the landward side by a system of faults that looks very much like others we know in this Caledonide world, extending in a generally south-westerly direction very close to Strumble Head on the Pembrokeshire coast. Although a great deal of over-optimistic talk has tried to make the Irish Sea and the Celtic Sea to its south into something comparable with the North Sea, it seems extremely unlikely that they will yield vast hydrocarbon resources. So far the successes have chiefly been in the form of gas close to the Irish coast in the south-west, and elsewhere (including the Cheshire Basin), but exploration continues.

Central Ireland

What can one say about central Ireland if one is not an Irishman? Most prejudiced Englishmen think of it as a vast peat-bog, which is unfair to one of the most beautiful (if wettest) countries in Europe. But certainly the geological map is not encouraging, for almost everything between the Caledonides and the Variscan Front is coloured the blue of the Lower Carboniferous. The inliers of the Lower Palaeozoic have already been mentioned. These are surrounded by aureoles of 'Old Red Sandstone' in broad, gentle dome-like structures such as the one forming the Slievefelim Mountains, east of Limerick.

So far as the main mass of 'Carboniferous Limestone' is concerned, there really is not a lot to say unless one goes into inappropriate detail. Shallow-water conditions seem to have prevailed everywhere, although exposures for the most part are few under the extensive superficial cover. On the coast, fossils are often extremely abundant, for example the twisting corals of the 'Serpent Rock' near Sligo. A belt of algal-bryozoan reefs extends west from Dublin. A very good one is seen not far from the city at Feltrim Hill near Swords, with a windmill still standing on the topographical feature formed by the core of the reef. The other widespread feature in the 'Carboniferous Limestone' is mineralization; lead, zinc, silver, copper, and barytes are widely exploited on a much bigger scale than in the underdeveloped country on the other side of the Irish Sea. There are some volcanics, but nothing that could be called tectonism.

A broad tract of Namurian runs up from the Variscan Front to the coast of Clare. This produces some of the most spectacular cliffs in Europe. I know nothing comparable with the effect of crossing the monotonous plain north-west from Limerick and coming suddenly on the Cliffs of Moher dropping 200 m straight into the Atlantic. The cliffs are formed of a great heap of flat-lying sandstones which display a shallowing upwards succession. Elsewhere along this coast there are intercalated marine shales and phosphatic horizons marking non-sequences, but the outstanding feature of the Namurian of west Clare is the remarkable collection of large slump structures and associated sand volcanoes. The former evidently slid down towards the centre of the trough, which was roughly along the line of the Shannon estuary. They are up to nearly 400 m across and nearly 60 m thick, repeated over and over again in what must have been waterlogged sediment. In places (e.g., on the coast at Quilty) they fill channels and one can even see ripple-marked surfaces wrapping round boulders that 'balled up' in the process of slumping.

Finally the 'Coal Measures' are only seen in scattered patches that have survived later erosion. The largest is the Castlecomer coal-field, north of Kilkenny. This is a basin-shaped upland area with outward-facing scarps of Namurian sandstones (with similar sedimentary structures to those seen on the coast). Only the lower part of the 'Coal Measures' is preserved and the coals are thin, but they are worth working because of the gentle nature of the earth movements that have affected them. In the last century there was discovered here a remarkable assemblage of late Carboniferous amphibians.

Everything else is Quaternary, and Ireland is a great place to study the effects (and the deposits) of the Pleistocene glaciations.

Irish continental shelf

The Rockall Trough, which marks the edge of the continental shelf west of Scotland, continues down to the west of Ireland, although the shelf here bulges noticeably into the Atlantic. Whereas most of the shelf west of Scotland must be regarded as 'Eo-Europa', that to the west of Ireland must be largely 'Palaeo-Europa' since it lines up with the Caledonides of Scotland and Ireland. In the south, off Munster, it must occupy a little of 'Meso-Europa' as well.

It is mainly known from geophysical surveys, although oil has now been struck in deep water about 100 miles west of Ireland. The most notable feature is Porcupine Bank, which forms the core of the bulge in the shelf west of Galway and is presumed to be formed of Caledonide rocks. South-west of Ireland there is a considerable embayment in the continental shelf. This passes northwards into the Slyne Trough which is parallel to, but smaller than, the Rockall Trough. It is thought to be filled with a considerable thickness of Tertiary sediments, resting on a less definite and generally thinner development of Mesozoic. As on the Scottish shelf and in the Irish Sea, faulting along Caledonide lines seems to have controlled sedimentation, at least in Mesozoic times, although there is not the strong asymmetry of the Hebridean troughs. The possible presence of diapirs of Triassic salt in the north is particularly interesting.

Selected references to Chapter 5

Section 5(a) Spitsbergen

Birkenmajer, K. (1972), 'Tertiary history of Spitsbergen and continental drift', *Acta Geol. Polon.*, **22**, 193–218.

Harland, W. B. (1961), 'An outline structural history of Spitsbergen', in G. O. Raasch (ed.), *Geology of the Arctic*, Univ. Toronto Press, vol. 1, pp. 68–132.

Harland, W. B. (1978), 'The Caledonides of Svalbard', in *IGCP Project 27, Caledonian–Appalachian Orogen of the North Atlantic Region*, Geol. Surv. Canada, paper 78-13, pp. 3–11.

Wisnes, T. S., A. Heintz, and N. Heintz (1960), 'Aspects of the geology of Svalbard', in *Guide Excurs. A1b*, 21st Internat. Geol. Congr., Norges Geol. Undersøk, No. 212p, 35 pp.

Section 5(b) Scandinavian Caledonides

Gee, D. G. (1978), 'The Swedish Caledonides—a short synthesis', in *IGCP Project 27, Caledonian–Appalachian Orogen of the North Atlantic Region*, Geol. Surv. Canada, paper 78-13, pp. 63–72.

Gustavson, M. (1978), 'Caledonides of north-central Norway', in *IGCP Project 27, Caledonian–Appalachian Orogen of the North Atlantic Region*, Geol. Surv. Canada, paper 78-13, pp. 25–30.

Holtedahl, O. (ed.) (1960), *Geology of Norway*, Norges Geol. Undersøk. No. 208, Oslo, 540 pp. + atlas.

Kulling, O. and P. Geijer (1960), Guide to Excursion No. A25 and C20, 21st Internat. Geol. Congr., Copenhagen, 45 pp.

Kvale, A. (1976), 'Major features of the European Caledonides and their development', in D. V. Ager and M. Brooks (eds), *Europe from Crust to Core*, Wiley, London, pp. 81–115.

Roberts, D. (1978), 'Caledonides of south central Norway', in *IGCP Project 27, Caledonian–Appalachian Orogen of the North Atlantic Region*, Geol. Surv. Canada, Paper 78-13, pp. 31–37.

Störmer, L. (1967), 'Some aspects of the Caledonian geosyncline and foreland west of the Baltic Shield', *Quart. Jl Geol. Soc., Lond.*, **123**, 183–214.

Strand, T. and O. Kulling (1972), *Scandinavian Caledonides*, Wiley, London and New York, 302 pp.

Sturt, B. A. (1978), 'The Norwegian Caledonides—Introduction', in *IGCP Project 27, Caledonian–Appalachian Orogen of the North Atlantic Region*, Geol. Surv. Canada, Paper 78-13, pp. 13–15.

Sturt, B. A. and D. Roberts (1978), 'Caledonides of northernmost Norway (Finnmark)', in *IGCP Project 27, Caledonian–Appalachian Orogen of the North Atlantic Region*, Geol. Surv. Canada, Paper 78-13, pp. 17–24.

Sturt, B. A. and A. Thon (1978), 'Caledonides of southern Norway', in *IGCP Project 27, Caledonian–Appalachian Orogen of the North Atlantic Region*, Geol. Surv. Canada, Paper 78-13, pp. 39–47.

Section 5(c)   British metamorphic Caledonides

Charlesworth, J. K. (1963), *Historical Geology of Ireland*, Oliver and Boyd, Edinburgh and London, 565 pp.

Craig, G. Y. (ed.) (1965), *The Geology of Scotland*, Oliver and Boyd, Edinburgh and London, 556 pp.

Harris, A. L., M. R. W. Johnson, and D. Powell (1978), 'The orthotectonic Caledonides (Moines and Dalradians) of Scotland', in *IGCP Project 27, British Contrib. No. 1C, Caledonian–Appalachian Orogen of the North Atlantic Region*, Geol. Surv. Canada, paper 78-13, pp. 79–83.

Johnstone, G. S. (1966), *British Regional Geology, The Grampian Highlands*, 3rd edn, Inst. Edinburgh and London, 280 pp.

Johnstone, G. S. (1966), *British Regional Geology. The Grampian Highlands*, 3rd edn, Inst. Geol. Sci., Edinburgh, 107 pp.

Owen, T. R. (1976), *The Geological Evolution of the British Isles*, Pergamon, Oxford, 161 pp.

Phemister, J. (1960), *British Regional Geology Scotland; The Northern Highlands*, 3rd edn, Geol. Surv. and Mus., London, 104 pp.

Phillips, W. E. A. (1978), 'The Caledonide Orogen in Ireland', in *IGCP Project 27, Irish Contrib. No. 1, Caledonian–Appalachian Orogen of the North Atlantic Region*, Geol. Surv. Canada, paper 78-13, pp. 97–103.

Section 5(d)   British non-metamorphic Caledonides

Charlesworth, J. K. (1963), *Historical Geology of Ireland*, Oliver and Boyd, Edinburgh and London, 565 pp.

Craig, G. Y. (ed.) (1965), *The Geology of Scotland*, Oliver and Boyd, Edinburgh and London, 556 pp.

Greig, D. C. (1971), *British Regional Geology; The South of Scotland*, 3rd edn, Inst. Geol. Sci., Edinburgh, 125 pp.

Kelling, G. (1978), 'The paratectonic Caledonides of mainland Britain', in *IGCP Project 27, British Contrib. No. 1E, Caledonian–Appalachian Orogen of the North Atlantic Region*, Geol. Surv. Canada, paper 78-13, pp. 89–95.

McKerrow, W. S., J. K. Leggett, and M. H. Eales (1971), 'Imbricate thrust model of the Southern Uplands of Scotland', *Nature*, **267**, 237–239.

Owen, T. R. (1976), *The Geological Evolution of the British Isles*, Pergamon, Oxford, 161 pp.

Phillips, W. E. A. (1978), 'The Caledonide orogen in Ireland', in *IGCP Project 27, Irish Contrib. No. 1, Caledonian–Appalachian Orogen of the North Atlantic Region*, Geol. Surv. Canada, paper 78-13, pp. 97–103.

Smith, B. and T. N. George (1961), *British Regional Geology; North Wales*, 3rd edn, Inst. Geol. Sci., London, 97 pp.

Taylor, B. J. *et al.* (1971), *British Regional Geology; Northern England*, 3rd edn, Inst. Geol. Sci., London, 121 pp.

Wood, A. (ed.) (1969), *The Pre-Cambrian and Lower Palaeozoic Rocks of Wales*, Univ. Wales Press, 461 pp.

Section 5(e)   Post-Caledonian basins

Charlesworth, J. K. (1963), *Historical Geology of Ireland*, Oliver and Boyd, Edinburgh and London, 565 pp.

Craig, G. Y. (ed.) (1965), *The Geology of Scotland*, Oliver and Boyd, Edinburgh and London, 556 pp.

Edwards, W. and F. M. Trotter (1954), *British Regional Geology; The Pennines and Adjacent Areas*, 3rd edn, Geol. Survey and Mus., London, 86 pp.

MacGregor, M. and A. G. MacGregor (1948), *British Regional Geology; The Midland Valley of Scotland*, 2nd edn, Geol. Survey and Mus., London, 92 pp.

Max, M. D. (1978), 'Tectonic control of offshore sedimentary basins to the north and west of Ireland', *J. Petrol. Geol.*, **1**, 103–110.

Naylor, D. and S. N. Mounteney (1975), *Geology of the North-west European Continental Shelf*, vol. 1. Graham Trotman Dudley, London, 156 pp.

Owen, T. R. (1976), *The Geological Evolution of the British Isles*, Pergamon, Oxford, 161 pp.

Whittow, J. B. (1974), *Geology and Scenery in Ireland*, Penguin Books, Harmondsworth, 301 pp.

Chapter Six

Danish Triangle

One of the most startling facts of European geology is that if you stand on the Pennine backbone of England and look eastwards, were it not for the curvature of the earth and the weakness of the human eye, the next high land you would see would be the Urals on the borders of Asia.

This vast stretch of lowland is the Great Northern Plain of Europe, extending from eastern England across the North Sea to Byron's 'waterland of Dutchmen and of ditches', thence via northern Germany and southern Scandinavia to Poland and the vast Russian plains. To any but the Quaternary geologist, it is at first sight the dullest part of the continent. In recent years it has proved one of the most exciting.

This chapter deals only with the western part of the Great Northern Plain (Fig. 6.1), delimited to the east by the Tornquist or Danish–Polish Line which is taken as the edge of Eo-Europa. To the south, the Variscan front is deeply indented (e.g., down the Rhine to Cologne), but the northern limit of intense Variscan folding is fairly sharply defined. To the west lie the Caledonides, so bounding a triangular area, centred on Denmark which gives its name to this chapter. Its least well defined boundary (in England) corresponds roughly with the frontier of the 'Danelaw' of ninth century times, which was that part of eastern England settled by Danish invaders from across the North Sea, hence making the name appropriate here too.

Until a few years ago, all that one could say of the solid geology of most of this vast area was that it consisted of late Mesozoic strata (especially Chalk) overlain by Tertiary strata, all largely hidden beneath glacial and periglacial deposits.

6(a) Baltic Plain

The plain which extends from the Baltic Sea down to the Variscan massifs of the Ardennes, Eifel, Rheinisches Schiefergebirge, and Harz is mostly covered with Quaternary deposits. In the west, a coastal belt of sand-dunes, marshes, and reclaimed land gives way inland to a low-lying belt of glacial sands extending as far east as the River Weser. Inland again is a third, parallel lowland belt of Mesozoic outcrops, which also floor the large embayments between the Variscan massifs. In the east, the cover is all glacial: a northern belt of moraines from Denmark into north Germany with many lakes, and a southern belt of moraines running from the North Sea, between the Elbe and the Weser, eastwards

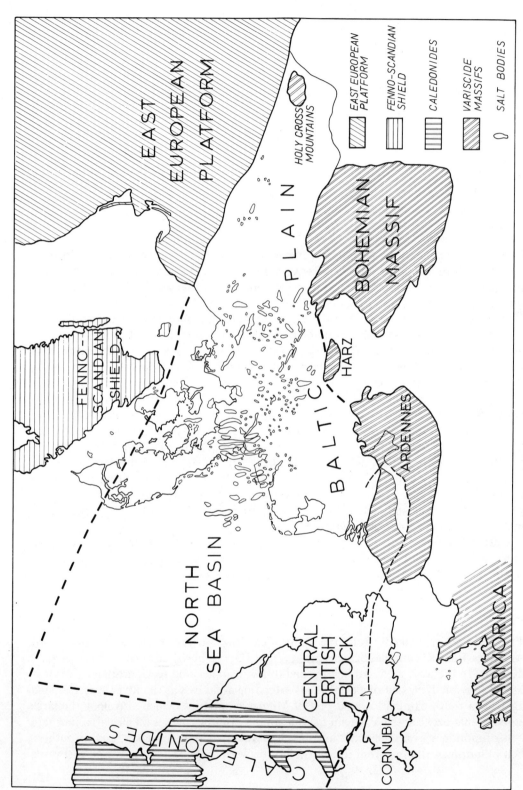

Fig. 6.1 Geological sketch-map of the Danish Triangle.

for some 800 km into Poland. In between these two morainic belts is an area where glacial streams, filled with outwash deposits, flowed westwards parallel to the ice-front, like those of the American Mid-West.

In the southern part of the Baltic Plain, Cretaceous rocks come to the surface around Hanover (Hannover) and south of Münster in the usual north-west European facies with continental 'Wealden'-type sands below and Chalk above. A narrow outcrop of Jurassic extends along the River Weser, south-west of Hanover, and this is succeeded southwards by a great area of Triassic sediments in the Thuringian Basin and in the fault-defined basin between the Rheinisches Schiefergebirge and the Bohemian Massif. This is the classic Trias of Swabia, with its three-fold division into 'Keuper', 'Muschelkalk', and 'Buntsandstein'. It extends eastwards around the Alps and north-westwards as far as Heligoland, and is now known to go much further.

Permian sediments appear in places, notably around Karl Marx Stadt (Chemnitz) in East Germany on the rim of the Bohemian Massif. The most famous and valuable Permian rocks, however, are those of Stassfurt, 30 km south of Magdeburg, where a tremendous thickness of late Permian (Zechstein) salt deposits have been worked for centuries. Beds of potash and other rarer salts, up to 40 m thick, are particularly valuable, while rock-salt and anhydrite reach hundreds of metres in thickness. The whole complex has been thought of as a series of desiccation cycles in an enclosed sea, with the soluble salts being preserved under an impervious clay. The amount of evaporation required is almost inconceivable, however, and it is doubtful if the salts would be preserved as they are by this means. An explanation more complex than the simple evaporating dish is probably required involving the sabkha environment seen on present-day desert shorelines.

The Permian evaporites here, like the Silurian evaporites in the American Mid-West and the Devonian evaporites in western Canada, are associated with organic reefs. Fossiliferous dolomites below and some rare marine fossils in the beds overlying the salts provide evidence of a late Zechstein age. Also belonging to the lower part of this Series is the *Kupferschiefer*: a series of bituminous limestones rich in sulphides of silver, zinc, iron, and especially (as the name implies) copper. These ores have often replaced the hard parts of the fauna, leading to spectacular and virtually perfectly preserved specimens. Best known are the fish and beautiful crinoids which are seen in museums throughout Europe.

The lower part of the two-fold German Permian is the Rotliegende or 'red beds' which are highly oxidized sandstones, conglomerates and marls with plant remains (such as the araucarian trees near Karl Marx Stadt), and poor coal seams. There is also, significantly, evidence of contemporaneous earth movements and volcanicity (both intrusions and extrusions) which were evidently connected with the emplacement of the ore deposits.

It is generally presumed that the Stassfurt deposits were laid down in marine basins that lapped against the Variscan massifs to the south, but did not pass between them to enter what is now France or connect in any way with the Permian seas of southern Europe. From Stassfurt the Zechstein deposits thin markedly southwards, but in other directions they extend very much farther. Eastwards, the Zechstein limestones and dolomites with their characteristic fossils continue as far as Klaipeda (Memel) in Lithuania, well on to the East European Platform, although the sea evidently did not connect with that of Perm and the Urals. Westwards, with similar fossils, they reached north-east England and even the Isle of Man.

We now know that salt of this age is developed extensively and thickly underneath all this vast area. Deep borings revealed a fascinating picture of salt tectonics right across north Germany into the Netherlands and up into Denmark, with some of the salt evidently still moving. Abnormal thicknesses of salt have been found in many places (e.g., 1200 m at Sparenberg near Berlin and 1500 at Wietze-Steinforde) due to diapiric movements. In many places also (e.g., at Hanover) oil and gas have been found trapped in salt dome structures. Exploration of these has stimulated most of the subsurface work in recent years and underground north Germany is now known in remarkable detail. We also now know that the diapirs extend under the southern North Sea.

Much more extensively developed and exposed along the northern margin of this area are the Upper Cretaceous Chalk and other chalky sediments of the eastern islands of Denmark and the island of Rügen off the north coast of East Germany. These strata have become the classic uppermost Cretaceous rocks of Europe, subdivided by means of echinoids, belemnites, and occasional ammonites. The higher beds of the Chalk, both in southern Sweden and in Denmark, display a remarkable development of bryozoan reefs. These are particularly well seen in the long exposures of Stevns Klint, south of Copenhagen.

Here the Maastrichtian Chalk, with its black flints and its abundant bryozoans and echinoids, passes up into remarkably similar Danian Chalk, now regarded as belonging to the Tertiary. The actual junction is marked by an undulating surface and a thin, impersistent clay which has been said to contain volcanic dust. It is not surprising that the Danian was so long regarded as of Cretaceous age. In all its obvious characters it resembles the Chalk below. Even the common echinoid genera are the same.

The definitive Cretaceous fossils such as ammonites and belemnites are already rare in the topmost Maastrichtian beds, so we have here a splendid example of a lithological facies crossing a major stratigraphical boundary. The so-called 'stratotype' of the Danian is the famous quarry at Fakse (Faxe) west of Copenhagen, where there is a wealth of Mesozoic-looking fossils and a development of ahermatypic coral reefs.

Earlier divisions of the Chalk are well seen in the cliffs of the small Danish island of Møn, where they have been considerably disturbed by the Pleistocene glaciation. Great masses of Chalk have been pushed over Pleistocene tills and, in fact, the whole island looks as though it has been deformed bodily by the force of the ice coming from the north-east.

The Danian deposits are succeeded by Paleocene glauconitic clays and then by the rest of the thick Tertiary succession. Almost the only exposures in Denmark above the Chalk are low cliffs of Paleocene on the west side of Sjaelland and the north-east side of Fyn (Funen). Of particular interest in the Danish Eocene is the Mo Clay, in which no less than 179 layers of volcanic ash have been recognized (although only amounting to some 4.3 m of ash altogether). Thus in one formation we have brought together the two completely different forms of the Palaeogene in north-west Europe. The clay is probably the equivalent of the London and Flanders clays of the Anglo-Belgian–Paris Basin, while the ash bands remind us of the Thulean volcanic province to the west, with its strong hint of an opening Atlantic Ocean. Ash bands are also now recognized in the Eocene of the Netherlands, northern Germany, and eastern England.

In considering the Palaeogene deposits of the Danish Triangle, we cannot conveniently confine ourselves to its constituent parts. The Eocene and Oligocene deposits of the Baltic Plain continue under the North Sea to the London and Hampshire Basins of southern Britain. They also continue southwards into the Belgian and Paris Basins. All together they may be regarded as the deposits of an enclosed but pulsating sea, with its centre in the south of the present-day North Sea. In these deposits we have a classic of cyclic sedimentation, with the margins of the sea periodically extending outwards transgressively and then withdrawing again. Thus the transgressions which come from the east in the London Basin come from the west in the Baltic Plain.

Six or seven major cycles have been recognized in the Eocene alone, each with its continental phase, its intertidal or estuarine phase, and usually (although not always) its fully marine phase with glauconite and abundant faunas. These will be discussed in the sections on the London and Paris Basins where they are best developed. So far as the Baltic Plain is concerned, the first major transgression happened in Lattorfian times, variously placed at the end of the Eocene or the beginning of the Oligocene. Although the Oligocene is a very minor 'system' compared with the Eocene, it is vastly more extensive in northern Europe. The Lattorfian sea evidently extended right into the Soviet Union, where it connected with the Tethys in the south and with a proto-Arctic Ocean in the north. Its deposits are the oldest Tertiary over much of the north German plain. The first marine transgression was followed by the usual continental phase in the form of lignitic sands.

In the south of the region, along the edges of the Variscan Massifs, important 'brown coals' or lignites are developed in similar Tertiary continental deposits. They are difficult to date accurately and probably formed both in Eocene and Oligocene times: some were as late as Neogene or even Quaternary. They have been worked extensively for the manufacture of briquettes as fuel. A second shorter cycle, attributed to the Rupelian (or Stampian) usually completes the story, although a later Chattian Stage is commonly recognized in Germany at the end of the Oligocene.

The earliest Miocene deposits are only known in Denmark and in Schleswig-Holstein near Hamburg. The Miocene seas evidently extended more widely, although the topography seems to have been very similar to that of the present day and the deposits pinch out against the Variscan uplands. The sediments are mainly marine in the west and pass laterally into continental facies to the east, with evaporites in Poland. The marine faunas are immensely abundant and have been the subject of many monographs. They indicate sea temperatures comparable with those off Portugal today. The late Miocene sea was more limited again and only slightly more extensive than that of the earliest part of the period.

Pliocene marine deposits were generally even more restricted, as the sea retreated again into the North Sea Basin. It has long been known that these deposits thicken in that direction both from the Franco-Belgian border northwards and across the Netherlands from east to west. The thickest late Tertiary deposits known on land are in the vicinity of Amsterdam.

This complex Tertiary story and the comparatively simple late Cretaceous one that preceded it were virtually all that was known of the stratigraphy of Denmark and the surrounding region until a few years ago. Then started a programme of deep drilling which has accelerated in proportion to its economic value. Borings in Jutland revealed a Mesozoic succession similar to that of eastern England below the Chalk. Lower

125

Cretaceous 'Wealden'-type continental sediments rest in places on a Jurassic succession like that of Yorkshire in north-east England. Below that again is the classic Swabian Trias and then the Zechstein evaporites of the Upper Permian.

The deeper boreholes went down to steeply dipping Lower Palaeozoic shales, 'Eocambrian', and Precambrian metamorphics. The fact that the Lower Palaeozoic beds are tectonically disturbed, as they also seem to be in eastern England to the west and Poland to the east, is the only real evidence we have which places the Danish Triangle in Palaeo-Europa rather than Eo-Europa. The present view seems to be that there are comparatively little disturbed Lower Palaeozoic rocks under Denmark and its surrounding seaways, but that there was an east–west fold belt farther south. The real evidence, however, is very scanty.

It soon became obvious from the boreholes that there was a Precambrian 'high' under Denmark (the Fyn Grinsted Ridge*) with 'lows' on either side. This seemed to be comparable with the well-known London–Brabant Ridge farther south. The Danish high runs slightly south of east, under the island of Rügen and on towards the Holy Cross Mountains of Poland. Superimposed upon this Fyn Grinsted Ridge is a series of northwest trending horsts and graben. The Oslo graben in Norway, with its famous Permian lavas, is the continuation of one of these that runs down the west side of the Jutland peninsula. Permian volcanic rocks have also been found in borings off the Netherlands, Sweden, and north Germany, where they rest directly on the Cambrian.

An interesting feature of the Triassic sediments on the ridge is the way they thicken rapidly into the graben, indicating that sedimentation was controlled by faulting (as it was in Britain). Considering the Fyn Grinsted Ridge as a whole, the sedimentary pile there is distinctly thin compared with that to the north and south. The Permian evaporites, although having an important influence on movements on the ridge, are much thinner there than in the salt dome country of Germany to the south. Each unit of the Trias behaves in the same way, as do the Zechstein carbonates. Thus the 'Bunter' is about 100 m thick on the ridge compared with about 1000 m to the north and 700 m to the south.

The ridge still had a considerable influence on early Jurassic sedimentation. Until recently, Middle and Upper Jurassic rocks were only known under north Jutland, but then they were found in borings between Helsingfors in Denmark (Hamlet's 'Elsinore') and Helsingborg in Sweden. The feature was still going strong in early Cretaceous times (like the London–Brabant Ridge) and the big change only came with the late Cretaceous. Then white chalk was deposited more or less evenly everywhere, except close to the Fenno-Scandian Shield where it is very thick (nearly 2000 m) perhaps due to a contemporaneously moving fault. It also contains much more terrigenous material.

This sort of evidence led to the famous concept of *Randtröge* or Border Troughs. The idea is comparable with geosynclinal theory without the orogenic phase and the metamorphism. The troughs differ from classic geosynclines quantitatively rather than qualitatively. Starting from an old stable massif, such as the Fyn Grinsted Ridge, a long depression or 'Border Trough' is formed on either side and filled with sediment. The prisms of sediment are then domed up or 'inverted', with only slight folding and faulting, but with the production of an anticlinorium or *Schwelle*. 'Subsequent Troughs' are then

* Shown as Fyn-Ringkobing High in Fig. 6.4.

formed either internally (i.e., on the old massif) or externally. As a result of this, the old massif or ridge may disappear beneath the sediments of a subsequent internal trough. This is why they were not recognized earlier.

This process was important in the Mesozoic and Cainozoic history of northern Europe. We can distinguish a series of structures running parallel to the north-west trending edge of the East European platform (Fig. 6.2). Immediately adjacent to this, the Danish–Polish Furrow (a 'Subsequent Trough') runs down from the Fyn Grinsted Ridge to the Holy Cross Mountains in Poland. Parallel again is the Pompeckj Schwelle running from southern Denmark down into East Germany. The Lower Saxony Trough was a secondary structure on top of the north-westerly extension of the Bohemian Massif. Then comes the West Netherlands Trough extending into the Rhineland Massif and the London Ridge (concealed beneath the secondary London Basin, with the primary trough of the Weald and the Paris Basin to the south).

The importance of the mid-Cretaceous movements here can hardly be exaggerated. It has long been known that in areas such as Dorset in southern England and the Boulonnais in northern France, the Lower Cretaceous sediments form a structural unit with the Jurassic. Both were affected by faulting and gentle movements which did not affect the Upper Cretaceous. It now appears that through much of northern Europe, the end of early Cretaceous times was the time of the inversion of 'Border Troughs' and the beginning of 'Subsequent Troughs'.

Figure 6.3 shows isopachs for the Lower Cretaceous compared with those for the Eocene in the western part of the Netherlands. The 'Subsequent Trough' to the south is burying the ancient rocks on the north side of the Brabant Massif. There are more than a 1000 m of Lower Cretaceous in the 'Border Trough'. Similarly, in the Lower Saxony Trough, south-west of Hamburg, there are up to 1000 m of Upper Jurassic and 2000 m of Lower Cretaceous.

The general picture in every case seems to be thick Mesozoic sedimentation up until the end of early Cretaceous times and then inversion, with the development of 'Subsequent Troughs'. We shall see later how important were the mid Cretaceous movements in the fold mountains of southern Europe also.

6(b) North Sea Basin

Some twenty years ago a couple of American oil geologists came to my room, excited by the oil recently discovered in the Devonian reefs of Alberta and sniffing at the shattered little Devonian reefs of south-west England. I remember pointing to the North Sea on the geological map on my wall and saying: 'I'd much rather look there!' It's a pity I could not invest in my idea at that time, otherwise I might now be sitting on a sun-bathed balcony in Provence, toying with my *brochette de foie de veau* and my vintage Chambertin.

But why did I, and presumably others, think that way? Superficially the North Sea appeared to be nothing more than the flooded edge of the monotonous north European plain, but there were some hints that it was different from the rest. We knew about the westerly thickening of Tertiary sediments in the Netherlands and their easterly thickening in eastern England. We knew about faults along the north-east coast of Britain that threw down thicker Mesozoic successions on their seaward side. We also knew that the

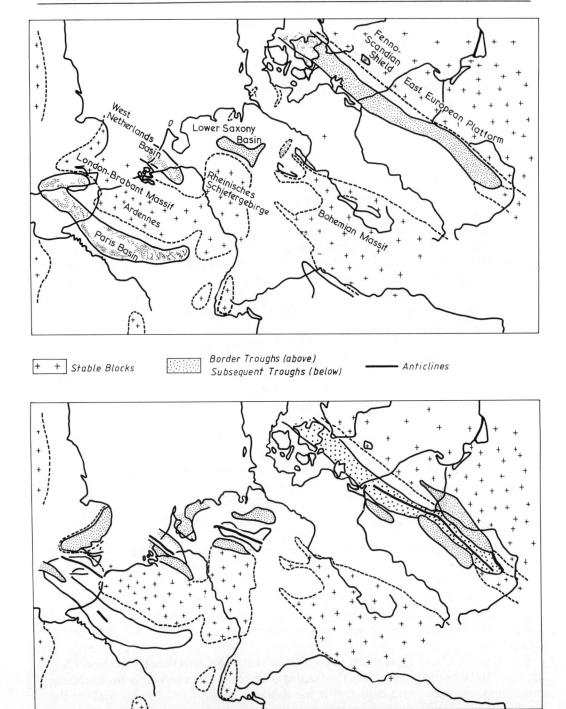

Fig. 6.2 'Border Troughs' (above) and 'Subsequent Troughs' (below) in north-west Europe (after Voigt, 1963, by kind permission of the author and the Deutsche geologische Gesellschaft).

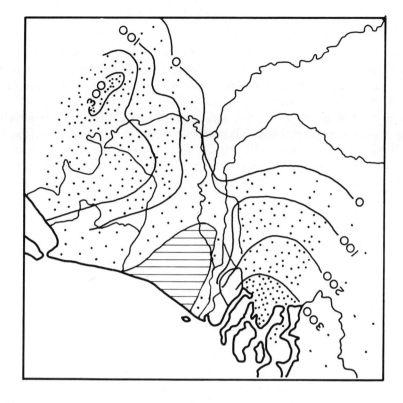

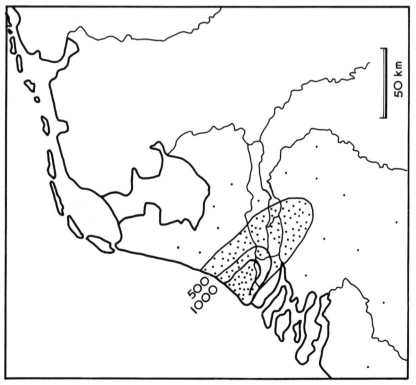

Fig. 6.3 *Comparative isopach maps of the western Netherlands for the Lower Cretaceous (left) and the Eocene (right), showing the replacement of a primary 'Border Trough' by two secondary 'Subsequent Troughs' (after Voigt, 1963, by kind permission of the author and the Deutsche geologische Gesellschaft).*

sweep of Permian evaporites across north Germany (with salt-domes and hydrocarbon accumulations) continued into Yorkshire. All this should have made us suspect that there was a lot of young sediment out there under the stormy North Sea and that tensional faults had played a large part in its accumulation.

The North Sea Basin, in the wet sense, was the virgin territory of Europe so far as geology was concerned and has only surrendered to the geological world in the last few years. It was only surpassed in its chastity by the basins between and to the west of the British Isles and perhaps those north of Russia. Much information is still in the confidential files of oil companies, but what has emerged is a fascinating picture of a deep, epicontinental basin that owes its present form to the same processes that formed the Atlantic Ocean.

Investigations started in earnest following the discovery of a valuable gas reservoir in Permian sands at Groningen, near the north coast of the Netherlands. Political and legal problems proved at first more difficult than the geological and technical ones. Then followed two different stories: gas in the south and oil in the north. It so happens that the order in which they were developed is also the way they are arranged stratigraphically.

North Sea gas was first found (in 1965) in the West Sole field off Yorkshire. It occurs in the Rotliegende (Lower Permian) as it does in most of the other gas-fields, although some is also found in the 'Bunter' (Lower Triassic). The gas is thought to have come from the Carboniferous rocks below, which are rich in organic material.

We now know quite a lot about the older rocks. Crystalline basement is known from more than a dozen wells and has given ages ranging from about 440 to about 410 million years, indicating a Caledonian metamorphism unknown in the Anglo-Welsh region. Schists and gneisses are overlain by sediments as old as the 'Old Red Sandstone' and include granites. Only under the seaways around Denmark does the Lower Palaeozoic appear to be unmetamorphosed and relatively undeformed.

This is the best evidence we have for including the North Sea in Palaeo-Europa and it was presumably as an early Palaeozoic trough that the North Sea first expressed itself as a negative area. After the orogeny it continued to sink. All round it there were positive areas and the London–Brabant Massif crossed its southern margin. Within this newly subsiding basin there accumulated considerable thicknesses of flat-lying Devonian sediments, although they are only known in a comparatively few boreholes. They are mostly of an 'Old Red Sandstone' facies and are continuations of the intermontane cuvettes onshore. There are also volcanics and, most significantly, marine carbonates right out in the middle opposite Edinburgh. This implies that a proto-North Sea was already in existence as an embayment of the extensive sea that we know lay away to the south. So the North Sea is another of the seas around Europe that is a very ancient feature.

Then followed a Carboniferous succession very like that of the neighbouring land-masses, that is to say, massive limestones in the lower part (with thick oil shales like those of eastern Scotland) and 'Coal Measures' above. We knew, of course, that the thick 'Coal Measures' of eastern Britain disappeared under the sea and reappeared at depth beneath the Netherlands and north-west Germany. It was therefore completely reasonable to expect them in between.

It was presumably at this stage that a structure came into existence as a positive feature that is very important in all North Sea studies. This is the Mid North Sea 'High' (Fig. 6.4) which seems to be a direct continuation of the Southern Uplands of Scotland.

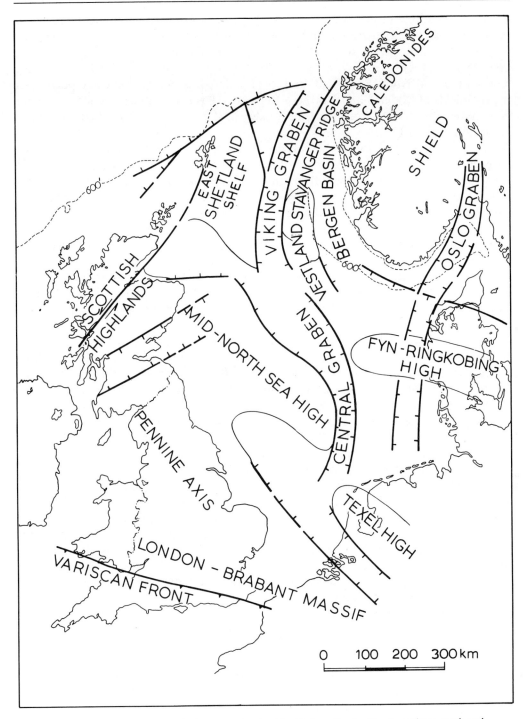

Fig. 6.4 Main structural elements in the North Sea Basin (from various authors).

It separates the oily region of the northern North Sea from the more volatile region in the south. Like the Southern Uplands, it is crossed by little north–south faulted troughs of 'Coal Measures'. Generally speaking the Upper Carboniferous sediments (both Namurian 'Millstone Grit' and Westphalian 'Coal Measures') are concentrated in a basin between the Mid North Sea 'High' and the London–Brabant Massif, corresponding to the coal-fields of Midland and Northern England. All this fluviatile and deltaic sediment must have been derived from the Caledonides (and perhaps the 'Old Red Sandstone' basins to the north).

The basin continued to subside in the Permian with the thick, continental Rotliegende sandstones which hold most of the gas that now cooks for and heats Britain. They too were derived from the surrounding positive areas. Most of them are dune sands in a belt up to 200 km wide, seen on shore as the 'Yellow Sands' of Durham. They pass basinwards into gas-less shales and evaporites, which is hard luck for the Dutch and the Germans to whom this part of the sea belongs. All this fits in with the picture deduced long ago in the British Upper Permian of easterly winds blowing across a desert basin with the sand accumulating around its western margin. Nowadays such winds are uncommon and bring us the cold and the snows of continental Europe, but this was evidently not the case at the end of Palaeozoic times. There was also some volcanicity east of Scotland, which is hardly surprising in view of what was going on in the Oslo Graben at this time.

The basin continued with the cyclic dolomites and evaporites of the late Permian (Zechstein) well known in a marginal facies in north-east England. The little reefs of the Magnesian Limestone of Durham evidently faced on to a deep salty basin, just as do the Devonian reefs of Alberta and other examples around the world. We also know that there was now another basin north of the Mid North Sea 'High' up to the east of Scotland and over towards Denmark. This northern basin may have been operating earlier, but we can say that at least the southern part of the North Sea Basin was subsiding through late Palaeozoic times and all of it was certainly subsiding by the Permian. Only the 'High' in the middle resisted the general sinking feeling and that too was cut by sediment-filled graben in Permian times.

Graben were operative on a bigger scale in the Triassic. There is the usual German trinity of 'Buntsandstein', 'Muschelkalk', and 'Keuper', although there have been problems in the translation of these terms into the way they have been misused in Britain. Salts were concentrated in the centre of the basin both in early and late Triassic times and we now have evidence that the 'Muschelkalk' Sea reached the English Midlands, albeit briefly. The graben are particularly obvious in the northern North Sea and controlled sedimentation, as similar graben did farther west in Britain. In the south, the Permian salt started a series of punch-ups, forming the salt-domes that were already affecting sedimentation. The Mid North Sea 'High' was only a partial barrier and Triassic sediments accumulated in the central graben that cut it from north to south.

There is a break above the Trias which is commonly referred to 'Early Kimmerian' movements, although the Crimea (whence that name comes) is a long way away and I am not sure that it is useful to talk of Alpine-type orogenic phases in this context. Distortions produced by the rising salt were probably more significant than anything tectonic.

In the Jurassic, the North Sea really came into its own as a petroleum province. A limited amount of oil does occur in the Permian rocks of the southernmost fields of the northern North Sea, but by far the most important reservoirs and the source rocks are in the Jurassic. The first oil was found in Norwegian waters, west of Jutland, in 1969. There followed the discovery of over twenty other fields, including the giant ones up in the north, west of Bergen and north-east of Shetland.

However, before considering the Jurassic of the North Sea it would be useful to return briefly to dry land to consider the faults on the north-east coast of Britain, referred to at the beginning of this chapter. The Helmsdale Fault runs close to the sea in Sutherland, in the north-east corner of Scotland. It throws down a narrow strip of Mesozoic sediments on the seaward side against the usual country rocks of north-east Scotland, that is to say: Moinian metamorphics, Caledonian granites, and 'Old Red Sandstone'. The present fault coincides very closely with a fault that was operative in Jurassic times and with both the Jurassic and the present coastline. It is also very close to the edge of the 'Old Red Sandstone' basin mentioned in Chapter 5(c). All this cannot be a coincidence. This ancient line is the edge of the North Sea Basin. The Mesozoic strip starts in the south with Triassic conglomerates exposed on the beach near the Victorian castle of the notorious Duke of Sutherland (who cleared the humans from the highlands to make room for his sheep). Northwards there is a little marine Lias and then the rest of a mainly marine Jurassic succession, including a notable development of mid Jurassic deltaic sediments with coal, spasmodically worked at Brora. The highest beds are Kimmeridgian and include the famous Helmsdale Boulder Beds. These were interpreted as everything from glacial erratics to fallen sea-stacks, but are more reasonably understood as repeated submarine landslip deposits along a contemporary fault. The landslips carried huge boulders, mainly of 'Old Red Sandstone', into relatively deep-water Kimmeridgian shales. They took with them tree-trunks, corals (the northernmost Jurassic ones in Europe), and drifts of shallow-water shells. This happened many times and has been called 'a natural seismograph'.

Not usually thought of in the same context, but equally significant, is the Peak Fault of the Yorkshire coast near Whitby. This has a much thicker and more complete Jurassic succession on its seaward side than on its landward side. Similar 'growth faults' are now well known in east Greenland and we must not forget the little downfaulted trough of Jurassic and early Cretaceous sediments preserved on the island of Andøy off the west coast of Norway—Chapter 5(b). All these features show us on dry land, the successions and structures that are now studied with such difficulty and expense under the troubled waters of the North Sea.

We know that similar growth faults and graben structures dominate the Jurassic story out in the North Sea. They are also very important in that they provide most of the traps for the oil. The accumulations are most abundant in the same Middle Jurassic deltaic sandstones that are seen on shore in Yorkshire, in the Brora coal-field of Sutherland, and in underground Denmark (they go all the way to east Greenland). The source of the oil is the thick marine clay formations of the Lower and Upper Jurassic. In England there are three such bituminous formations—in the Lower Lias (Hettangian to Lower Pliensbachian), the Oxford Clay (Callovian–Oxfordian), and Kimmeridge Clay (Kimmeridgian). The first and last of these produce self-igniting 'burning cliffs' on the Dorset coast. It seems probably that the largest contributor is the Kimmeridgian, which may seem odd

133

if the oil accumulates in older sandstones, but this is due to the reservoirs being mainly on the tilted sides of the graben and the oil migrating from the down-faulted centres.

The graben were actively developing at this time, as is shown by erosional breaks on the horsts, while sediments continued to be deposited in between, controlled by the fault movements. This again matches the situation onshore in England, where we now know, for instance, that the Severn Graben continued to operate at least as late as mid Jurassic times. Sedimentation was particularly thick in the Viking Graben in the north, but by Kimmeridgian times differential subsidence seems to have ended although graben formation continued into the early Cretaceous.

All this faulting is tensional in origin and the fact that it occurred at the same time as the early opening of the present North Atlantic makes a plate tectonic cause seemingly inescapable. The North Sea graben would nowadays be interpreted as 'failed arms' of a triple junction.

Tensional movements started in Triassic times and are seen on both sides of the Atlantic, all the way down the American seaboard and from Britain to Morocco on this side. With the faulting went fissure eruptions and intrusions (although not in northern Europe). There were minor marine invasions from the west in early Jurassic times and more important transgressions all round the North Atlantic in the late mid and early late Jurassic. The oldest known pelagic deposits of the North Atlantic are of very late Jurassic age in the Cape Verde islands and from the ocean floor in those latitudes. So the ocean as such probably started in late Jurassic times.

The British Isles hesitated for a long time whether to depart with North America or stay with Europe. The North Sea is perhaps the record of that hesitation with stretching and sinking going back at least to the Devonian and actual fracturing going back perhaps to the Permian volcanics. One of the most remarkable discoveries in the North Sea (at least to Jurassic-oriented eyes) was that of considerable mid Jurassic volcanic activity off northern Scotland. Even this should not have been all that surprising, for we have developments of bentonitic 'Fuller's Earth' at this level in southern England, but no one would believe anything as unlikely as a Jurassic volcano. So tension continued, but long before the end of the Cretaceous and more than 60 million years before the Common Market, Britain decided to remain in Europe.

Most of the faulting ended with the Jurassic and what are called the late Kimmerian movements. This was an erosional episode and post-Kimmeridgian Jurassic sediments are little known. The basal Cretaceous often provides a cap-rock. In the south the Neocomian transgresses across the truncated Jurassic, but farther north it was later (probably Aptian–Albian). The Mid North Sea 'High' was finally eliminated and a single simple basin formed for most of Cretaceous times. Generally speaking the Cretaceous succession is what we would expect from what we know on land, passing up from clays in the lower part to white Chalk at the top. The troughs were still encouraging thicker sedimentation and the Chalk passes into shales northwards up the Viking Graben. This is assumed to be a matter of depth, but it might also be one of latitude. By Coniacian times all faulting had ceased and it was just gentle subsidence from then on.

A fundamental change took place in late Cretaceous times and continued into the early Tertiary. This was the 'inversion' of some of the troughs, so that they became positive areas. This is comparable to what was described in the previous section under the Baltic Plain. In particular, there was inversion along the Weald–Boulonnais structure, on the west side of the southern North Sea Basin and along the Central Graben that cuts the Mid North Sea 'High'.

Reference has already been made to the thickening of the onshore Tertiary towards the North Sea. It reaches 3500 m in the deepest part of the northern basin. The structure had become very simple. It is just a north–south basin, swinging into the Netherlands, which subsided fairly continuously right through to the Pliocene. At the bottom, as in Denmark, the Chalk facies persisted through into the Paleocene and this Danian Chalk with the sands that immediately followed form the second most important oil reservoir after the Jurassic sands. Above is a monotonous sequence of shales, representing the central trough of a sea that expanded periodically to flood the London, Hampshire, Paris, and Belgian Basins. The only variation is provided by volcanic ashes in the Paleocene and Eocene, presumably from the same source as those in southern Scandinavia.

Sandy deposition returned in the Pliocene as the basin shallowed and above are just the mixed-up deposits of the Quaternary. Trees and mammoths on Dogger Bank prove a land connection when Britain was in every sense part of the continent.

In summary then, the North Sea Basin can be said to be a side-effect of the opening of the Atlantic, and a very valuable one for at least some of the countries that surround it.

6(c) Central British Block

We are concerned here with that part of England and Wales that lies south-east of the Caledonides and north of the Variscan Front (Fig. 6.5). Part of it is commonly called the London–Brabant Massif (extending just to the Low Countries) and that name is sometimes used for the much larger unit. However, to avoid confusion I prefer to restrict the London–Brabant Massif to its original sense and to coin a new term for the large area which escaped the Caledonian movements, although they passed on either side. Some authors have used the term 'craton' but that to me has a much larger connotation. The Block may be compared (although certainly not scenically) with the Colorado Plateau in the south-western United States, which is a detached fragment of the Stable Interior cut off by Mesozoic fold belts. In that it escaped all tectonism after the Precambrian, the Central British Block may be regarded as part of the East European Platform, and I have long discussed the proposition that the platform extends all the way to the Severn Bridge (the frontier station between England and South Wales) or even past the Swansea Valley to South Pembrokeshire. However, now that we know for certain that there was a Caledonian orogenic belt passing down through the North Sea, it is more convenient and logical to deal with it here.

I remember that it worried me, as a student, having learned about our Anglo-Welsh early Palaeozoic geosyncline (which ended with the Caledonian orogeny), to go to the classic Welsh Borderland. For there all one sees are gently-dipping, well-preserved Lower Palaeozoic rocks, in a thin shelf-type succession with frequent breaks in deposition. They were really very little different tectonically from the familiar Mesozoic rocks of south-east England. What is more, they passed placidly up into the 'Old Red Sandstone' with no sign of anything that could be called an orogeny. Such structural complications as

135

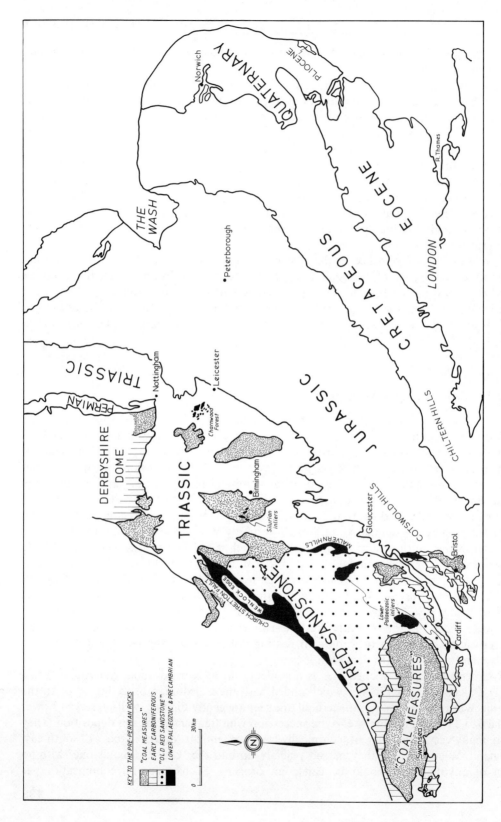

Fig. 6.5 *Geological sketch-map of the Central British Block.*

The following labels appear within the figure:

QUATERNARY

PLIOCENE

Norwich

THE WASH

EOCENE

LONDON

R.Thames

CRETACEOUS

Peterborough

TRIASSIC

PERMIAN

Nottingham

DERBYSHIRE DOME

Leicester

Charnwood Forest

JURASSIC

TRIASSIC

Birmingham

Silurian inliers

CHILTERN HILLS

Gloucester

COTSWOLD HILLS

MALVERN HILLS

CHURCH STRETTON FAULT

WENLOCK EDGE

"OLD RED SANDSTONE"

Lower Palaeozoic inliers

Bristol

"COAL MEASURES"

Cardiff

Swansea

KEY TO THE PRE-PERMIAN ROCKS

"COAL MEASURES"

EARLY CARBONIFEROUS

"OLD RED SANDSTONE"

LOWER PALAEOZOIC & PRECAMBRIAN

0   30km

existed were confined to the major fault zones, of which by far the most notable was the Church Stretton Fault with its various branches.

In fact the Church Stretton line is a clearly defined boundary that was much more than merely a dislocation. It relates to important facies changes in the Lower Palaeozoic rocks and it can be shown to have continued to operate right through to the end of Palaeozoic times. This latter point is particularly clear in the direct continuation of the Church Stretton feature in South Wales, where it is known as the Careg Cennen Disturbance.* Parallel structures, near the edge of the block, are the Vale of Neath and Swansea Valley Disturbances.

High-grade metamorphic basement rocks are only well seen in the Central British Block in the long narrow ridge of the Malvern Hills, which forms the geological (if not political) boundary between England and Wales. They have been compared with the Mona Complex of Anglesey and are overlain by late Precambrian acid volcanic rocks. The latter are comparable with those seen on the east side of the Church Stretton Fault, notably in the Wrekin, south of Wellington, and in Caer Caradoc near Church Stretton in Salop. Similar acid volcanics are found further east in the Lickey Hills near Birmingham and in Charnwood Forest near Leicester.

It may be significant that there are no thick late Precambrian sedimentary sequences immediately east of the Church Stretton Fault, although they are thickly developed in the Longmynd, immediately to the west. It may be that the Church Stretton Fault was already controlling sedimentation in Proterozoic times.

The Charnwood Forest rocks show on the map as a rash of spots where jagged pinnacles push up through a cover of Triassic desert deposits. These are the peaks of ancient highlands appearing again after burial for some 200 million years. The rocks are mostly volcanic in origin, but much is ashy sediment and agglomerates, yielding some of the oldest fossils known in Europe. The Charnwood rocks are folded on north-west lines as discussed in Chapter 4.

Above the acid volcanics of the Welsh Borders come the Cambrian sediments of the Church Stretton and Malvern areas, classic but thin, poorly exposed, and bedevilled by faults. The sediments are marginal in character with unconformities, conglomerates, basal white quartzites, glauconitic sandstones, thin limestones, and abundant trilobites, of a distinctly 'European' nature. These are comparable with those of the Baltic area and contrast markedly with those of north-west Scotland. So they have long been placed on the opposite shorelines of an early Palaeozoic ocean, many years before anyone thought of calling it the proto-Atlantic or (worse) that unnecessary classicism the 'Iapetus Ocean'. Basal Cambrian quartzites are seen again in the Lickey Hills, near Birmingham, and at Nuneaton, where they are worked to provide the ballast that goes between the lines of British Rail.

The thick Ordovician sediments and volcanics of the Caledonides to the west thin abruptly as one crosses the Church Stretton Fault. Only the Caradoc is represented on the eastern side, with only the merest trace of volcanism. The deposits are of a shelf nature, with breaks above and below, and within a few kilometres eastwards they too have disappeared. There is no sign of the Ordovician (apart from a few intrusions) in the

---

*'Disturbances' are geological phenomena only known in South Wales, just as 'accidents' are only known in France and French-influenced countries.

English Midlands proper, where transgressive Upper Llandovery rests directly on the Cambrian.

Further east, near Cambridge, borehole and geophysical evidence suggest the sort of Ordovician volcanics known in the Caledonides to the west with some degree of folding. This must be connected with the orogenic belt down the east side of the block, but the real knowledge here is scanty.

The Lower Palaeozoic story of the Central British Block is mainly one of the Silurian. Above the thin Cambrian and Ordovician sediments of east Salop comes the real 'Siluria' of Sir Roderick Murchison. Sandstones, shales, and above all highly fossiliferous limestones, dominate the scenery with gently dipping escarpments. This is the country of A. E. Housman and 'A Shropshire Lad', with the wooded scarp of Wenlock Edge (Upper Wenlock) and View Edge (Upper Ludlow) being the most obvious features. Besides well-known names such as Much Wenlock and Ludlow, many of the modern plethora of Silurian stage names originate from here. The story is basically one of a late Llandovery transgression, of shallow-water calcareous mudstones and limestones (with mini-reefs), and then regression again in the late Ludlow. The transgression spread right across the English Midlands. The wonderfully preserved Wenlock faunas at Dudley Castle Hill (now a zoo) and Wren's Nest near Birmingham have been famous since the early days of geology. A trilobite is part of Dudley's coat of arms. Everything is indicative of a platform and apart from their age the Silurian escarpments of Salop do not differ in kind from the Jurassic escarpment of the Cotswolds or the Cretaceous of the Chilterns. These follow each other in regular succession as one heads towards London.

Farther south, inliers of similar Silurian rocks are seen west of the Malverns, in the Woolhope Dome and in other smaller inliers. They carry the pattern down into south-east Wales. Nowhere here is the Lower Palaeozoic geosynclinal in the traditional sense, nor has it suffered anything that can be called an orogeny. I therefore feel justified in extending the 'platform' of Central England all the way to the continuation of the Church Stretton Fault north of Swansea.* It is really not narrow chauvinism that makes my present home city close to the meeting place of several of the major features of European geology.

Late Palaeozoic

Everyone associates South Wales with the Carboniferous coal-field, which is a structural, topographical, and sedimentary basin. In fact it is part of a much larger basin that extends up to the Malvern Hills in the Welsh Borderland. The rest of that wider basin is represented at the surface by considerable thicknesses of 'Old Red Sandstone', centred on Hereford. The Malvern line and the Severn Graben cut across the Block here and separate South Wales from the rest. The main structures seen are on north–south lines parallel with other gentle late Palaeozoic movements north of the Variscan front.

One of the great natural features of Wales are the Brecon Beacons. This is a splendid north-facing, red escarpment that forms a barrier between the Celtic twilight of Caledonide Wales and the busy, industrial, highly populated (but still very beautiful) southern

---

*This does somewhat extend the 'Danelaw' part of the Danish Triangle, but Swansea was a Viking name long before the Welsh told us to call it 'Abertawe'.

basin. The escarpment is made of Upper 'Old Red Sandstone' and there is a broad area of more low-lying country to the north on the softer lower division. There is a break between the lower and upper divisions but one needs a light aircraft, some faith, and a slight mist to imagine the angular unconformity between them. Not much has happened to these rocks since they were laid down and even a major break would have gone unnoticed if it had not been for the missing fish.

There are also some early land plants not far from Brecon and there is even, in the upper beds, a brief marine incursion of Frasnian age which conveniently ties this succession to the open seas of Variscan Meso-Europa to the south. This large area has a character of its own with thick red soils, red cliffs, and red sandstone cathedrals and churches. It is sometimes called the 'Anglo-Welsh Cuvette', as though it were a narrow valley between the new Caledonide mountains. In fact much of it must have been a broad alluvial plain, not far above sea-level, with occasional torrential rushes of conglomerates and breccias from the hills. The abundant plants (and the absence of evaporites) belie any idea of arid deserts and the sediments suggest derivation from an area to the north that was undergoing intense chemical weathering.

The next barrier one meets as one advances south towards the coal-field is the escarpment of the 'Carboniferous Limestone'. A parallel was drawn earlier with the Colorado Plateau. Our local equivalent of the Grand Canyon is the road that climbs this scarp near Bryn Mawr ('big hill' in Welsh). At the bottom one sees a cutting in flat-lying Silurian, then glimpses of 'Old Red Sandstone', then one climbs up past the whole of the 'Carboniferous Limestone', the whole of the 'Millstone Grit', and the lower beds of the 'Coal Measures' in a continuous section. The 'Heads of the Valleys' road continues round the northern rim of the coal-field with glimpses down into the famous mining valleys such as the Rhondda and Ebbw Vale.

Both the 'Old Red Sandstone' and the 'Carboniferous Limestone' pass round and under the coal-field to appear again in the lovely cliffs of the Gower Peninsula and south Glamorgan. Although there are differences in detail and a score of studies yet to be made, the generalities are the same. The early Carboniferous was mainly a time of shallow marine carbonate deposition with rich coral and brachiopod faunas, occasional breaks, and passages into muddier and more brackish facies.

The 'Millstone Grit', on the other hand, differs markedly from one side of the coal-field to the other. On the north side the sandstones predominate and one is reminded of the deltaic situation in the Pennines. On the south side everything passes into marine shales (e.g., in Swansea Bay) and the open sea was clearly in this direction. What is more, these Namurian deposits cut across the earlier formations so that they rest on older and older beds to the north and east. The situation to the east is particularly significant because it is evident that the north–south Malvern line and its continuation was operating within Carboniferous times.

For all its past poverty, the South Wales coal-field is (in my opinion) the only attractive coal-field in Britain and perhaps the only such in Europe. The chief reason for this is the thick sandstone developed in the lower part of the upper Westphalian. The productive 'Coal Measures' are mostly below this. The sandstone dominates the scenery and the coals beneath it are mainly worked in deep narrow valleys into which people, mines, railways, and rivers are all crowded. It may not be very pleasant to live in the mining valleys, even though many of them are becoming green again as the mines are worked out, but it is certainly very pleasant to be able to climb quickly out of the valleys on to the broad sandstone moorlands all around.

The South Wales coal-field is a broad, gentle, east–west syncline with an anticline across the middle. The mining valleys trend north-west and are controlled by faults. There are also, however, major structures running across the coal-field from north-west to south-west, reminding one of the Caledonides structures to the north. These are the 'disturbances' mentioned earlier and appear to have operated spasmodically through a considerable period of time. The most obvious are those that follow the Swansea and Neath Valleys.

Perhaps the most interesting feature of the late Carboniferous sediments of South Wales is the way that derivation from the north in Namurian (and earlier) times is replaced by derivation from the south by late Westphalian times. This must reflect both the wearing down of the Caledonian mountains and the rise of the new Variscan mountains across the Bristol Channel. Again marine intercalations ended by late Westphalian times, but they did last slightly longer than in most places and there was probably an open sea away to the south-west. What is more, unlike all the other British coal-fields there is nothing that can really be called red beds. The highest Carboniferous is probably missing anyway and there is nothing more to be seen, although we know that Triassic and Jurassic deposition occurred not very far away in what is here grouped with Meso-Europa—Chapter 8(b).

Moving back to Salop one sees the 'Old Red Sandstone' in the Clee Hills above the Silurian scarps, but beyond that it disappears beneath younger sediments. As a crude generalization it may be said that, south of London, boreholes go into marine Devonian, while under London itself there are either interdigitations of marine and non-marine facies of (not far under Soho) typical 'Old Red Sandstone'. In other words, the London–Brabant Massif was an important palaeogeographical feature in Devonian times. Northwards the 'Old Red Sandstone' pinches out and there is nothing really to be seen of this age until one comes close to the Scottish border. Lower Carboniferous rocks are similarly absent under the southern Midlands, so that there is a gap between the Silurian and the Upper Carboniferous or higher strata. Along the London Massif, Jurassic and early Cretaceous formations feather-edge against the Lower Palaeozoic, and the Albian was the first stage to climb over the barrier. This is the feature commonly seen on palaeogeographical maps as the 'Mercian Highlands', although it is doubtful if mountaineers would ever have found anything here worth climbing. We know from boreholes near Oxford, that thick late Carboniferous 'Coal Measures' passed this way. It may be that these were preserved in faulted troughs like those that cross the Fyn Grinsted High under Denmark.

Farther north we come into an early Carboniferous basin in which were laid down the thick carbonates that build the Pennines. The story is continuous with that of the English Caledonides to the west, and the sea invaded the Danish Triangle from that direction.

The Dinantian 'Carboniferous Limestone' and the Namurian 'Millstone Grit' dominate the scenery of Northern England, but this part of our 'green and pleasant land' is the 'Black Country' dominated by Westphalian 'Coal Measures' and their associated mining and industry. The Midland coal-fields radiate from the south end of the Pennines like the fingers of a hand, with the great conurbations of Birmingham, Wolverhampton, the Potteries, Nottingham, and the rest. The positive area to the south controlled sedimentation and the thin coal seams run together in that direction. Birmingham owes its existence to the 'Thick Coal' of the South Staffordshire coal-field, although it is long since exhausted. Besides the coals there are the valuable clays for china manufacture, notably around Arnold Bennett's 'Five Towns'. These are part of a storey of red bed sedimentation which moved south with time during the Westphalian. There is no trace of anything marine in the upper part of that division and the top is lost in a thick blanket of red mudstones, sandstones, and breccias.

The five main coal-fields of the English Midlands are all preserved in graben which started to develop in Permo-Triassic times. The horsts between show mainly Trias at the surface, although we know that there are more 'Coal Measures' at depth beneath. Beyond and to the east, in the fox-hunting Vale of Belvoir, a huge new coal-field has been proved and is currently the subject of much conservationist debate.

North from here, up the east side of the Pennines, is the great Yorkshire, Derbyshire, and Nottinghamshire coal-field which carries its coals down gently in an easterly direction. North again is the Northumberland coal-field which plunges under the sea and used to supply the capital in the days before the industrial revolution (hence 'carrying coals to Newcastle'—the epitome of useless enterprise). The north–south structures impressed upon northern England at around the end of Carboniferous times are cut across obliquely by the Permian, which rests on a great variety of older rocks. This serves to define the north-west margin of the Central British Block.

The basal beds of the Permian are yellow sands, frequently showing subaerial dune structures with a prevailing wind from the east. These sands are highly porous and permeable, providing a good water reservoir on land just as they provide a good gas reservoir out in the North Sea. They may be equated with the Rotliegende of Germany.

Above comes the so-called 'Marl Slate', which yields occasional fish and other fossils which make it an obvious correlative of the German *Kupferschiefer*. The most interesting formation in the British Permian is the Zechstein 'Magnesian Limestone', which extends from the coast at Sunderland down to Nottingham. The name refers to the highly dolomitized condition of this rock (making it a highly unsuitable building stone for the Houses of Parliament, which rapidly turned into Epsom Salts in London's acidic atmosphere). This formation is famous for its curious organic-looking concretions and for its succession of little reefs, the faunas of which became progressively scarcer and more stunted upwards into the high salinities of the highest Permian.

Cyclic evaporites are much in evidence and one of the most important discoveries in Britain since the Second World War was that of late Permian potash and other salts in a deep boring at Robin Hood's Bay in Yorkshire. These are comparable to those of Stassfurt in Germany and it is sometimes suggested that the two localities were at opposite ends of a single great evaporating dish. It is more likely that they were separate elements in a whole series of salt basins extending across northern Europe.

Mesozoic

The Trias which follows is of the usual continental facies, although without the 'Muschelkalk'. With the characteristic English love of paradox (and no evidence of a major break in the middle) the terms 'Bunter' and 'Keuper' have been used to cover the whole succession, with resultant confusion when correlation is attempted with the continent. The sandstones in the lower part of the Trias gave rise to Robin Hood's Sherwood Forest near Nottingham.* The soft red mudstones of the so-called 'Keuper', together with the Rhaetian and Lias, form the great lowland valley that extends up from the Vale of Severn through Newark and Gainsborough to the Vale of York and the sea near Middlesbrough.

In the Midlands this was the time of the formation of the horsts that are now the exposed coal-fields and the graben with thicker Trias in between. After the compressions of the Variscan orogeny, tension became the fashion throughout western Europe and north-west Africa. This was far more important than any early shudders of the Alpine orogeny. North America was again going west.

All the evidence is of aridity and of a generally lifeless desert. Sometimes the evidence is very precise as with the sand-blasted sub-Triassic surface of the Precambrian rocks in Charnwood Forest. There is no real evidence before late Triassic times that Britain was yet feeling fresh sea breezes from the west, but certainly these islands were a long way removed from the happenings on the continent at this time. We know that the 'Muschelkalk' Sea twice spilled out of its Alpine basin, and in Ladinian times came as close to Britain as Heligoland (Helgoland).

Some years ago a student party was visiting the Eakring oil-field in Nottinghamshire. As they walked past the usual monotonous red Trias, a student asked, 'Are there any fossils here?' 'Of course not', replied the lecturer in charge. With the healthy scientific scepticism and independence of thought that we like to think is encouraged in British universities, the student struck the rock and discovered the first definite marine fossils ever found in the British Trias below the Rhaetian. This is the farthest manifestation of the 'Muschelkalk' Sea, although there are hints of something more to the west.

The Lower Jurassic consists mainly of typical shaly clays and thin limestones, with shelf faunas. A notable feature is the development of sedimentary ironstones in the Sinemurian around Scunthorpe in Lincolnshire and in the Upper Pliensbachian across the Midlands from Banbury in Oxfordshire up into the Cleveland Hills of Yorkshire. This latter was formerly the most valuable source of iron-ore in Britain, a pre-eminence later taken over by a similar deposit in the Middle Jurassic of the east Midlands.

The Lower Jurassic rocks are nowadays little seen inland, but are beautifully exposed in a series of gentle anticlines and synclines along the Yorkshire coast, second only in importance to the classic sections of Dorset. Local ammonites from the Upper Lias used to be sold at Whitby with carved snakes' heads as testimony to the fact that the local Saint Hilda (who gave her name to *Hildoceras*) changed all the snakes into stones.

The Middle Jurassic has a complex story with mainly carbonates in the south passing, rather abruptly, into mainly deltaic deposits to the north. The carbonates are the quaintly named 'Inferior' and 'Great Oolite' of the glorious Cotswold Hills, which form a splendid escarpment above Gloucester and Cheltenham and face west over the Triassic–Liassic lowland Vale of Severn. This was a great graben controlling sedimentation in Triassic times, and we know that it went on influencing sedimentation at least up till mid Jurassic times. It was at the little village of Churchill in the Cotswolds that

*That folk-hero is also recorded in many other parts of England, including the Yorkshire bay mentioned above.

William Smith and stratigraphy were born and I cannot think of a better place in the whole continent. The shallow-water oolites, oncolites, and shelly limestones, of the Bajocian and Bathonian are much used as building-stones (notably for the Oxford colleges and a thousand Cotswold villages). Abundant fossils, often of strongly southern affinities, probably represent the northern limit of the Jurassic tropics. The deltaic deposits which replace them to the north include marine incursions, such as the scarp-forming Lincolnshire Limestone, and the extensively quarried Northampton Sand Ironstone. But much of it is sandy and it includes poor coals and plant beds which provide one of the best records of the flora of these times.

Of the Upper Jurassic, mention must be made of the Oxford Clay which is worked on a huge scale (notably near Peterborough) in the world's biggest, most automated brickworks. Reefs in the late Oxfordian, near Oxford and elsewhere, are the equivalent of those developed right across Europe and north-west Africa at this time, but again may well represent the northernmost limits of these fussy creatures. Recent evidence suggest that they only managed to colonize the area for a few hundred years.

All the Jurassic and Lower Cretaceous formations above thin out markedly over a 'high' in south Yorkshire that is still generally known as the Market Weighton axis. The exact nature of this is a matter of some dispute, but it is a gravity low and clearly affected sedimentation for a very long time.

The uppermost part of the Jurassic is usually missing and in the north of the area the whole of the Upper Jurassic is only patchily preserved as clays and thin sands. It is chiefly notable for the Boreal nature of its faunas, which have strong affinities with those of the Soviet Union. This has encouraged the belief among some Mesozoic palaeontologists that this is part of the East European Platform. A further link with the cooler seas of the north is recorded in the Lower Cretaceous sands of the royal country around Sandringham in Norfolk. Evidence of an early transgression, comparable to that of Ryazan in Russia, was found in excavations bringing ashore the pipes carrying North Sea gas.

The 'Red Rock' of Hunstanton, on the Norfolk coast, is a condensed deposit of Albian age and its brilliant red colour immediately below the white Chalk makes this one of the most distinctive cliffs in Europe. Its significance may be what it tells us about arid conditions prevailing along the margins of the Chalk sea.

The Upper Cretaceous is perfectly normal for northern Europe with the Chalk forming the high cliffs of Flamborough Head and sweeping inland as the Yorkshire Wolds, through Lincolnshire, across to Norfolk, and eventually all the way to outer suburban London as the beech-wooded Chilterns. The Chalk dives down below the capital to provide its underground water supply and emerges again as the North Downs on the other side. It was shown before the war that a careful tracing of zones within the Chalk indicates that this basin was already subsiding in late Cretaceous times. Earlier this was not so, however, as has already been emphasized. Both the Jurassic and the Lower Cretaceous pinch out against the London–Brabant Ridge. In other words, what had been a positive ridge inverted at the end of early Cretaceous times and became a basin instead. This is the same pattern that we have seen already across the northern plain of Europe.

Cainozoic

By Tertiary times this region had forgotten whether it belonged to Eo-, Palaeo- or even Meso-Europa. The London Basin story is very much part of the saga that extends from Jutland to beyond Paris, and it straddles what is commonly called the Variscan Front. A new trough was superimposed on the old ridge. The sea came and went repeatedly from the east leaving poorly exposed cyclic records of shallow marine and fluviatile sediments through most of the Eocene. There were four transgressions and four regressions. The first brought the Thanet Sands (of obviously Thanetian age) into Kent, the second took the Woolwich Beds into London (where the famous Woolwich Arsenal was sited to make use of the moulding sand). The marine facies pass gently into estuarine and then into the fluviatile Reading Beds over to the west. With the sort of meticulous studies that have been inflicted on these urbanized sediments, it can be shown that variations in thickness and facies can be related to north–south structures in the basement, not so very far beneath.

The marine London Clay (Ypresian) spread farther and thicker than any of the others and provides a suitable medium for the digging of underground railways. In the Isle of Sheppey in the Thames estuary a prolific fauna and flora records a teeming crocodilian river flowing through a rain-forest into a tropical sea. Westwards and upwards the London Clay passes into the continental Bagshot Sands which cap the capital's mountain heights of Hampstead, Highgate, and Harrow. At the west end of the London Basin it is almost all sand, providing a suitable environment for birch trees and rhododendrons, and for military training at Aldershot and Sandhurst.

There is a little more of the Tertiary story: no Oligocene or Miocene but the much later 'crags' in East Anglia. These are shelly sands like the *faluns* of western France. They outcrop over a considerable area of Norfolk and Suffolk and were all formerly thought to be Pliocene in age. We now know, however, that only the lowest of the 'crags', near Orford in Suffolk, belongs to a warmish spell in the late Pliocene.*

The later 'crags' record the climatic oscillations of the early Pleistocene before the ice reached England. They culminate in the Cromer Forest Beds of Norfolk, with an abundant flora and vertebrate fauna, which is immediately overlain by the first glacial deposits. When the ice did come it left a jumble of tills and outwash deposits, some with erratics brought from the Permian volcanics of the Oslo graben, some with Caledonian granites from the west of the Pennines, some with metamorphic rocks from the Scottish highlands. For those brought up on the four glaciations of the Alps, it was essential to find four here too, if only out of pure patriotism. If you expect a thing, almost inevitably you find it, and it has taken years to put the record straight again in terms of minor phases within the last glaciations. I must mention this because 'perfidious Albion' has erected an excessive number of Pleistocene stage-names based on scruffy and ephemeral exposures in these flat and windswept lands beside the North Sea. Some, such as that founded on the seaside resort of Clacton in Essex, are probably worth while because of the excellent record of early human industry, but most are probably best forgotten.

---

*I found my first fossil in these while digging a hasty slit trench in the early forties, when an invasion was imminently expected.

Every English schoolboy knows that, long before General de Gaulle, England was joined to the continent by muddy swamplands across which the Thames and the Rhine flowed together in amity towards a northerly ocean. England's protective moat was formed when the ice melted and the upstart North Sea is still gnawing away at the cliffs of glacial till. Whole towns have disappeared since mediaeval times and it is little consolation to the locals to know that in Wales and elsewhere the land is gaining over the sea.

Selected references to Chapter 6

Section 6(a)   Baltic Plain

Voigt, E. (1963). 'Uber Randtroge vor Schollenrändern und ihrer Bedeutung im Gebiet der Mitteleuropäischen Senke und angrenzender Gebiete', *Zeitschr. deutsch. geol. Ges.*, **114**, 378–418.

Ziegler, P. A. (1978). 'North-western Europe: tectonics and basin development', *Geol. Mijnb.*, **57**, 589–626.

Section 6(b)   North Sea Basin

Hay, J. T. C. (1978), 'Structural development in the northern North Sea', *J. Petrol.*, **1**, 65–77.

Kent, P. E. (1975), 'Review of North Sea Basin development', *J. Geol. Soc., Lond.*, **131**, 435–468.

Pegrum, R. M., G. Rees, and D. Naylor (1975), *Geology of the North-West European Continental Shelf*, vol. 2, *The North Sea*, Graham Trotman Dudley, London, 225 pp.

Ziegler, P. A. (1975), 'Geologic evolution of North Sea and its tectonic framework', *Bull. Amer. Ass. Petrol. Geol.*, **59**, 1073–1097.

Ziegler, P. A. (1978), 'North-western Europe: tectonics and basin development', *Geol. Mijnb.*, **57**, 589–626.

Ziegler, W. H. (1975), 'Outline of the geological history of the North Sea', in Woodland, A. W. (ed.), *Petroleum and the Continental Shelf of Northwest Europe. I. Geology*, Applied Science Publishers, London, pp. 165–187.

Section 6(c)   Central British Block

Chatwin, C. P. (1961), *British Regional Geology: East Anglia and Adjoining Areas*, 4th edn, Inst. Geol. Sci., London, 100 pp.

Dunning, F. W. (1977), 'Caledonian–Variscan relations in north-west Europe', *Colloq. Internat. CNRS, Rennes*, No. 243, 165–180.

Earp, J. R. and B. A. Hains (1971), *British Regional Geology: The Welsh Borderland*, 3rd edn, Inst. Geol. Sci., London, 118 pp.

Hains, B. A. and A. Horton (1969), *British Regional Geology: Central England*, 3rd edn., Inst. Geol. Sci., London, 142 pp.

Owen, T. R. (ed.) (1974), *The Upper Palaeozoic and Post Palaeozoic Rocks of Wales*, Univ. Wales Press, 426 pp.

Owen, T. R. (1976), *The Geological Evolution of the British Isles*, Pergamon, Oxford, 161 pp.

Sherlock, R. L. (1960), *British Regional Geology: London and Thames Valley*, 3rd edn., Geol. Surv. and Museum, London, 62 pp.

Chapter Seven

General conclusions on Palaeo-Europa

Palaeo-Europa is the smallest of the four major natural divisions of Europe. This is simply because its main part, the Caledonides *sensu stricto*, is related to the Atlantic line and therefore, by definition, to the very margin of the continent. A comparable division would be the Uralides, at the opposite end of Europe, which is included here with Meso-Europa because their terminal orogenies happened to coincide. Palaeo-Europa is dominated by the Caledonides but much more happened here than just the Caledonian orogeny, although most of the events can be related more or less directly to the Atlantic Ocean (Fig. 7.1).

Even very eminent geologists have misunderstood Stille's concept of Palaeo-Europa and thought it to be synonymous with the Caledonian movements in Europe wherever they might occur. Once more it must be said that it is the age of the last significant tectonism that is important. Whether or not Caledonian age movements also occurred in Meso- or Neo-Europa is the concern of those parts of this book, it has nothing to do with Palaeo-Europa.

No one nowadays can doubt that the Caledonides of Scandinavia and the British Isles were once part of the same mountain range as the Appalachians of eastern North America. The tearing apart which formed the Atlantic Ocean was a comparatively recent incident, but what concerns us chiefly here is an earlier episode during which there accumulated the rocks which now form most of Palaeo-Europa.

The first point to be made about these is to reverse our thoughts a little to Eo-Europa and to consider the comparatively close similarity of the rocks of the Fenno-Scandian Shield and those of the Hebridean Province. If it were not for the chance that preserved the latter sliver for us on the north-west coast of Scotland, our interpretation of Europe might be very different. It was long said that the Caledonides divided these two disproportionate fragments of ancient Europe. It is more likely that, far from separating them, most of the Caledonides did little more than intrude on to the margin of Eo-Europa.

So far as the Scandinavian Caledonides are concerned it is now thought that much of the Precambrian there is more or less *in situ* and not allochthonous as was formerly believed. Coupled with the fact that there is a marked scarcity of ocean floor material, except perhaps in the extreme north-west, there seems to be little justification in postulating a proto-Atlantic Ocean up through the centre of Scandinavia in early Palaeozoic times. The ophiolitic elements that are present are probably far-travelled or, if more local

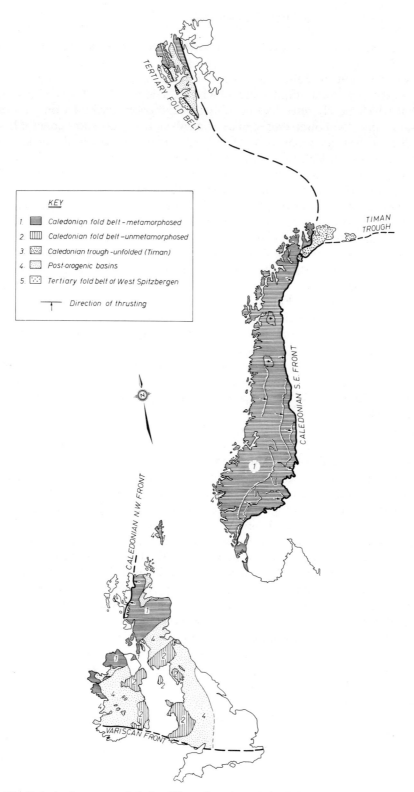

Fig. 7.1 *The Caledonian orogenic belt of Scandinavia and the British Isles (after Ager, 1975, by kind permission of the Council of the Geologists' Association).*

in origin, probably relate to small basins behind island arcs rather than to the main ocean itself.

The evidence from the Jotun nappes inland from Bergen is most impressive. Here we have allochthonous Precambrian material which is said to belong to the Fenno-Scandian Shield but which closely resembles possibly autochthonous basement on the west coast. At the same time, the Lower Palaeozoic sediments in the upper slices contain Baltic-type fossils. There is just not room to bring this from anywhere east of the present Atlantic. Such evidence and that already mentioned of autochthonous basement in the north of Norway mean that the main suture cannot have lain on or near the south-east Caledonian front, as was formerly postulated, but far to the west.

If a proto-Atlantic ocean existed in these latitudes, it seems more likely that it and the subduction zone down which it disappeared were west of the present Norwegian coastline. Perhaps the ultra-basic masses we see in the northernmost islands are all the good evidence there is. The nappes of Proterozoic and Lower Palaeozoic sediments were then thrust south-eastwards as the result of the coming together of a Greenlandian plate and a Scandinavian plate at various times in the early Palaeozoic. They were squeezed out of a trough or series of troughs that might or might not merit the term 'ocean'. It is surely significant that truly 'American'-type faunas have only been found in the westernmost nappes of Norway, such as those of Trondheim and Spitsbergen (in the same way that they are only found in the extreme west of Scotland and Ireland). I strongly suspect from the Greenlandian and Canadian affinities of much of what we see, that these present parts of the earth's crust were not then very far apart. The Scandinavian Caledonides may be compared with the Apennines of peninsular Italy which formed in a similar way at a much later date.

When we turn to the Caledonides of the British Isles, we are lost in a turmoil of rival theories. We have sutures in many different places with subduction zones facing in different directions and moving at different times. In particular a great deal of paper has been expended setting out different ideas on the timing and mode of closure of the proto-Atlantic. From some of the contradictory evidence one might presume that it was opening and closing all through late Precambrian and early Palaeozoic times like a swing door. Presumably something was already happening at the end of Proterozoic times to produce the Cadomian orogeny of western France and the western part of the Iberian Peninsula (discussed under Meso-Europa). It could be that the same events produced the early metamorphic dates in the Moinian of Scotland as well. There are alleged Proterozoic ophiolites at several places (e.g., Anglesey and Brittany) but these are extremely suspect, although there are certainly thick flysch sequences and pillow lavas.

So far as the Cambrian is concerned, orogenesis has been postulated at this time in Norway and it is possible that some of the Dalradian metamorphism occurred during the period. We know that major deformation with amphibolite grade metamorphism was followed by uplift and erosion before the deposition of early Ordovician sediments in Mayo in western Ireland. There are also the ophiolites of the Highland Boundary Fault which may be as old as Cambrian and may represent an early phase in the subduction of a proto-Atlantic Ocean under the Scottish Highlands.

Most specialists would say that the proto-Atlantic functioned as an effective faunal barrier throughout Cambrian times. To my eyes the contrasts in the Lower Palaeozoic assemblages on the two sides may be attributable as much to environmental differences as to geographical isolation. This point is particularly obvious in the Lower Cambrian facies with quartzites and carbonates on the one side and shales and greywackes on the other. So it seems probable that the proto-Atlantic was never very wide. We are probably influenced subconsciously by the present-day map, but it could well be that never previously in its long and complex history was the Atlantic as wide as it is today. We must remember that we are only concerned with a rather narrow belt of sedimentary rocks with no tectonic evidence of more than—at the most—a few scores of kilometres of foreshortening and in many areas (such as Wales) perhaps not that.

It is clear that the Ordovician closing of the proto-Atlantic was a very important event, especially in the area that is now the British Isles. This was the 'Grampian orogeny' which is so well seen in the Dalradian rocks. The movements reached their climax in early to mid Ordovician times on the evidence of sections such as that at Girvan, in the west of Scotland. The orogeny is also well known in Norway, especially around Trondheim and Bergen, and is now also recognized on the other side of the Atlantic in the Appalachians. The famous Ballantrae rocks, south of Girvan, are probably as good an ophiolite suite (or at least fragments thereof) as we have anywhere in Palaeo-Europa, although their significance remains a matter of dispute. Similar suites are recognized in Scandinavia and in the west of Ireland. The supposed ophiolites of the Dalradian (e.g., at Tayvallich) are alkaline in composition and not oceanic; what is more they appear to rest on good Lewisian continental crust.

The latest of the many interpretations of the closing of the proto-Atlantic in the British Isles envisages three subduction zones ranging from early Ordovician to early Devonian in age. In north-west Scotland, the Moine Thrust is interpreted as the site of repeated east-south-east directed subduction of the Lewisian continent under the Dalradian basin. Along the line of the Southern Uplands and on into Ireland there was a north-north-westerly directed subduction zone (represented at Girvan) carrying lithosphere below the Scottish Highlands in the opposite direction. The convergence of two subducted plates here was presumably responsible for the prolonged history of tectonism, metamorphism, intrusion, and uplift in between. The fact that the two zones were set at an angle may also explain the considerable lateral displacements such as the Great Glen Fault. Transcurrent movements between the two continents have been suggested as the cause of the subsidence of the 'Old Red Sandstone' basins.

The early Palaeozoic Atlantic is then postulated along the Anglo-Scottish border with the third subduction zone trundling down to the south-east and seen in the English Lake District and south-east Ireland. This still does not necessitate a very wide ocean that had to be lost somewhere in the Southern Uplands. It also does not explain some of the phenomena in Wales, such as the splendid pillow lavas of Snowdonia and Strumble Head in Pembrokeshire, but this does not mean that I am looking for oceanic interpretations for them too. As in Scandinavia I think we are usually looking at comparatively small basins between island arcs and the continent rather than the open ocean itself.

The evidence of the granites, many of which have now been radiometrically dated, appears to fit in well with the main orogenic episodes. In Ireland, for example, they appear to fall into three groups, at about 500 million years (i.e., end Cambrian), 460 (mid Ordovician), and 415 (late Silurian). Those in other regions appear to fit into this pattern. This must point to the persistence of subduction zones at depth below continental crust. There were clearly a long continuing series of events associated with the

151

Atlantic closure. There is for example the very widespread sedimentary break below the Upper Ordovician (Caradoc) seen in south-west Scotland, the English Lake District, and the Anglo-Welsh area. At the same time intense volcanicity continued in areas such as North Wales.

The final Silurian closing of the Proto-Atlantic seems to have been a comparatively gentle affair of a quite different kind, in which the eugeosynclinal piles of southern Britain were 'scuffed up' without metamorphism, long after the cessation of important volcanicity. The pattern seems to have been imbricate thrusting and associated folding, with progressive migration of the sedimentary troughs south-eastwards towards the continent. This is similar to the pattern envisaged in many modern accretionary prisms.

The post-orogenic basins of the Caledonides are small affairs compared with those of the other major divisions of Europe. In Scandinavia they have all but disappeared due to the deep level of erosion, but the intermontane cuvettes filled with 'Old Red Sandstone' in Scotland show that although tensional forces with down-warping were now the rule, the old Caledonoid fractures were not dead. Compressional forces still expressed themselves in features such as the Great Glen Fault and indeed continuations of such lines were still operative as late as the Jurassic. Much of northern and western England must be regarded as a post-orogenic basin filled with gently warped and faulted Upper Palaeozoic sediments, superimposed on a deformed Lower Palaeozoic basement. From the local evidence of intense Caledonian folding (as in Ribblesdale) and of Caledonian magmatism (as in the sub-Pennine granites) we can confidently say that we are still within the Caledonian belt.

A special problem, however, attaches to the region here called the 'Danish Triangle' and for a long time I hesitated whether to include it in Eo- or Palaeo-Europe. The critical issue was whether or not this sizable chunk of northern Europe had suffered significant deformation after the end of Precambrian times. I was inevitably influenced by that part of the continent that is most familiar to me, the part that is here called the Central British Block. Little had happened here after the Precambrian and I was tempted to suggest that south-west Wales was unique (perhaps only rivalled by the Danube delta) in being the meeting point of three major divisions of our continent (Eo-, Palaeo-, and Meso-Europa). However, the latest evidence from the deeper borings in the North Sea has proved what has long been suggested by some geologists, that there was a separate belt of Caledonian folding and even metamorphism running down in a south-easterly direction as far as the Holy Cross Mountains in Poland. For this reason I have included much of northern Europe, with its interesting evidence of mid Cretaceous 'inversions', in this part of the book. Whether or not we should talk about another ocean here is a problem I would prefer to ignore, since the evidence is so scanty, but certainly there were both 'orthotectonic' and 'paratectonic' zones (in the North Sea and eastern England, respectively). But everything that happened after the Caledonian movements was wholly within a continent.

Europe may be said to have only come into existence as a separate recognizable plate with the formation of the proto-Atlantic ocean in late Precambrian times. Palaeo-Europa formed as a reversal of this trend, when the New World hesitatingly came back to rejoin the Old in early Palaeozoic times. But the integrity of our continent was preserved by the fact that Palaeo-Europa continued as a dynamic phenomenon. The huge Euro-American craton of Precambrian times was never re-established. The Atlantic line has been an active suture, or bundle of sutures, ever since.

The story is confused by the slice of Eo-Europa known as the Hebridean Province, which is delimited on both sides by Caledonoid structures. It might have been easier to consider it as just an aberrant tectonic slice caught up in the confusion of the Caledonides and it could be compared with that other slice of continent, the Rockall Bank, abandoned out in the North Atlantic at a later stage.

In summing up Eo-Europa I emphasized the importance of Atlantic lines in the later history of the Hebridean Province as expressed by Proterozoic and Palaeozoic facies changes, Caledonoid structures, Mesozoic and Tertiary sedimentation and volcanicity, and present-day geography. All this could be said again in summing up Palaeo-Europa. Nearly all the features summarized in the past few chapters can be matched and continued in eastern North America; indeed there has been a direct correlation of the structural zones in the Caledonides with the Appalachians.

What we also see in Palaeo-Europa is the evidence of the opening of the present Atlantic Ocean from early Mesozoic times onwards. The graben (such as that of the Severn Valley) which opened in Triassic times show a remarkable parallelism with those that formed to hold the Newark Group down the east coast of North America. At times the sediments and structures are so alike as to be almost silly. Thus the formation known as the 'Building Stones' of the English Midlands matches the 'Brownstone' that was used to build much of old New York. One difference is the absence of basic intrusions and extrusions in the Trias of Palaeo-Europa, but these are present farther south in western Europe and north-west Africa in the latitudes that would have come opposite the same phenomena in North America. Presumably they reflect the fact that the splitting started in the south. It has been shown that similar Triassic dikes in eastern North America, western Europe, north-west Africa, and north-east South America, form a perfect radial pattern from a centre in the Blake Plateau north of the Bahamas.

But there is no evidence of a sea to the west (and certainly not an ocean) through the greater part of Triassic times. When the sea did arrive in western Europe in the Rhaetian, and even more so in the Hettangian and Sinemurian, it may well have come from the west as it did in Scotland, in Portugal, and in western Morocco. It also spread at this time into the coastal districts of east Greenland. Although sadly we have no record from the eastern seaboard of the USA, it is reasonable to presume that there was some sort of shallow seaway affecting all parts of the North Atlantic borderlands at this time. There is no evidence from Palaeo-Europa (nor I would think from anywhere in western Europe or north-west Africa) of the great Atlantic evaporating dish postulated by some geophysicists for early Jurassic times.

By the late Mesozoic I think there was already an oceanic-type circulation with a proto-Gulf Stream taking some of my brachiopods from the south all the way up to east Greenland. Cretaceous and Tertiary sediments thicken westwards on the European shelf, as they do in Morocco and as they thicken eastwards on the coastal plain of the USA. We could hardly expect to see anything that we can call 'ocean' on a spreading edge, beyond the continental slope, but the intense Tertiary volcanicity is evidence of the tension that forms oceans. It may be significant that the Mesozoic volcanicity is confined to the 'failed arm' of the North Sea, where spreading started earlier but ended when the British Isles decided to stay in Europe.

153

The one great exception to all this story is the Tertiary fold belt of Spitsbergen, which is clearly compressional. This may be regarded as the farewell embrace of the brash young American continent before she left the Old World and went west. If the opening of the present Atlantic started in the south, as it clearly did, then it is to be expected that rotation would force Greenland against the northern tip of the European plate, perhaps in the process shearing off the Barents microplate and causing it to rotate and produce the very significant curved tear fault of northernmost Norway.

Selected references to Chapter 7

Ager, D. V. (1975), 'The geological evolution of Europe', *Proc. Geol. Assoc.*, **86**, 127–154.

Bowes, D. R. and B. E. Leake (eds.) (1978), 'Crustal evolution in north-western adjacent regions', *Geol. Jl.* spec. issue No. 10.

Dewey, J. F. (1969), 'Evolution of the Appalachian/Caledonian orogen', *Nature*, **222**(5189), 124–129.

Dewey, J. F. (1971), 'A model for the Lower Palaeozoic evolution of the southern margin of the early Caledonides of Scotland and Ireland', *Scot. Jl. Geol.*, **7**, 219–240.

Gayer, R. A. (1973), 'Caledonian geology of Arctic Norway', *Mem. Amer. Assoc. Petrol. Geol.*, No. 19, 453–468.

Kennedy, M. J. and E. R. W. Neale (1972), 'Similarities in the early structural development of the northwestern margin of the Newfoundland Appalachians and Irish Caledonides', '24th Internat. Geol. Congr., Montreal', sec. 3, pp. 516–531.

Kvale, A. (1976), 'Major features of the European Caledonides and their development', in Ager, D. V. and M. Brooks (eds.), *Europe from Crust to Core*, Wiley, London, pp. 81–115.

Lambert, R. St. J. and W. S. McKerrow (1976), 'The Grampian orogeny', *Scot. Jl. Geol.*, **12**, 271–292.

Phillips, W. E. A., C. J. Stillman, and T. Murphy (1976), 'A Caledonian plate tectonic model', *J. Geol. Soc., Lond.*, **132**, 579–609.

Part Three

Meso-Europa

That part of Europe which was affected by a major orogeny at or near the end of the Palaeozoic, but has not since suffered major tectonism

Chapter Eight

Northern Variscides

There appears to be no really satisfactory way of dividing Meso-Europa, so after a great deal of juggling I decided to treat it as three roughly latitudinal belts which had many features in common, although there are inevitable complications. Each will include both the Variscan massifs themselves and the sedimentary basins in between. The first extends from south-west Ireland across northern Europe as far as Poland. It is characterized by evidence of a Caledonian orogeny preceding the Variscan, possibly along the same general lines, and by the later movements occurring mainly late in the Carboniferous. The massifs also tend to be covered by Cretaceous sediments.

The Bohemian Massif is included here, although it has many points in common with the Vosges and Black Forest of the central belt. It has been suggested that there is a fold belt (called the 'Sudetides') that extends along the western part of the Northern Variscides, as here defined, but then turns north and passes round the top of the Bohemian Massif. I find no strong arguments one way or the other and my classification remains one of convenience.

8(a) Munster Variscides

If one flies eastwards across the Atlantic, the first one usually sees of Europe are the long, low peninsulas of south-west Ireland projecting towards the New World. Munster is the old name for this corner of the Emerald Isle and includes the part of that island which is here placed in Meso-Europa. The peninsulas just mentioned are anticlines of Devonian 'Old Red Sandstone'. The synclines between are formed of softer Carboniferous sediments (Fig. 8.1). The fact that these rocks have been quite strongly folded compared with their peaceful state in the rest of Ireland indicates that we are here in Meso- rather than Palaeo-Europa. The Variscan orogeny crumpled Munster, and hardly anywhere in Europe is there a clearer contrast between the Atlantic line and what I will recklessly call the Variscan–Alpine–Mediterranean line. The breaking off of the fold belt is brutal and sudden; earlier geologists could not be blamed for wondering if the chain continued under the Atlantic waves. But we must remember that if we project the Caledonian front down from the Moine Thrust in this direction, it will come very close to this termination.

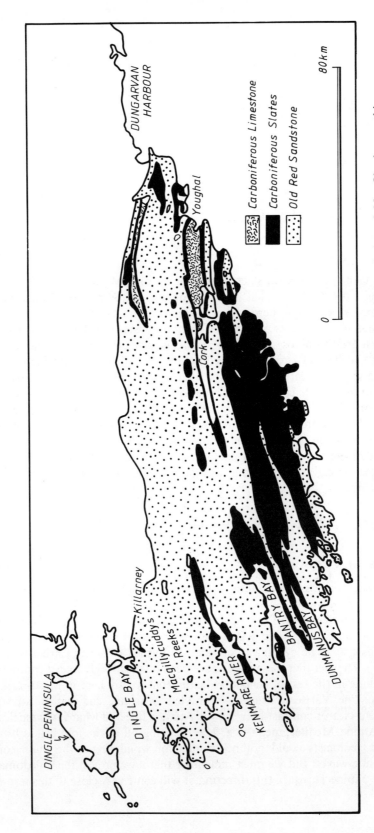

Fig. 8.1 Geological sketch-map of Munster (after Charlesworth, 1963, by kind permission of Mrs Charlesworth).

Legend:
- Carboniferous Limestone
- Carboniferous Slates
- Old Red Sandstone

DUNGARVAN HARBOUR

Youghal

Cork

DINGLE PENINSULA

DINGLE BAY

Killarney

Macgillycuddy's Reeks

KENMARE RIVER

BANTRY BAY

DUNMANUS BAY

80 km

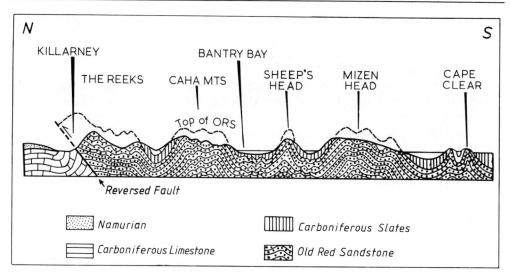

Fig. 8.2 *Cross-section of the western end of the Variscan fold belt in south-west Ireland (after the Irish Geological Survey).*

Perhaps it is a coincidence, but more likely it is a reflection of a very ancient and deep-seated line of weakness.

This is quite a small area and not the whole of the ancient kingdom of Munster. Its northern limit—the Variscan front—can be simply defined at the northern edge of the main outcrop of 'Old Red Sandstone' running from Dingle Bay in the west to Dungarvan Harbour (east-north-east of Cork) in the east. This line marks the last of the steep north-facing anticlines that make up the Irish Variscides. The line is a pronounced hollow, filled in the west with the beautiful lakes of Killarney (of the sad Irish songs) and passing along the River Blackwater (An Abhainn Mhor) through Mallow and Fermoy to Dungarvan. At Killarney the glacially eroded lakes, with their remarkable Mediterranean-type flora, are dominated by the highest mountains of Ireland, with the unlikely name of Macgillycuddy's Reeks. These splendid peaks are formed of 'Old Red Sandstone', but with a stiffening of volcanic rocks and elegant sculpturing by Pleistocene ice.

The dips of the incompetent Lower Carboniferous are reversed beneath the impressive scarp on the north side of the Reeks, marking a major northerly-directed thrust (Fig. 8.2). This thrust is supposed to be present all along the Variscan front, but is more often imagined than seen.

The surface rocks in Munster* are wholly of Devonian and early Carboniferous age. It is noteworthy, however, that just in front of the 'Variscan front' is the famous Dingle Peninsula, which has many features reminiscent of the northern Variscides. Thus at Clogher Head, at the west end of the peninsula, there is a notable development of lavas, tuffs, and agglomerates, in the Silurian, just as there are in south Pembrokeshire, the Mendip Hills, and the Tortworth inlier, along the line of the Variscan front to the east.

---

* Never to be confused with the Hanseatic city of Münster, in West Germany.

There is more volcanism (chiefly in the form of bentonites) in the Silurian than was formerly supposed in this part of Europe generally, but nevertheless the main episode of violent volcanism in my corner of the world ended with the Ordovician, and only along this line did it continue much later.

The 'Old Red Sandstone' has always been regarded as the continental facies of the Devonian, although it has long been realized that it probably ranges well down into the Silurian, all the more so since the Silurian–Devonian boundary has been redefined in Czechoslovakia. The answer to the dating of this boundary in the British Isles (where it used to be easy) will probably lie in isotope and fission-track dating of the volcanic horizons that are now being increasingly recognized within the succession. We can only guess at what happened in or before the Caledonian orogeny in this part of Ireland, but a gravity 'low' south of Killarney suggests a possible Caledonian granite just south of the Variscan front.

The story of the 'Old Red Sandstone' is comparable to that farther east. Thick conglomerates start the succession, and are well exposed on the south side of Dingle Bay. Farther north there is an unconformity between them and the rest of the 'Old Red Sandstone', leading to the suggestion that they are Silurian in age. But within Munster, as here defined, there appears to be a direct passage from the one into the other. The conglomerates are torrential deposits derived from an early stage in the wearing down of the Caledonian mountains. There is then a general fining-upwards succession through massive sandstones to slates, showing a range in colours through reds and purples and greens. Although modern sedimentological work is still lacking over many areas, there seems little doubt that they are dominantly fluviatile deposits, interdigitating with alluvial fans (often showing very rapid deposition) and passing up into shoreward mudflats awaiting the arrival of the early Carboniferous sea.

Since the general plunge of the structures is eastwards, the oldest beds are seen in the west, but the long headlands mainly show the eroded tops of complex anticlines and it is only along the thrust front that much is seen of the lower strata. Immense thicknesses have been estimated, but await confirmation. There is also a much greater volcanic element than had previously been supposed, with lava flows, tuffs, and agglomerates. Before the discovery of copper in Zambia and other parts of southern Africa, copper (and associated barytes) were mined in what was then a big way in south-west Ireland, notably at Mount Gabriel, south-south-west of Bantry on the southernmost of the main peninsulas.

The various clastic formations lumped together as the 'Old Red Sandstone' are succeeded by the formation known as the 'Carboniferous Slate' although, with a typically Irish paradox, a fair proportion of the Carboniferous Slate is of Devonian age. This is the late Devonian transgression, which is seen in an argillaceous facies in many places, notably on Whiddy Island, at the head of Bantry Bay and in the prominent promontory of the Old Head of Kinsale, south of Cork.

The Carboniferous of the Variscide belt in Ireland is generally referred to as 'Culm', by analogy with south-west England. Like the succession in Devon and Cornwall, it is not really geosynclinal in the traditional sense, but consists of a great thickness of slates, mudstones, and sandstones, with shallow-water benthos and plant material. It thickens westwards and may approach 2500 m under Bantry Bay. The evidence of cross-bedding suggests derivation of the deltaic material from the south-west.

Due to the easterly plunge of the structures, the Lower Carboniferous (mainly Tournaisian) is seen just as the narrow pinched-in centres of synclines at the western end of the belt. Only at the head of Bantry Bay is there a wide outcrop of the 'Carboniferous Slate'. Eastwards, however, the outcrops widen and the slates form the greater part of the country south and south-west of Cork.

Also in this direction the term 'Culm' becomes inappropriate because a massive carbonate development appears in the upper part of the Lower Carboniferous, unlike anything seen in south-west England (although like the Variscide part of South Wales). It is best seen to the east of Cork and was used for building the splendid old buildings of that city (and for Blarney Castle in the next syncline to the north*).

A massive Waulsortian-type reef is well seen in Little Island, just east of Cork. This is said to be more than 1000 m thick, but disappears within the width of a golf course. The reef forms part of a barrier that separated a deeper argillaceous facies to the south (which weathered into the splendid harbour) from the great limestone platform that covered the rest of Ireland and forms most of its surface geology. This fits in with a general picture of a progressive transgression from the south in early Carboniferous times.

Back around the lakes of Killarney, the limestone facies is seen immediately on the north side of the Variscan front, with fantastic caves and other solution features. So it is clear that besides being a structural feature, the north side of the Munster Variscides was also an important palaeogeographical feature in early Carboniferous times.

Namurian rocks are also involved in the structure and are preserved for example, in the Bantry syncline, but it is not possible to date the Variscan movements here very accurately. They were intense enough to impart a slaty cleavage in the more argillaceous rocks and to produce the reversed faults and overturned folds which contrast so markedly with the placidity of the late Palaeozoic rocks throughout the rest of the soft green island. It may be that this is only a local feature and doubt has been thrown on the usual picture of northerly-directed folds all along the Variscan front. In fact there is a clear divergence of folds in the vicinity of Mount Gabriel. South of that point the folds tend to be overturned to the south. Such changes in the orientation of the folding will be seen to be a feature of many of the Variscan massifs of Europe. It could be that we only see these masses today because of special local circumstances, such as tight 'knee-bends' which may not be characteristic of the belt as a whole. Mineralization of these late Palaeozoic rocks, which was once of economic importance, took place at the same time, but although volcanicity persisted in a minor way through the Carboniferous, there is no sign of the granites which are such a feature of the other Variscan massifs.

Apart from the glorious reshaping of the landscape in the Pleistocene, that might have been the end of the story but for a remarkable discovery a few years ago, just north of Killarney. This was a pocket of Upper Cretaceous Chalk far removed from any that had previously been recorded. Since the exposure is right beside a main road, it is surprising that it was not noted by the officers of the Geological Survey when they mapped the area. One theory is that they were so terrified of the autocratic director of that time that they did not have the courage to record anything so unlikely. We now know that similar Chalk underlies a great part of the sea area to the south of Ireland. It seems inescapable

---

* Kissing a sample of this formation, set in the wall of the castle, allegedly gives the Irish the loquacity and persuasiveness for which they are famous.

that the Chalk formerly covered virtually the whole of Ireland, but all that is left of this great transgression in the south-west is a few pockets of brecciated material preserved in fissures.

8(b) Cornubia

The gently wild Palaeozoic country of south-west England forms the greater part of the counties of Devon and Cornwall. To the English it is a country of misty moors and craggy cliffs, for ever associated with the Hound of the Baskervilles and the wreckers who lured ships to their doom so as to loot their cargoes. Some would say that the farthest part of the peninsula is not England at all, but out in the Celtic twilight where the Anglo-Saxon never feels fully at home. It is closer in fact, both geologically and culturally, to Armorica across the Channel, so that here again human affairs relate directly to geological history.

I must also include here the Bristol Channel to the north and a narrow strip of South Wales that was also affected by the Variscan movements. This takes us up to the so-called Variscan Front which is much more difficult to define here than it was in southern Ireland. It may be that there is not a direct connection between them.

South-west England

The oldest rocks of Cornubia are seen in the Lizard peninsula (Fig. 8.3), the southern-most point in mainland Britain, and in some other southerly-projecting headlands along this coast. The Lizard consists largely of a complex of metamorphic rocks, serpentinites, and basic igneous rocks, which make it quite different from the Palaeozoic sediments and Variscan granites which form the rest of the region. This may be a fragment of a Caledonian orogeny since the complex includes Lower Palaeozoic rocks and the metamorphism has been dated as Devonian, that is, much earlier than that in the rest of Cornubia. Some rocks involved possibly range back into the Precambrian. The serpentinites, which take a variety of forms, a little squirt of pillow lavas, and what has been called a sheeted dike complex, naturally make people think of ocean floors and a subduction zone has often been postulated here. The relationship to the rest of south-west England is far from clear. The Lizard complex is limited to the north by a belt of shattered rocks that include fossiliferous Lower Palaeozoic sediments, and farther along the coast are some very Gallic-looking Ordovician quartzites. The most popular interpretation is to have a major thrust along this coast with the evidently exotic rocks being thrust up from the south. The full explanation presumably lies below the young sediments of the English Channel, but if the alleged thrust is only a Devonian sedimentary breccia, we may here be looking at the foundations of Cornubia.

The rest of that Variscan massif consists mainly of Devonian and Carboniferous rocks. The Devonian takes its name from the lovely county of Devon, but beautiful though it may be it is difficult to imagine a worse place to choose as a type area. Without wishing to appear treasonable, it really would have been much better if the system had been called Newyorkian or Rhinelandian or Antiatlasian or even Pasdecalaisian. The rocks

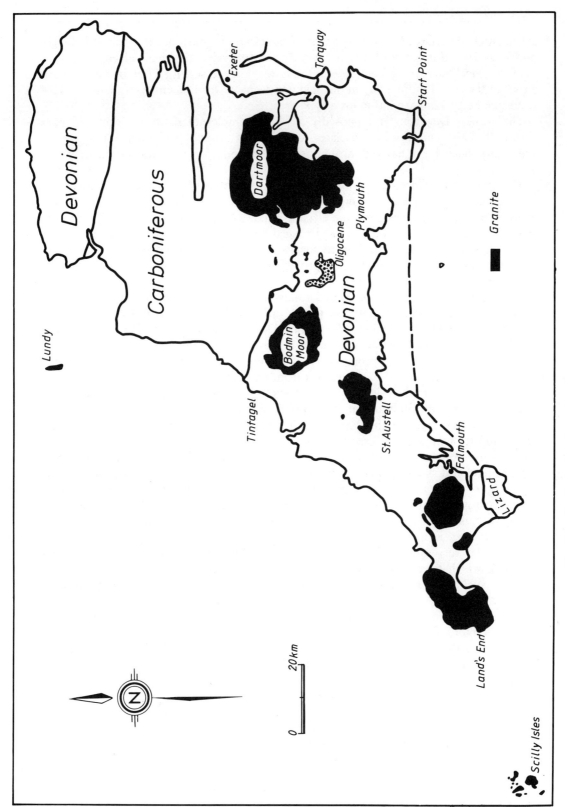

Fig. 8.3 Geological sketch-map of south-west England.

are intensely deformed, the successions far from clear, and most of the fossils appallingly preserved. Indeed it is recorded that when Robert Etheridge, the chief palaeontologist of the Geological Survey, was sent here in the last century to sort it all out, he sat down on a rock at the end of his first day in the field and wept 'at the immensity of his task'. This is not the best recommendation for a type area.

The earliest Devonian is supposedly a whole complex of sediments down in west Cornwall. These sandstones and slates, outcropping around the granite boss west of Falmouth, have been hawked around several periods for the lack of good faunal evidence.

The main Devonian outcrops form the north and south limbs of the main east–west synclinorium of this peninsula, but each limb is complexly folded within itself. In the south, the outcrop extends from the elegant holiday coast of Torquay and Paignton in south Devon to the more romantic and rugged coast of King Arthur's Tintagel, in north Cornwall, where the thrusting is particularly well displayed. Inland exposures are comparatively poor, but the sheer cliffs provide magnificent sections in intensely folded sediments.

The succession starts with slates and sandstones which seem to show a passage from fresh-water to marine conditions, so that 'Old Red Sandstone' type fish are in close proximity to corals and brachiopods. By mid Devonian times carbonate-depositing conditions had been established and we have the limestones that form the complex harbour of Plymouth, including the promontory of Plymouth Hoe, where Drake played bowls before leaving to defeat the invading fleet from another Variscan massif (and from below which the Pilgrim Fathers left for better Devonian sections in another continent). The limestones just range up into that climactic stage of reef formation, the Frasnian.

Mini-reefs are seen on the coast near Torquay and these limestones, packed with corals and stromatoporoids, used to be worked in several places as an ornamental stone (particularly popular, for some reason, in bakers' shops and urinals). The limestones pass up into reddened slates with goniatites. A feature of the outcrop that crosses from south Devon into Cornwall is the presence of tuffs and pillow lavas, notably at Pentire Head near Padstow, together with intrusions (including picrites), although whether there are enough to justify 'megathoughts' is extremely doubtful. The whole succession, including the pillow lavas, is probably a shallow-water one, with nothing remotely oceanic about it. Only at the very top does it become a little deeper, but even there the argillaceous deposits, which have become workable slates, are still characterized by shallow-water benthos such as the so-called 'Delabole Butterfly', which is a tectonically flattened spirifer.

In north Devon, on the opposite side of the synclinorium, the Devonian succession shows an interdigitation of shallow marine and continental 'Old Red Sandstone' type of conditions, indicative of the transition to the continental conditions of central and northern Britain. Three times do sandstones come into the succession and again limestones appear at the top of the Middle and the bottom of the Upper Devonian, around the seaside resort of Ilfracombe. Devonian clastics also form most of the upland areas of Exmoor and the Quantock Hills in neighbouring Somerset. Again the story is confused by folding and northerly thrusting. There are major repetitions and these with the facies changes make the stratigraphy very difficult.

In north Devon, as in the south, the facies gets slightly deeper at the top and there is a direct passage through into the Carboniferous sediments which occupy the greater part of the region. As one looks north from the hog-back cliffs of north Devon and Somerset, one looks into a region of Dinantian limestones and Westphalian 'Coal Measures', but here we are in a very different facies. Limestones are largely absent, as are the valuable coals, the latter to be replaced here by poor, thin sooty coals known as 'Culm' which gives its name to the whole facies. It would be convenient in this orogenic belt if one could say that everything had passed into a deep trough, but this is just not true.

The 'Culm' succession is dominantly shales and thin sandstones, suggesting no great depth of water and in many places clearly continental in origin. There is a certain amount of volcanicity, with pillow lavas (e.g., near Launceston in Cornwall). The whole succession is probably thick, but this is difficult to estimate because of the intense contortions such as the much-photographed concertina folds in the cliffs near Bude. Only at the Lower–Upper Carboniferous boundary is there a development of siliceous sediments that might mean deep water, but much of the Upper Carboniferous is missing and elevation was evidently well under way before the end of the period. By Namurian times, coarse sediment was coming into the area from the south, where the new Variscan mountains were rising.

The Variscan movements began earlier here than elsewhere in the British Isles, indeed there is evidence of a wave of movements, of diminishing intensity, moving north with time across Cornubia. The dominant trend is east–west and, unlike other Variscan massifs, there does not seem to be a distinct virgation within the Cornubian folds, although the structure as a whole seems to be a huge fan.

The outstanding feature of south-west England geologically is the Variscan granites; indeed the peninsula would not be here were it not for them, since they form its stegosaurian-type backbone. What is seen at the surface is a series of five main granite uplands, ranging from Dartmoor in the north-east to Land's End and then on into the sea as the Scilly Isles and another beyond, discovered recently. Each shows large felspar phenocrysts (much seen in British kerb-stones), tor topography, and metamorphic aureoles in the enclosing sediments. They also all have radiometric ages of about 280 million years. It is evident that they are nothing more than protuberances of a single great batholith that disappears under the Mesozoic cover to the east and under the waters of the Western Approaches to the west. This is further confirmed by the belt of mineralization that extends through Cornubia, taking in all of the granites *en route*. Along this belt a variety of metals have been worked in the past, including the tin that allegedly brought the Phoenicians to Cornwall and us into history. This is still mined, although abandoned mine buildings are one of the most characteristic features of Cornish scenery. Much of the tin was obtained in the past from the short hurrying Cornish streams. The weathering products of the granites are important. In particular the granite mass of St. Austell, west of Plymouth, is always associated with the china clay produced by the kaolinization of felspars in the granite as a late pneumatolytic process. Another scenic feature of this part of Cornwall is the high white cone of the spoil heap where the kaolin is still worked on a big scale. It used to be exported all round the world in sailing ships from the little nearby port of Fowey and is still one of Britain's largest exports (although nowadays as a filler for paper, not for china).

We are accustomed in most of Britain to the red soils of the Devonian outcrops, but paradoxically the red soils of Devon itself are not due to the Devonian 'Old Red Sandstone' but to what many British geologists still call the 'New Red Sandstone' or 'Permo-Trias'. Along the south Devon coast from Torquay to Seaton and on the north Somerset coast on either side of Minehead, there are flaming red cliffs built of the detritus of the new Variscan mountains. The Permian part of them is best seen on the coast near Teignmouth and inland past Exeter and Taunton, with a prominent tongue of outcrop running west along the centre of the synclinorium. These rocks are clearly post-orogenic. On the coast one can see raw, felspathic breccia full of fragments of hypabyssal rocks not otherwise preserved. Dune sands testify to a prevailing wind direction very different from what it is at the present (and used to demonstrate a rotation of the British Isles since Permian times that was only later confirmed by palaeomagnetic evidence). Around Exeter there is a series of potassic lava flows which are also dated as Permian. The only fossil evidence is in the form of a few land vertebrates and it is almost a convention that the base of the Trias is taken at the thick conglomerates that appear in the cliffs at Budleigh Salterton, south-east of Exeter. This fits, however, with the onset of graben formation and reactivated erosion throughout north-west Europe. Many of the pebbles are identical with the *Grès Armoricains* and the *Grès de May* in the Ordovician of Brittany.

The conglomerates pass up into the usual cross-bedded red sandstones, seen near Sidmouth, and these into the red and green mudstones that are always (improperly) called the 'Keuper Marl'. Although there are hints of the mid Triassic transgressions of the continent, the first marine deposits of the Mesozoic are in the Rhaetian bone-beds, black shales, and white limestones, which appear on the very edge of our area, near Lyme Regis and on the north Somerset coast near Watchet. This was the beginning of a marine cycle that was to last right through the Jurassic, but is the concern of the next section. It has been estimated from the geotechnical properties of one of the Permo-Triassic formations that it had an overburden of up to 1300 m of sediment. But nearly all of this must have been Permo-Trias or lowermost Jurassic.

The later record of Cornubia is scanty. There are high-level sands and gravels which probably record a Cretaceous shoreline when this massif was already an island. There are white kaolin clays and black lignites around Bovey Tracey in south Devon which are late Oligocene continental deposits derived from the weathering of the nearby Dartmoor Granite. There are similar deposits to the north-west which show that the old fault lines were still active at that time, and this may also be reflected in the erosion surfaces of south-west England. It has been shown that a series of dextral tear faults probably brought south-west England to the form it is today from a very odd-looking country.

The most obvious erosion surface is at about 130 m. It carries some patches of gravel and marine deposits which date it as Pliocene. It forms the flat interior of most of Cornwall, above the sheer cliffs, and is probably equivalent to a similar plateau in South Wales. There is a good record of later raised beaches and a whole chronology for the Pleistocene has been worked out on their basis. The ice did not reach this side of the Bristol Channel, although a few exotic boulders were dropped by wandering icebergs. Finally man came to live in some of the caves in the Devonian limestones. Localities such as that of Kent's Cavern, near Torquay, saw some of the earliest investigations into prehistory and some of the bitterest arguments about the antiquity of man.

Bristol Channel area

The Bristol Channel is the stretch of pleasant (although often turbulent) water which flows past my windows and separates me from my native England. It is a great westward-facing estuary into which are funnelled the storms of the North Atlantic. Geologically it is more than an estuary; it is not just the flooded northern margin of Variscan Cornubia but is a trough filled with Mesozoic sediments resting on an older trough that dates back at least to Devonian times.

Here, as in so many other places around the coasts of north-west Europe, the basic shape was blocked out long ago and the geology under the waves is quite different from that forming the dry land on either side. Come to see the geological delights of the Gower Peninsula, west of Swansea, and we will proudly show you a miserable patch of supposedly Triassic conglomerate near Port Eynon as the sole outcrop of Mesozoic rocks in our corner of Wales. But now we know that, little more than a lithoclast's throw from the cliff, there is a great thickness of Trias and nearly all the Jurassic as well (Fig. 8.4).

Farther west, in south Pembrokeshire the only evidence of the Mesozoic is some fault breccias stained Triassically red, although offshore oil-men have drilled through the whole triumvirate of Mesozoic systems. Eastwards, the land and sea merge as the Triassic and lowermost Jurassic rocks climb ashore in the Vale of Glamorgan between Swansea and Cardiff on the north side of the Channel and in the Somerset levels to the south.

The division between Palaeo- and Meso-Europa depends on the state of the late Palaeozoic rocks. Northwards the Devonian and the Carboniferous are gently folded in the broad anticlines and synclines of the South Wales coal-field. In south Pembrokeshire and the Gower Peninsula these rocks are much more deformed. The coals of the Pembrokeshire coal-field, which is the western extension of the main coal-field, have long since been abandoned because of their intense folding, typified by a much photographed angular anticline on the beach near Saundersfoot. Recent work suggests that the dividing line is much farther north than was generally supposed. But it is nice to think that this major European frontier passes under the campus of the University College of Swansea.

It is possible that the Variscan Front is a much older line. This is difficult to discuss because of our ignorance about pre-Devonian rocks to the south, but the point has already been made that volcanic activity only really persisted into the Silurian along this line. Silurian lavas have long been known in south Pembrokeshire, but only recently has the notable volcanicity of Skomer Island been attributed to that period. At the other end of the area, near Bristol, Silurian volcanics occur in the Mendip Hills and in the Tortworth inlier to their north.

Although we think of the Caledonian mountains as away to the north, something was happening here towards the end of early Palaeozoic times. Caledonoid lines can be traced down through the South Wales coal-field, and the sedimentary evidence in late Silurian strata on the north side of the coal-field indicates derivation from the south. We know nothing about Lower Palaeozoic rocks in south-west England until we get to the south coast, so it may be that there were Caledonian mountains here before the Variscides.

The late Palaeozoic rocks change as they approach the Bristol Channel. The plants of the 'Old Red Sandstone' continent began to feel sea breezes among their slender dicho-

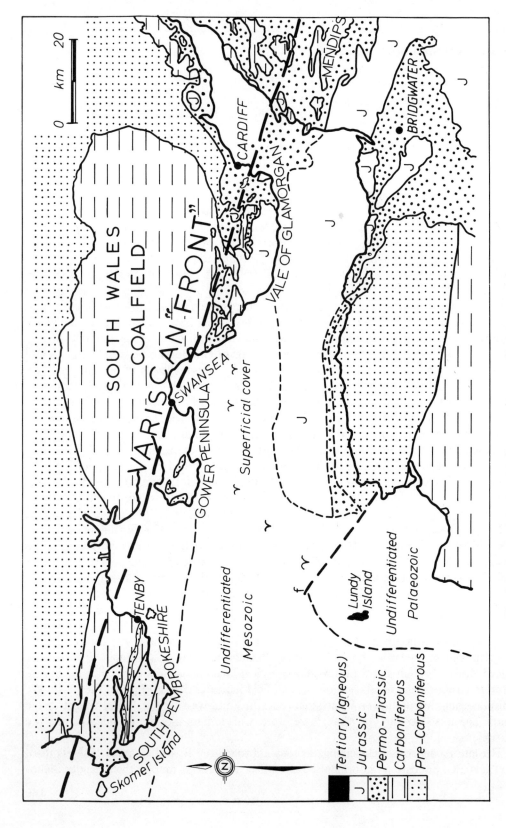

Fig. 8.4 Geological sketch-map of the Bristol Channel and adjacent areas.

tomous branches; marine deposits of late Devonian age occur in south Pembrokeshire and even extended briefly as far as the north side of the coal-field. The Namurian, which is deltaic to the north, has changed to marine shales by the south coast of Wales, and their relative softness produces its broad bays. The Westphalian reaches its thickest development around Swansea and the marine bands it contains reach their highest degree of 'marineness' in southern Pembrokeshire.

When one reaches the equivalent rocks on the south side of the Channel, nearly everything has changed. Some 'Old Red Sandstone' facies remain, but most has passed into the marine Devonian of its home county. The 'Carboniferous Limestone' persists as far as the tiny, faulted inlier of Cannington Park near Bridgewater. It can be traced seismically under the Channel, but the beautiful white cliffs of Gower contrast with the grimmer cliffs of North Devon, and limestone was formerly transported from South Wales to relatively limeless Cornubia. The Carboniferous in general changes, almost out of recognition, from what we see in South Wales to the 'Culm' facies of south-west England, deposited in the frontal trough of the new Variscide fold belt.

What lies beneath the Bristol Channel is still one of the mysteries of this region. One problem is to predict where the Westphalian 'Coal Measures' and the thick marine Namurian shales change into the 'Culm'. Northwards lay the Welsh uplands, with a coastline of fluviatile and swamp deposits. Southwards, usually, lay the open sea. At times, particularly in the Devonian, we would have seen the tide disappear over the southern horizon.

Evidently the Variscan movements started back in Carboniferous times and there are notable breaks in the shallow-water sequences of the Dinantian limestones, with their rapid lateral facies changes, their small local reefs, and the ecological zonation of their abundant bethos. But everything had changed by the time we pick up the story again in the Triassic, although the basic structure remained the same. The main trough in late Palaeozoic times was on the south side of the Channel, as has been shown by geophysical surveys. This was probably exaggerated by Variscan thrusting from the south. The asymmetric Mesozoic trough was centred on the same line.

Triassic rocks are only well seen at the eastern end of the South Wales coast where torrential and scree deposits pass southwards into more typical fine-grained red beds. The breccias can be seen literally climbing a staircase of bedded Carboniferous Limestone and dropping down into solution pipes. Similar breccias form an apron along the south side of the Mendips to the east. In fact all the early Mesozoic formations change into marginal facies around islands or ridges of 'Carboniferous Limestone' which were populated by early mammal-like reptiles that have been found in the solution pipes of a karstic surface. Away from the uplands, evaporites were developed, notably the thick salts in a boring at Puriton on the Somerset levels.

Conglomerates of the earliest Lias surround the islands of the Vale of Glamorgan as they do the similar islands of the Mendips. These pass outwards into bedded sandy limestones and then into the alternations of limestones and shales that are the usual offshore facies of the lowermost Jurassic over a great part of western Europe. This is a classic area of lateral facies change and of early Jurassic marine faunas, as is the coast of north Somerset on the other side of the Channel, where one can literally map the ammonite zones and subzones on the beach.

The same strata continue the line of the Channel eastwards into the Somerset Levels south of the Mendips, where the little town of Street formerly had a museum full of ichthyosaurs. Unfortunately later strata are not preserved in Wales, while in Somerset a string of hill outliers saves for us some cappings of Middle and Upper Liassic limestones. The most famous of these—Glastonbury Tor—is one of the holy places of mythological England, where St. Joseph of Arimathaea (whose hawthorn tree staff flowers here at Christmas) is said to have brought the Holy Grail and where King Arthur and his queen are said to be buried. The little chapel on the Toarcian top of this sharp hill was destroyed by an earthquake in the Middle Ages, which makes one wonder in this seismically stable land whether there may not yet be life along the old line.

That, until recently, was the end of the pre-Pleistocene story. We now know, from bottom sampling, that practically the whole of the Jurassic is preserved in the Channel. Unfortunately (thinking of hydrocarbon reservoirs) it is all in the form of mudstones plus a few thin silts, so this depositional trough was far from a shoreline. Westwards, out in what is now called the Celtic Sea, the Jurassic is overlain unconformably by Cretaceous.

The one thing that shows, out in the Channel, is the lonely granitic island of Lundy, with its puffins, private stamps, and buried giants. Until the coming of radiometric dating, this was assumed to be a somewhat errant member of the long line of Variscan granites of Cornubia. Then we heard to our surprise that it was only 50–55 million years old, although far removed from its Tertiary contemporaries in the west of Scotland and northern Ireland. More recently the Lundy granite has proved to be no more than a marginal development of a large area of basic rocks, hidden under the sea. This is much more in keeping with what one expects of a Tertiary igneous emplacement. It also indicates that something was still happening along this line of weakness very late in geological times.

We also know this from the faulting. On both sides of the Channel our normally peaceful Triassic and Liassic rocks are repeatedly faulted and in places crumpled. The major north-west shear faults which shuffled Cornubia into the form it has today, can now be traced across the Channel and are certainly of mid-Tertiary age. One of them is connected with the Lundy igneous mass. Others, more or less east–west, determined the form of the Bristol Channel. Prominent erosion surfaces, well seen in Pembrokeshire and Gower, testify to high sea-levels in late Tertiary times.

Most of us think that the Bristol Channel halted the Pleistocene ice-sheets, although erratic blocks are found on the North Devon coast, carried by floating ice. One geologist at least, however, thinks that a tongue of ice moved on east to carry blocks of igneous rocks from the Preseli Hills of Pembrokeshire to Stonehenge on the Chalk uplands of Salisbury Plain. Most of us prefer the older idea of toiling humans, who may have been helped by a late marine invasion, up the old line of the Somerset Levels, which lasted until Roman times. This is a wet, marshy land, with an excellent post-glacial pollen record, and stayed that way until modern times.

8(c) Wessex, the Weald, and the Boulonnais

The most difficult thing to teach is that which one knows best. One's prejudices make it almost impossible to present a balanced assessment and one's reservations make it difficult to produce any generalizations that are not wrapped around with 'ifs' and 'buts'. The same is true in writing an account of one of the best-known parts of the earth's surface and one that is particularly well known and well loved by the writer.

'Wessex' was the old West Saxon Kingdom that was revived by Thomas Hardy. It is used here to cover the Hampshire Basin of Tertiary sediments in the centre of southern England and its rim of Mesozoic rocks, especially to the west in Hardy's own county of Dorset. The 'Weald' is the great anticline of Cretaceous rocks south of London, although in a stricter sense it applies only to the centre of that structure. The anticline closes westwards in the Chalk upland of Salisbury Plain. The 'Boulonnais' shows how geology laughs at nationalism, for it is the eastern closure of the same structure, across the Straits of Dover in northern France.

Throughout southern and south-east England no Palaeozoic strata reach the surface, but we know that we are south of the ridge of older rocks that runs roughly along the line of what is regarded here as the junction of Palaeo- and Meso-Europa. The Palaeozoic rocks have mainly only been reached by the boreholes and mines of the Kent coal-field, in the extreme east, where they are set relatively high up on the London ridge. Although the Palaeozoic is only about 300 m down below central London, the nearest place to see it at the surface is far away, in fact in France. Thus the Boulonnais can be said to be the best place to study underground south-east England, where we can peep beneath the surface, as it were, and study the earlier Mesozoic and Palaeozoic sediments that are hidden under all that Cretaceous of the Weald and by both Mesozoic and Tertiary sediments in Wessex.

For that reason I will start with the Boulonnais and then move westwards. It is also convenient to deal with the three areas separately since (apart from the glorious lines of Chalk hills), they have little in common at the surface.

Boulonnais

This is the truncated dome on the north French coast roughly between Calais and Boulogne. We may separate the *Haut Boulonnais*, which is a great horseshoe of Chalk hills, continuous with the Chalk plateau of northern France, and the *Bas Boulonnais*, which is the low-lying country of Palaeozoic, Jurassic, and early Cretaceous sediments within the horseshoe (Fig. 8.5).

The oldest rocks seen (very poorly) at the surface are Silurian shales which, with a few boreholes in east Kent, are all the real evidence there is for an early Palaeozoic geosyncline which is postulated in palaeogeographical maps for this part of the world. Equally poorly exposed Devonian sediments of 'Old Red Sandstone' facies follow with drifted plant remains. That is a lot farther south than this facies is seen in England. Upwards there is a magnificent succession of mid to late Devonian carbonates of a shallow-water aspect packed with a great diversity of fossils. In particular the *Calcaire de Ferques* (Frasnian) is the source of many of the most familiar brachiopod and coral names in Devonian palaeontology. They are magnificently preserved compared with the deformed faunas of Cornubia at the opposite end of Wessex. The Famennian which follows is, as usual, strongly regressive with beach sands and a totally different fauna.

Carbonates returned in the early Carboniferous with spectacular algal developments in

173

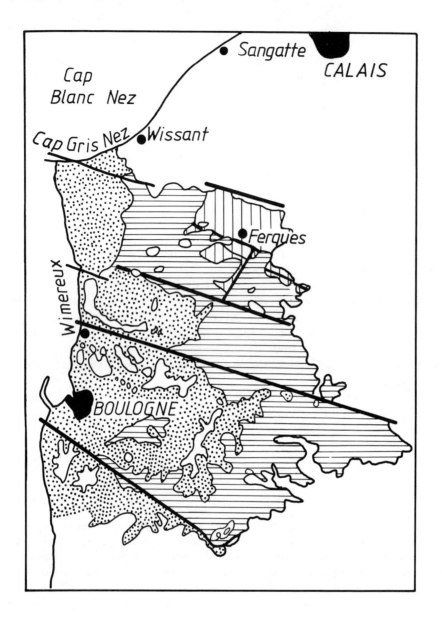

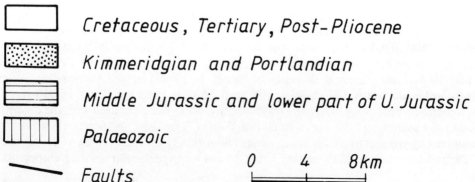

Cretaceous, Tertiary, Post-Pliocene

Kimmeridgian and Portlandian

Middle Jurassic and lower part of U. Jurassic

Palaeozoic

Faults

0   4   8km

Fig. 8.5 *Geological sketch-map of the Boulonnais (from Ager and Wallace, 1966, by kind permission of the Council of the Geologists' Association).*

place of the corals and stromatoporoids seen below, well displayed in wire-cut quarries and in the monument to *La Grande Armée* outside Boulogne (on which Napoleon stands with his back firmly turned on Britain). The Upper Carboniferous is of the usual 'Coal Measure' facies and it was here that coal was first mined in France, although there is very little to be seen of it now. Superficially the Palaeozoic rocks seem to be little disturbed, but in places—notably the railway cutting near the delightfully named *Vallée Heureuse*—it can be seen to be strongly thrust towards the north, and locally the limestone is pushed right over the coals.

All these Palaeozoic wonders are contained within the tiny Ferques inlier. They disappear northwards under the Upper Cretaceous and southwards under the Middle Jurassic. The latter rests on a karst surface of Lower Carboniferous limestone, with clay fillings in the solution pipes that have been dated as Rhaetian. There is no other evidence in the Boulonnais of Mesozoic rocks older than the mid Jurassic. One is reminded constantly of the stratigraphy and structure in the Mendip Hills south of Bristol, at the other end of this region.

In the Boulonnais we are probably fairly high up on the Brabant Massif, as is suggested both by the state of the Palaeozoic rocks and the presence of coarse conglomerates in the Jurassic, which look very much out of place to an Anglo-juraphile. The alleged Triassic in borings under the Boulonnais is probably nothing of the sort and, apart from the fillings in the karst surfaces, the Mesozoic starts with richly fossiliferous Bathonian oolites. Callovian and Oxfordian sediments are hardly to be seen at the surface nowadays, although the latter contains coral reefs, as usual, in its upper part.

The story resumes in the magnificent cliff sections of Kimmeridgian and later Jurassic rocks, which extend from south of Boulogne nearly to Wissant. The rocks consist of cyclic shallow-water sands and clays with splendid trace-fossils, sand diapirs, conglomerates, and other evidence of repeated emergence. Limestones are very minor and there is no sign of the thick carbonates of the 'Portlandian' and only a hint of the fresh-water limestones of the 'Purbeckian' such as are seen in southern England. The whole succession is repeated several times thanks to faults and monoclines, steep to the north, such as the one clearly displayed to the left of the harbour entrance as one sails into Boulogne. A similar, although more complex, structure forms war-battered Cap Gris Nez and is seen at low tide on the beach below, where Channel-swimmers emerge.

Wealden sands rest unconformably on the Jurassic in places but are said to have been folded with the latter in what would now be called late Kimmerian movements, before the deposition of the later Cretaceous sediments. These latter are moderately well displayed around the rim of the Bas Boulonnais, notably along the beach from Wissant to Cap Blanc Nez. They consist, as in the Weald, of glauconitic sands followed by dark clays packed with pyritized ammonites and grade up into white Chalk.

Where the shell-holed Chalk ridge runs inland from Blanc Nez, dark mounds with deeper shell holes ('Mottes Noirs') indicate the presence of late Tertiary outliers of soft late Pliocene sands, comparable to the Lenham Beds of south-east England. From the Chalk ridge one looks down on the muddy levels of the *Plaine Maritime* around Calais, and just down the slope near Sangatte (where the Channel Tunnel was due to come ashore) a Pleistocene cliff-line cuts obliquely into the modern cliff and marks the limit of a very late transgression. This is similar to the one seen across the Channel at Black Rock, Brighton.

Weald

At the surface this is wholly composed of Cretaceous rocks (Fig. 8.6) apart from some tiny inliers of late Jurassic 'Purbeckian' north of Hastings. The largest inlier is at Battle, named after the combat in 1066 when the Normans accomplished the last successful invasion of Britain and contributed their blood and culture to an already multi-racial nation.

The Palaeozoic floor drops steeply southwards from the London ridge and is only well known in the gently folded concealed coal-field of east Kent, between Canterbury and Dover, but this is clearly north of the line of intense Variscan folding and should strictly be regarded as part of Palaeo-Europa. The Mesozoic above becomes progressively thicker southwards. It used to be said that the Weald consisted of an anticline sitting on a syncline. This is not true, since there is nothing to suggest the Palaeozoic floor rising again to the south, but certainly it is a typical case of a marginal trough (*Randtröge*) bordering an old massif (the London ridge) which has subsequently suffered tectonic inversion.

The Wealden pericline is a virtually continuous Tertiary structure but the Palaeozoic rocks are curiously off-set across that narrow stretch of water that has protected us from so many misfortunes (from Napoleon Buonaparte to driving on the right). The marine to continental transition in the Devonian, the 'Coal Measures', and the Variscan thrusting are farther south on the French side. One is tempted to postulate a tear fault through the Straits of Dover that might worry the builders of the long-delayed Channel Tunnel. But the most obvious difference is that pre-Cretaceous rocks are exposed on the French side, but hardly at all on the English side. This is partly due to the much greater thickness of the earliest Cretaceous (pre-Aptian) rocks in the Weald. This is the classic 'Wealden' in its type area, but it so happens that the 'Purbeckian', although barely exposed, is much thicker too. Both these units, and those below, thin markedly northwards against the London ridge, although some members of the Mesozoic succession go farther than others; the first formation to go right over the London ridge is the Albian Gault Clay. This rests directly on the Devonian under central London. From then on the London ridge stopped being a ridge and became the London Basin.

Apart from the Kent coal-field and a few borings, little is known of the Palaeozoic floor beneath the Weald except what can be deduced from geophysics. In Kent, the 'Coal Measures' are thickly developed and for many years four mines and their attendant miners seemed curiously out of place in this 'Garden of England'. Now the industry is dying as it did long ago in the Boulonnais.

The 'Coal Measures' in their usual form of non-marine deposits with occasional thin marine bands in the lower part, rest directly on the Dinantian 'Carboniferous Limestone' without the intervention of a Namurian 'Millstone Grit'. In many ways the succession is comparable with that where the strata come to the surface westwards around Bristol. The 'Carboniferous Limestone' is now known almost as far south as Brighton, and the 'Coal Measures' in a boring at Middleton-on-Sea near Bognor Regis.

Below the Carboniferous, Devonian and Silurian rocks were encountered in several of the east Kent boreholes. All the main Silurian divisions seem to be present, chiefly in a shaly graptolitic facies. The Devonian is in the form of 'Old Red Sandstone' with plant remains. Pebbles of 'Old Red Sandstone' have also been identified in conglomerates of

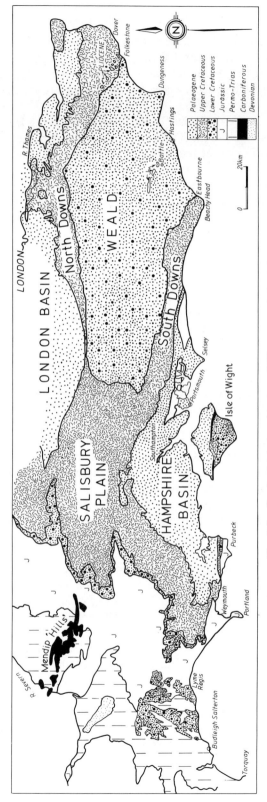

Fig. 8.6 Geological sketch-map of Wessex and the Weald.

later date suggesting that outcrops were not too far away. Marine Devonian is also now known under London and the Central Weald. It has been suggested, largely on the basis of geophysical evidence, that there are major thrusts in the Palaeozoic rocks under the Weald, comparable with those seen where the same rocks reach the surface to the east and west.

The deepest borings in the main part of the Weald and in the Hampshire Basin to the west, do not usually get below the Trias in its normal Germanic form. The Jurassic is also very much as it is known at the surface to the west, with the interesting feature of coral reefs fringing the London ridge.

The 'Purbeckian' non-marine facies at the top of the Jurassic is exceptionally thick. Although in Dorset there are indications of hypersalinity, in the centre of the Weald gypsum is thickly enough developed to be worth mining for plasterboard and other purposes.

But it is the Cretaceous that one comes to the Weald to study, especially the Wealden facies which supposedly ranges from Berriasian to Barremian or even Aptian in age. Its succession of thick sandstone and clay formations, for the most part lacking fossils, have nevertheless attracted palaeontologists from the beginning of geology. Fresh-water ostracods are often abundant in the clays and there are plant levels with horse-tails and other swampy plants often in position of growth. There are also thin limestones made up entirely of fresh-water bivalves or snails (the latter used for some of the most distinguished tombs in Westminster Abbey). But after the marine delights of most of the rest of the British Jurassic and Cretaceous, many of my kind find it boring. Nevertheless one of the most exciting discoveries in palaeontology was made by Gideon Mantell (or rather his wife) in finding the first dinosaur near Cuckfield in Sussex. Mantell, who was an embittered Brighton doctor, went on to discover many more dinosaur fragments and to quarrel about them with Richard Owen (who refused to accept them as giant reptiles). Another misunderstood man, Charles Dawson, who was to be blamed (probably unjustly) for the Piltdown Man hoax, also genuinely discovered the first Cretaceous mammals in the Wealden near his home in Hastings.

Most of the palaeontological evidence of the Wealden points to a non-marine origin, but sedimentologists have been wavering for years as to its precise environmental situation. It has been a lake (with no apparent southern margin), a delta, and currently just a 'morass'.

One feature of the Wealden that should not be forgotten is the presence of thin ironstones, hardly worthy of the name today, but which were the main source of iron for 'the horse-shoes red at Flodden Field, the arrows of Poitiers' and other less bloodthirsty uses way back before the industrial revolution. The great oak forests of the Weald were mainly cut down to smelt this iron.

At the very top of the Wealden are the first hints of marineness creeping back into the story, and the Aptian 'Lower Greensand' swept across the Wealden deposits from the south. It is so called because of its glauconite and is clearly marine, although fossils are generally scarce. The Gault Clay, into which it passes is, on the other hand, packed with a diversity of marine fossils, especially pyritized ammonites. At the east end of its outcrop, in the famous sections at Folkestone, the Gault passes almost directly into the Chalk of the 'white cliffs of Dover'. But at the western end, down in Wessex, the Gault is only a few metres thick and has been mainly replaced laterally by the 'Upper Greensand'. Both are Albian in age and this is a clear demonstration of lateral facies change towards shallower water conditions around Cornubia.

The Chalk used to be divided into 'Grey Chalk' below, the 'White Chalk with few flints' in the middle, and the 'White Chalk with many flints' at the top. This still serves as a crude rule and indicates the progressive deepening of the Chalk sea, with decreasing land-derived material, until at the top it is an almost perfectly pure coccolith limestone. The Chalk forms a distinctive landscape unlike any other. Nearly everywhere in the Weald one can see 'along the sky the line of the Downs, so noble and so bare . . .'.

The North and South Downs which encircle the Weald are uplands, in spite of their name, and are characteristically all smooth curves with few trees apart from occasional cathedral-like clumps of beeches where the weathering products of the chalk ('clay with flints') are thicker than usual. There are 'no waters to delight our broad and brookless vales'; it all sinks into the Chalk to form much of the water supply of south-east England. The North Downs finish at the white cliffs of Dover and the 'Isle' of Thanet (which was still an island in Roman times), while the South Downs plunge into the sea at Beachy Head, a favourite spot for suicides near Eastbourne.

There are no later deposits in the Weald other than sub-Recent deposits (such as make the broad headland of Romney Marsh) and some fascinating marine deposits high up on the North Downs near Folkestone, the Lenham Beds, which have been dated as late Pliocene and correlate with similar sands on the continent. These indicate a marine incursion over much of this part of Europe, leaving deposits up to nearly 200 m above present sea-level, and now all but disappeared. It is an object lesson in how easily all evidence for a major geological event may be completely lost. The North and South Downs run together westwards in Salisbury Plain, the traditional training ground of the British Army. This is Thomas Hardy's 'Great Plain' and we are on the borders of Wessex.

Wessex

Great Britain (i.e., England, Scotland, and Wales) has benefited from being an island in many ways. One of the less obvious ways is that it has provided us with a magnificent series of coast sections in which geological successions can be studied with relative ease and reasonable completeness. Not least among these are the sections of Mesozoic and Tertiary strata exposed along the coastlines of the counties of Hampshire and Dorset.

So far as older rocks are concerned, these are even less well known than those of the Weald. Between the Kent coal-field and Cornubia, the London ridge and the Mendips, this was called 'the unknown triangle' so far as the potentially valuable Carboniferous rocks were concerned. The Mesozoic sedimentary rocks are very thick, so that a very deep boring in the Isle of Wight still finished in the Trias. Geophysical studies have not helped much except to suggest northerly thrusting of Palaeozoic rocks as under the Weald.

A recent idea is of a Variscan granite mass under central Dorset and another under the Salisbury–Southampton area to explain aureole rocks found in the Trias of the English Midlands. In the extreme north of this area the textbook anticline of Kingsclere, near Newbury, was an obvious place to bore (unsuccessfully) in the early days of oil exploration, and pebbles of Carboniferous Limestone were found in the thick Mesozoic. This must be near the northern edge of Meso-Europa.

The Trias is not seen at the surface in this area at all; it only appears from beneath the easterly dipping Jurassic to the west of Lyme Regis, just across the county boundary in Devon. But it was convenient to discuss the Trias under Cornubia, since it is made of its detritus.

When the Jurassic sea, preceded by a Rhaetian one, invaded the area all was calm and placid. Shelf muds and limestones were laid down, packed with ammonites and other fossils that have made the Lyme Regis area one of the most hammered parts of the island. A local girl, Mary Anning, found the first ichthyosaur here, early in the last century, and spent her life supplying fossils to the great geologists of her day. There are still at least two fossil shops in Lyme showing a regrettable lack of conservationist spirit. Fine sands join the dominating grey clays in the Middle and Upper Lias, but the whole forms perhaps the best reference section in the world for the Lower Jurassic, with the beds mapped individually and every layer known intimately by generations of geologists.

There is a remarkable condensation of the strata at the Pliensbachian–Toarcian junction and then again in the Bajocian. It has been said, with truth, that in places the zones are thinner than the ammonites which characterize them. This has been taken as evidence of a positive ridge existing in the Dorset coast area at these times, but generally this was a subsiding region throughout the greater part of Mesozoic times.

The Bathonian has thick clays and fissile limestones, best seen in the Fleet Lagoon behind the long shingle bank of the Chesil Beach, which extends for nearly 30 km from the shore near Burton Bradstock to the distinctive silhouette of the Isle of Portland south-west of Weymouth. The ammonitiferous Oxford and Kimmeridge Clays are separated by the varied shallow-water sands, clays, and limestones, of the 'Corallian', of late Oxfordian age and here mostly lacking corals. The Jurassic is capped, spectacularly, by the Portland and Purbeck Beds, here on their home ground. The 'Portlandian' culminates in the Portland Limestone which was used to rebuild the official and ecclesiastical buildings of London after the great fire of 1666 and has been the sign of British officialdom ever since. Being the most resistant of the Jurassic rocks it forms most of the steeper cliffs of the Dorset coast and some of the most spectacular coast scenery in Europe, including the Isle of Portland itself. The fauna of the Portland Beds consists of remarkably large individuals (notably the giant ammonites which decorate many gardens along the outcrop) but is remarkably low in diversity, with notable absentees. This probably marks an increase in salinity, heralding the end of a great cycle of marine sedimentation that began in the Rhaetian. The cycle is completed with the Purbeck Beds which are mostly fresh-water limestones with soil horizons (and cycadophyte trees still in life position). They are also famous for their early mammals, roughly contemporaneous with those in the Morriston Formation of the USA. There are brackish episodes in the Purbeck and a marine band (mostly oysters) in the middle, which has been taken by some to represent a marine transgression at the beginning of the Cretaceous.

Wealden deposits are well developed in the Isle of Wight (although without the massive sandstones of the Weald) and at their base have a jumble of tree trunks like those which accumulate at the mouth of the Mississippi or any major river. It is a poor, barnacle-covered counterpart of the 'Petrified Forest' of Arizona. The Lower Greensand, too, makes fine cliffs along the south-west and south-east sides of the island. Westwards, however, this formation dies out fairly rapidly and the Albian Gault Clay marches over everything, resting in turn on each unit of the Jurassic until, near Seaton, it rests directly on the Trias. At the same time the Gault Clay facies becomes very thin and the Upper Greensand grows more important, marching on westwards into Cornubia. Although early for the classic 'Cenomanian transgression', this was the major event seen in many other parts of Europe (and the world). Whether or not it covered the ancient lands to the west is a matter of dispute, but certainly there is evidence of shallowing conditions in the lead-up to the whitest of white chalk at the top. The glorious chalk hills of the Weald continue as the spine of the Isle of Wight and then hit the mainland at Ballard Down and encircle the earlier Mesozoic already discussed to reach the sea again at Lulworth, Weymouth, and beyond.

But Wessex (as here defined) is quite as important for afficianados of the Tertiary as it is to Mesozoic specialists. The delightful Isle of Wight, which still has an aura of Queen Victoria who lived there so long, is one of the best places in Europe for studying the Palaeogene. This is seen also on the mainland to the west around Bournemouth and to the east in Bracklesham Bay, but it is in Whitecliff Bay at the east end of the island and Alum Bay at the west end, that the strata can be studied with ease. This is thanks to the Alpine movements which obligingly stood them on end for inspection.

The Tertiary story in the Hampshire Basin, as in the other Tertiary basins of western Europe, is one of repeated transgression and regression. Five cycles of marine clays, intertidal mud flats, and continental sands, can be recognized in the Eocene alone. A useful student exercise is to correlate the east end of the Isle of Wight, where all the cycles are clearly developed with the west end, where they are more continental in aspect. The same story is continued on the mainland (if the larger island can be called that). The sea again came from the east as in the London Basin. There are further complications, inevitably, one of the most interesting being that sometimes the faunas indicate a chilly splash of the Boreal Ocean to the north and sometimes there is 'a deep draught of the warm south' with nummulites and exotic molluscs.

The Oligocene story continued that of the Eocene for two more main cycles, but only brief marine episodes. Continental conditions, including noteworthy fresh-water limestones, dominate. The later Oligocene strata fade out in the poorly exposed north part of the Isle of Wight and nothing more is seen of the record apart from Quaternary sands and gravels, notably over the sparsely wooded 'New Forest' in mainland Hampshire, where William Rufus met with his fatal 'accident' while hunting.

Structurally, Wessex repeats the pattern of the Weald with broad, open anticlines that have steeper northern limbs. Nowhere is this better shown than on the Isle of Wight where the steep northern limb forms the east–west backbone across the central part of the island, while the gentle southern limb caps St. Catherine's Down in the south. In fact, there are two anticlines in the island, slightly off-set in an *en echelon* manner, as are the other Tertiary folds now known out in the English Channel.

A gentle southern limb is displayed in the outline of the Isle of Portland, already discussed, while the corresponding steep northern limb is displayed in the best imaginable 'textbook' of marine erosion along the coast around Lulworth Cove. Here the sea has broken through the first line of defence provided by the Portland and Purbeck Beds, to wreak havoc among the weak Wealden and greensands behind and to be stopped by the massive rearguard of the Chalk, which is in places so steep as to be actually overturned (an almost unimaginable situation for the British Mesozoic). The result is a marvellous series of natural arches, caves, and offshore reefs, and that most perfect piece of scenery—the geometrical perfection of Lulworth Cove. The less competent Purbeck Beds have been contorted between the massive jaws of the Portland Stone and the Chalk to produce the structure known as the 'Lulworth Crumple' in Stair Hole just west of the cove. This is the outermost manifestation of the Alpine orogeny. Many of these gentle anticlines have been drilled hopefully, but until recently unsuccessfully, for oil, and renewed interest has come from the evident productivity of the Jurassic shaly formations in the North Sea. Both the Lias and the Kimmeridge Clay have so-called 'burning cliffs' on the Dorset coast, caused by the spontaneous ignition of the hydrocarbons in these shaly clays. There are also a number of oil 'shows' along the coast (including one in the 'Lulworth Crumple'). It must also be said that the first well operating in the south of England produces from the Jurassic and stands on the 'stratotype' of the Kimmeridgian at Kimmeridge Bay. There is evidence of the 'Late Kimmerian' movements in Wessex, mainly as repeated movements along faults, but all this adds up to very little tectonically. This is all very much Meso-Europa.

8(d) English Channel

The English Channel as the English like to call it, or *La Manche* (the sleeve) as the French (and others) like to call it, would appear at first sight to be simply the wet space covering up the connection between Cornubia and Armorica, the Hampshire and Paris basins, the Weald and the Boulonnais. In fact it has a separate existence of its own, as have so many parts of the European continental shelf.

From its position it clearly belongs in Meso-Europa, as is also apparent from its structure. The Precambrian and Palaeozoic rocks on either side of the western part of the Channel disappear not very far from the shores, but it is probable that the structures that affect the Mesozoic and Tertiary sediments are directly related to those of the ancient floor beneath. These structures all trend east-north-east or thereabouts, parallel to the trends in the Variscan massifs on either side.

Like so many basins in north-west Europe, the English Channel began in the Triassic with down-warping at its western end (i.e., west of a line from Portland to the Cotentin Peninsula). Some of the earliest records of Channel geology are of red mud brought up on anchors, and there is a large outcrop of 'Permo-Trias' filling the arcuate embayment off south Devon and Cornwall (Fig. 8.7). This is immediately overlain by Upper Cretaceous rocks, in keeping with the transgressive relationship seen along the south-west coast of England. Thereafter there is an ascending sequence in the simple syncline that is the western Channel, although there is some faulting on the south side and a separate Palaeogene basin in the large embayment west of the Cherbourg Peninsula.

The first serious consideration of the geology of the Channel was probably that in connection with 'PLUTO'—the pipeline laid from England to supply petrol to the invasion bridgehead in Normandy in June 1944. This crossed Jurassic and Cretaceous

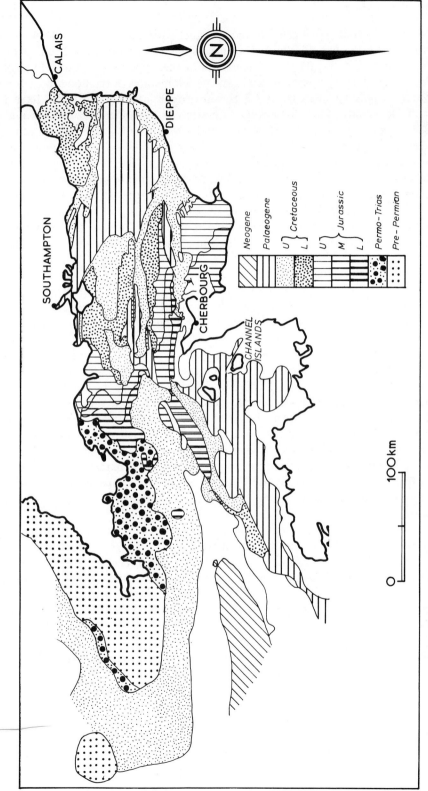

Fig. 8.7 *Geological sketch-map of the English Channel (after Dunham et al., 1972, by permission of the Director, Institute of Geological Sciences. Crown copyright reserved).*

rocks thrown in a series of *en echelon* folds parallel with and complementary to those seen on dry land in the Isle of Wight. The successions are, on the whole, similar on the opposite shorelines, but the Bajocian limestones of the 'type area' around Bayeux are unfamiliar to English eyes, as are the sands and conglomerates of the uppermost Jurassic in the *Pas de Calais* farther east. To a certain extent intermediate facies have been recorded off Normandy. The Cretaceous succession is remarkably consistent and the 'white cliffs of Dover' are exactly comparable with the cliffs of Blanc Nez, west of Calais, or of Le Tréport, east of Dieppe.

Sampling of the sea-floor has revealed a uniform story in the central and eastern channel from mid Jurassic times onwards. There was emergence and erosion at the end of the Jurassic (seen well at Cap d'Antifer). There was further subsidence in the early Cretaceous and then slight folding before the deposition of Upper Cretaceous sediments. Thus the 'Wealden' is said to have been folded with the Jurassic in the Boulonnais (which story can be traced offshore) and the same phenomenon is seen on the Dorset coast.

The east–west Cenomanian transgression provided the best rock (the argillaceous Lower Chalk) in the *Pas de Calais* area in which to excavate the long-awaited Channel Tunnel. Detailed studies in connection with the last plans for the tunnel revealed missing foram zones in places within the Cenomanian, implying continuing movements during that time, as have also been recognized in south Devon.

The central and eastern Channel only really got that sinking feeling in Tertiary times and the soft Palaeogene sediments of the Hampshire Basin extend right across the Channel almost to the French coast. There was slight folding in the early Eocene in the west but the Palaeozoic basement reasserted itself in late Eocene times with faulting on the old lines during the Lutetian. This has been correlated with the opening of the Bay of Biscay and the Atlantic. However, there are scarcely any Neogene rocks except at the western extremity of the Channel and it is difficult to date accurately the main, gentle east–west folds with their steeper northern limbs that are so characteristic of the whole region. Only some scraps of marine late Pliocene on the chalk hills around the Straits of Dover testify to a late Tertiary marine transgression that spread over an already folded landscape.

An even later feature of the English Channel was the development of a large river system such as that which formed the Solent waterway that separates the Isle of Wight from the English mainland. A buried channel here some 50 m below the present sea-floor was evidently rapidly filled by the products of the erosion of the crumbling cliffs to the west.

A much larger feature, probably of the same nature, is the Hurd Deep along the centre of the Channel which drops to as much as 240 m below the present floor. This has been argued about for years. Its general east-north-east orientation makes one think of faulting along the old Variscan lines, and perhaps faulting played a part in its original location, but it is now thought to be fluvial in origin on the evidence of tributaries at the north-east end. It was probably modified by tidal scour during the rising sea levels of the Pleistocene interglacials and has been kept clear by tidal action ever since.

Quaternary sediments only provide the meerest veneer and the Straits of Dover were probably only cut not more than 2500 years ago. The separation of Britain from the continent is a very recent phenomenon and hopefully only a very temporary one.

8(e) Ardennes, Eifel, and Rheinisches Schiefergebirge

A large dark patch on the geological map of Europe covers these three adjacent areas of ancient rocks which include one of the largest areas of unmetamorphosed late Palaeozoic rocks on the continent. Towns and villages here give their names to many stages of the Devonian and Carboniferous. Although the three areas are contiguous, their sedimentary and tectonic histories are different and it will be convenient to consider the first two separate from the third.

Ardennes and Eifel

The forests of the Ardennes sweep across the borders of north-east France and Belgium and are roughly bounded to the east by the German frontier. The general impression of the region is one of darkness, with fast rivers in deep valleys cutting through the dense pine forests in which deer and wild boar are still common. Across in Germany, however, the Eifel presents a quite different appearance: a gently undulating bare plateau, dotted with the volcanoes for which the region is famous.

The Ardennes–Eifel Massif consists of three great synclinoria separated by two narrower anticlinoria, all trending roughly east–west, although swinging round to the north-east at the German frontier (Fig. 8.8). The synclinoria, from south to north, are those of the Eifel, Dinant, and Namur, with the main Ardennes anticlinorium between the first

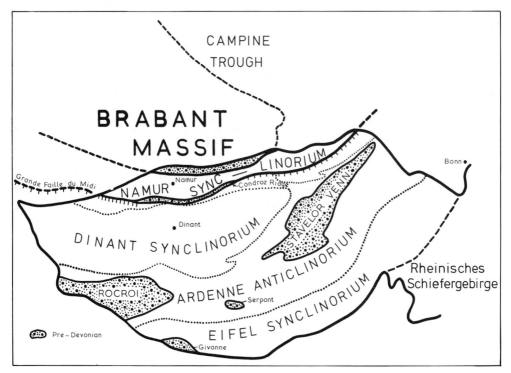

Fig. 8.8 Geological sketch-map of the Ardennes and Eifel.

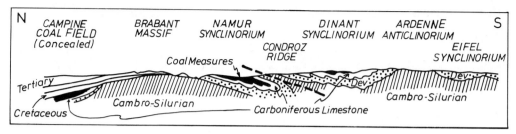

Fig. 8.9 *Cross-section of the Belgian Ardennes (after Stamp* et al.*, 1922, by kind permission of the Council of the Geologists' Association).*

two. The Dinant synclinorium has been thrust northwards on to that of Namur, almost cutting out the structure in between (Fig. 8.9). Indeed it is here that runs one of the most famous faults of northern Europe—the *Grande Faille du Midi*—which can be traced westwards to the Variscan Front in Britain.

The oldest rocks at the surface are pyritic slates in the Rocroi area, in the most north-easterly corner of France. This has been doubtfully dated as mid Cambrian. A sandier slate in the middle of what is thought to be an isoclinal syncline may have yielded *Dictyonema* and may be Tremadocian in age. That is the state of chronostratigraphy in these rocks. All the slates have been much used in the past for roofing purposes (e.g., in the beautifully arcaded Place Ducale of Charleville-Mézières), although the efficiency of the slates is impaired by the tendency of the pyrite crystals to fall out. The slates are intruded by a few small sills of microdiorite, which are the only evidence of igneous activity in the Ardennes as a whole, apart from some possible altered bentonites. Other Cambrian rocks near Stavelot, which continue into Germany, are sometimes said to be younger in age, but without real evidence.

Cambrian, Ordovician, and Silurian, sediments seem to form the greater part of the Brabant Massif to the north, which is almost hidden under young sediments. They are seen chiefly in valley inliers north-east of Mons, cut by intrusions such as the quartz porphyry that has been quarried on a vast scale (notably at Quenast) for hundreds of years. The Brabant Massif is one of those massifs of western Europe that were 'inverted' in mid Cretaceous times to transform what had been a positive area into a negative one. It seems to have been comparatively rigid in late Palaeozoic times and was almost unaffected by the Variscan movements, but the condition of the older rocks points clearly to a Caledonian orogeny. The older rocks in the anticlinorium to the south are also usually said to have been affected by both major movements.

After the events at the end of the Silurian, a Devonian transgression advanced steadily from the south spreading a basal conglomerate. Some of the older masses may have stood up as islands. Something was supplying fairly fresh felspar to the early Devonian deposits, although there is no trace in the region of anything that could be called a Caledonian granite.

Towards the end of Gedinnian times, a slight regression brought 'Old Red Sandstone' type of sediments into the region of the Dinant synclinorium, but the sea reasserted itself and the marine advance continued. Most of the marine beds of the Lower Devonian fall into what has been called the 'Rhenish Magnafacies', which may be summarized as poorly sorted sandstones with a specialized benthonic fauna. The distribution of this magnafacies contrasts fairly clearly with that of the 'Hercynian Magnafacies' of limestones and shales with abundant corals. The two names refer specifically to the Rhineland and the Harz, respectively, but in the Ardennes there is a gradual passage from one to the other.

By the end of early Devonian times the marine transgression had reached the Condroz axis between the Dinant and Namur structures. From there it moved on northwards, so that Frasnian sandstones rest on the Brabant Massif at the northern edge of this area.

It was in the mid and late Devonian that the classic Eifel district came into its own. The outcrop there is cut up into separate synclines, each of which differs from its neighbours in detailed stratigraphy, resulting in a complex and tedious nomenclature. With immense energy, German palaeontologists dug trenches across the structures and sampled the abundant and well-preserved faunas exhaustively. I am still confused by a splendid but detailed excursion there soon after the Second World War, in which *Schwellen* and *Becken* (ridges and troughs) were correlated in the most intimate detail. Further complicating the picture, the palaeogeography forms a compressed 'S' (the 'Eifel sigmoid') with a well-developed ecological zonation including a fringing reef along its edge.

The superabundant brachiopods, corals, and other fossils of the Eifel are surprisingly different from those of the neighbouring Ardennes. This goes far beyond the usual differences that result from nothing more than the differing nationalities of the palaeontologists studying them, although some of the stage-names (e.g., Couvinian/Eifelian) change at the frontier. The other classic area is that of Couvin, Givet, and Frasne, in Belgium, where a superb story has been worked out of a Middle–Upper Devonian reef belt along a hinge-line between the stable Rocroi Massif to the south and a relatively unstable basin to the north. A whole series of small reefs was developed, each about 100 m high and 500–800 m in diameter. They are surrounded by softer shales which have weathered out. If one stands on a view-point north of Couvin, every small hill one sees is a Devonian reef. Most of them are quarried, often being wire-cut for ornamental stone. A complex series of ecological zones has been worked out, based on depth of water and energy levels. The story elucidated here, studying quarry-sized reefs, was found to apply equally well to the vast Devonian reefs of the Canadian Rockies which are such important oil reservoirs where they plunge under the prairies.

At the end of Frasnian times, the reef belt was swamped and stifled by an influx of fine mud and then a general regression set in (as in so many parts of Europe). Shoreline and tidal-flat deposits were laid down in the Famennian and these form the cores of many of the anticlines in the northern part of the Dinant synclinorium, where they are quarried for roadstone.

The centres of the synclines are chiefly occupied by early Carboniferous limestones of the next transgression. This is the type area of the Dinantian, and the town of Dinant is dominated by its Citadelle, perched high on cliffs of steeply dipping Dinantian limestone. Tornai and Visé (which give their names to the main divisions of the Dinantian) are not far away and the Meuse valley here provides a classic section in the Lower Carboniferous. The facies is essentially what most Europeans think of as 'typical Carboniferous Limestone' and very similar to the equally 'typical Mississippian' along the banks of the Mississippi. Indeed this was a time of shallow-water carbonate deposition in many parts of the world, ranging from Alaska to the Himalayas.

A special variant is the 'Waulsortian facies', with bryozoan–algal reefs, which is named after the village of Waulsort, just north of Dinant. This also has been recognized in many other parts of Europe. There was a slight break at the end of the early Carboniferous and, near Visé, the Namurian rests on a karstic surface.

Later Carboniferous rocks are hardly seen at all in the Dinant synclinorium, but are well preserved in the Namur synclinorium to the north. That town in its turn gives its name to the Namurian, which is here in the form of thick cycles of sandstones, coals, and marine shales, with land plants and goniatites alternating. These pass up into the familiar 'Coal Measure' facies of the Westphalian. There were movements at the end of the Namurian which produced a useful conglomeratic marker horizon. Altogether there are several kilometres of Namurian and Westphalian sandstones, shales, and coal-seams in the Namur synclinorium. The main folding here was undoubtedly Asturian in age. Strata up to Westphalian 'B' are involved in the Namur synclinorium and possibly later Westphalian strata in the concealed Campine coal-field on the north side of the Brabant Massif. In the Dinant structure the youngest beds preserved are Namurian. All the Variscan structures tend to be overturned towards the north and the thrusts have moved in the same direction. Many of the folds are angular and would be called 'box-folds' in the Jura, but are here 'chair-folds' (*pli en chaise*) instead. This together with the major thrust of the *Grande Faille du Midi* (which could be likened to the frontal thrust of the Jura) suggests a *décollement* type of folding, on the margin of a major tectonic belt. Unlike the Jura, however, the Ardennes has no underlying layer of salt to provide the lubrication, although there is plenty of evidence of slipping along the coal seams of the north French and Belgian coal-fields. There is also no real evidence of a palaeoslope down which the sliding may have occurred, although it could be that the intrusion of Variscan granites (e.g., in the Vosges to the south) provided the necessary elevation, but these may have been a little early for the known date of the movements. There remains the question of earlier movements. In the Ardennes anticlinorium there are several striking structures such as the mushroom fold of the Rocher d'Uf at Fumay in the Rocroi Massif and the so-called 'thunderbolt' nearby. These are tightly folded Cambrian slates, but the cleavage that crosses them is Variscan and the Caledonian must remain problematical.

Late stage Variscan movements are seen in the form of transverse faulting of Permian age, accompanied by a limited amount of volcanic activity. After that there is little evidence that the Ardennes were anything other than an island in a sea of Mesozoic sediment. The folded and faulted surface of the Eifel was unconformably overlain by Triassic conglomerates and red sandstones, which in places are seen to spill down into the synclinal valleys. The Ardennes only came close to submergence at the very end of the Cretaceous when coarse, littoral deposits of the Maastrichtian lapped on to the massif from the north.

The Alpine movements did little more than gently reactivate existing fault lines, breaking the regular horizontal skyline of the Ardennes peneplain. Some indeed are still moving, as the *Grande Faille du Midi* itself moved in the 1930s, perhaps as a warning of the human disturbances that were to happen in this area so soon afterwards.

The Ardennes are unlike almost all the other Variscan massifs of continental Europe in lacking any evidence of Tertiary volcanism. Almost the only thing of this kind are the thermal springs of the town of Spa (yet another 'type locality'). This stands on the

Stavelot Massif and takes its mineral-rich, slightly radioactive waters from a deep-seated fault.

The Eifel, on the other hand, is one of the best places in Europe for studying sub-Recent volcanicity. Ash cones are scattered widely as are tiny circular lakes (*maar*) filling old craters. Lava flows are not so common, although there are columnar-jointed phono-lites. Apart from olivine bombs and biotite crystals, the ash is quite unconsolidated and is used everywhere to make paths for the omnipresent hikers. Here, as in the Auvergne, Palaeolithic man was terrified, or at least impressed, by the last eruptions.

Rheinisches Schiefergebirge

The anticlinoria and synclinoria of the Ardennes and Eifel plunge beneath Triassic and younger sediments of the Luxembourg region to emerge again as the slate mountains that stand astride the Rhine along its most industrious length. The Rheinisches Schiefergebirge spread more widely in a north–south direction and so display more structures than the Ardennes and Eifel (Fig. 8.10). Essentially they consist of the upstanding block of the Hunsrück and Taunus in the south, the Hesse synclinorium and broad Siegerländ Block in the centre, the Sauerland synclinorium, and then the Ruhr coal basin with all its industries along the northern edge.

Topographically the slate mountains are a plateau, with a main erosion surface at about 700 m, deeply dissected by the Rhine and its tributaries, of which the most specta-cular is the Moselle with its snake-like incised meanders. This is the northernmost commercial wine-growing region in Europe and the vines only prosper on the steep, south-facing slopes. Along the Moselle, therefore, the vineyards leap from bank to bank every kilometre or two. What is more, because of the latitude the wine-growers spread broken up local Lower Devonian slate on the ground beneath the vines to absorb a little of the Hunsrück and Taunus in the south, the Hesse synclinorium and broad Siegerlünd the night. Also the slates provide better drainage and stop the vineyards being washed down the steep slopes in heavy rain. Geology has its bearing on every aspect of human endeavour!

The pre-Devonian history of the Rheinisches Schiefergebirge is inadequately known, since Lower Palaeozoic rocks are only seen in the cores of a few anticlines, notably in the extreme south. In general, however, it seems to be comparable with that of the Ardennes.

The main story of the massif is that of the Devonian and the Carboniferous, but it is complex both palaeogeographically and tectonically and there are many different pos-sible interpretations. Early in Devonian times, this region lay to the south-east of the 'Old Red Sandstone' continent which provided coarse sediments at least to the northern part of the massif. Islands to the south, out in the main central European trough, also provided some material, but of a finer-grained nature. Uplift was already occurring, however, in what is now the Hesse synclinorium, with a local condensed carbonate facies.

In the south and in the Moselle region to the west, the generally sandy deposits of the Gedinnian were followed by a famous argillaceous formation, the Hunsrück Schiefer. This is the black slate of the vineyards, but it is better known for its fantastically preserved starfish and other fossils at localities such as Bundenbach. It presents quite an environmental problem so far as depth is concerned, and in the mixture of 'Old Red Sandstone' type fish with what were obviously fully marine forms.

189

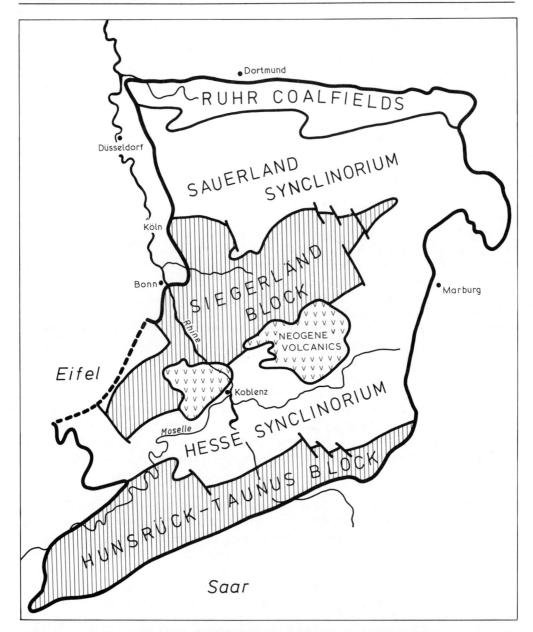

Fig. 8.10 Geological sketch-map of the Rheinisches Schiefergebirge.

True 'Old Red Sandstone' spread into the northern part of the area in the later part of the early Devonian, with some acidic volcanicity, while greywackes with shallow marine faunas were accumulating in the south. All this comes within the 'Rhenish Magnafacies'. Only in the extreme east were there limestones of the 'Hercynian Magnafacies' which were to become more important later.

In mid Devonian times organic limestones began to develop on the northern shelf, although apparently in fairly deep water below the range of wave action. A complex story has been worked out of vertical and lateral changes related to fluctuating currents or minor eustatic oscillations. The Givetian transgressed on to the Brabant Massif and passed into the 'Old Red Sandstone'. Only locally did small reefs build up above the general carbonate platform. Near Attendorn, on the edge of the shelf, a large well-preserved atoll developed, originally about 10 km in diameter. In the basin to the south-east, iron, zinc, and barium, accumulated in fetid muds to give the finely laminated sulphide ores mined at Meggen. South again, spilitic lava flows built up on the basin floor and grew their own reefs, well seen in the Lahn valley near Limburg. Increased subsidence drowned most of the reefs in late Devonian times and shales were widely deposited, with goniatitic limestones on the old reef ridges and on the persistent ridge in the middle of the area. 'Turbidites' swept into the northern part of the massif and greywackes interfingered with basinal cherts and shales in the south.

This story continued into the Carboniferous and herein lies the biggest difference between the Rheinisches Schiefergebirge and the Ardennes. In the latter, carbonate deposition was the rule in the early Carboniferous, while in this area it is all siliceous shales and clastics of a 'Culm' facies. Pure quartz sands accumulated along the ridge that is now the Hesse synclinorium and extensive spilitic lavas flowed from this into the deeper basins, associated with tuffs. Only in the extreme north is there anything that can be called 'Carboniferous Limestone'.

It is evident that the Variscan orogeny began in the south-east part of the slate mountains in late Devonian times, and then moved progressively northwards to reach the farther end of the massif by mid Westphalian times. In Dinantian times the basin filled with greywackes and a belt of pelagic sedimentation moved northwards to occupy a basin on the site of the former shelf. This in turn was filled with greywackes in Namurian times. Finally in late Namurian times, there was a transition from flysch-type sedimentation to coal-bearing molasse as the orogeny spread across the basin. The Westphalian of the Ruhr coal basin is extremely thick, as is only proper since this is its type area. It is very similar to the Westphalian of the Namur synclinorium but with a large number of very valuable coals which make this the foundation of West Germany's economic success. One important difference from the Ardennes coal-field is that here the coals continue under the Mesozoic cover to the north, while north of Namur the Variscan movements evidently reactivated old structures resulting in the uplift of the Brabant Massif. Many marine horizons are recognized within the cyclic Coal Measures of the Ruhr and it is thought that these represent the first incursions of an eastern sea rather than one from the west.

In the Ruhr the main movements can be shown to be Asturian in age, but it cannot be proved if these were also the movements that affected the older rocks of the Rheinisches Schiefergebirge. It may be significant that the movements in the Saar coal basin, 50 km to the south, were earlier (i.e., Sudetian).

There are no Mesozoic rocks here, but the Tertiary volcanic province of the Eifel continues into the Rhine area with the Siebengebirge ('Seven Mountains') near Bonn, the Westerwald near Koblenz, and the great Vogelsberg (although this is discussed under the Rhine Graben). They are related to Tertiary block faulting and are mainly acidic, although much of the original acidic explosive material may have blown right away leaving the occasional basalt. The Siebengebirge is a group of seven hills produced by such basaltic necks standing high above the general peneplain, with their former seven castles appealing much to Germanic romanticism. A little to the south is the equally volcanic Drachenfels, where lived the dragon slain by Siegfried. The blood in which he bathed to become invincible may be interpreted as trachyte. The Westerwald and Vogelsberg are complex basaltic centres consisting of many necks and small flows. Again early man saw the last eruptions.

8(f) Harz

The Harz Massif blissfully ignores the political division of Europe and sits firmly astride the boundary between East and West Germany. It is a small, low-lying massif, appearing from beneath a flat-lying Mesozoic cover, and is largely composed of late Palaeozoic rocks. It gives the alternative name 'Hercynian' to the late Palaeozoic earth movements; it gives the same name to the general trend of its rocks and to a facies of the Devonian. It is because of this confusion that the term 'Variscan' is preferred in this book for the orogeny.

The rocks of the Harz are commonly thrust and overturned towards the north-west. They are divided by two major dislocations (trending the same way) into three distinct units: the Upper, Middle, and Lower Harz (*Oberharz*, *Mittleharz*, and *Unterharz*), shown diagrammatically in Fig. 8.11.

Pre-Devonian

The oldest rocks known at the surface are the siliceous schists, phyllites, and greywacke-type gneiss seen in the extreme south-east which (from comparisons elsewhere) may be of late Precambrian age. These are isoclinally folded and strongly thrust. They correspond to the southern edge of the Rheinisches Schiefergebirge.

Silurian graptolitic shales are much better known and are very thick, including inter-bedded quartzites, greywackes, and keratophyre tuffs. All divisions are recognizable in the graptolitic facies, from Llandovery to Ludlow, and there is a carbonate facies at the top which passes into the Devonian.

There is no clear sign of the Caledonian orogeny in the Harz, although there was probably general uplift at the end of the early Palaeozoic, demonstrable near Zorge, and there is an angular unconformity between the Silurian and the Devonian. The late Palaeozoic folding, on the other hand, is intense, while the Mesozoic round about is all placidity.

Devonian rocks are very widespread in all parts of the Harz and in surprisingly different facies. The occurrence of contrasting facies close together has led in the past to the postulation of considerable overthrusting. In the Lower Devonian there is a general passage from the shallow-water sandstones of the Upper Harz in the north-west (where they form the anticlinal ridges) to more carbonate facies in the south-east.

In mid and late Devonian times this became a classic region of the peculiarly Germanic feature of *Schwellen* and *Becken* which controlled sedimentation. Limestones were developed on the rises and shales in the troughs. The latter are often associated with basic volcanic rocks, of submarine origin, forming for example the 'Diabase zone' in the

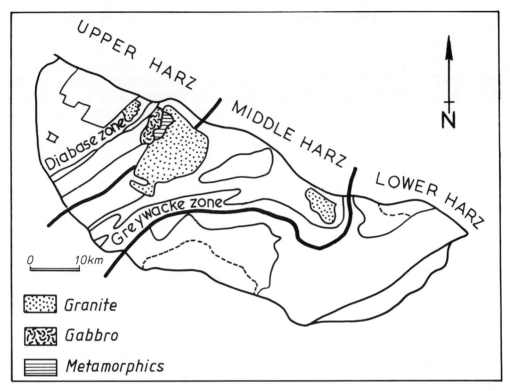

Fig. 8.11 *Geological sketch-map of the Harz (after Mohr, 1973). The thicker lines show the principal dislocations and the thinner lines the anticlinoria.*

Upper Harz. Not far from here in the Rammelsburg, north-east of the famous mining town of Clausthal, the Middle Devonian shales contain rich sulphide ores which have been exploited for over a thousand years. They are thought to be synsedimentary in origin, deposited in an isolated trough and possibly derived from contemporaneous igneous activity. There are over 500 m of Middle Devonian volcanics in the Elbingeröder area of the Middle Harz, in what may be a tectonic window of autochthonous material seen through rocks overthrust from the south.

In the Upper Devonian, there is a notable development of reef limestones, for example near Ilfeld in the north-west, while elsewhere there are brachiopod and ammonoid limestones. In the troughs, however, there are fine-grained clastics and flysch-type sediments which pass through into the Lower Carboniferous. The latter include some spilitic lavas which have been somewhat overworked in oceanographic theorizing. These and the reefs come within less than 20 km or so of each other in the Upper Harz. All through the Middle and Upper Devonian are thin intercalations of fine-grained siderite which have been interpreted as derived from weathered basic volcanics.

The flysch-type rocks pass through into the Lower Carboniferous and there is some uncertainty as to whether there were any movements at this time (i.e., the Bretonic phase). All along the dislocated southern edge of the Middle Harz there seems to be a break and this may be a critical suture in the history of Meso-Europa with the present

193

overturned synclines perhaps related to a sudden change in facies along the edge of a trench.

Farther north, the Lower Carboniferous takes the form of a thick, dominantly shaly, sequence in the 'Culm' facies. In the central syncline of the Upper Harz, this facies is some 500 m thick, but thins markedly on to the anticlinal ridges both to the north and south. So it is clear that differential subsidence and sedimentation went hand in hand.

Further evidence of a Bretonic phase may be provided by the sudden appearance of coarse clastics in the Lower Carboniferous, and pebbly basal deposits have been shown to be strongly diachronous. Basic volcanism continued well into early Carboniferous times and then the late Carboniferous only appears to be represented by basic and acid intrusions. This marked the beginning of the main phase of movements. After the faulting and uplift of the Bretonic phase, chiefly seen in the Lower Harz, the climax came in the Sudetic phase, between early and late Westphalian times. The later rocks are not, in fact, seen in the Harz at all, but in the neighbouring coal-field areas.

In the Sudetic movements the Palaeozoic rocks were intensely folded and faulted, including the 'Culm', but the Upper Westphalian is almost undisturbed. Some minor movements in the Asturic phase may have been responsible for thrusting and a general foreshortening of the outcrops, but the Upper Westphalian sediments of the neighbouring coal-fields are generally seen lying flatly on the folded 'Culm'. Minor movements in the Permian produced the unconformities which are well known in this region.

Besides the folding there was considerable igneous activity associated with the Variscan orogeny. The largest mass—the Brocken pluton—cuts right across the dislocation between the Middle and Upper Harz. It consists of a gabbro, injected along the north-easterly trend, which passes laterally into norite and is succeeded by the much more extensive Brocken granite, forming a laccolith. Associated with these intrusions are some high-grade metamorphic rocks, which have been thought by some to be a fragment of basement brought up with the igneous rocks, but the more common view seems to be that they are Lower Carboniferous shales that have suffered contact metamorphism.

Other smaller granite masses occur in the Upper and Middle Harz and commonly show crystal orientation parallel to the Variscan trend. They have been dated as around 296 million years old. There are dioritic and granodioritic dikes along the same lines. Mineralization was widespread, often modifying the earlier Devonian ores. Finally there was acid volcanism in the earliest Permian, associated with Lower 'Rotliegende' conglomerates and sandstones.

The whole of the Harz Massif was swamped by the Zechstein Sea and reefs developed on pre-existing highs. Such bryozoan–algal build-ups form important hydrocarbon reservoirs. The flooded landscape was generally of low relief and was soon evened out. In the upper part of the Zechstein there was a tremendous development of evaporites, and salt from this level has often combined with salt from the *Muschelkalk* to form the huge composite salt instrusions of the north German plain.

Although the prevailing trends within the Harz are oriented towards the north-east, the actual edges of the massif are roughly west-north-west and are probably fault-controlled. Such faults may be very old and probably developed mainly during the Variscan, but they were reactivated at various times during the Mesozoic and Tertiary, keeping the Harz standing up as a positive area above the surrounding seas. It is not certain whether the late Cretaceous sea ever completely drowned the Harz, although pebbles in the surrounding Turonian and Senonian Chalk show that the Brocken pluton was already unroofed and suffering erosion.

Late Cretaceous movements are indicated by Eocene gravels resting unconformably on steeply dipping Trias in the vicinity of the Harz, but since Miocene times this has been an area of erosion with a partial glaciation in the Pleistocene.

Perhaps the Harz is too small to be compared meaningfully with the main Variscan Massifs, but it might be noted in passing that it lacks the Cainozoic volcanicity of such larger masses as Bohemia, the Eifel, and the Massif Central.

8(g)   South-west German Plateau

This large area of south-west Germany, with mainly Mesozoic rocks at the surface, does not—at first sight—appear to be clearly defined structurally or geographically. Nevertheless, it is one of the classic geological areas of the world and was one of the great nurseries of European geology. It is defined by its margins (Fig. 8.12). To the north lies the vast, monotonous northern plain of Europe; to the west lie the Variscan massifs of the Black Forest and Odenwald along the Rhine Graben; to the south lies the frontal molasse trough of the Alps, and to the east lies the Bohemian Massif. Within this region are several of the foremost geological schools of Germany (notably Tubingen) and the successions where Quenstedt and his pupil Oppel laid the foundations of stratigraphical palaeontology in the best traditions of careful German scholarship. Also here are such classic geological localities as Solnhofen with its early birds, Holzmaden with its many wonders, and the meteoritic impact craters near Nordlingen.

The metamorphic rocks of the Variscan massifs to the west enclose graben with recognizable late Carboniferous sediments, but the basement rocks reached in deep boreholes here appear to be of early Palaeozoic age. There is therefore no direct evidence that this region was affected by Variscan movements, although this must be assumed from its position within the Variscide belt. It could equally well be put in either the northern or the central belt.

The sedimentary story starts with the Permian, which surrounds and buries the jagged landscape of the Variscan massifs to the west in coarse detritus from the new mountains. These are the typical Rotliegende of the Lower Permian. They vary considerably in thickness from place to place and in the larger basins pass laterally from torrential deposits and screes at the margins to fine-grained deposits in the middle. The Zechstein Sea invaded the area from the north in later Permian times, but did not reach south of roughly the latitude of Heilbronn and did not bring the evaporites which are so important at this level farther north in Germany. Permian rocks are not found everywhere and over wide areas it is the 'Buntsandstein' of the Lower Triassic which rests directly on the basement.

The Trias is here in its usual form of 'Buntsandstein', 'Muschelkalk', and 'Keuper'. These extended into south-west Germany from the main trough under the North German Plain. So the 'Buntsandstein' thins southwards with internal overlapping. The 'Muschelkalk' represents a narrow straits of shallow sea between the northern trough and the Alpine basin. Its varied carbonates and fauna indicate high temperatures and salinities, but reduced topography. Evidently the new Variscan mountains were already

195

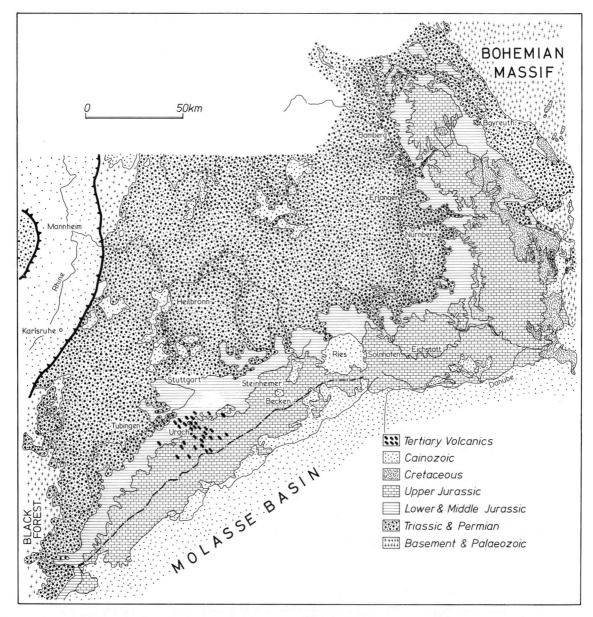

Fig. 8.12 *Geological sketch-map of the South-west German Plateau (after various authors).*

very much subdued, even though there is evidence, up to the end of early Triassic times, of repeated local uplift affecting sedimentation. The story continued into late Triassic times with fine-grained desert deposits. Although varied in places, notably in its lower part and towards the detritus-producing margins, the monotonous mudstones of the 'Keuper' typify the situation at the end of Triassic times, when a vast red plain, relieved only by migrating herds of herbivorous dinosaurs, lay waiting the inevitable marine invasion.

This came in Rhaetian times, at the very end of the period, and the deposits of the strange sea of those times, with its limited and undersized faunas, pass up gently into those of the earliest Jurassic. It was in the Jurassic that the South-west German Plateau really came into its own. This area rivals western England as the capital of the Jurassic world. Here we have Quenstedt's traditional divisions of the 'Black Jura', 'Brown Jura', and 'White Jura', in their home ground and it is almost ridiculous how well these seemingly naive terms apply, not only here, but elsewhere in Europe.

While the Triassic rocks outcrop over the central and western part of the triangular plateau, Jurassic rocks form the base of the triangle and (together with some Cretaceous rocks) its right side. These two broad outcrops are, respectively, the Swabian Alb and the Franken Alb and form a continuation of the French and Swiss Jura, except that they do not show the Alpine folding and faulting of that range. As one leaves the beautiful old university city of Tübingen, one sees the flat-lying Trias forming ridges round the city. One then climbs a series of escarpments to the south-east, representing the different divisions of the Jurassic, and then rolls down the final dip slope into the valley of the young Danube (Donau).

The Black Jura or Lias consists of dark shales and limestones with abundant faunas, monographed by the great masters. Offshore sands in the transgressive beds at the bottom soon pass up into the muddy marine deposits of the Sinemurian and Pliensbachian. The latter takes its name from a village here, as does the Aalenian higher up. The great Goethe himself, who was a keen geologist of the peaceful 'Neptunist' persuasion, described a Lias section here, near Ofterdingen, full of giant arietitid ammonites. It is still preserved. The top stage of the Lias, the Toarcian, consists of black bituminous shales, which seem to represent unoxygenated bottom muds without benthos or the agents of decay. As a result the pelagic organisms are often incredibly well preserved, most notably at Holzmaden, world famous for its marine saurians complete with skins, large logs supporting waving clusters of crinoids, and many other wonders. The early Jurassic sea extended right across the area, but there is evidence from boreholes that the Black Forest was still an island to the west, as were the other major massifs of Europe. Deposition was thickest, however, near Plochingen in the middle of the Swabian outcrop, so this trough was an ancient feature, reflected in the present outcrop, the front of the Alps, the Molasse trough, and the course of the Danube.

The Middle Jurassic continues the same story, but the rocks are now brown due to the presence of ferruginous oolites and sandstones. The sea had shallowed and the palaeogeography had changed. The harder limestones and sandstones among the usual clay sediments form further escarpments, notably the one on which the castle of the Hohenzollerns theatrically stands near Hechingen, although somewhat shaken by a recent earthquake.

With late Jurassic times, this part of Germany became an area of clear limestone-depositing seas, continuous with those of the Alps. Clean limestones and lime muds gave us the 'White Jura'. The most notable features were massive reefs, especially those of Oxfordian age formed by massive siliceous sponges, such as that well displayed at Lochen near Balingen. Here the reef forms a prominent feature on the skyline and passes laterally into bedded inter-reef material. Sponge reefs occur at several levels in the Upper Jurassic, while corals and algae also play their part in reef building. The Upper Jurassic rocks are fairly evenly distributed through Swabia and Franconia, although they swell and pinch around the frequent bioherms. Their generally calcareous nature makes them much more resistant than the beds below and they form the major north-westerly facing escarpment of the Swabian Alb and the major westerly facing escarpment of the Franken Alb. They dominate the landscape on the left bank of the upper Danube.

Whereas the reefs and associated deposits are clearly of shallow-water origin, there are others that are clearly basinal. Thus in the Franken Alb, reef barriers have been recognized at three places (north-east of Ulm, west of Regensburg, and north of Nürnberg) which separate basins in which calcareous shales were deposited. In one of these is the most famous rock of the region—the Solnhofen lithographic stone. For a long time this was thought to be a lagoonal deposit which accumulated in very quiet conditions behind the sponge-reefs. The low energy level made it particularly useful both for printing purposes in the old days and for preserving delicate fossils in even older days. However, it is now thought that it passes laterally into deep basinal sediments and probably accumulated in hollows on the sea-floor. If this is true, it differs from its contemporary analogues at Cerin in the French Jura and above the Tremp gorge in the Spanish Pyrenees, both of which were certainly shallow deposits. The remarkably preserved fauna and flora of the Solnhofen Stone, especially of course its *Archaeopteryx*, are on the whole very scarce. It is only because of the extensive quarrying around Solnhofen (about halfway between Ulm and Nürnberg) that the famous fossils were found.

The top of the Jurassic is missing in the South-west German Plateau. There is evidence of a shallowing sea in early Tithonian times and it is assumed that there was a general withdrawal of the sea at the end of the period as in many other parts of Europe. Cretaceous beds are only preserved in the east of Franconia, between Regensburg and Bayreuth. They rest unconformably on all divisions of the Jurassic and on the Triassic; they are best considered with their more extensive equivalents in the neighbouring regions. There are also small areas of Tertiary sediments in the extreme east.

The South-west German Plateau was tectonically quiet during Tertiary times, although the front of the Alps was not very far away. All that happened was a gentle uplift and a tilting to the south-east, producing the dip and scarp topography of today, together with a drainage system down into what was at first the Molasse Trough and later the Danube Valley. The foundering of the Rhine Graben at the same time mainly affected the neighbouring massifs, but some of the drainage of the plateau—notably that of the Neckar—flowed that way.

Two surprisingly violent happenings did take place here during Tertiary times, however. The first was the eruption of some 200 volcanoes, with associated tuffs, basalts, and small dikes. There are three main clusters of volcanic necks: near Nordlingen at the north-east end of the Swabian Alb, around Urach in the centre, and in the south-west near the Swiss frontier. This last group at least may be associated with the contemporaneous volcanism in the Rhine Graben.

The other, even more surprising happening in Tertiary times was the creation of two other craters also near Nordlingen. These were the huge Ries structure, some 22 km across, and the much smaller Steineimer 'Basin', about 2.5 km across. These are found in the vicinity of the first of the volcanic areas mentioned above, north-east and north of Ulm, respectively. For a long time they were also thought of as volcanic craters, but—incredible coincidence though it may seem—they are now generally accepted as meteoritic in origin. The one at Ries is therefore one of the largest known on earth. Neogene fresh-water sediments have accumulated within the rims of shattered rocks, providing a clear date for the meteorites' arrival.

The Pleistocene glaciations did not reach this pleasant, rolling land, either from the Scandinavian north or the Alpine south.

8(h) Bohemian Massif

If the Fenno-Scandian Shield is the core of Europe, then the Bohemian Massif is its heart (Fig. 8.13). Near its western rim there is a small monument that marks the geographical centre of our continent. The massif stands out clearly on the geological map as a seemingly stable nucleus in a confusion of fold belts. It is one of the largest and best known of the Variscan massifs and occupies almost the whole of the western part of Czechoslovakia (the old kingdom of Bohemia). This is the lovely land of Smetana's 'Má Vlast', with the winding Vltava, legendary Šárka, and 'Bohemia's Meadows and Forests', with the golden city of Prague in its centre.

The massif extends over the borders for a short distance into Austria, West and East Germany, and Poland. To the west and south it is mainly fault-bounded, with the horst of the Thüringer Wald extending to the north-west. To the north it dips gently under the great northern plain and to the south-east it is separated from the Carpathians by a series of deep faults. For the most part it is rugged, peneplained, and thickly forested.

Although it looks so stable and seems to have functioned as a breakwater to the waves of the Alpine orogeny, this was only so in post-Palaeozoic times. Earlier, from way back in the Precambrian until the Variscan orogeny, it was a mobile belt with thick sedimentation and frequent movements. The truly stable edge of the East European Platform extends to within a short distance of the north-east frontier of Czechoslovakia, but this was very much part of Meso-Europa.

Precambrian

The oldest part of the Bohemian Massif, the nucleus of the nucleus, is the large area to the south of Prague extending into West Germany and Austria and known as Moldanubicum—from Moldan, the German name for the River Vltava. This is a complex of late Archaean and/or early Proterozoic rocks which were reworked in the Variscan orogeny and became the most rigid part of the massif. The original sedimentary succession was thick (probably several kilometres) and typically 'geosynclinal', with intercalated volcanics. Two distinct sequences can be recognized, one including carbonates and the other almost entirely shaly. Due to later intense folding and metamorphism it is not clear how these two relate to one another, but it may be that the monotonous argillaceous succession is in fact two formations, one below and one above the carbonate-bearing succession. It is also not clear how all these rocks relate to a complex series of granulites which seem to have originated from a variety of acid to basic extrusives.

199

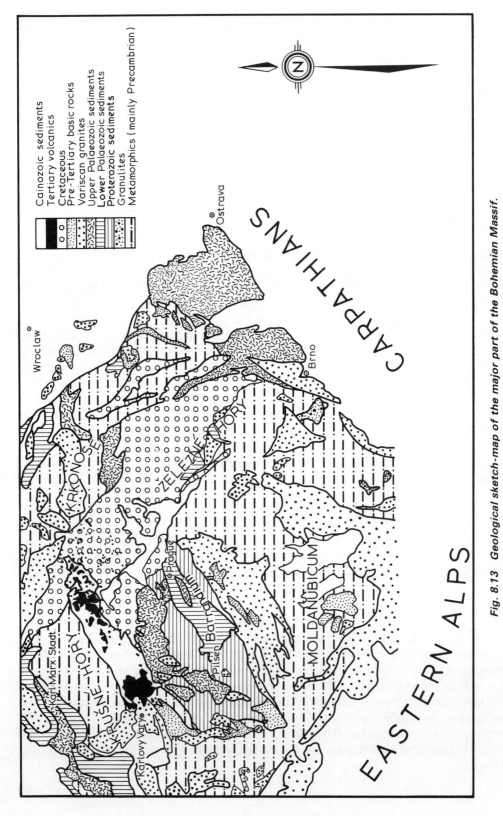

Legend:

- Cainozoic sediments
- Tertiary volcanics
- Cretaceous
- Pre-Tertiary basic rocks
- Variscan granites
- Upper Palaeozoic sediments
- Lower Palaeozoic sediments
- Proterozoic sediments
- Granulites
- Metamorphics (mainly Precambrian)

Wroclaw

Ostrava

Brno

CARPATHIANS

KRKONOSE

ZELEZNÉ HORY

Karl-Marx-Stadt.

KRUŠNÉ HORY

Karlovy Vary

Pilsen

Prague

Barrandian

MOLDANUBICUM

EASTERN ALPS

Fig. 8.13 Geological sketch-map of the major part of the Bohemian Massif.

Strong folding and metamorphism, together with migmatization, took place in early Proterozoic times and roughly correspond with the Svecofennian orogeny of the Fenno-Scandian Shield. Deep-seated metamorphism is represented by pale gneisses and granitoid rocks, while at a higher level there formed mica-schists, gneisses, and synorogenic granites. Later-phase granites are only known as pebbles in the conglomerates of the overlying Proterozoic succession. The orogeny (usually called 'Moldanubian') was followed by a long period of uplift and erosion. It was then that Moldanubicum became the rigid nucleus of the whole region, standing up as a positive area right through to Variscan times. Because of this, most of the higher crustal levels have been eroded away and the present peneplained surface was achieved by late Carboniferous times.

So we have a block forming the greater part of the southern half of the Bohemian Massif with a confusion of structural trends. Most distinctive are the granitic masses which trend roughly north or north-east, especially the great mass in the centre which extends from just east of Prague south-west towards Regensburg on the Danube. This forms a boundary with the largest metamorphic outcrop, which trends in the same direction.

The main mass of Moldanubicum formed an island in late Precambrian times, albeit of somewhat subdued relief. At first, sedimentation was gentle, with thick graphitic shales. These pass up into sandier deposits and there was faulting accompanied by extensive basic volcanism. This latter is mainly in the form of spilites and spilitic tuffs with associated cherts and forms a convenient dividing line in the middle of the Proterozoic. It was a classic eugosynclinal succession and was ended by earth movements which were the opening phase of the orogeny that reached its climax at the end of the Precambrian. This is well displayed in the Železné hory to the east of Prague. Anticlinal ridges and synclinal valleys developed with resultant differences in sediment thickness. There was also metamorphism and the emplacement of granites.

The later ('post-spilitic') sedimentation was therefore different in distribution, being concentrated in mobile troughs. Besides the new ridges, the old mass of Moldanubicum had been uplifted and was episodically supplying conglomerates and other clastics to the sedimentary pile, and coarse deposits interdigitate with black shales. Some Czech workers believe that some at least of the conglomerates are glacial in origin and it is tempting to correlate them with the 'Eocambrian' glaciation of northern Europe.

In the Krušné hory (Erzgebirge or 'iron mountains') along the Czech–East German frontier, the Proterozoic sediments are thick and mainly argillaceous and flysch-like in origin, although now metamorphosed to mica schists and gneisses. They include conglomerates and basic volcanics and appear to have been deposited contemporaneously with a late phase of the end Precambrian orogeny. They pass up into the Lower Palaeozoic, and with more volcanics through the Cambrian into the Ordovician, but there may be an unconformity at the base of the Cambrian that has been missed in the metamorphism.

The end-Precambrian orogeny is commonly called 'Assyntian' by the Czechs, but it certainly is not recorded at Assynt in the western highlands of Scotland, and I prefer to call it Cadomian, from Caen in Normandy. The general trend in the Cadomian structures—the anticlinoria, the cleavage, and the faulting—is to the north-east.

Eastwards in Moravia, the 'waist' of Czechoslovakia, there is a belt of schists of similar trend which are assumed to have been affected by the movements, but the dating here is somewhat uncertain. The same north-easterly trend is also seen in Lower Palaeozoic rocks, most notably in what may be regarded as the most famous rocks in Czechoslovakia.

Palaeozoic

From the centre of Prague one can take a tram with the destination board 'Barrandium'. This is one of the few places in an unkind world where a palaeontologist's name has been given to a locality, in this case a whole area of richly fossiliferous Lower Palaeozoic rocks (Joachim Barrande was a refugee from the French Revolution who settled in Prague and wrote more than thirty folio monographs on the local faunas). Barrandium is a long synclinal structure that stretches south-west from King Wenceslas's capital and includes up to Devonian sediments in its centre.

The basal Cambrian sandstones and conglomerates rest with a sharp unconformity on the folded Proterozoic basement. They pass up into shales with abundant, beautifully preserved trilobites,* while in late Cambrian times there was renewed volcanicity, related to late phases of the Cadomian movements, with emergence near the centre of the massif. Similar successions are seen elsewhere, with variations, but the coarse molasse-type deposits after the Cadomian orogeny in the early Cambrian are general.

After its period of thick sedimentation and orogenesis in the Proterozoic, the Bohemian Massif again became the site of a geosynclinal trough in the early Palaeozoic. This is sometimes called the 'Caledonian Tethys' and is pictured as wrapping round the Moldanubicum core. An inner 'Bavarian' facies, which is thinner and has many breaks, is distinguished from an outer 'Thuringian' facies, which is thicker and more continuous.

Truly thick sedimentation only really started in the Tremadoc and the subsiding trough was oriented, like the structures, to the north-east. Black graptolitic shales and sandstones predominate through the Ordovician, with an almost complete absence of carbonates. The shales passed up into the Silurian, but there was then an interesting development of volcanic islands, each of which developed concentric facies belts. The shallowest zone of coarse, crinoidal limestones (with terrestrial volcanics) passes out through coral and brachiopod zones to a belt of molluscs and trilobites and then to the deepest facies of graptolitic shales.

In the upper part of the Silurian there is a thick development of limestones, and the Silurian passes through into the Devonian in a richly fossiliferous marine facies that contains both shelly and graptolitic faunas. The local stage-names of Přidolian and Lochkovian, on either side of the boundary, are now used internationally. After years of discussion, the carbonate succession here at Klonk—a most appropriately named place to hammer in the first 'golden spike'—was chosen by the Stratigraphical Commission to define this much-disputed boundary. A monument now marks the spot. It is appropriate for another reason because here graptolites continue fairly commonly into undoubted Devonian rocks, although it does put the limit higher than where it has commonly been recognized elsewhere. But stratigraphical boundaries are essentially arbitrary and I am all for accepting such decisions, however uncomfortable it may make it for some of us.

One reason that Barrandium is so suitable for this purpose is that there is no sign of anything that could be called a Caledonian orogeny. Nevertheless, elsewhere in the

* There is a 'Trilobite Bar' overlooking the Vltava, with a most unlikely species as its sign.

massif, especially along its north-eastern edge, there was intense folding, thrusting, and metamorphism, at the end of Silurian times. The folds are oriented to the west-north-west, notably in the Sudetenland, and are probably the best documented Caledonian movements in central and eastern Europe. They added to the core and provided a new and larger massif that stood firm in the later Variscan spasms. Part of the evidence for the movements is the complete change in palaeogeography that followed. While the story continued unchanged in Barrandium, elsewhere—for example in the Sudetenland (well remembered politically by my generation)—much of the Devonian is missing and the rest is represented by conglomerates and greywackes.

The calcareous facies of the Devonian is one of the chief glories of Bohemia. This is, of course, a type area of the calcareous 'Hercynian magnafacies' (here called 'Bohemian') as distinct from the sandy 'Rhenish magnafacies'. In Barrandium there is marked lateral variation from detrital facies at the edge of the trough to dense limestones with well-developed reefs in the centre. North of Brno in Moravia there is the famous area of the Moravian Karst, with its spectacular caves and glorious limestone scenery. Here mid and late Devonian limestones rest directly on Precambrian granite and have remained almost flat-lying, being hardly affected by the Variscan movements. There is a remarkable development of reefs, for example in the Josef Valley. All was very shallow water and at Červený kopec ('red hill'), on the outskirts of Brno, there is even a tiny patch of typical 'Old Red Sandstone' facies, perhaps its southernmost development in central Europe, although farther north-east the limestones thin and pass into a deeper water facies with volcanics.

As in the Lower Palaeozoic there is a sharp contrast in Silesia to the north, where the Devonian is in a geosynclinal facies with much volcanism implying instability. The first stirrings of the Variscan were probably felt during the Givetian, but in Moravia limestone deposition continued throughout early Carboniferous times producing a 'Carboniferous Limestone' as in so many parts of Europe. But in the north-east, flysch-type 'Culm' sedimentation had begun in late Devonian times and the axis of the trough in which it was deposited moved slowly south through early Carboniferous times. So younger and younger stages of the 'Culm' facies overstep in that direction. This seems to have happened round both sides of the central core.

The main Variscan movements seem to have happened towards the end of early Carboniferous times. In Barrandium, all the Palaeozoic sediments are folded but not so intensely as to destroy the marvellous fossils. The tectonism was stronger to the north-east, with some thrusting of the Precambrian over the Lower Palaeozoic. The Variscan orogeny reactivated the Precambrian structures and generally followed the same lines. This is most obvious in the trend of the Barrandium synclinorium. Round the edge of the massif, all the way from Thuringia in the north-west to Moravia in the south-east, Variscan structures are much more obvious and intense. This is commonly called the 'Variscan Arc'. Within the anticlinal structures there are inliers of basement and the general east–north-east trend of the structures again seems to be a reactivation of Cadomian lineaments. There are also prominent later, cross-cutting faults, which seem to reflect deep structures.

Granite emplacement was an important feature of the Variscan orogeny, including famous ones such as Karlovy Vary (Karlsbad) with its equally famous felspar twins, at the western end of Czechoslovakia. Another is that of the scenic Krkonose ('giant')

Mountains, on the borders of Poland. Deep borings have shown that these granites, like those of Cornubia, are merely surface bulges on an almost continuous sub-surface body. They are elongated transversely to the main structural trend.

The Variscan granites may be grouped into three or four distinct phases, of which the latest was associated with valuable mineralization. Tin, wolfram, lead, and zinc, are particularly important and it was from Bohemia that the Curies got the pitchblende from which they first isolated radium. Jachymov (Joachimstal), north of Karlovy Vary, is still an important source of uranium. The general pattern of the veining swings from east-north-east in the west to north-north-east in the east but it is all parallel to the Precambrian trends. In fact it is almost impossible to define a distinctive Variscan trend in the Bohemian Massif. The only important exceptions are on the south-west border of the massif, along the Czech–Austrian border, where the veining and other features run parallel to the north-westerly trending fault zone that delimits this side of the massif.

By the end of the Variscan orogeny, Bohemia had become a rigid massif. A series of small late Carboniferous and Permian basins are scattered across the surface and in the east there is the important Silesian coal basin running into western Poland. The small basins are preserved in little graben structures that began to develop in early Westphalian times with shales and some coals. But they are not everywhere of the same age. Later Westphalian deposits are mainly conglomerates and arkosic sandstones, derived from the already unroofed granites. Movements were still going on, and further uplift preceded Stephanian barren red beds with a few local coals. Another break heralded the red mudstones, sandstones, and conglomerates, of the early Permian.

The migration of sedimentary troughs had changed direction, with the result that the Permian is best developed in the north-west. This is linked with the general uplift of the old Moldanubian Massif which began in late Carboniferous times. In general, sediment was derived from the south-west during the late Carboniferous and from the north-east during the Permian.

By far the most important area of Carboniferous rocks is that of Upper Silesia. In Czechoslovakia, this is the basin around the industrial and mining city of Ostrava (the 'iron heart of Czechoslovakia') at the north end of the country's 'waist'. This extends under a much larger area of Poland in that concentration of mining and industry west of Krakow. A paralic basin existed here from Namurian until Westphalian times. Whereas the little faulted basins within the massif proper were cut off from the sea, the Silesian coal-field formed part of the great belt of marginal basins that extended all the way from Ireland to the Donetsk. It has given its name to the upper division of the Carboniferous.

The Visean marine sedimentary basin here was affected by the Sudetic movements with uplift and dry land to the west while marine incursions came in from the east. Brackish deposits passed up into late Namurian coal-bearing strata and then a thick series of limnic formations in the Westphalian when the sea was completely excluded. The Asturian movements produced an unconformity below barren Stephanian conglomerates and sandstones which pass up into the Permian.

Mesozoic

During the late Permian, Triassic, and early Jurassic times most of the Bohemian Massif was an uplifted land-mass. Late faulting produced depressions and then erosion produced peneplanation. Triassic sediments are extremely local and mainly limited to the Sudetenland in the north, where they consist of conglomerates and arkoses from the local granites. Similarly, Jurassic seas lapped around the edges (as they did round other Variscan massifs) and Jurassic sediments are only known as slivers in fault zones on the north side of the massif and as denudation relicts on the Palaeozoic near Brno.

The great post-Variscan event was the Cenomanian transgression which here really was Cenomanian in age! The whole northern half of the massif subsided and was flooded by late Cretaceous seas. So most of the country north of Prague as far as the Krkonose mountains on the border with Poland, are covered with flat-lying Cretaceous sediments. The pre-Cenomanian topography was probably a gently undulating peneplain. There is evidence of lateritic weathering, perhaps of Jurassic age, and the basal Cenomanian sediments are mostly fine grained and well sorted. This is not the case where the sea transgressed on to the more rugged landscape farther south. Near Kolin and Kutná Hora, east of Prague, one can see one of the finest unconformities in Europe. Coarse Cretaceous littoral deposits fill pockets in a very irregular surface of Precambrian amphibolite gneiss.* The Upper Cretaceous deposits become progressively more fine-grained as one moves away from the shoreline towards the north.

Regressions and transgressions continued through the rest of the Cretaceous, but the main part of Moldanubicum was never submerged and there were local islands, in the Sudetenland, which provided sediment to the surrounding area. Thus in the Sudetic region east of Dresden there were granitic islands around which there accumulated thick cross-bedded sands. These weather out as great blocks known locally as 'rock cities'. The amateur geologist Goethe visited them several times. It is interesting to compare them with the Nubian sandstone of North Africa. The Cretaceous sediments lie in a broad trough that extends in a north-westerly direction parallel to the edge of the massif. Only locally is there steepening and overturning associated with Tertiary faulting.

Although the Moldanubian core remained dry land for most of the Mesozoic, up to 200 m of fresh-water sands, gravels, and clays, accumulated in tectonic depressions in the south-east corner of the massif during the Senonian. Due to their flat-lying nature and temporary protection by overlying Neogene they have an outcrop far out of proportion to their thickness.

Cainozoic

The massif remained above sea-level during the Tertiary and marine deposits are only found where it borders the Carpathian trough to the east. There shallow seas spread over a mature land surface in Miocene times, depositing sands and clays. At Černotin one can see Devonian limestones bored by Miocene piddocks.

Within the massif proper, Tertiary sedimentation was a matter of tectonic control in little graben and flooded valleys. Thus in southern Bohemia, the valleys formed in tectonic depressions in Cretaceous and Eocene times became lakes in the Oligocene accumulating sands, clays, and peats, some of which are now worked as lignites.

* The classic locality is at Kaňk, near an interesting church with an ossuary and a statue of St. Barbara, the patron saint of geologists (now sadly desanctified).

Volcanism began in early Miocene times and there is a large area of north-west Bohemia (known as the 'Czech Auvergne') that is dotted with volcanoes like the Massif Central. As in the French massif, the volcanoes are often arranged in straight lines of 'puys' along fault lines, and the whole belt of volcanism is oriented in a north–east direction. We again see the influence of the Precambrian structures. The volcanism was synchronous with sedimentation and the thin-bedded argillaceous deposits are often baked to lurid colours (and the lignites burned) as a result of the local eruptions. Much of the volcanism was confined to the subsiding areas, where the landscape is dotted with large and small ash cones and volcanic necks. Presumably the same faults were responsible for both. The volcanoes vary widely in composition, but andesites, trachites, and phonolites dominate while the more basic types are confined to areas with major fault dislocations.

Brown coals accumulated extensively in the Miocene and are intruded by later basic volcanics, but younger sands and gravels are only preserved in a few small graben. The volcanism continued spasmodically through the Pliocene and Pleistocene and is seen continuing today in the hot springs of north-west Bohemia, notably in the world-famous spas of Marian Lazne (Marianbad) and Karlovy Vary (Karlsbad), where the faded glories of once-regal spas are preserved for deserving workers and geologists. Besides the medicinal properties of the volcanic waters, Kieselguhr and similar deposits present a considerable problem to the local plumbers and provide visitors with beautiful examples of rapid petrification, such as the perfect siliceous rose I have on my bookcase.

8(i) Holy Cross Mountains

Only a local can pronounce Góry Swiętokrzyskie, so I hope my Polish friends will excuse me if I use the English translation. The Palaeozoic rocks which underlie Poland and the north German plain only appear at the surface in the Sudetenland and in this small group of hills in central Poland (Fig. 8.14). Their interest and importance are quite out of proportion to their size, since their interpretation is vital to our whole understanding of the structure of our continent.

The Holy Cross Mountains come right in the corner of the Danish Triangle, squeezed between the Variscan Front and the Danish–Polish Line. The critical issue is the importance of the movements that affected them in mid Palaeozoic times. What is more, the northern part of the massif, the Łysogóry (Mussorgsky's 'Bare Mountain') has a different sedimentological and tectonic history from the southern part, the Kielce area.

The metamorphic Precambrian is nowhere seen at the surface or in boreholes. The oldest rocks present are late Proterozoic unmetamorphosed siltstones with limestone intercalations which seem to have been deposited in a shallow trough running parallel to the edge of the East European Platform. The main axis of deposition was to the south and the depositional basin probably extended as far as the Carpathian fore-deep, where the equivalent sediments are now phyllites. Although the contact is nowhere seen, an unconformity is presumed between this and overlying fossiliferous Cambrian. There does not seem to be much evidence for important movements at this time.

Cambrian outcrops are quite extensive in the Holy Cross Mountains. All three divisions are present and they form the main ranges. Right from the start there is a clear differentiation between calcareous facies in the north and mainly argillaceous facies in

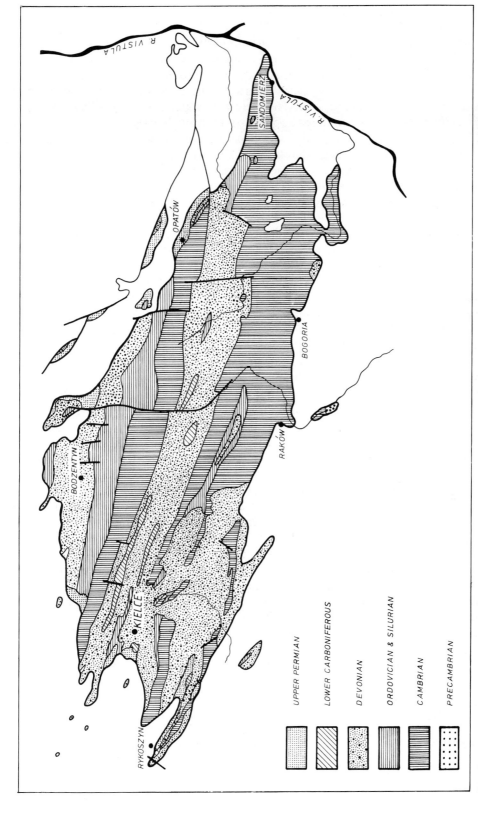

UPPER PERMIAN

LOWER CARBONIFEROUS

DEVONIAN

ORDOVICIAN & SILURIAN

CAMBRIAN

PRECAMBRIAN

Fig. 8.14 Geological sketch-map of the Holy Cross Mountains (after Książkiewicz et al., 1968, by kind permission of the authors).

the south. Trilobites and their trace fossils are particularly abundant. The axis of sedimentation moved north in mid Cambrian times, with coarse quartz sands accumulating in the south. The Upper Cambrian is only preserved in the Łysogóry chain with a passage from clastics in the east, near the East European Platform, to fine-grained highly fossiliferous sediments in the west. The picture of a north–west trending trough, with slight shifts in the location of its axis, persisted all through early Palaeozoic times.

The Lower Ordovician is nearly everywhere absent following the shallowing of late Cambrian times. Then a trough developed again in the north, with Middle Ordovician oolitic limestones (and even conglomerates) passing up into graptolitic shales in the Caradoc and Ashgill. In the south, a series of small ridges and troughs was formed, with contrasting facies and many local breaks. Only in the extreme south, near Brzeziny, is the Lower Ordovician preserved, but even here the top of the system is missing. The whole of this region seems to have suffered emergence at the end of the Ordovician, but again does not justify the title of orogeny.

Due to slight movements, the lowermost Silurian is missing, but generally speaking the greater part of that period is represented by graptolitic shales (ranging from late Llandovery to early Ludlow in age). The succession is most complete in the north, where there was a deep basin through most of the period. In the south, as in the Ordovician, was an area of troughs and rises. Towards the end of the period, however, changes began to express themselves. Thick greywackes and occasional limestones and tuffs replace the monotonous graptolitic shales. This change started in the Łysogóry, but soon spread throughout the massif. It has been called the 'Cracovian' orogenic phase after the fascinating (and learned) city in southern Poland. Here it is datable as late Wenlock–early Ludlow, but is hardly more than an inrush of material from elsewhere.

Later in Silurian times came another more severe phase. This affected the southern part of the Holy Cross Mountains earlier and far more than it affected the north. As a result, there is nothing preserved above the Wenlock in the Kielce area, while there is at least Ludlow in the south of the Łysogóry. Only in the north is there continuous sedimentation through the Silurian–Devonian boundary in a clay–silt facies with tuff horizons. In the Kielce area, sedimentation did not recommence until the Emsian, leaving a large break spanning most of the late Silurian and early Devonian.

Thus only the southern part of the Holy Cross Mountains was really affected by 'Caledonian' movements and then only in a comparatively minor way. Certainly there was nothing in the way of intense deformation or metamorphism, and no major intrusions, although isoclinal folding and angular unconformities at up to 70 degrees are recorded. To the casual geological visitor from the Celtic fringe, this is not the Caledonian orogeny as we understand it. One just sees wooded ridges formed by gently folded, argillaceous Lower Palaeozoic sediments cut across at a low angle by harder beds of the Devonian.

The general trend of the folding is towards the west-north-west with overturning towards the south. It may be significant that to the south of the Holy Cross Mountains, in the Silesia–Cracow uplands, Silurian sediments are intruded by a series of spilites and keratophyres, although pillow lavas have not been recorded. Small intrusions of dolerite and lamprophyre cut rocks up to Lower Devonian age, notably around Kielce. They presumably indicate the presence of a granite at depth, although none has been encountered in boreholes.

Some have postulated plate margins and continental collisions on the basis of the above evidence. If present, the vital information must be sought in deep boreholes to the south, in the vicinity of the front of the Carpathians where we shall be talking about plates at a much later stage of European history. The Devonian succession at least fits closely to the specification of an Atlantic-type ocean–continent margin, with the edge of the continental shelf coinciding with the Kielce–Łagów line.

The earliest Devonian (Gedinnian) strata of the Holy Cross region are of both marine and continental origin. Marine facies are present in the west and centre of the Łysogóry, in the form of highly fossiliferous shales and silts. To the east lay the 'Old Red Sandstone' continent which extended on to the great Russian plain. In Siegenian times the sea retreated towards the western trough and shallow-water sands and shales containing an abundant fauna (comparable with those of Belgium) came into the area, followed by coastal plain deposits.

In Emsian times the sea extended again, even invading the Kielce rise to the south, with a basal conglomerate that locally passes into a bone-bed. In the Eifelian, the generally sandy sediments gave way to mudstones and limestones, with more rich and varied faunas. Both the Rhenish and the Hercynian 'magnafacies' are represented. Later the basin became more saline and dolomites dominate the succession until the end of the mid Devonian. In the Kielce area there are some reef associations, although many still suggestive of a restricted environment. What may be called 'normal' marine conditions are local and only returned with more varied sedimentation in the north towards the end of the Givetian.

In the Frasnian of the Holy Cross Mountains, as in so many parts of the world, reefs took over, especially in the south. 'Bioherms' and 'biostromes' abound in the lower and middle part of the stage. In the north, the water became deeper with pelagic faunas in shales and thin limestones. The separation of a trough to the north and shallow water in the south continued into the Famennian, but became progressively less clear. Both facies were calcareous, but with abundant evidence of submarine slumping with tumbled material from the old reefs. Some debris also came from the north side of the trough. There are many stratigraphical breaks and we may be seeing the vanguard of the Variscan orogeny.

The Carboniferous is relatively poorly developed in the Holy Cross Mountains, although it is so important in the Silesian coal basin to the west. Only the Lower Carboniferous is preserved, as small patches in the south. Much has been removed by later erosion. There was still a differentiation of facies, but the distinction between the Łysogóry and Kielce areas had disappeared and the main facies variations were now between the south-west and the central area. In the former there is a direct transition from the Devonian through shales and marly limestones, with pyroclastic deposits appearing in the lowest Carboniferous and continuing sporadically until the end of the Visean. The Lower Carboniferous consists of shales and siltstones, with cherts, siderites, and phosphatic deposits in the central area. Limestones are only developed locally, but in the south-west one sees the usual 'Carboniferous Limestone' facies, albeit with considerable breaks.

Earth movements started again in the late Visean and terrigenous clastics of the usual 'Culm' facies came into the south and slowly moved north and west. There was fairly strong folding in the late Carboniferous and the Permian lies almost flat, with a marked unconformity, on the older strata. The early Zechstein transgressed on to folded rocks, forming a complex, deeply indented shoreline. Conglomeratic and other high-energy basal deposits pass up into a more calcareous facies which are part of the general story of northern Europe, as is the rest of the Mesozoic and Tertiary.

The massif did not form an island in the Mesozoic seas like others of its kind. In fact it was often the opposite, with most Mesozoic formations thickening into a trough hereabouts. Only the lowermost Permian contains material derived from the massif. Thereafter subsidence was the rule and the present outcrop of the Holy Cross Mountains results from Tertiary rather than Palaeozoic movements. The trough ran parallel to the front of the East European Platform and persisted as late as the Maastrichtian and Paleocene. Miocene folding produced an approximately east–west arch in front of the Carpathians and it is where this arch crosses the north-westerly trending mid-Polish rise that a piece of the Palaeozoic basement came up to form the Holy Cross Mountains.

Selected references to Chapter 8

Section 8(a)   Munster Variscides

Charlesworth, J. K. (1963), *Historical Geology of Ireland*, Oliver and Boyd, Edinburgh and London, 565 pp.

Gill, W. D. (1962), 'The Variscan fold belt in Ireland', in K. Coe (ed.), *Some Aspects of the Variscan Fold Belt*, Manchester Univ. Press, pp. 44–64.

Naylor, D. (1978), 'A structural section across the Variscan fold belt, southwest Ireland', *J. Earth Sci., Dublin*, **1**, 63–70.

Walsh, P. T. (1965), 'Cretaceous outliers in south-west Ireland and their implications for Cretaceous palaeogeography', *Proc. Geol. Soc., Lond.*, **1629**, 8–10.

Whittow, J. B. (1974), *Geology and Scenery in Ireland*, Penguin Books, Harmondsworth, 301 pp.

Section 8(b)   Cornubia

Brooks, M. and D. G. James (1975), 'The geological results of seismic refraction surveys in the Bristol Channel, 1970–1973', *J. Geol. Soc., Lond.*, **131**, 163–182.

Brooks, M. and M. S. Thompson (1973), 'The geological interpretation of a gravity survey of the Bristol Channel', *J. Geol. Soc., Lond.*, **129**, 245–274.

Dearman, W. R. (1970), 'Some aspects of the tectonic evolution of southwest England', *Proc. Geol. Ass.*, **81**, 483–491 (and earlier papers).

Edmonds, E. A., M. C. McKeown, and M. Williams (1975), *British Regional Geology: South-west England*, 4th edn, H.M. Stationery Office, London, 136 pp.

Evans, D. J. and M. S. Thompson (1979), 'The geology of the central Bristol Channel and the Lundy area, South Western Approaches, British Isles', *Proc. Geol. Ass.*, **90**, 1–14.

Lloyd, A. J., R. J. G. Savage, A. H. Stride, and D. T. Donovan (1973), 'The geology of the Bristol Channel floor', *Phil. Trans. Soc. A.*, **274**, 595–626.

Owen, T. R. (1971), 'The structural evolution of the Bristol Channel', *Proc. Geol. Soc., Lond.*, **1664**, 289–294.

Section 8(c)   Wessex, the Weald, and the Boulonnais

Ager, D. V. and P. Wallace (1966), 'The environmental history of the Boulonnais, France', *Proc. Geol. Assoc.*, **77**, 385–417.

Ager, D. V. and P. Wallace (1966), 'Easter field meeting in the Boulonnais, France', *Proc. Geol. Assoc.*, **77**, 419–435.

Chatwin, C. P. (1960), *British Regional Geology: The Hampshire Basin and Adjoining Areas*, 3rd edn, Geol. Surv. and Mus., London, 99 pp.

Gallois, R. W. (1965), *British Regional Geology: The Wealden District*, 4th edn, Geol. Surv. and Mus., London, 101 pp.

Wills, L. J. (1973), 'A palaeogeological map of the Palaeozoic floor below the Permian and Mesozoic formations in England and Wales', *Mem. Geol. Soc. Lond.*, No. 7, 23 pp.

Wills, L. J. (1978), 'A palaeogeological map of the Lower Palaeozoic floor below the cover of Upper Devonian, Carboniferous and later formations', *Mem. Geol. Soc. Lond.*, No. 8, 36 pp.

Section 8(d)   English Channel

Cnexo (1971), 'Colloque sur la géologie de la Manche' (papers in French and English), *Mém. Bur. Rech. Geol. Min.*, Paris, No. 79, 326 pp.

Dunham, K. D. *et al.* (1972), 'The Sub-Pleistocene Geology of the British Isles and the adjacent continental shelf' (map), Inst. Geol. Sci., London.

Section 8(e)   Ardennes, Eifel, and Rheinisches Schiefergebirge

Beugnies, A. (1964), 'Essai de synthèse du géodynamisme paléozoique de l'Ardenne', *Rev. Géogr. Phys. Géol. Dyn.*, **6**, 269–277.

Erben, H. K. and K. Zagora (1967), 'Devonian of Germany', *Internat. Symp. Dev. Syst.*, *Calgary*, pp. 53–68.

Hoeppener, R. (1955), 'Tektonik im Schiefergebirge', *Geol. Rundschau*, **44**, 26–58.

Lecompte, M. (1958), 'Les récifs paléozoiques en Belgique', *Geol. Rundschau*, **47**, 384–401.

Stamp, L. D., E. Mailleux, G. Delepine, P. Pruvost, and J. Cornet (1922), 'The Geology of Belgium and Long excursion to Belgium', *Proc. Geol. Ass.*, **33**, 1–72.

Tilmann, N. *et al.* (1938), 'Summer field meeting. The Rhenish Schiefergebirge', *Proc. Geol. Ass.*, **49**, 225–260.

Wallace, P. and D. Laurentiaux (1973), 'Summer field meeting in the Ardennes and Vosges', *Proc. Geol. Ass.*, **84**, 181–206.

Waterlot, G. (1969), 'Le Paléozoique en Ardenne française', *Ann. Soc. Géol. Nord*, **89**, 5–22.

Waterlot, G. and A. Beugnies (1973), *Ardenne*, in *Guides géol région. Ardenne and Luxembourg*, pt 1. Masson, Paris, pp. 1–125.

Section 8(f)   Harz

Knetsch, G. (1963), *Geologie von Deutschland*, Enke, Stuttgart, 386 pp.

Möbius, G. (1966), *Abriss der Geologie des Harzes*, Teubner, Leipzig, 219 pp.

Mohr, K. (1973), *Sammlung geologischer Führer: Harz*, Westlicher Teil, Borntraeger, Berlin, and Stuttgart, 200 pp.

Schriel, W. (1954), *Die Geologie des Harzes*, Schr. wirtschaftswiss. Stud. Niedersachsen, **49**, 308 pp.

Skiba, R. (1966), *Moderner Harzer Bergbau*, Pieper, Clausthal-Zellerfeld, 94 pp.

Section 8(g)   South-west German Plateau

Dietl, G. (1977), 'The Braunjura (Brown Jurassic) in southwest Germany', Stuttgarter Beiträge zur Naturkunde, B, No. 25, 41 pp.

Geyer, O. F. and M. P. Gwinner (1962), *Der Schwäbische Jura*, Sammlung Geologischer Führer, No. 40, Borntraeger, Berlin, 452 pp.

Gwinner, M. P. (1977), *Geological Structure and History of Southwestern Germany*, Sammlung Geologischer Führer, No. 23, Borntraeger, Berlin, 6 pp.

Urlichs, M. (1977), *The Lower Jurassic in Southwestern Germany*, Sammlung Geologischer Führer, No. 24, Borntraeger, Berlin, 41 pp.

Zeiss, A. (1977), *Jurassic Stratigraphy of Franconia*, Sammlung Geologischer Führer, No. 31, Borntraeger, Berlin, 32 pp.

Ziegler, B. (1977), *The 'White' (Upper) Jurassic in Southern Germany*, Sammlung Geologischer Führer, No. 26, Borntraeger, Berlin, 79 pp.

Section 8(h)   Bohemian Massif

Anon (1967/68), 'Regional geology of Czechoslovakia', geological atlas, 1:1 000 000, Geol. Surv. Czechoslovakia (7 sheets with text) + series of excursion guides for *23rd Internat. Geol. Congr., Prague, 1968*.

Buday, T. *et al.* (1960), *Tectonic Development of Czechoslovakia*, Naklad. Českoslov. Akad. Věd, Prague, 224 pp.

Svoboda, J. (1966), *Regional Geology of Czechoslovakia*, pt I, *The Bohemian Massif*, Geol. Surv. Czechoslovakia, Prague, 668 pp.

Svoboda, J. and F. Prantl (1958), *Barrandium*, Naklad. Československ. Akad. Věd, Prague, 118 pp.

Section 8(i)   Holy Cross Mountains

Anon (1968), 'The Palaeozoic and Mesozoic in the Świętokrzyskie Mountains and the Cainozoic in the Carpathian Foredeep', *Excursion Guide C45*, 23rd Internat. Geol. Congr., Geol. Inst., Warsaw, 81 pp.

Głazek, J. and J. Kutek (1970), 'The Holy Cross Mountains area in the alpine diastrophic cyle', *Bull. Acad. Pol. Sci.*, **18**, 227–235.

Książkiewicz, M., J. Samsonowicz, and E. Rühle (1965), *An outline of the Geology of Poland*, Central Inst. Sci. Tech. Econ. Inf., Warsaw, 414 pp.

Sokołowski, S. *et al.* (1970), *The Geology of Poland*, vol. 1, *Stratigraphy*, pt 1, 'Pre-Cambrian and Palaeozoic', Publ. House Wydawnictwa Geol., Warsaw, 651 pp.

Chapter Nine

Central Variscides

This chapter concerns the central belt of Variscide massifs, with intervening basins, that form the major part of France, but just extend into Germany as far as the Black Forest. It is also convenient to include here the isolated fragment of Meso-Europa preserved in eastern Romania.

The belt is characterized by the complete lack of evidence of a Caledonian orogeny, but by a major spasm coming at the end of the Devonian. This is even true of remote Dobrogea. There was also a late Carboniferous spasm and most of the massifs are characterized by high-grade metamorphism.

9(a) Armorica

Armorica since their serpentinites and associated rocks are clearly related to the Armorican complex and are only thrust against the very different rocks of the Cornubian Variscides. ('les Îles Anglo-Normandes'). It might be argued that the English Channel and parts of south-west England, notably the Lizard Peninsula and Start Point, are really part of Armorica since their serpentinites and associated rocks are clearly related to the Armorican complex and are only thrust against the very different rocks of the Cornubian Variscides. However, these related areas are discussed elsewhere and this chapter is only concerned with Armorica in the strict sense (Fig. 9.1).

Like several of the other Variscan massifs of Europe, Armorica is not a rugged mountainous area, but a plateau of rather dull, undulating country, where the softer rocks have weathered to form broad valleys. The harder formations and intrusive granites retain the sharp peneplain of supposedly Cretaceous age, as seen (though dated later) in south-west England and South Wales. This drops steeply to the sea as spectacular cliffs.

Its abundant granites probably solidified at intermediate depths in the crust, being neither the tips of batholiths like the granites of south-west England nor the deep-seated granite gneisses of the Massif Central. It may be significant that the block of Breton granite on my front gate-post is remarkably like one of the Caledonian granites of the English Lake District.* The structure of Armorica is very complex, largely because of

*It is also historically significant that it comes from a locality with a Celtic name—Aber Ildut—that sounds familiar in South Wales.

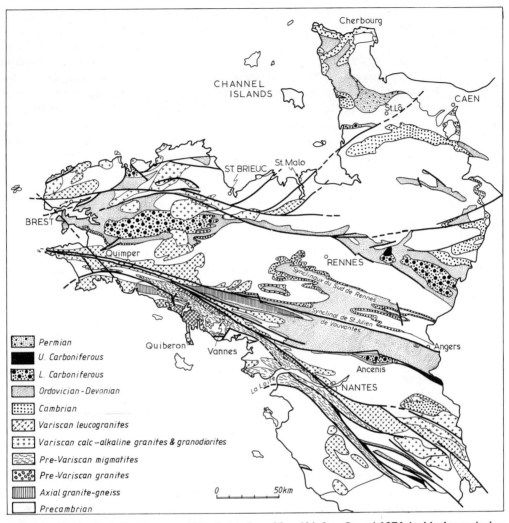

Fig. 9.1 *Geological sketch-map of the Armorican Massif (after Cogné 1974, by kind permission of Doin Editeurs and Prof. Debelmas).*

successive episodes of tectonic reworking and the influence of later movements on some of the oldest trends. Undoubtedly part of the complexity is only apparent due to the contradictory views of the many independent and individualistic geologists who have worked here, and there is a surprising lack of syntheses of the geology of the whole region. Once more I wonder at my temerity in rushing in where Gallic angels have feared to tread.

Precambrian

The Precambrian rocks of Armorica are normally divided into the Pentevrian below and the Brioverian above, although not all local geologists are agreed on the reality of this division. These terms are also used more widely, especially in France.

The Pentevrian was first described from the north coast of Brittany, near St. Brieuc, and is best known to British geologists through its forming the whole of the tomato-growing island of Guernsey and possibly the Lizard peninsula of Cornwall. It is a strongly reworked complex of granitic and granodioritic gneisses which were probably largely sedimentary in origin and which were metamorphosed in an orogeny locally known as the Sarnian. Its radiometric age remains uncertain, although dates around 800–1000 million years (and locally some as old as 2900) have been found. It may be that the Sarnian orogeny corresponds with the Gothian event in the Fenno-Scandian Shield and that this represents a detached edge of the craton, with fragments of the Archaean crust reminiscent of the Lewisian of the Hebridean Province. In the south of Brittany and in the Vendée there is a migmatitic and gneissose complex at the bottom of the succession cut by amphibolites. This seems to be the equivalent of the Pentevrian in the north. After the Sarnian (sometimes called the Pentevrian) orogeny there seems to have been general uplift in the centre of Armorica, forming a land-mass that is often called 'Sarnia'.

The Brioverian is very much a highlight of Armorican geology. This is a thick late Precambrian sedimentary sequence, commonly metamorphosed at the end of the era, but also still preserving many original features. It may be said in general of Armorica that the older sediments (both Proterozoic and Palaeozoic) are much less metamorphosed than in the Massif Central or in the other massifs of northern France and western Germany. They are more comparable to the Bohemian Massif of Czechoslovakia.

The Brioverian is seen in close proximity to the Pentevrian in northern Brittany and an angular unconformity has been claimed between them. On the coast at Jospinet, east of St. Brieuc, one can see arkosic sandstones and conglomerates of the Brioverian and one can see Pentevrian gneisses, but the junction between them is far from obvious. The Brioverian evidently transgressed across the land-mass of 'Sarnia' and the earliest deposits were wholly clastic. Farther south the base is not seen and the early succession is unclear.

These deposits pass up into a thick succession of black shales with some sandstones, which are sometimes referred to as 'flysch'. This also contains ophiolite sequences such as the pillow lavas well exposed on Erquy Plage near St. Brieuc (and the association recently described from Audierne Bay as a Caledonian suture zone!). As we are here so close to the Atlantic, it is difficult not to think of a Proterozoic proto-Atlantic being consumed hereabouts. These sediments are much more widespread (albeit in a metamorphosed condition farther south) and there seems to have been a trench here (the 'Fosse Armoricain') in mid Brioverian times. The sediments include grey schists and phyllites around St. Lô at the foot of the Cotentin peninsula, which gives its Roman name, Briovera, to the whole sedimentary group.

Earth movements began at the end of mid Brioverian times, raising new cordillera to the north and south of the east–west central trough. These are the first manifestations of the Cadomian orogeny. The cordillera, called 'Mancellia' and 'Ligeria' respectively, were to persist through much of Palaeozoic times and cause much of the stratigraphical variation within the later deposits. So the general east–west Armorican trend had already established itself here before the end of Precambrian times. Some metamorphism had probably already occurred at this stage.

The late Brioverian is particularly famous for its glacial and periglacial deposits, well seen in the western cliffs and beaches of the Cotentin peninsula, notably near Granville.

There has been much argument about these and some are more persuasive than others. Nevertheless it now seems to be generally accepted that the conglomeratic beds near the top of the Brioverian are true tillites and it is natural that they should be correlated with the much more convincing 'Eocambrian' tillites of Varanger in northern Norway and at other places along the Caledonide chain. The boulders in the tillites are sometimes said to show ice scratches. They are largely granitic but include recognizable earlier Brioverian material. Presumably they came from the northern of the two elevated cordillera. Again there is no obvious unconformity below, but a regional discordance can be seen on small-scale maps.

The glacial episode in the north was followed by the deposition of flysch-type rocks. This was associated with the later and main Cadomian movements and the emplacement of granites such as that of Vire, south of St. Lô, which have been dated as around 580 million years, although they are eroded and overlain by Cambrian sediments.

In central Brittany there are again conglomerates in the Upper Brioverian, but these seem to be estuarine or shallow marine in origin as one enters the central trough. They too pass up into flysch-type sediments like those of the north. The metamorphic grade, however, is much higher here, rising from green schist to amphibolite level. This problem is more difficult in southern Brittany and the Vendée, where both the sedimentary and the metamorphic histories are complexly interwoven. In fact the last metamorphic phase seems to have obliterated all signs of earlier events in this region.

The Cadomian orogeny was preceded and accompanied by the emplacement of large granitic masses some of which (as already mentioned) are overlain unconformably by Cambrian sediments. Others appear to have been remobilized and re-intruded during the Variscan orogeny so that their original Cadomian age has, in some cases, been disputed. One particular problem relates to the Brest Gneiss which extends from the coast west of that port north-east towards Morlaix. It is a large area of granodiorite which becomes more foliated towards the north-east. This has been regarded, by many French geologists, as having resulted from the *in situ* metamorphism and granitization of Brioverian rocks. Others have claimed evidence of contact metamorphism and stoped margins, suggesting magmatic emplacement.

The trends and style of folding in the Cadomian orogeny were basically different from those which earlier affected the Pentevrian rocks. Undoubtedly there were several phases, of which the earlier are naturally the more difficult to distinguish, but it seems that in the first spasm there was tight folding with flat-lying axial planes and a general trend to the north-north-west. In a second phase there were upright folds, tighter in the north than in the south, producing the east-north-east trending axial plane cleavage and folding that dominates the Brioverian rocks. A third phase was probably related to this and produced the main metamorphism. Late granites and granodiorites, such as that of Pointe des Renards (mistakenly called Caledonian) post-date the main metamorphism but are cut by later basic dikes and affected by a final minor metamorphic phase. So the Cadomian orogeny was complex and has been particularly well studied in this area. This is one reason that I prefer it as a name for an orogeny at the end of the Precambrian, coming as it does from the Roman name for Caen in Normandy. Near here is the classic section at Orne where Cambrian and later sediments rest with marked unconformity on the tectonized Brioverian.

Early Palaeozoic

After the Cadomian orogeny, the Armorican Massif went through a long, quiet period during which the new mountains were worn down to a peneplain over which crept the early Palaeozoic seas. In the north there is a sharp, angular unconformity beneath the Cambrian, but in the south the story is again unclear and there may be a direct passage from the Brioverian into the Cambrian, with some of the former being classified as 'Infracambrian'.

It may be that much of the Cadomian orogeny in Armorica occurred during Cambrian times, for the position of that system here is anomalous. In the south, correlation is largely a matter of matching conglomerates, but one of these seems to be transgressive and is commonly blamed on the early Cambrian (e.g., at Rochers de Rocreus near Caen). There are a series of intercalations of molasse-type deposits (probably continental in origin) with bands that are probably marine. The former are largely missing over the two cordillera but fill in the old landscapes in between. There have been arguments about a micro-fauna only found once and then (almost certainly wrongly) attributed to the Carboniferous!* But there does seem to be some definite evidence in the form of archaeocyathids (previously identified as corals).

Generally speaking the Cambrian consists of reddish-coloured beds with frequent conglomerates and plenty of evidence of transgressions and regressions. This applies to the whole Palaeozoic of Armorica, which is never anywhere near complete, has frequent breaks, and varies wildly in thickness from place to place. Although wholly epicontinental, it is clearly the result of constant up and down movements.

The sedimentary and stratigraphical history of Armorica becomes much clearer in the Ordovician. The period began with a marked transgression in which inter-tidal and shallow marine deposits overlie a thin development of fluviatile sandstones and conglomerates. In places, notably over the cordillera, these rest directly and with angular discordance on the Brioverian.

The shallowest water facies of the early Ordovician (Arenig) in Armorica is one of the most famous formations in Europe—the *Grès Armoricains*. These sandstones are characteristically pure white or purplish (so-called 'liver-coloured'), clean-washed, well-sorted, and often cross-bedded. They are seen in many of the cliffs of northern Brittany, for example in high white cliffs around Camaret across the inlet (or 'gullet') from Brest (in the bay sadly called *Mort Anglaise*). They form high points in the same area, such as Roche Maurice and the hill of Menez Hom near Chateaulin which provides a splendid view of Brittany. They are also well seen farther east in Normandy, forming the impressive escarpment south of Caen on which stands William the Conqueror's castle at Falaise. But the most striking thing about them is their wide extent. Not only do they occur throughout the whole of Brittany (somewhat thicker in the north than in the south) but exactly similar sandstones of the same age are seen in the Cantabrian mountains of northern Spain, on the southern edge of the Iberian Massif, and even stretch well into North Africa. In the opposite direction, they are known in Britain as pebbles in the basal Triassic conglomerates up as far as the English Midlands (and distributed in glacial deposits). It has become conventional to derive these from Brittany, even though this

---

*Leading to a paper with the delightful title: '*Une hypothèse discutable basée sur un fait doutex*' ('A questionable hypothesis based on a doubtful fact').

implies the transport of boulders up to 50 cm in diameter some 650 km. An alternative possibility is that this facies formerly extended much farther north and may in fact be represented by the Stiperstones Quartzite of Shropshire, which happens also to be white, pure, and Arenig in age, with similar trilobite traces.

The Ordovician transgression seems to have come from the east, sweeping up the *Fosse Armoricaine* and then gradually submerging the two land-masses raised by the Cadomian orogeny. Late Ordovician strata are thicker to the south of Finistère and it seems likely that the main source of sediment lay in that direction. Sedimentary slumping in north Finistère confirms this interpretation. Volcanism in the Upper Ordovician also thins out northwards.

The Ordovician succession is well developed in the May syncline of Normandy, in the valley of the Laize south-south-west of Caen (Fig. 9.2). The *Grès Armoricains* are there overlain by sedimentary iron-ores, seen in large quarries near May, and then by shales with abundant trilobites. Next comes another sandstone which is often confused or associated with the *Grès Armoricains*. This is the *Grès de May*, which is Caradoc in age but remarkably similar to its Arenig predecessor. It is more purplish coloured and many of the 'liver-coloured quartzite' pebbles scattered around western Europe may well come from it or its equivalents. It is also similar to formations seen on the south coast of Cornwall in Cornubia.

It was at this time that important basic volcanism started in Brittany, for example in the Crozon peninsula, south of Brest, but this did not last long. The sedimentary story became a monotonous one of black graptolitic shales which top the Ordovician succession and occupy most of the Silurian. There is a basal conglomerate to the latter in eastern Brittany and Normandy and some more quartzites, indicating continuing instability, but generally speaking deposition was quiet and the pattern continued of a trough of no great depth, running from west to east, complicated by oscillating ridges.

Late Palaeozoic

There is no evidence of a Caledonian orogeny here at the end of Silurian times, only gentle uplift that brought an increasing influx of clastic material into Armorica. At the present day, Devonian rocks only outcrop extensively in the Chateaulin syncline, south-east of Brest, and in the Laval syncline, east of Rennes, but there are numerous other scattered outcrops, especially in the Vendée and along the Loire east of Nantes. These make it possible to piece together a general picture.

The earliest Devonian rocks (Gedinnian) occur chiefly in the north, especially near Brest, where they are another quartzite. They contain a poor fauna and have slump structures which suggest a sea-floor sloping down to the south. This fits in with the interpretation of sands around St. Brieux as continental 'Old Red Sandstone'.

Siegenian sands with rich faunas are very much of the so-called 'Rhenish magnafacies' of the northern massifs and the limestone deposition which started in the Emsian is closely comparable with that of the Ardennes. There was a general trend towards deeper (although still shallow-water) environments and a decrease in land-derived detritus.

The Middle and Upper Devonian are thicker in the south of Brittany, especially along the lower reaches of the Loire, where they are seen in narrow outcrops pinched between the Silurian and the Carboniferous in tight folds. There is a great wine-growing area

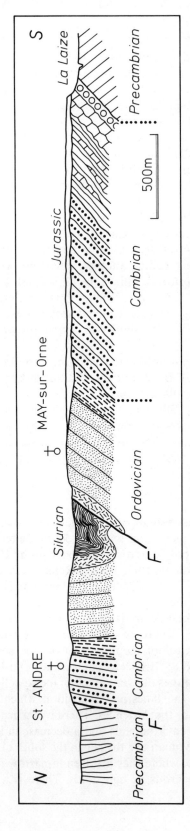

Fig. 9.2 Cross-section of the May syncline, as an example of an Armorican structure (after Doré, 1957, by kind permission of Masson Editeur).

220

along the Loire and its tributaries, but unlike other areas of France it is the Muscadet grape rather than the geology that counts. Although quarries in Devonian limestones can be seen in the middle of the vineyards, one of the best (the famous Savennières vineyard) surrounds the crag known as the Roche aux Moines made of *Grès Armoricains*. Probably the best of all grow on the Dinantian in the middle of the syncline.

Details of the Devonian succession do not concern us here except that they are variable, of shallow-water origin, and show affinities with the Devonian farther north and south in Europe. The period ended with black shales replacing the usual Frasnian calcareous deposits, but with uplift at the end with lake deposits around Brest and south of the Loire. Near St. Malo and St. Brieuc there was a remarkable episode of dike emplacement at this time. Swarms of dolerite dikes, trending roughly north–south, cut through every pre-Carboniferous formation and imply a considerable east–west distension. They are seen running across the wide rocky beaches, where the allegedly largest tidal range in Europe* seems to take the sea out over the horizon. They are well seen on both sides of the Rance estuary, west of St. Malo, where the huge tides have been harnessed for power generation and where the deep north–south inlet itself must be related to the same episode of tension.

The Devonian commonly grades into the Dinantian, especially on the northern shores of Brittany and the Cotentin, but along the Loire there is an unconformity and the Carboniferous only starts with the Upper Visean. This follows the main spasm of the Variscan movements in Armorica, which has been called the 'Bretonic phase'.

The Lower Carboniferous is almost entirely in a 'Culm' facies, that is to say alternations of sandstones and shales, often with graded bedding and bottom structures making it into an acceptable 'flysch'. However, most of it is apparently continental in origin with abundant plant remains. Marine fossils only occur at a few levels, in calcareous lenses, although in the south there is a Waulsortian facies with corals and bryozoans, But exposures are few and these rocks suffered badly in the continuing tectonic violence and the Carboniferous history is not yet fully understood. In the south there is nothing more preserved until the Tertiary. In the north there are some very small coal basins without workable coals, such as that of Littry in Calvados and St. Pierre-la-Cour near Rennes. These rest unconformably on various basements and with floras indicating the Westphalian and Stephanian. There are no marine horizons, so we have left the paralic basins of northern Europe and are seeing the first of the limnic basins, formed between the mountain ridges of the new Variscides. Stratigraphically they are most comparable with the Saar Basin of Germany.

The climax of Armorican history, was of course, the Variscan orogeny, for which 'Armorican' is one of the several synonyms. It must be remembered that, during the whole of the Palaeozoic, this massif was never completely stable. Small epeirogenic movements, especially in the ridges to the north and south, went on all the time, controlling the vagaries of the Palaeozoic seas. The first real movements of the Variscan orogeny occurred in mid Devonian times, but the climax came at the end of that period and the Bretonic phase, is, of course, named from this region.

The Palaeozoic succession tended to move as a cover, semi-independent of the Precambrian basement, but along similar trends to those already established in the

---

*Swansea Bay claims to have the second largest tidal range in the world, after the Bay of Fundy.

Cadomian movements. The folding was largely in the form of broad anticlines and synclines, with their steeper limbs facing the south-south-east. It is clear from what has already been said that the folding started in the south, but the differences in trends between the north and south may relate to adjustments to differences in the basement rather than to differences in the age of the movements.

An outstanding feature of Armorica is the divergence of the Variscan structures. In the north they trend slightly north of east and are clearly heading for the Ardennes. In the south they trend almost south-east and are only separated by the narrow 'Straits of Poitou' from their direct continuation in the western part of the Massif Central. Indeed it might have been more logical to treat this as two massifs, with the north one placed in the 'Northern Variscides' and the south one in the 'Central Variscides'. It is clear that their histories are also somewhat different.

After the Bretonic folding, there were powerful vertical movements and the injection of masses of migmatite. These latter were chiefly emplaced parallel to the grain of the country, following the earlier zones of dislocation. Then came the main phase of granite emplacement, following the same lines. There are two main belts of these granites and granodiorites heading inland from the coast north and south of Brest. The northern belt does not extend as far as the Cotentin peninsula, but the southern one is much more extensive and a massive granite is the last thing to disappear under the Mesozoic of Poitou. In the south they are mainly light-coloured granites with muscovite, while in the north there are more calcalkaline granites and grandiorites. There were also some very late, post-tectonic bodies such as the Aber Ildut granite on my gate-post (from north-west of Brest). These are generally smaller and more widely distributed, including masses in the Channel Islands and the Cotentin peninsula (such as the neat little Flamanville granite, south-west of Cherbourg). These are thought to have been punched up into an already rigid massif.

Some volcanism occurred in the central trough in Dinantian times and a later episode between post-Dinantian and pre-Stephanian movements. Such is the uncertainty about Carboniferous history in these parts that some geologists still maintain that the main movements only occurred at the end of the period and that the concept of the Bretonic phase was all a misunderstanding. That pebbles of granites are found in Westphalian conglomerates, but not in the Dinantian 'Culm' has been claimed as evidence of their post-Dinantian age, but may be simply a matter of the time taken to unroof them.

Very late in the orogeny, major tear faults developed parallel to the main structural trends. These are *cisaillements* or shears, closely related to the granites. They are all sinistral in displacement and converge westwards, pinching out the Carboniferous basins. They are like the structure of Alaska and make one think that Armorica was situated on the edge of a Variscan plate that was moving in much the same way that the Alaska–Pacific plate system is moving at the present day. One must not forget in any discussion of Palaeozoic Armorica that the Bay of Biscay was probably closed at that time and we are in close proximity to the Palaeozoic rocks of northern Spain.

Post-Palaeozoic

At the end pf Palaeozoic times, the Armorican Massif had emerged as a land-mass with a fairly high relief. This relief was considerably reduced by erosion in Permian and Triassic times to produce the sediments of the 'New Red Sandstone' deserts which lay to the north and east and which extended, probably continuously, as far as south-west England. In early Jurassic times these deserts were swamped by the sea which lapped on to the old massif. At Laize and at May-sur-Orne south of Caen one can see the Lower Jurassic resting unconformably on the Lower Palaeozoic.* This passes up into Middle Jurassic, with breaks, and then the classic sections of the Normandy D-day coast. But this Mesozoic is really the edge of the Paris Basin and is best considered there. A further transgression occurred in Albian–Cenomanian times which is thought to have produced the marked peneplain at about 300 m above sea-level. The sea withdrew again in the Turonian.

Finally, although one would not think of Armorica as a place for the Tertiary, there are scattered deposits (ranging from Eocene to Pliocene) over most of the massif, but concentrated in a central region down from St. Malo to the Loire. In effect the rapid transgressions and regressions, so well documented in the Paris and Aquitaine Basins, are seen here in their marginal expressions. Arms of the sea swept up structural lows in the massif, especially along the lines of the major wrench faults. The Ypresian and Lutetian cycles of the Eocene are clearly recorded. Their deposits lie, for example, on the old rocks of the Quiberon peninsula on the south coast and on the Ile de Ré off La Rochelle. Mangrove swamps and *Nipa* palms lined the sides of inlets which brought abundant nummulites to the heart of the massif. Later in the Eocene, kaolinitic clays and continental sands with plant remains were widespread. There was deep lateritic weathering in a humid tropical climate. This situation continued into the Oligocene with lacustrine and brackish water deposits. Evidently faults were still active and controlling sedimentation in little graben (as in other Variscan massifs). A particularly pronounced belt of Stampian deposits runs from the coast near St. Brieuc in a south-easterly direction all the way to the Loire east of Nantes.

The Miocene is only represented by the Helvetian, which is remarkably widespread in the eastern part of the massif, although only in faulted basins of no great thickness. Most of the deposits, and those of the Pliocene sea which followed in the same area, are what are known locally as 'faluns'. These are unconsolidated shelly sands and clays with marine fossils such as bryozoans. To English eyes they are very reminscent of the late Cainozoic 'crags' of East Anglia. A trail of these is the only connection between the Paris and Aquitaine basins over the Mesozoic rocks of the Straits of Poitou. There is evidence of increasing aridity and there are extensive red sands in the Pliocene. By this time the faulting seems to have come to an end.

Quaternary raised beach and similar deposits can be omitted as usual, but one can hardly leave Brittany without at least mentioning the remarkable Stone Age monuments for which it is famous, especially the long avenues of standing stones at Carnac, near the base of the Quiberon peninsula.

9(b) Paris Basin

The Paris Basin is one of the most clearly defined geological regions of Europe, although it has never been a distinct and separate sedimentary basin. Its rocks form a direct

*In one road-cutting south of May one can see two unconformities—the Jurassic on the Cambrian and the Cambrian on the Brioverian.

continuation of those in the surrounding regions and it is essentially a structural and physiographical unit rather than a depositional one.

The glorious city of Paris, cradle of so much civilization, including geology, stands proudly in the centre of the central, Tertiary, basin (Fig. 9.3). This is somewhat elongated in outcrop, on a north-north-east axis, and is surrounded by a neat rim of Cretaceous rocks. This in turn stands in an almost complete saucer of Jurassic sediments, plus a little

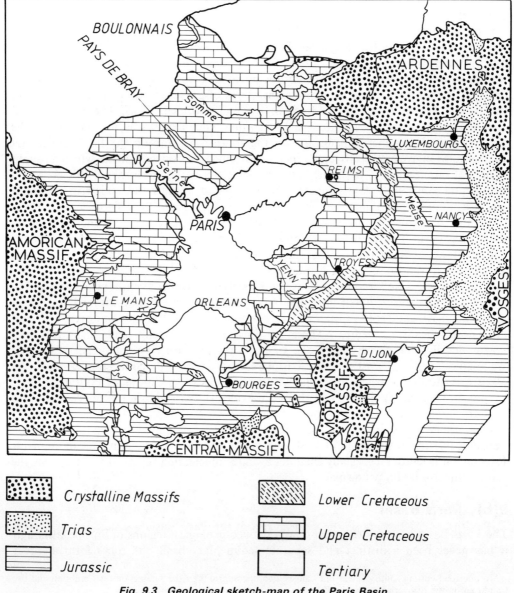

Crystalline Massifs		Lower Cretaceous	
Trias		Upper Cretaceous	
Jurassic		Tertiary	

Fig. 9.3 Geological sketch-map of the Paris Basin.

Trias here and there. Beyond and below this is a slightly warped table of Palaeozoic and Precambrian rocks.

The structural basin is particularly obvious on its eastern (and to a lesser extent its northern) rim, where successive stratigraphical divisions form as many as eight escarpments.

Palaeozoic Table and Triassic

The Paris Basin is delimited by the ancient massifs of Armorica in the west, the Massif Central in the south, the Vosges in the east, the Ardennes in the north-east, and the Boulonnais continuation of the Wealden structure in the north-west.

Palaeozoic and Precambrian rocks have been reached by a number of deep borings within the Paris Basin. These show up rather clearly the trough-like nature of the structure, with the greatest depths to the floor roughly along a north-west trending axis (2440 m at Nantouillet, 30 km north-east of Paris and 3186 m at Courgivaux, 80 km east of Paris). The depths decrease to the north-east and south-west. Thus this basin is of the same order as that in the North Sea. It may be that the Paris Basin began as a Protero-zoic graben.

Triassic rocks form a very discontinuous series of outcrops around the basin. They are seen in a small area near Bayeux in the west and flanking the Massif Central in the south. The best outcrop is in the east where Triassic sediments outcrop over a considerable part of Lorraine and Luxembourg, east of Nancy, flanking the Vosges Massif. Nevertheless, we have a fairly complete picture of the Trias due to the large number of boreholes by which it has been pierced. In Lorraine and Luxembourg, the three divisions of the German classification are clearly displayed and form a useful connecting link between the marine succession of the Alps, the German succession, and the succession in the north-west Europe (notably Britain) which lacks obvious marine horizons below the Rhaetian.

Jurassic Saucer

The Jurassic rocks form an almost complete ring of outcrops around the Paris Basin, except in the north, where they are overstepped by the Upper Cretaceous, and in the north-west, between Boulogne and Trouville, where they are hidden beneath the sea.

The only place within the main structure of the Paris Basin where the Jurassic out-crops over any significant area is in the north-facing monocline of the Pays de Bray. Like the Boulonnais, this is a fold on a north-west trending axis and can be related to structures in southern England. However, the succession in the Pays de Bray is quite different from that of its near neighbour the Boulonnais. This was shown by a deep boring at Ferrières-en-Bray which revealed a Jurassic succession four times as thick as that seen in the cliffs between Boulogne and Calais. This seems to be another 'bordering trough'.

The Jurassic sediments on the western rim of the Paris Basin are best seen along the D-day invasion coast of Normandy. The Lower Jurassic is not particularly good here, although where it is exposed it is extremely fossiliferous and comparable with that seen across the English Channel on the Dorset coast. Middle Jurassic limestones form cliffs for a considerable distance around Arromanches, with the well-remembered beaches of 6

June 1944. The most famous and interesting of the Middle Jurassic formations is the Bathonian Caen Stone, which is a shallow marine or supra-tidal deposit that has been used extensively for building purposes. It was taken with them in great quantities by the Normans in an earlier invasion, to build castles in England. Presumably their military geological intelligence did not inform them of the many excellent building stones already available in their conquered territory. Upper Jurassic clays and sands are exposed in the cliffs near the small resort of Villers-sur-Mer and are similar to the Boulonnais in many respects including their abundant trace fossils. To the south-west, Jurassic strata fill the 'Straits of Poitou' between Armorica and the Massif Central. They connect with the story in Aquitaine. The widest outcrop of Jurassic rocks is on the south-east side of the basin. They are exposed along the valley of the Yonne, between Auxerre and Avallon, with a remarkable development of coral reefs and associated deposits in the Upper Jurassic.

Towards Dijon, as one heads towards the Jura and the Alps, one descends a series of fault escarpments, running roughly parallel with the rim of the basin. Each of these takes one higher up the Jurassic again, so that one crosses the gently-dipping succession many times. The faults produce a series of steep valleys, such as the one that contains the delightful village of St. Seine-l'Abbaye. The River Seine rises in an enclosed and coin-filled spring nearby on one of the uppermost faulted steps.

The final step takes one down into Dijon, the capital of Burgundy and the best wine-growing area in the world. The vineyards of the Côte d'Or extend south of Dijon where the last Jurassic escarpment faces on to the young low-lying sediments of the Rhône–Saône Trough. The vines are limited to remarkably small areas of outcrop. The more argillaceous sediments, such as the Oxfordian 'marls', tend to produce the best white Burgundies such as Montrachet, while the Middle Jurassic limetones produce the delectable red Burgundies such as Beaune, Nuits St. George, and my favourite (and Napoleon's!), Chambertin.

Jurassic rocks are also known in deep borings within the Paris Basin and are important, for the fissured limestones of the Bathonian have (together with the 'Wealden' sands) proved the most valuable reservoir for oil and gas. There are also oil and gas reservoirs in several other Jurassic limestones and in the sands of the Trias. At Chateaurenard, south of Paris, oil was found (to the surprise of the drillers) at less than 600 m depth, but usually it is much deeper.

Cretaceous Rim

Until one drives across it one does not appreciate how much of northern France is underlain by Cretaceous rocks. The vast upland plateau of Picardy is formed of Senonian and Turonian Chalk, generally flat-lying, although rising over the continuation of the Boulonnais axis to form the hills of Artois. This dry upland has formed the main highway for successive invasions of France, being equally suitable for cavalry and tanks. Farther south along the outcrop the large westward-flowing rivers form barriers, notably the Loire with its famous chateaux guarding every crossing place. The Chalk can be seen in river cliffs along the Seine and the Loire (where numerous caves have been dug for the storage of wine). Chalk is quarried almost everywhere for cement manufacture and agricultural lime. In contrast the Lower Cretaceous is hardly exposed at all.

The Cretaceous country of Champagne around Reims is chiefly associated with the perhaps overrated wine of the same name. It is the well-drained countryside called the 'Dry Champagne', extending along or near the top of the Chalk, which supports the famous vineyards. The thick sticky clays on the Tertiary escarpment constitute the 'Wet Champagne', unsuitable for grapes. The best Champagne grapes are said to grow 'with their heads in the Tertiary and their feet in the Chalk', that is to say, in the feather edge of Sparnacian clays of the Tertiary immediately above the Tertiary–Cretaceous junction. This is what the locals call the 'true' champagne. There is also 'false' champagne, which is grown on the broad Chalk outcrop, but with Sparnacian clay brought down from the escarpment to spread on the vineyards.

The highest Chalk normally seen around the Paris Basin belongs to the Campanian Stage, but it is possible that some Maastrichtian is preserved in places and as derived fossils in residual deposits that are found here and there on the Chalk surface. Certainly there was a great deal of erosion of the Chalk before the first Tertiary deposits were laid on top, and the basal layers of the latter commonly contain only slightly worn, glauconite-stained flints as in England. The Palaeogene transgression generally seems to have been a gentle one and the top of the Chalk is neatly planed off.

Tertiary Basin

It was in Palaeogene times that what is now Paris and the surrounding region of the 'Ile de France' came into its own. In an earlier chapter, the general relationships of the Tertiary sediments of north-west Europe were touched on briefly. The essential picture is one of a vast sedimentary basin with its centre roughly in the southern part of the North Sea. The sea within this basin periodically expanded and contracted so that, in the Paris Basin, we find evidence of a series of marine transgressions coming from the north-west or north. As in north-west Europe generally, there is a fascinating picture of lateral and vertical passages each time into brackish and fresh-water deposits.

The first such transgression to reach Paris was the Danian–Montian, now generally accepted as the initial phase of Tertiary deposition. The sea evidently reached Paris from the north-west, extended beyond Paris to Montereau and from thereabouts a gulf extended north-eastwards to Vertus, south of Epernay—Fig. 9.4(a). These are actual deposits, but it is impossible to say what others existed that were later eroded, or whether there was ever a direct connection with the deposits around Mons in Belgium.

Usually (but not always) the basal deposit of the Danian is an organic limestone, containing great quantities of encrusting algae besides a varied marine fauna which enable the deposit to be correlated with those of Belgium and Denmark. The limestone is thickest between Paris and Mantes, downstream on the Seine. The coincidence of the Montian strata with the present valley of the Seine may mean that this valley is a very ancient structure. Perhaps the most interesting of the Montian deposits is that in the large quarries at Vigny (about 40 km north-west of Paris). Here the algal and coral limestones, in reef-like form, are banked up against a cliff of Campanian Chalk. For a long time this was thought to be a lateral passage, but evidently, at this point at least, the Montian sea was eroding and undercutting a cliff-line, and boulders of Chalk can be seen within the Tertiary deposit. Above the limestones along the Seine come continental clays, which complete the first Tertiary cycle and in places rest directly on the Chalk.

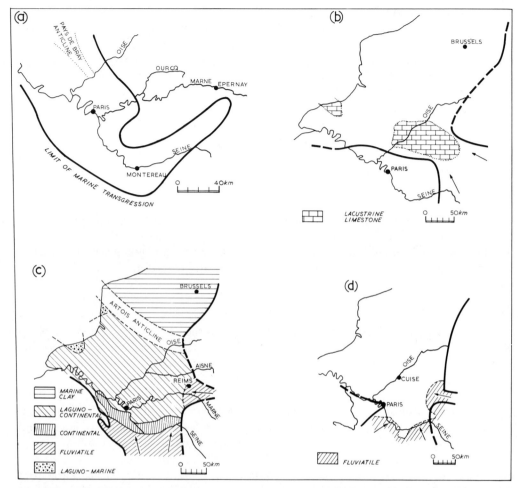

Fig. 9.4 *Distribution of Paleocene and early Eocene sediments in the Paris Basin: (a) Danian/Montian, (b) Thanetian, (c) Sparnacian, (d) Cuisian (after Pomerol and Feugueur, by kind permission of Masson Editeur).*

The second cycle is usually called the 'Thanetian' in France (after Thanet in England) and the 'Landenian' in England (after Landen near Brussels). Such are the paradoxes of Tertiary stratigraphical nomenclature! The sea came again from the north, but the deposits are more continuous with those of Belgium and the sea did not reach as far south as Paris. The marine sands pass into lacustrine limestones north-east of Paris and into fluviatile deposits, with evidence of rivers entering the sea from the direction of Armorica to the south-west and the Champagne region to the south-east—Fig. 9.4(b). The marine fauna of the Thanetian has a more northerly, cooler water aspect than that of the Montian, but abundant plant remains in the continental facies, notably in the famous Sezanne travertine (formed as a petrifying waterfall round a spring issuing from the Chalk), still suggest a tropical climate. Even flowers with stamens are preserved. It is evident that there was a break between these first two marine invasions of the

228

Palaeogene, for the Thanetian deposits usually rest directly on the Chalk. With the withdrawal of the sea at the end of the Thanetian, lacustrine limestones and plant-bearing sands spread northwards and into Belgium.

The Sparnacian deposits which follow consist of lagoonal clays and sands with lignites and detritus from the Massif Central—Fig. 9.4(c). The name comes from Epernay. These deposits might be regarded (with their equivalents in England) as part of the continental phase of the previous cycle, but the mammalian remains found in them near Reims suggest a later age, and the marine equivalent in Belgium (the Ypres Clay so intimately known by British soldiers of the First World War) seem to represent a distinct episode which probably correlates with the transgressive London Clay.

The major transgression so far as the Paris Basin was concerned came in late Ypresian times with the *Sables de Cuise*. These are sometimes regarded as a separate and later cycle (the Cuisian) as it seems to be in the Hampshire Basin. Alternatively it may be a contemporaneous transgression coming from a generally southerly direction, while the Ypresian transgression was moving in from the north. A southerly derivation is suggested by the fossils (which are locally fantastically abundant in the Cuisian sands), notably the abundant nummulites and molluscs only living today in the Indian Ocean. It is these Cuisian sands particularly, under a capping of Lutetian limestone, that give rise to the wooded escarpment round the northern edge of the Paris Basin. The marine deposits did not reach as far as the present course of the Seine, Fig. 9.4(d), but passed into a fluviatile facies with detritus again coming from the Massif Central. There is also a passage eastwards into a fresh-water facies around Reims.

Continental sands and clays follow in the usual pattern to complete the cycle, although the sea does not seem to have withdrawn completely and in the west marine deposits pass up directly into those of the Lutetian cycle which followed. Then the sea again extended to the south and east—Fig. 9.5(a). *Lutetia* was the Roman name for Paris and it is not possible in that city to get far from the Lutetian deposits, for the *Calcaire Grossier* is the building stone of Paris and is seen everywhere in all the famous buildings and in the balustrades along the Seine. This highly fossiliferous limestone was formerly quarried all round and even under the city. The old subterranean workings caused much disastrous subsidence during the past century; on one occasion even a theatre suddenly disappeared into a hole in the ground. One can visit some of the old adits, known as the '*catacombes*', which have been used to store—often in fanciful designs—the skeletons from many of the old cemeteries of Paris, which were evacuated during the urban development of the latter part of the last century. The *Calcaire Grossier* can be seen at Montmirail, south-east of the capital, near the scene of Napoleon's last victory. The supply of detritus from the Massif Central seems to have ceased and the marine deposits (after an initial sandy and glauconitic phase) are largely in the form of limestones. These Lutetian limestones cap the north- and east-facing Tertiary escarpment and many of the hill outliers (*buttes témoins*) that stand out in front of it, for example Mont Ganelon near Compiègne. An easily recognized level is the so-called 'money stone' (*pierre à liards*) packed with the characteristic, large coin-like *Nummulites*.

Another change which occurred during Lutetian times was the uplift of the Artois anticline, separating a sandy facies in Belgium and northernmost France from the car-bonate facies of the Paris Basin proper. The Remarde anticline south of Paris is aligned on the same north-west lines and limited the southerly extent of the Lutetian sea. All the

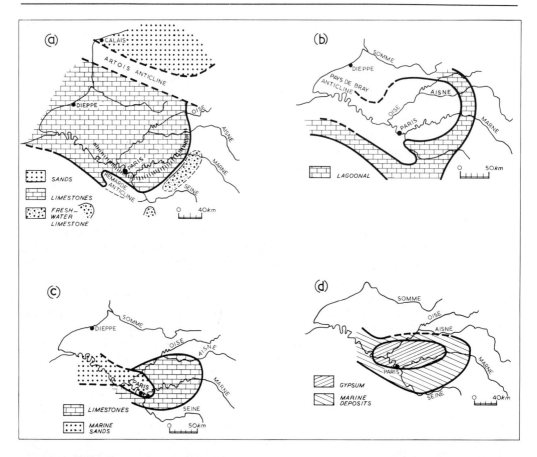

Fig. 9.5 *Distribution of late Eocene and Oligocene sediments in the Paris Basin: (a) Lutetian, (b) 'Auversian', (c) 'Ludian', (d) Oligocene (after Pomerol and Feugueur, by kind permission of Masson Editeur).*

gentle anticlines of the Paris Basin were on similar parallel lines, and several of them were already active, as is shown by local sandier and thinner developments of the Lutetian. Thicker sedimentation occurred in the synclines, for example at Thérain (south-east of Beauvais) where the limestone has been worked since Roman times. The first Tertiary evaporite deposits appear in the regressive phase of the Upper Lutetian.

The next cycle is called 'Bartonien' by the French, although it does not correspond with the Bartonian of Barton-on-Sea in southern England, and is more complex in its history than the earlier cycles. Emergence at the end of Lutetian times led to the lithification of the limestones (with splendid styolites) and to the development of a karstic surface over much of the Paris region. There were intermediate lagoonal deposits and then the sands and clays of a sea slightly less extensive than the one that went before. This is commonly known as the 'Auversian' after the poorly exposed locality at Auvers, 40 km north-north-west of Paris. Here, locally derived pebbles indicate that the Pays de

Bray axis was a positive feature and the Artois anticline again separated the Paris Basin from that of the Belgium. All round the margins of this early Bartonian sea were lagoonal and beach deposits in which many mammalian fossils have been found—Fig. 9.5(b). In the various facies of the marine sediments, nummulites (of a smaller size than their Lutetian predecessors) are fantastically abundant (up to 600 000 per kilo of rock). It is hardly surprising that the French commonly call the Eocene the *Nummulitique*.

A temporary emergence at the end of the 'Auversian' perhaps justifies its being regarded as a separate cycle. Tropical podzols developed together with blown sands which are used for glass-making. Another marine flooding (sometimes separated as the 'Marinesian') came into the western part of the basin, but generally facies were developed that are regarded as intermediate between fully marine and lagoonal. The limestones and marls of this division give a first preview of the Oligocene situation that was to follow.

The last phase of the complex Bartonian cycle is commonly known as the 'Ludian', but probably equates with the Bartonian of England. It is represented by marine deposits which spread along the valley of the Seine and up to Reims—Fig. 9.5(c). The incursion was short-lived and the cycle approached its end with gypsum accumulating in the Paris area, which now seemed to be subsiding more than anywhere else. In the old days the gypsum was worked in the Bohemian district of Montmartre, below Sacré Coeur, for the manufacture of 'Plaster of Paris'. It was here that the 'father of vertebrate palaeontology', Baron Cuvier, did most of his famous work on early mammals, although he accepted no form of evolution (but this may have been political expediency). The gypsum is still worked today, although mainly in the *buttes temoins*, especially in the huge quarries at Cormeilles near Pontoise, west of Paris. This outlier shows the topmost Eocene and the whole of the Oligocene, including thick developments of gypsum at several levels. The vertebrates occur mainly in the marls overlying the main gypsum, and since they are clearly early Oligocene in age, imply that the Eocene–Oligocene junction probably lies within the gypsum.

The first stage of the Oligocene, commonly called 'Sannoisien' in France, is represented at first by semi-marine deposits and fresh-water limestones. A widely recognizable oyster bed (well seen at Cormeilles) is more marine, and may mark the beginning of the 'Stampien' (named after Etampes, not Sir L. Dudley Stamp as British students used to think). This is the last marine transgression to affect the Paris Basin. The well-known *Sables de Fontainebleau* of the beautiful forest of that name (well seen along the main southbound autoroute towards Lyon) follow immediately above and have yielded a poor marine fauna at several levels. They are very extensive—Fig. 9.5(d)—and were formerly even more so, for they have been found in boreholes as far south as Orléans. In the north-west they seem to have been stopped by the Bray Anticline and there are many problems connected with the contemporary palaeogeography. The sands have been widely used for glass-making. After this, the sea seems to have progressively withdrawn to the north-west and fresh-water limestones, of Aquitanian age, follow.

It is evident throughout Palaeogene times in the Paris Basin that sedimentation was much controlled by the structures. It was thicker in the synclines and thinner on the anticlines, most of which trended north-west or west-north-west.

The general uplift of north-west Europe at the end of Oligocene times meant that the Neogene is very little represented in the Paris Basin. Above fresh-water limestones of Aquitanian age come continental clays and sands, especially near the splendid Université de Paris (Sud) at Orsay, south-west of Paris. These have been attributed to the Burdigalian Stage and are developed in a trough running south-east from Rouen. The remains of many large mammals have been found in these deposits, but they are better seen in the Low Countries.

9(c) Aquitaine Basin

The low-lying country of Aquitaine, famous for its vineyards and forests, seems to be a country without geology. Apart from its north-westerly Mesozoic rim, the geological visitor will see almost nothing unless he goes to the far south, to the elegant cliffs of Biarritz. But sub-surface Aquitaine is probably known as well as anywhere in Europe, especially through the work of the Institut de Bassin d'Aquitaine in the University of Bordeaux at Talence and the Société Nationale des Pétroles d'Aquitaine at Pau.

This is a great Tertiary basin (Fig. 9.6), comparable with, but quite different from, the Paris Basin. To the north and east are the ancient massifs of Armorica and the Massif Central, subtending a broad northerly belt of dominantly carbonate rocks of Jurassic and Cretaceous age. These form low cliffs along the coast and along the river valleys such as the Dordogne. In the south-east, the Tertiary beds rest directly on the old rocks of the Montagne Noire and extend through the Lauragnais Gap (or Straits of Carcassone) to the Tertiary basin of Languedoc along the Mediterranean coast. To the south is the fold belt of the Pyrenees with its extensive alluvial fans. To the west is the Bay of Biscay (or Gulf of Gascony) with its own story of geophysical anomalies and its fringe of sand-dunes and alluvial plains.

Basement

The 'basement' rocks of Aquitaine, ranging from Precambrian to late Palaeozoic in age, are known in more than 70 boreholes. The floor dips southwards towards the Pyrenees and westwards towards the coast, reaching a maximum depth of more than 7000 m on the coast south of Bordeaux. The most obvious complication of this pattern is a major south-south-west trending fault running down from the north-west side of the Montagne Noire. This terminates the Mesozoic plateau of the north side of the basin, by throwing down Jurassic rocks against the Palaeozoic of the massif. The fault can be traced beneath the Cainozoic east of Toulouse, where its throw is reversed and the Palaeozoic is brought very near the surface. Along the west side of the Massif Central, the supposedly Proterozoic slates of Bas Limousin form low-lying country which, in a topographical sense, is also part of the Aquitaine Basin.

The 'basement' rocks encountered in the boreholes within the basin are very similar to the ancient metamorphic rocks of Armorica and the Massif Central. There are granites, gneisses, and schists of Precambrian or later age. The Palaeozoic rocks have presumably all been affected by the Asturian phase of the Variscan orogeny, since no post-Asturian Palaeozoic sediments (i.e., Stephanian 'Coal Measures' or Permian red beds) have been recognized within the basin.

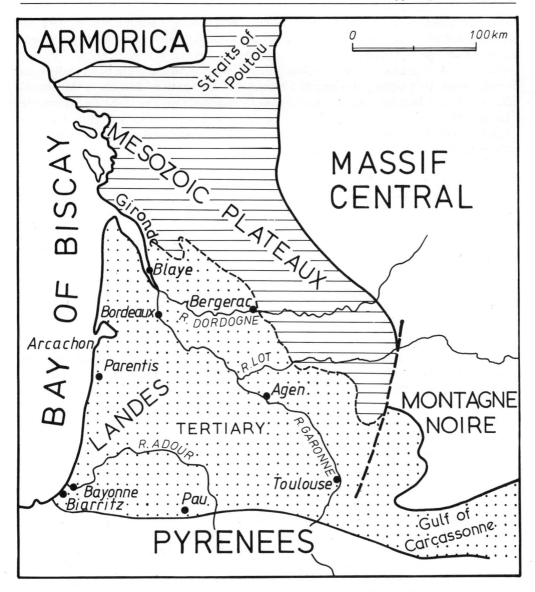

Fig. 9.6 Geological sketch-map of the Aquitaine Basin.

Mesozoic

Triassic rocks are of the usual Germanic facies, especially along the borders of the Massif Central, where they are dominated by red sandstones and conglomerates and are difficult to separate from the Permian. Sedimentation began early in Triassic times in the south and spread progressively northwards. Towards the centre of the basin the sediments are mostly finer grained, implying that it was already functioning as a negative area. There

233

are considerable thicknesses of variegated shales with dolomite and noteworthy developments of anhydrite and salt. These last give rise to diapiric structures, which have been actively investigated because of their association with oil and gas seepages.

Marine 'Muschelkalk' is well developed in the Pyrenees to the south but its full extent is not known. In a boring at Roquefort (about 100 km south of Bordeaux) 'Muschelkalk' was found between typical 'Keuper' with anhydrite and salt and an anomalous 'Bunter' below, also with salt. At this locality the Trias reaches its greatest known thickness within the basin; this is more than 1400 m, compared with little more than 100 m bordering the Massif Central.

Another feature of this borehole, now known generally in the south of the basin, is the presence of dolerite sills. This is a feature of the Trias not seen in north-west Europe, but known farther south, perhaps significantly at the other end of the Pyrenees on the Spanish side and then down to Morocco. Such volcanicity is characteristic of the very similar Trias of the Newark Group along the eastern seaboard of the USA. Finally in the Aquitanian Triassic, there was a great spread of sands and mudstones which covered everything else north-east of a line from Arcachon to Toulouse.

The Jurassic rocks which follow are nearly all marine and epicontinental. They show a similar pattern of isopachytes to that of the Trias, with the greatest thickness around and (for the uppermost Jurassic) to the east of Roquefort. The 'basement' was evidently emergent at this time along the present coastline between the Bay of Arcachon and Biarritz. Perhaps this was the Spanish meseta before its rotation to its present site. Also, a broad ridge immediately to the north of Bordeaux separated a northern basin from the main basin to the south. The northern basin is obvious at the surface, with a broad belt of Jurassic and Cretaceous limestones dipping gently to the south-west under the Tertiary.

At the beginning of Jurassic times there was a marine incursion from the south-east providing shallow-water deposits around the borders of the basin and extensive evaporites in the centre. Although the former are completely normal for the Lower Jurassic, the latter are completely atypical. Nevertheless there are more than 500 m of early Jurassic salt and anhydrite known in boreholes to the south of the Garonne. This has encouraged the idea (which I dislike) of the early Jurassic North Atlantic as a great evaporating dish. Later in early Jurassic times, after several regressions, normal marine conditions became generally distributed. By this time the Basin of Aquitaine had been blocked out on the lines seen today, and filled with shallow marine sediments.

Shallow-water deposits, now limestones with important developments of oolites, also dominate the Middle Jurassic and spread on to the massif to the east. The limestones are well seen up the valley of the Dordogne and its tributaries. The Bathonian, in particular, forms the characteristic dry karst-like plateaux or 'Causses'. The Upper Jurassic continues the same story, only more so, with Callovian and Oxfordian limestones forming typical 'causse' country. This is characterized by shrunken rivers, underground streams, steep valley sides, and flat hill-tops with patchy vegetation. Cultivation (especially of tobacco) and population are concentrated on the alluvium of the valleys. Dips are gentle and the only obvious tectonism is the occasional east–west fault, seen for example in the spectacular valleys of La Cave and the pilgrimage centre of Roc-Amadour.

Limestone plateaux are difficult country for the biostratigrapher. Unfossiliferous micrites predominate and almost the only animal fossils are small non-cephalopod molluscs. A special feature is the extensive development of algal limestones, including quite sizable reefs. There are also some coral reefs, for example near Charente. All the time that these shallow-water carbonate facies were persisting in the east, there were deeper water, more argillaceous sediments with abundant ammonites accumulating in the west, suggesting that the Atlantic was already in that direction.

Towards the end of the Jurassic a change set in. To the north there were still reefs, in the form of coral 'biostromes' (seen for example around the Pointe du Chay, just south of La Rochelle). But generally, marine conditions ended with the extensive, rhythmic, argillaceous limestones of the Kimmeridgian, which are extensively worked for cement. Then a general regression set in, and this shallow area emerged from the sea. Farther south, for example around Cognac, dolomites, breccias, and evaporites were deposited, and brackish water 'Purbeckian'-type conditions became widespread.

By the end of the Jurassic, the greater part of the Aquitaine Basin was dry land. The sea did not return over most of it until the Aptian. Boreholes reveal typical 'Wealden' continental deposits south of Arcachon. But nearer the Pyrenees there are important marine Neocomian deposits, although with intercalations of anhydrite. A marine gulf evidently spread into the area from the south-east, as a frontal trough along the north side of the Pyrenees. This extended during Aptian and Albian times, with the accumulation of considerable thicknesses of limestones and shales, including the continent-wide Urgonian reef facies.

These thick accumulations of early Cretaceous limestones, together with the underlying Jurassic limestones, are the chief oil and gas reservoirs of France. The Parentis Basin, south of Arcachon, provides 80 percent of France's home-produced oil from these rocks, while the Adour Basin (around Pau and Lacq in the Pyrenean foothills) supplies the whole of France's onshore natural gas. There are many seepages of oil and gas in the flysch zone along the Pyrenees, often associated with Triassic salt diapirs. There are also conglomerates, breccias, and sandstones, spreading into the area from the south, presumably indicating an uplift of the Pyrenees at this time. Great thicknesses of late Cretaceous calcareous flysch, perhaps as much as 3000 m thick, accumulated in the frontal trough. This is well seen on the beach at Bidart, south of Biarritz, near the Spanish frontier. The same conditions persisted into the Palaeogene at the western end of the trough.

This frontal Pyrenean trough corresponds with the similar, but much larger, frontal troughs of the other Alpine ranges of Europe. However, the filling of this particular trough began in the Cretaceous. The late Cretaceous sediments are transgressive, with sandstones and breccias, in the north-east of this region around Aurignac and Gensac (nearly all Gascon place-names end in '-ac'). But the trough was quite separated from the other persistent basin of deposition, south of Arcachon. Here a triangular depression with its base on the Atlantic coast extends its apex up the historic and prehistoric valley of the Dordogne.

Shaly in the middle of the Aquitaine Basin, the Upper Cretaceous is known here best as the chalky and sandy limestones seen at outcrop. These are known to extend underground as far as Carcans, north of Bordeaux. Up the Dordogne they are seen as cliffs and were intimately known by Palaeolithic man in the caves and rock-shelters around Les Eyzies. Names such as Le Moustier, Crô-Magnon, and Madeleine are known to every schoolboy. Crô-Magnon man himself was first found in what is now the garage of the Hôtel Crô-Magnon at Les Eyzies. Stone Age man drove his prey over the overhanging Cretaceous cliffs of the Vézère, a tributary of the Dordogne. The pictures he drew of them are thought of as the beginning of art. The most famous of all caves, the Grotte de Lascaux, is higher up the same valley. The Grotte de Rouffignac with its multitude of mammoths is not far away; its underground railway also provides the visitor with a fine section of chalky Upper Cretaceous thick with flint nodules replacing arthropod burrows.

Besides its prehistoric wonders, this is the country of great rivers, wonderful wines, and famous swordsmen. The Three Musketeers came from here, as did Cyrano de Bergerac. The two greatest rivers are the Dordogne and the Garonne, which are the two 'seas' that delimit the extent of the Entre-Deux-Mers wines. They meet just south of Blaye, with its cliffs of Eocene limestone, and they flow together as the mighty Gironde. It is along the sides of this great inlet that the Upper Cretaceous rocks appear again as the north rim of the basin.

The Cenomanian is everywhere transgressive, but does not extend very far to the east. Thus it passes into a non-marine facies with lignites along the Dordogne south-east of Périgueux, in the region just discussed. Near the Pyrenees it is noteworthy for its layers of volcanic tuff around St. Marcet. On the north rim, however, it is not very important and is dominated by the later Cretaceous stages of which this is the 'type' area. The Turonian is also transgressive and of a shallow-water limestone facies. It is notable for its developments of rudist biostromes, well seen, for example, in a large quarry at Chateauneuf, some 26 km south-east of Cognac.

East of the Gironde estuary is a classic region of Upper Cretaceous stratigraphy, having the type localities of three of its stages within a few, poorly exposed kilometres. 'Coniacian' refers to the town of Cognac, where the 'stratotype' is within a stone's throw of the famous distilleries (one never gets far from the vine in Aquitaine). 'Santonian' takes its name from the small town of Saintes and 'Campanian' from the vine-growing *campagne* or countryside around Segonzac. The rocks are all sandy limestones, packed with broken shell debris.

In the south, flysch deposits spread out from their trough into the basin proper. At the same time the trough became much deeper, and a new marly facies developed north of Pau. The last Cretaceous stage, the Maastrichtian, continued in the flysch facies in the south. In the north it is the usual pure carbonates, packed with bivalves and well seen in the cliffs of the Gironde estuary at Meschers, south of Royan.

Cainozoic

So we come to the Tertiary sediments of the Aquitaine Basin, which are the best known but the least seen. Besides the boreholes drilled through the Tertiary to the oil- and gas-bearing Mesozoic, there are an immense number of drillings for water.

In his classic work on the Tertiary, Charles Lyell chose the Paris Basin to typify his early Tertiary and Aquitaine his late Tertiary. Apart from the age difference in the main Tertiary developments, the two basins are in any case difficult to correlate because of their different lithological and palaeontological facies. The only connecting links between the Paris Basin and that of Aquitaine are the scattered outliers of the shelly sands ('faluns') between Armorica and the Massif Central. These are difficult to date accurately.

The trough in front of the Pyrenees persisted through from Mesozoic to Cainozoic, and the flysch facies continued in the east, around Torbes, as it did in northern Spain. But the flysch or flysch-like rocks are not so thick, and are surrounded by shelf carbonates. There is clear evidence of ridges rising in the Pyrenees at this time, following on movements initiated at the end of the Jurassic.

Danian and Montian stages have been recognized; the former, for example, as rose-coloured micrites in the cliffs at Bidart which rest directly on Upper Cretaceous flysch.

The Eocene sea spread northwards and eastwards intermittently reaching its greatest extent in Ypresian and Lutetian times, when marine sands were laid down as far north as the Gironde and as far east as the marvellous castle town of Carcassonne. Along its northern coast the sea cut hard rocky surfaces, which the French call paradoxically 'haut fonds'. To the north-east all was land, with some local deltas in the south.

The best sections are those around the faded glories of Biarritz and its ancient neighbour Bayonne (which in spite of its beauty is believed to have given its name to the bayonet). The Eocene proper began with a sandy and conglomerate white limestone, seen in the Falaise de Handia, south of the town. The exact age of the lowest beds was for long uncertain and a local stage-name, the 'Biarritzian', has been created for them. It is now thought, however, that the main Biarritz section only begins with the Lutetian.

The Pyrenees were already rising not far away. Immense alluvial fans spread out over the southern part of Aquitaine. By late Lutetian times the frontal trough finally disappeared with the Pyrenean orogeny and with it the flysch. The great basin became split up and the shoreline retreated. In the north-west the late Eocene sediments are famous for their echinoids and well seen below the Citadel of Blaye on the Gironde. To the north-east, on the Mesozoic carbonate plateaux, there are extensive areas of sediment thought of as 'molasse' but for the most part impossible to date.

The later Eocene at Biarritz is well seen below the ruined Chateau de Lady Bruce (used before the Mediterranean and Caribbean became *de rigueur* for aristocratic British holidaymakers). Nummulites become fantastically abundant along the Côte des Basques.

Similar sandy limestones extend up into the basal Oligocene. Large forams fill burrows and form a large part of the Rocher de la Vierge and the cliffs near the casino in the fashionable centre of Biarritz. North of the town below the Saint Martin lighthouse, far less disturbed calcareous sandstones and silts of the Rupelian stage are displayed in a broad syncline ending at the romantically named cliff, the Chambre d'Amour.

The sections north and south of Biarritz are worth considering in detail because there is so little to be seen elsewhere. But the many boreholes have made possible a detailed reconstruction of the repeated transgressions coming from an ever-opening Atlantic. The story is similar to that of the London, Paris, and Belgian Basins, but the sediments are quite different, especially in their highly calcareous nature.

Throughout this period of Mesozoic and Eocene sedimentation one can separate the 'tabular Aquitaine' to the north from the 'folded Aquitaine' to the south. The former is represented by the great plateaux and forested plains, where the tectonics consist chiefly of broad gentle folds and east–west faults. In the 'folded Aquitaine', however, the tectonics are much more severe and increase in intensity towards the Pyrenees.

The main trend of the folds within the basin is to the west-north-west, parallel to the Pyrenees. Away from the mountains, movements tend to be in blocks, probably related to a basement control. The anticline of Parentis, south of Arcachon, where the most valuable oil-field was found in 1954, may be taken as typical. The fold trends east–west with a steeper southern limb and the oil occurs in the limestones and dolomites of the Lower Cretaceous. Aptian–Albian marls form the cap-rock although, farther east, Eocene marls perform this function. Other oil-bearing structures, such as that at St. Marcet, are related to salt-domes coming from the Triassic.

The chief folding episodes in Aquitaine were four in number. The first was at the end of the Jurassic, when the frontal Pyrenean trough came into existence. There were further movements before the Cenomanian transgression and at the beginning of the Campanian, where there is a marked discordance. But by far the most important movements were during the Eocene, when the flysch trough came to an end and was thrust up on to the foreland. There was no mid-Tertiary orogeny as in the other Alpine belts, and the later Tertiary strata lie almost horizontally and are disturbed only by north-west trending faults. This exemplifies the distinctiveness of the Pyrenean folding. So here Neo-Europa is intruding upon Meso-Europa, but the Tertiary folding is only of a minor nature.

The isopach map of the basin for the Oligocene is much simpler than that for the Eocene. The little depressions and basins, including the great trough in the south, have disappeared. The north and east of Aquitaine continued as dry land, but there are extensive spreads of poorly dated sediment, generally called 'molasse'. There is now a simple picture of deeper water clayey limestones to the west extending on into the Atlantic, which from now on can be regarded as the western end of the Aquitaine Basin. Connections to the Mediterranean in the south-east and to the Paris Basin in the north-east have come to an end.

Around and to the east of the deeper water deposits there is a shallower limestone facies, which forms a great plateau between Saint-Laurent-du-Medoc and Lesparre and a smaller plateau on which stands the perfect mediaeval town of Saint-Emilion, with its church actually cut into this formation. Every name hereabouts reminds one of a famous wine, but unlike the other great wine-growing regions of Europe there is little direct geological control. The vines grow for the most part on Quarternary alluvium with drainage rather than solid geology as the most important environmental factor.

We now come to the junction between the Palaeogene and the Neogene. This is important here, not because one level matters more than another in the stratigraphical record, but because most Tertiary palaeontologists, have unwisely chosen 'type' sections in the Aquitaine Basin to define this global reference point.

The lowest two stages of the Miocene, the Aquitanian and the Burdigalian, both take their names from here (the latter from the city of Bordeaux). The 'stratotype' of the Aquitanian is defined as outcropping between two mills on a small stream about 20 km south of Bordeaux. It is necessary to wade up the stream and push aside the vegetation to see the miserable sections that illustrate the futility of such 'stratotypes'. A similar unconformable section nearby at Pont Pourquey attempts to define the Burdigalian stage. Besides the unsatisfactory nature of the type sections, the situation is further complicated by the fact that 'Aquitanian' is commonly associated with brackish water and lacustrine facies, while 'Burdigalian' is characteristically shallow marine. A further term—'Girondian'—has been coined (although fortunately not much used) for deeper water glauconitic facies.

Transgressions from the west and their associated regressions continued through the Miocene (Fig. 9.7) and typify the whole pattern of Tertiary sedimentation. Brackish

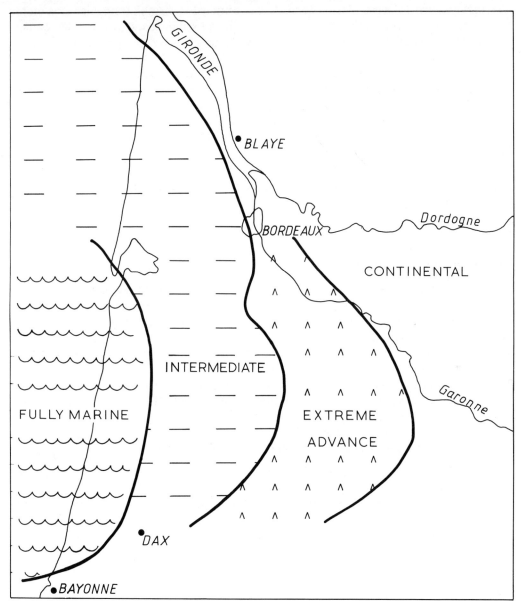

Fig. 9.7 Palaeogeography of the Aquitaine Basin in early Miocene times (after Alvinerie, J., 1969—thesis—by kind permission of the Director of the Institut de Géologie du Bassin d'Aquitaine).

and fresh-water deposits came and went in the east. Soft marine calcareous sands predominate in the west. Coral and bryozoan reefs flourished locally and every kind of fossil, from forams to mammals, are found in great abundance. The Helvetian stage, at the end of the Miocene, is represented by a sandstone transgression that went even further than the two preceding stages, nearly reaching Agen in the east. This was the last fling of the Tertiary sea and Pliocene marine deposits are restricted to a small triangular area on the coast, between Parentis and Bayonne. The continental sediments, that were always there in the east, then took over, and their clays and lignites reached the present shoreline, as for example at Biarritz.

The last trace of this great marine basin is seen in the Bay of Arcachon, the playground of Bordeaux, with its beaches, yachts, and oysters. But one must not leave Aquitaine without mentioning its most characteristic feature. This is the vast, gloomy monotony of the Landes, the wide, flat, coastal plain with its thick, frequently burned pine forests and its shepherds (traditionally at least, on stilts). The Landes is a region of Quaternary fluviatile deposits and wind-blown sands. The latter come from the great line of sand-dunes along the Atlantic coast, culminating in the Grande Dune de Pyla, just south of Arcachon. This is said to be the highest dune in Europe and it is constantly marching inland, smothering the pine forests.

9(d)   Massif Central

The Massif Central is the ancient heart of France and is often taken to be the most typical of the Variscan massifs of Europe. It is characterized by the ancient rocks, rugged topography, dark forests, and gloomy villages, that go with spiritous liquors, religious extremism, and bagpipes, in many parts of our continent. In the geographical sense it comprises something like one-sixth of the total land area of France. In a geological sense, it is even larger, since to the west of the main upstanding mass is the Bas Limousin, which is a low-lying slate belt. To the north is the Paris Basin, to the east the Rhône–Saône trough, to the west the Aquitaine Basin, and to the south the broad hollow which joins the Aquitaine to Lower Provence.

The rocks of the Massif Central fall into three main groups, of completely different character and studied by completely different people. These are:

1. The ancient rocks, deformed and altered in the Variscan orogeny, which makes the massif what it is.
2. The Mesozoic rocks, mainly carbonates wrapping round the sides, notably in the Ardèche and the Tarn gorges.
3. The Tertiary rocks, mostly volcanic, forming especially the classic landscape of the Auvergne.

Pre-Stephanian rocks

The older history of the Massif Central, at least that before the Stephanian, is thoroughly studied but poorly known. The lack of fossils and of sufficient radiometric dates leaves many uncertainties. There are strongly contrasting views and many of the structural interpretations are open to doubt. It seems to be generally accepted, however, that the region was affected by several different tectonic phases, the effects of which are almost inextricably mixed. We know that the metamorphic basement includes rocks as young as the Dinantian in places, although elsewhere (notably in the Montagne Noire in the south) even early Palaeozoic rocks are in a fairly healthy condition with well-preserved fossils. The major folding seems to have been in places, if not everywhere, post-Viséan and pre-Stephanian. After that the main story was one of erosion.

The general conclusion seems to be that one can recognize an ancient core in the Massif Central and then successive belts wrapped around it, rather in the manner of the supposed accreting continents. It is convenient therefore to consider the pre-Mesozoic rocks of the Massif Central in this way.

Auvergne Core. This is the *Noyau arverne* of French authors, comprising the northerly regions of the Auvergne (with its thick volcanic blanket), Forez (east of Clermont Ferrand), Lyonnais (above Lyon), and the long finger of Morvan pointing to the north; it also includes parts of Marche in the north-west, Limousin in the west, and the northern part of the Cevennes in the south-east. This region (Fig. 9.8) was stabilized long before the Variscan orogeny and its tectonism is commonly blamed on the Cadomian (end-Precambrian) movements, although it is still impossible dogmatically to confirm or deny the presence of Precambrian rocks in this region.

The plutonic rocks of the Auvergne Core have been the subject of some of the most famous studies in petrology, especially by the distinguished school at the University of Clermont Ferrand. Processes of metamorphism, metasomatism, and granitization, have been worked out in these ancient rocks. It is clear that the metamorphic grade reached varies markedly from place to place, and a general zonation can be recognized, reaching a higher intensity in the south than in the north. Generally speaking the French distinguish a deeper zone of migmatization from a higher zone of so-called 'ectinites' in which there has not been appreciable addition of granitic material. In this upper zone would come the majority of the gneisses and schists of the Auvergne Core, while in the lower zone of migmatites, the foliation has been progressively lost.

In spite of all this and the shortage of dates, a general succession can be worked out for the Auvergne Core. At the bottom there is a remarkably persistent and very thick succession of what must have been argillaceous sediments; these are followed by a volcanic series of a very varied nature, but including some spilites and serpentinites (although mostly transformed into migmatitites, amphibolites, etc.). Resting on these and cutting down through them in places to the pelites is a very thin development of carbonates, now marbles, which provides a useful marker horizon (if we knew what it meant). It is followed by another extremely thick argillaceous succession with some flysch-like bands, basic volcanics, and what seem to have been carbonaceous layers.

This is the whole of the succession in the north-west, but in the centre and east of the Auvergne Core there is a further volcanic succession, mainly acid, with both lava flows and tuffs, although like all the rest usually in a high-grade metamorphic condition. There is no apparent evidence of any major discordance or orogenic disturbance. There is, for example, no tectonic repetition of the marker horizons within the whole succession, which must reach 15 km in thickness.

All that we know of the age of this record is that it is certainly pre-Devonian, since up in the north-east, in Morvan, the crystalline rocks are overlain by Devonian sediments. It

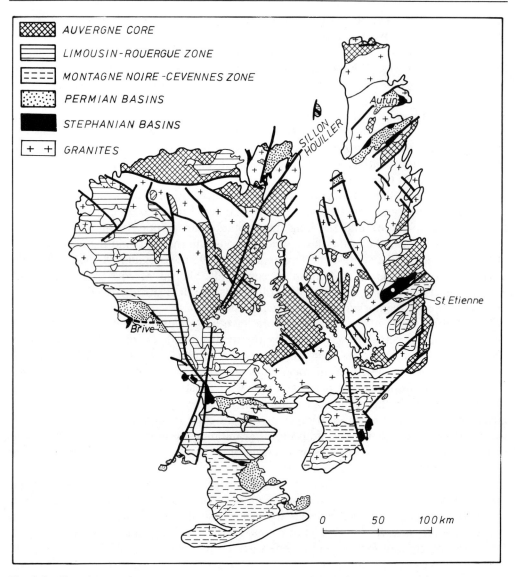

Fig. 9.8 Sketch-map showing the main geological units in the Massif Central (after Chenevoy, 1974, by kind permission of Doin Editeurs and Prof. Debelmas).

may well be all Proterozoic, as the top of the succession can be matched fairly well with the Lower and Middle Brioverian of Armorica. There may be some evidence of a pre-existing metamorphic basement below this.

The exact age of the pre-Devonian metamorphism is uncertain, although the fact that the Devonian of Brevenne, west of Lyon, rests on rocks that had already been eroded to the level of migmatites, makes it probable that it was already very ancient. The most popular approach is to call the metamorphism Cadomian, by analogy with Armorica, and this is supported by a few whole-rock dates which range around 670–650 million years. There are a few 'Caledonian' dates too, but no convincing geological evidence of such an orogeny in the Massif Central. Perhaps here and elsewhere in southern Europe there was non-orogenic Caledonian metamorphism.

The main orogeny and metamorphism (which produced retrograde effects in the earlier rocks) was early Variscan, although several different phases seem to be represented. The Devonian sediments and volcanics of Brevenne have been affected by the later metamorphism, but not the Visean rocks on top. However, the most common radiometric dates on the metamorphics are about 345–320 million years, which would put it at the end of the Dinantian (e.g., near Lyon) while elsewhere (e.g., in Haut Allier) it is in the Westphalian, with dates as young as 290 million.

By far the most common dates are those on the granites which abound in the Massif Central, in bewildering variety. Some are as old as Devonian and might be regarded as late phase Caledonian plutons; some are Dinantian, some Namurian, but the great majority have given ages concentrated around 300 million years, or a little more, and may be regarded as Westphalian.

Limousin–Rouergue Zone. This is the *Ensemble Ruténo–Limousin** of French authors, which is a belt of country that wraps round the Auvergne Core, mainly on its southern side, and is chiefly seen in the two regions of its name. The succession is very different from that of the central zone, although again there may be an early phase metamorphic basement. White quartzites and associated basic volcanics immediately make one think of the Ordovician, and this has been proved by acritarchs in some of the slates. Other rocks have been attributed to the late Brioverian and Cambrian, but with rather less evidence (mainly lithological comparisons with Armorica). It could be that the clastics including conglomerates, which figure largely in the lower part of the succession, represent the detritus from a newly risen Auvergne Core to the north. A thick pile of lava flows, with gabbroic intrusions, followed and the sedimentation became finer grained, although mostly a flysch-like character prevailed. So we seem to have a classic eugeosynclinal situation, which may have ranged from late Precambrian until early Ordovician times. The white quartzites are overlain unconformably by conglomerates and sandstones (e.g., in Bas Limousin) which may be Devonian or Dinantian in age. Unfortunately the exact age of these and of the main metamorphism here is not known. Radiometric dates range wildly through the Palaeozoic from as old as 530 million years to as young as 290. Again the granites come at the end of the story and are appropriately late Variscan.

Montagne Noire–Cevennes Zone. This is the *Ceinture Cévenole* of French authors, but it may be conveniently referred to by the above title because it consists mainly of the almost detached part of the Massif Central in the south—the Montagne Noire— and that belt of hills in the south-east known chiefly to English readers from Robert Louis Stevenson's travels there with a donkey in the last century. The Montagne Noire often figures in the stratigraphical literature because of its well-preserved record of Palaeozoic sediments and their fossils, but it also has its nucleus of older rocks.

Basement gneisses and granites are overlain by a sedimentary series which is thought to pass from the uppermost Proterozoic through into the Lower Cambrian. A shaly and

---

*Ruténo refers to the people who in Roman times inhabited the region of Rouergue in the south of the Massif Central.

sandy sequence is followed by prominent dolomites and limestones yielding plentiful archaeocyathids. These fix one at the top of the Lower Cambrian (or the very bottom of the Middle Cambrian). More shales and quartzites follow and then there is a break where the Upper Cambrian ought to be. A flysch-like sequence takes one through the Tremadoc and Lower Arenig and then there is another, bigger gap below transgressive Devonian. Only in the extreme south-east, in the area of Cabrières, is there a record of thin Upper Ordovician (with volcanics) and shaly Silurian. Evidently there was a big break due to uplift before the Caradoc. Thus there are breaks, which some would blame on phases of the Caledonian orogeny, but there is no evidence of major tectonism, apart from some radiometric dates in the metamorphics of the Cevennes, and one or two granites may have been remobilized at this time.

The Devonian sediments are limited in extent and thickness and are dominantly carbonate, including the distinctive reddish and greenish nodular limestones which are known as *griottes*, from a supposed resemblance to a basket of cherries. In the Mesozoic they would have been called *ammonitico rosso*, or better *rosso ammonitico*, see Chapter 16(d), since they have very similar characters, including the dominance of pelagic fossils in what seems to have been an area of slow deposition. It is striking how common this particular facies is, at several different stratigraphical horizons, in various parts of southern Europe.

The succession in the Montagne Noire is usually capped by Visean flysch-like rocks (so-called 'Culm'), of no great thickness, ending with emergence that began the long period of erosion that gave this end of the Massif Central the perfect peneplained surface that is so obvious, for example, from the mediaeval walls of Carcassonne.

The Variscan orogeny was the great event here and it is doubtful if there was an earlier one since way back in the Precambrian. The Palaeozoic sediments, albeit well preserved, are intensely folded. This shows up particularly well, for example, in the thin-bedded limestones of the Devonian. At Pic de Bisson, for example, the goniatites show that it is overturned. These remarks apply particularly to the Montagne Noire, where the stratigraphy is recognizable. In the quiet rolling country of the Cevennes the whole succession becomes progressively more monotonously metamorphosed. Although the generalities of the succession remain true, the carbonates almost disappear and there is much more clastic and volcanic material. The higher systems are probably missing due to uplift in this direction.

The age of the Variscan movements and metamorphism was very late in this zone. Unlike the areas to the north, Stephanian coals are here transformed to anthracites, and radiometric dates for the metamorphics are as low as 280 million years. The granites (such as the Martys granite in the heart of the structure) are mostly well up in the Westphalian–Stephanian.

All this may lead one to the conclusion that there was an outward building of the massif from the original core in the north, before the whole was tectonized, granitized, and stabilized, in the Variscan orogeny. There then followed an episode that was largely, but not wholly, post-orogenic.

Stephanian–Permian Sedimentation

Scattered across the surface of the Massif Central are a large number of coal-fields, of which the largest and most famous is at St. Etienne in the east. Associated with some of them (e.g., Autun in the north-east) are Permian deposits. All rest discordantly on the older rocks and all are related to an extensive system of fractures. The most obvious of these fractures is the *Sillon houiller* (the 'coal furrow') which runs roughly north-south through the Massif Central and separates the generally north-westerly trends to the west from the generally north-easterly trends to the east. This was probably a very ancient line and marks the main about-face of the Variscan trends in western Europe. It also shows up on geophysical surveys since the crust is notably thinner (perhaps 23 km) to the east and thicker (around 30 km) to the west.

The coal-fields are all of the limnic type, which formed as basins between the new mountains and were completely cut off from the sea. It is not suggested that the literally dozens of little coal-fields seen today were all originally separate. They are all delimited by later faulting, but there were probably only a limited number of basins around the margins of the massif, as well as a few along the major fractures. The abundance of conglomerates and coarse sandstones, together with the drifted nature of the plant remains, testifies to the intermontane nature of the deposition. Volcanism was also active during the Stephanian and evidently emerged from tensional fissures, for example along the *Sillon houiller*. There were some later folding movements along this line but it may originally have been a transcurrent fault.

The Permian usually follows directly on the Stephanian and is of the same general lacustrine–swampy–fluviatile character. Only in the south-west is there a break between the two. The lower part of the Permian is here known as the 'Autunian', after the town in the north-east of the Massif Central, but this is a difficult stage to define in international terms, although famous for its flora. Above it comes the more Germanic 'Saxonian', which is coarser, redder, and drier, with a distinct flora and attributed to the Upper Permian. Volcanism had largely ended by the early Permian and by the end of that period the massif has been blocked out pretty much as it is today.

Mesozoic Sedimentation

The story was now one of uplift, with the Mesozoic seas lapping around the sides of a new island. The 'Muschelkalk' sea of the mid Trias just reached its eastern, faulted wall. Conglomerates, sandstones, gypsum, and dolomite, spread south from Morvan. The early Jurassic sea invaded the massif with shallow-water deposits, separating the Montagne Noire from the main island. There came into existence the remarkable feature that now forms that glorious part of France known as the Causses. Tremendous thicknesses of Middle and mainly Upper Jurassic carbonates invade the massif from either side. This is the dazzling white country of deep caves and huge gorges, notably that of the Tarn and its tributaries (now solidly jammed with tourist traffic in the summer). The purity of the Upper Jurassic limestones indicates that the massif by that time was very much worn down and no longer supplying detritus. Indeed it may have been largely under water, especially in the south. The limestones smell strongly of the Tethys and the Mediterranean; they pinch out as one comes up the east side of the massif, along the faulted margin of the Rhône–Saône trough. Almost the last one sees of them is in the splendid ridge of Mont Crussol, south of St. Péray (opposite Valence). Here the whole Jurassic succession is preserved in a faulted slice of hill. The ruins of the chateau on the top stand on the highest Jurassic and provide one of the finest views in Europe. To the west is the rugged peneplain of the Massif Central, below is the great trench of the

Rhône; to the north-east are my beloved Jura; to the east are the Sub-Alps and the Alps rising behind; to the south one might see, or at least imagine, the blue waters of the Mediterranean. There is even a trace of gravels from when the great river flowed at a much higher level than it does today.

The Massif Central seems to have stood out from the sea almost completely during the Cretaceous, with only very local marine incursions. However, in the Ardèche, north of the Tarn gorges, there is a broad spread of flat-lying Cretaceous limestones.

The tension that produced the fault-lined Stephanian coal basins continued on a grander scale in Mesozoic times, defining the main limits of the massif and separating it from Armorica to the north-west and the Vosges to the north-east. We know, however, that similar Variscan rocks and structures are continuous at depth under the Mesozoic sediments.

Cainozoic

When the early Tertiary folding began in the nearby Pyrenees, the Massif Central stood firm. All through Tertiary times the rigid block acted as a buttress to the waves of Alpine folding. As with similar blocks farther east (notably the Bohemian Massif), instead of folding there was a slight fracturing and a series of graben developed in which accumulated Tertiary continental sediments (Fig. 9.9).

This started as early as the Eocene in the small Menat Basin, where there is a rich flora and fauna of this age (notably insects, fish, and plants). The much larger basins of Limagne and Aurillac contain mainly Oligocene sediments, which are divisible stratigraphically by means of snails.

Also in the Oligocene began the famous Cainozoic volcanic activity of the Massif Central (Fig. 9.10), and this too was much controlled by faulting. The first eruptions were associated with the sedimentary basins and a feature of them is the formation of 'pépérites' which consist of glassy lava fragments embedded in limestones or other sediments. They appear to have been produced by sub-aqueous explosions when lavas flowed into lakes.

The volcanicity reached its maximum in the Miocene and Pliocene with the formation of the great mountain masses of Cantal and Mont Dore, now deeply eroded. At their prime, they must have been comparable with present-day Mount Etna.

These are great stratified volcanoes; the larger of the two—Cantal—is some 70 km across. They are characterized by enormous thicknesses of volcanic breccias and ashes, together with lavas that range from rhyolites to basalts. Locally, for example at Aubrac, the activity was far more placid and there were Hawaiian-type extrusions of lava without explosions. Pliocene plateau basalts and associated mud-flows reach as much as 1000 m in thickness.

Dating of the lavas is possible chiefly by means of interbedded sediments with terrestrial and fresh-water fossils. Locally there are vertebrate remains, for example near Aurillac in Cantal, where basalts are interbedded with sands yielding *Hipparion*. Around Le Puy, lavas rest on alluvial deposits with *Mastodon* and at Neschers, in the Mont Dore Massif, a basalt rests on alluvial deposits containing reindeer remains. This shows that

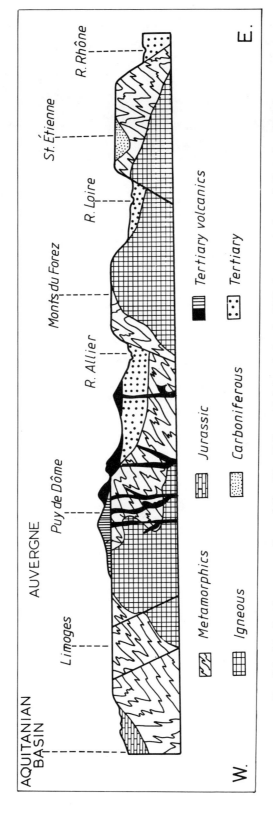

Fig. 9.9 Idealized cross-section of the Massif Central (after Lobeck, 1951, by permission of Hammond Inc.).

247

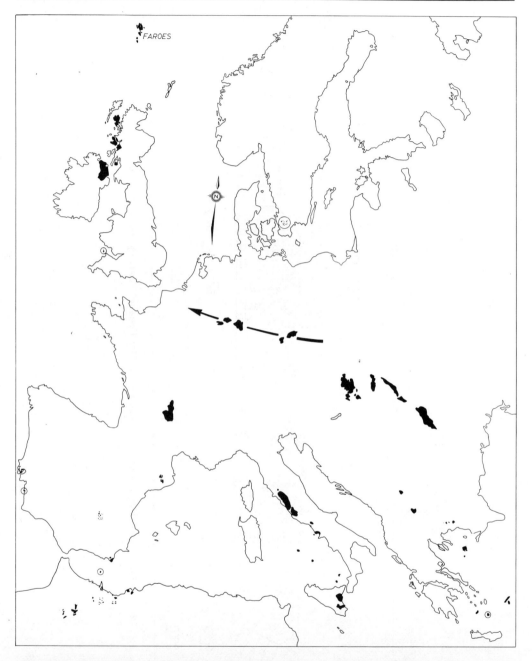

Fig. 9.10 Distribution of Cainozoic volcanism in Europe. The arrow indicates the supposed trace of a mantle plume, and it is tempting to draw others. Circles are intended to draw attention to smaller occurrences (from Ager, 1975, by kind permission of the Council of the Geologists' Association).

volcanic activity continued into the Pleistocene, as one might suspect from the fresh unweathered-looking appearance of many of the newer volcanoes.

These include the most famous 'puys'. The first eruptions of Quaternary times were simple upwellings of viscous, trachytic lavas forming steep-sided domes of the Mont Pelée type, such as the sudden sharp hills of the town of Le Puy itself with their precariously perched churches and holy statues. The best known of all is probably the Puy-de-Dôme, west of Clermont Ferrand, which has a spectacular spiral road leading up to the meteorological station at the summit, which is used for the observation of cloud formations (usually from above).

From this summit one can also see the magnificent Chaîne des Puys—a line of late Quaternary volcanoes some 35 km long—arising from a fracture in the granite below. These latest puys are usually perfect cones of stratified ashes with central craters. They represent eruptions of both the Stromboli and the Volcano type. Lavas can be seen to flow down existing valleys. In places, streams still flowed in natural tunnels under the lava and columnar basalt can be seen resting on river gravels that look as if they might have been laid down yesterday.

In fact, the sense of modernity is so much with one among the volcanoes of the Auvergne that one almost expects to see steam rising from the ground and to feel the rocks still warm to the touch. As elsewhere in the ancient massifs of Europe, Palaeolithic man must have gazed in terror at the last eruptions of the puys and perhaps acquired his fire from the conflagrations they caused.

9(e) Vosges, Black Forest, and Odenwald

The Vosges and the Black Forest stand as gloomy Variscan sentinels on either side of that great corridor of northern Europe that is the Rhine Graben. There is no doubt that the two massifs are connected beneath the waterway and are, in effect, very much part of the same block, split only by later rifting. But here the Franco-German frontier runs along the Rhine, so the Vosges lie in France while the Black Forest (and Odenwald to the north) lie in Germany. This should not affect their geology, but in fact it does, since the French inevitably draw parallels between the Vosges and the Massif Central while the Germans tend to look east towards the Bohemian Massif. So it is that migmatization was a dominant process in the Vosges granites and gneisses, but magmatic processes dominated the story (at least until recently) in the Black Forest.

Both the Vosges and Black Forest are in the belt of high-grade Variscan metamorphism. The Odenwald, on the other hand, with its little associated massif of Spessart, is closer to the 'paratectonic' fold belt to the north, and has suffered less.

Vosges

This is the massif that gives its name to the Variscan orogeny. The Vosges are not really very far from the Massif Central and a connecting link is provided by the tiny Serre Massif, in front of the Jura near Dôle. Unlike the Massif Central, the Vosges of the geographers is much larger than the Vosges of the geologists. The Variscan massif that is the concern of this chapter is just the 'crystalline Vosges' of French literature. This disappears gently westwards under the 'sandy Vosges' of flat-lying Triassic sandstones. The eastern borders of the massif are much more abrupt as the old rocks drop down in a series of step faults into the Rhine Graben.

The oldest rocks are the high-grade metamorphics of the central Vosges (Fig. 9.11) which seem to result from the Variscan remobilization of an ancient basement formed way back in the Precambrian. They include granulite facies rocks and lenses of peridotite, but mainly consist of a series of different kinds of gneisses and migmatites put together in a jigsaw puzzle of fault blocks cut by later instrusions. They may be compared with the Auvergne Nucleus of the Massif Central and the Moldanubian Zone of Bohemia. There were probably at least two different phases of metamorphism, working on what must have been an original composition that was largely clastic and pyroclastic. This fits with the fact that the high-grade metamorphics are overlaid by schists

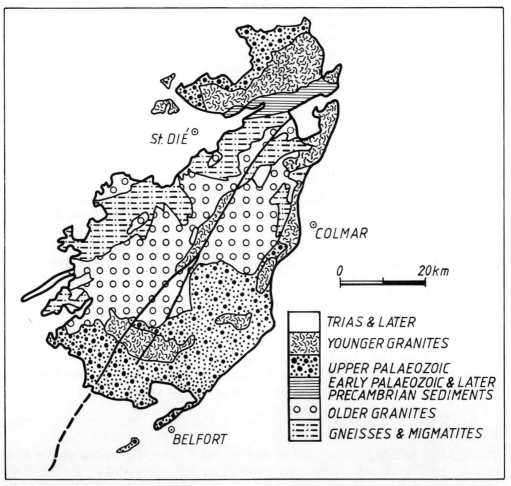

Fig. 9.11 *Geological sketch-map of the Vosges (after von Eller, 1976, by kind permission of Masson Editeur).*

near Villé, in the north-east corner of the massif, which are thought to be the equivalent of the Brioverian of Armorica. This is partly on the basis of their lithological characters (originally greywackes or sandy shales and quartzites) and on radiometric age determinations which are around 700 million years. They have twice been folded.

Immediately next to these Brioverian rocks, and forming part of the same outcrop, are further sandstones and shales (the latter said to be the colour of wine dregs) which have yielded Ordovician and Silurian chitinozoans. Unlike the Brioverian sediments they have been subjected to only one phase of folding—the Variscan. There is no evidence of Caledonian movements hereabouts, which links this masif to the central rather than the northern belt of Variscides, as does the high degree of metamorphism.

The Upper Palaeozoic of the Vosges is difficult to divide stratigraphically and is usually grouped as the Devono-Dinantian. It is seen over a large area in the south of the massif and at its northern extremity. The Lower Devonian displays a varied series of metamorphosed sediments in the valley of the Bruche in the north, where there is also considerable contemporaneous volcanism, ranging from spilites to andesites and much pyroclastic material. The Middle and Upper Devonian in the north is also a varied series of sediments and volcanics, including lenses of fossiliferous limestones that may represent reefs. The volcanism reached its acme in mid Devonian times. But the whole thing is in a very sorry state. In the south only the Upper Devonian is seen, with limestones and volcanics, near Belfort.

At the end of the Devonian, the Bretonic phase of the Variscan orogeny was important here, with major northerly thrusting and the emplacement of granites. The Tournaisian is everywhere absent as a result of this tectonism and the transgressive Visean is usually in the form of black slates, sandstones, and cherts, with further volcanicity, including more spilites. Fossils are few but include land plants which do not suggest an ocean floor. The Visean is well seen along the River Savoureuse in the south.

But it is almost misleading in the Vosges and Black Forest to mention the sediments, since the story is so much dominated by gneisses and granites. A notable series of the latter were emplaced in mid Visean times including the famous 'Ballon d'Alsace' granite which cuts across the Upper Palaeozoic outcrop in the south. It takes its name from the smooth, rounded weathering of the granite masses, which look like large balloons resting on the landscape.

The main Variscan movements revitalized the trends established in the Precambrian orogenies. The formation of the great north-easterly trending *Faille Vosgienne* (which runs across the centre of the massif and can be traced all the way south to the Jura) was contemporaneous with the emplacement of the granites, some of which can be seen squeezing up along it with parallel oriented felspars. Northerly thrusting occurred and then everything was reactivated once more in the Asturian movements at the end of the Westphalian. The granites in fact fall into two groups radiometrically at 320 and 300 million years.

Little coal basins were formed in the Westphalian and Stephanian but have only been worked on a minor scale. They are said to have migrated northwards as the movements continued. There is also Permian ('Autunian') in the north, especially around St. Die. Movements (which would be termed Saalian) and volcanism were still going on in Permian times, but from now onwards it was essentially a story of uplift and erosion.

The coarse Triassic deposits rest everywhere unconformably on the tectonized rocks of the Vosges. In places the coarse sediments have left outliers high up on the massif and they form the extensive 'Sandy Vosges' to the west. But this and the once all-enveloping blanket of Jurassic sediments are part of another story. There is no sign of any Cretaceous rocks in the region.

Black Forest

The Black Forest (*Schwarzwald*) stands on the opposite bank of the Rhine in Germany, and like the Vosges is a forested massif with few exposures. Its name is singularly appropriate, although the black conifers are relieved by the extensive cherry orchards which provide the raw material for the fiery local Kirschwasser liqueur.

Superficially it is simpler than the Vosges, with a similar core of ancient gneisses of both sedimentary and volcanic origin. But many aspects of its geology are, in a way, more difficult to explain. Thus the oldest rocks are not in the core but in the extreme south, where they have been brought up by a north-west trending fault (Fig. 9.12). The Germans compare the cordierite gneisses and migmatites here with the Moldanubian core of the Bohemian Massif. The main gneissose core farther north, may be more comparable with the Saxothuringian zone. Radiometric dates on this part of the massif have been surprisingly young, ranging around the 480–470 million year mark and therefore well into the middle of the Ordovician. This seems to be the only definite evidence of anything 'Caledonian' (in the broad sense) in the region. Nevertheless, there is no doubt that most of the gneissose core is much older, even though it may have been through several phases of folding and metamorphism. The whole thing was partially reworked during the Variscan orogeny, with the granitic and other intrusions which are such a feature of the Vosges and Black Forest massifs.

The old metamorphic rocks are overlain unconformably by a series of greywackes and shales of late Devonian and early Carboniferous age. This is seen chiefly in the south, preserved along an old zone of weakness, with only a small patch on the northern margin. Undoubtedly these sediments, now metamorphosed up to phyllite grade, once covered the whole massif. The sequence includes basic volcanic rocks and intrusives, but these are relatively rare. Sedimentation appears to have continued into earliest Carboniferous times (i.e., Tournaisian), although that interval is not known on the opposite side of the Rhine but, as there, it was interrupted by the movements of the Sudetian phase of the Variscan orogeny. Sharp folding and faulting produced steep ridges which were eroded again during the next phase of sedimentation. The main trend was to the northeast, but in the south it swings round to form a curious circular structure, south-east of Freiburg. As in the Vosges, this was also a time of granite emplacement with several different bodies.

Immediately afterwards, rapid erosion produced thick conglomerates, sandstones, and shales, in the Visean, while in the west a minor marine invasion laid down a thin limestone that is only a shadow of its massive equivalent in other parts of Europe. The 'Culm' sandstones include pebbles of granites that had already been unroofed. Extensive volcanism, including explosion breccias, agglomerates, and tuffs, accompanied the later Carboniferous sedimentation.

The Asturian phase of the Variscan orogeny was only a matter of block-faulting, although there was a second episode of granitic intrusion in Westphalian times with a

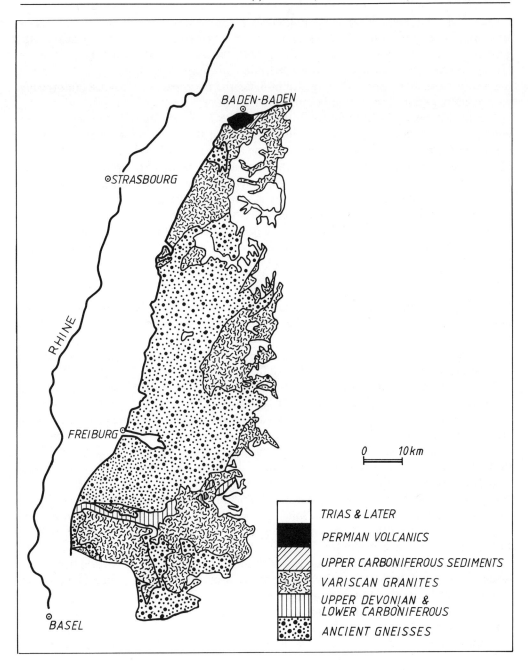

Fig. 9.12 Geological sketch-map of the Black Forest.

range of dates between 320 and 300 million years, similar to those obtained in the Vosges and Massif Central. Some of the granites have long, parallel-orientated felspars suggesting intrusion along a place of weakness. With the late faulting there was the start of late volcanism and extensive hydrothermal mineralization. A suite of north-west trending acidic intrusions appeared at this time. Thus the main part of the Variscan orogeny was virtually over before it even began farther north.

The mostly acidic volcanism continued into the Permian and was associated with continental sediments. On the east side of the massif these rest on a deeply weathered surface of Carboniferous granite, with the zone of alteration extending three metres into the substrate. Deep fault-bounded troughs, such as that at the northern tip of the Black Forest, acquired hundreds of metres of coarse, felspathic sediments derived directly from the old rocks. A last hint of the volcanicity is seen in the thermal springs of the area, of which those of the spa town of Baden-Baden are the most famous.

The continental deposits of the Permian pass eastwards up into the Triassic of the Swabian Alb. In paces these beds spread far on to the eastern flanks of the Black Forest, providing some of the best unconformities to be seen anywhere.

Odenwald

The little crystalline massif of the Odenwald lies north of the Black Forest, on the same side of the Rhine, and may be regarded as a detached continuation of that massif. With it may be associated the even tinier massif of Spessart, to the east-north-east. It is a wooded upland area like the others and forms a natural playground for the city of Mannheim and the other communities of this highly industrialized area.

The most striking feature of the Odenwald (as in so many of the Variscan massifs) is a major fault through its middle, trending north-north-east (Fig. 9.13). On the east side of this there is a dome (that continues into Spessart) formed of high-grade metamorphosed argillaceous sedimentary rocks of uncertain age which have been intruded by granitic gneisses and gabbro-amphibolites. All that can be said of these rocks as a whole is that they have suffered two phases of deformation like the older successions in the other massifs described in this chapter.

To the west of the main fault is a meta-sedimentary sequence of the Saxothuringian type as in the northern part of the Bohemian Massif. They are schists and phyllites of uncertain age, but some are comparable to the Middle Devonian slates of the Bruche valley, mentioned in the Vosges. There is also an interesting broken-up horizon of marble, originally probably continuous, which may represent a Devonian reef belt. Spectacular thermal–metamorphic minerals are found near Auerbach, as a marginal product of a hornblende granite. Younger granites are finer grained.

The main tectonic spasm is thought to have come in the Bretonian phase of the Variscan orogeny, i.e., very early, but some of the granites are certainly Sudetian. Many of these were syntectonic. The main fault moved at this time, but the whole massif was stable before the Triassic, which passes over it undisturbed.

9(f)   Rhine Graben

Between the massifs just described runs the Rhine Graben. It is a narrow, sharply defined belt, running roughly north–south, that cuts across all pre-existing structures and is filled with Cainozoic sediments (Fig. 9.14). On either side is a series of normal faults which

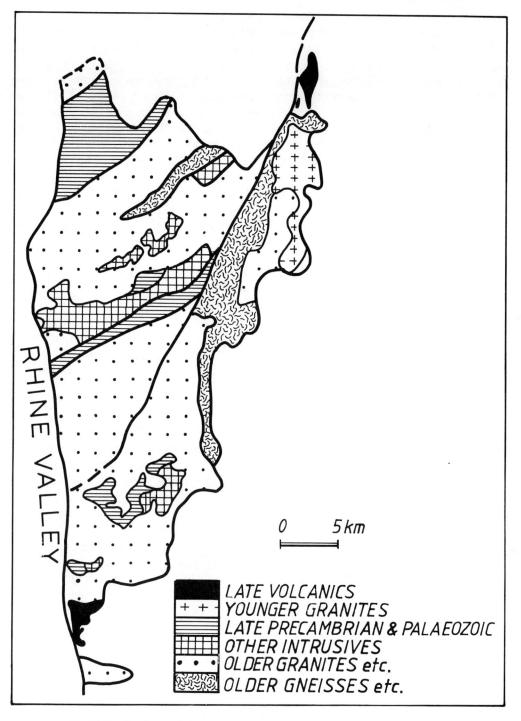

Fig. 9.13 Geological sketch-map of the Odenwald (after von Bubnoff).

converge downwards. In several places a staircase of faults can be observed delimiting the ancient massifs that form the margins. The graben is remarkably constant in width (about 36 km) for the whole of its 300 or so km and the master faults on either side consistently parallel each other's changes in direction. There is even a mirror-image in the geomorphology on either side, with the exposed Variscan basement of the Vosges and Black Forest uplifted about the same amount and much more so than the Permian and Triassic sediments farther north. The graben here is not the narrow, rocky gorge that I imagined, adorned with Rhine maidens combing their hair and singing seductive songs to passing sailors.* It is a wide plain with the bordering massifs away on opposite horizons. The central part of the graben is also cut by a large number of small normal faults defining small horsts of Jurassic rocks within the main trough. This is the pleasant wine and fruit country of Alsace, with the south-facing slopes of the little horsts ideal for growing the grape.

If one calculates that the original width of the graben before stretching was about 30 km and if one hypothetically extends the master faults downwards, then they would meet at about 31 km, which is also the depth of the Moho on either side of the graben. The depth to the base of the present crust within the graben is less than this and seismic refraction studies suggest the presence of a mass of high velocity here between the crust and the upper mantle proper. The question is then which came first? Did the rifting provide a space for a massive intrusion or did the intrusion produce the rifting effect?

The whole region was covered by Jurassic seas and evidence of thickening and thinning within the deposits of these seas suggests a series of submarine ridges that cross the area obliquely and completely ignore the later graben system. With the late Kimmerian movements the whole region became emergent with subaerial weathering in the Cretaceous.

The first signs of the Rhine Graben date back to the Eocene. Continental facies Lutetian sediments were deposited locally in troughs and some of these were already being reworked as a result of later movements to be redeposited as basal Lattorfian conglomerates at the end of the Eocene. This heralded an Oligocene marine transgression into the trough, probably from the south. A thick zone of salt deposits, mainly rock-salt but including two valuable potash horizons, ranges through the Upper Eocene and Oligocene. The potash is mined in the Mulhouse basin. A later Oligocene marine invasion came in from the north.

The movements on the faults intensified during the Miocene and were associated with volcanicity, notably the circular hill of the Kaiserstuhl (the 'king's chair') east of Colmar in the south. The Miocene sedimentation was concentrated in the north of the trough as though the great see-saw which had been tilted southwards in the Palaeogene had now reversed itself. A sort of 'Dead Sea' developed north of Strasbourg with further faulting and, at the end of the epoch, molasse-type deposits were forming in the south with the elephant-like *Dinotherium*.

It was during the Miocene that there were poured out the vast basaltic lavas of the Vogelsberg, which seems to have secured the main Rhine rift like a safety pin

---

*The type locality for the siren Lorelei is farther north, where a branch fault cuts through the Rheinisches Schiefergebirge and where the legend may have been invented by drunken bargemen to excuse the frequency with which they ran aground on the Palaeozoic slates in the dangerous rapids.

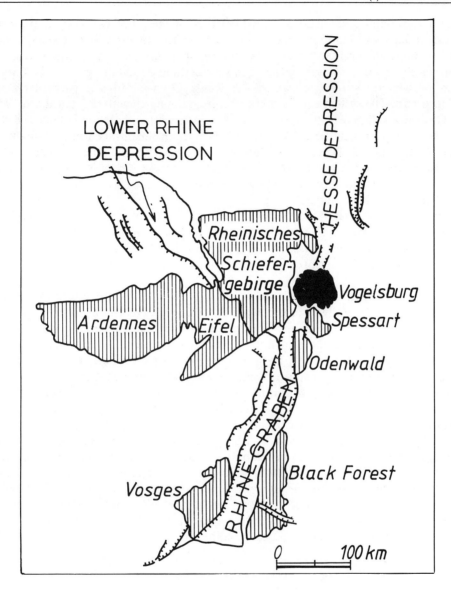

Fig. 9.14 *Sketch-map of the Rhine Graben.*

across a zip fastener. Previously it had continued northwards into the Hesse depression, but hereafter it was deflected north-westwards past the Lorelei into the Lower Rhine Depression.

The Rhine itself was diverted this way as a result also of movements and the deposition of coarse deltaic and alluvial sediments in the Pliocene. Previously it flowed south to join the Saône and thence into the Mediterranean, but henceforward it would be a

257

northern river joining (at least for a while) the Thames. The bordering massifs were elevated enough by mid-Quaternary times for glaciers to form and the major faults continue to operate until the present day with minor seismic activity and thermal springs.

This seems to be a suitable place to say something about the general Tertiary rift system of western Europe, of which the Rhine Graben forms a particularly well-developed part. The system can be said to begin in the north with the 'failed arm' of the Oslo Graben which may be traced south in structures west and east of Jutland and down under northern Germany (Fig. 9.15). It runs into the Rhine Graben near Frankfurt via the Hesse Depression. Beyond the plug of the Vogelsberg, the later branch heads off north-westwards via the Lower Rhine Depression into the southern North Sea and up into the Viking Graben. One must not forget in this connection the other graben of the North Sea and western England.

From the southern end of the Rhine Graben, the structures are deflected sharply to the west-south-west through the Belfort gap south of the Vosges and north of the Jura, before continuing in a southerly direction as the Rhône–Saône Trough. This deflection has been interpreted as a transform fault displacing the two north–south sections of the graben.

The Rhône–Saône structure is discussed in the Section 9(g) below, but beyond that we see the whole thing laterally displaced again as the Campidano rift of Sardinia, as a result of the rotation of the Corsica and Sardinia massifs in the shuffling of Mediterranean microplates. On again, as the Sicilian Channel between that island and Tunisia, our rift system leaves Europe to enter Africa near Sirte and then disappears under the sands of the Sahara with a spread of plateau basalts to the south-south-east.

Seismic records over the past century show that the Lower Rhine branch is now the more active of the two branches, with a line of epicentres running up its centre. The Hesse Depression is completely inactive, although there is minor seismicity near Cologne and beneath Belgium and the Netherlands. The general sense of movement along the faults seems to be lateral and sinistral, in relation to general compressional forces on north-west–south-east lines. Much of the Tertiary and Quaternary volcanism of western Europe is associated with the rift system, from the Rhineland right down to Sardinia, and the more separated volcanism such as that of the Massif Central is along parallel lines. One may speculate whether the Vogelsberg 'plug' arrested a splitting apart of western Europe far more fundamental than occurs politically.

9(g) Rhône–Saône Trough

It is logical to follow the Rhine Graben with its southern continuation, albeit off-set, the Rhône–Saône Trough. This is the great flat-bottomed graben that separates the Massif Central from the Jura and the Alps. Apart from the roaring motorway of the 'route to the sun', it is a quiet, low-lying, damp, peaceful place with very little geology to be seen along the greater part of its length. What *is* seen, in the customary paradox of geology, is for the most part atypical. Although it is essentially one structure, it falls neatly into four parts: the Bresse Basin, the Bas Dauphiné Basin, the Lower Rhône Basin, and the Camargue.

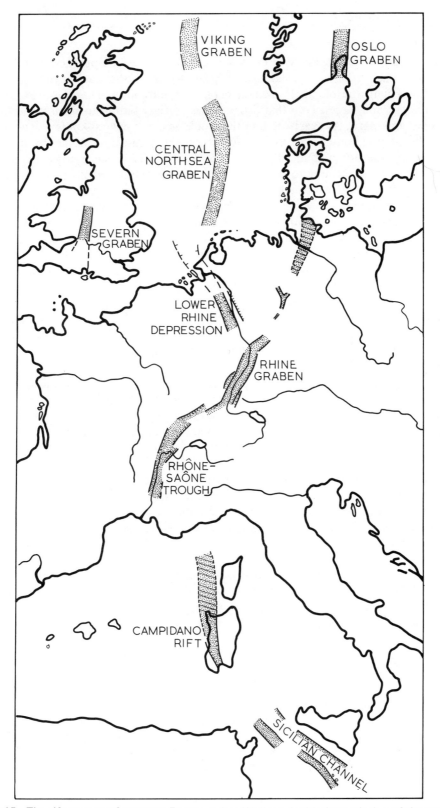

Fig. 9.15 The rift system of western Europe (after Wallace, by kind permission of the author).

Bresse Basin

This is the low, watery country of cows and cheese. The usual approach to it, from the direction of Paris, is down the staircase of faults that mark the cracked rim of the Paris Basin into Dijon, the old and splendid capital of Burgundy. The final descent is La Côte—the last and largest fault that drops down Tertiary sediments against the Jurassic limestones and marls. As everywhere in this book, it is difficult to know where to draw the line between regions. Logically the faulted slabs of Jurassic rocks that form the *Seuil de Bourgogne* (the Burgundian Sill) are part of the Paris Basin, since they are continuous with the other Mesozoic outcrops that circle the Tertiary infill. Equally logically, they are part of the Rhône–Saône Trough, since similar faults continue under the Tertiary cover of that feature and are the whole reason for its existence. The same could be said of the faulted western Jura on the other side of the great valley. But topographically it is the Tertiary-filled part of the graben that is obvious, so it will here be treated as a separate entity.

The name 'Bresse Basin' is often restricted to the part roughly east of the Saône, while that to the west is called the Châlon Trench. These two parts are separated by a slight tectonic ridge which runs up the centre of the valley, culminating in the north in the tiny La Serre Massif, north of Dôle, which is the only connecting link of crystalline rocks seen at the surface between the Vosges and the Massif Central. It only rises about 100 m above the plain and consists of metamorphic rocks of early Palaeozoic age and a cover of Permian red beds.

To the north-east, only the western part of the trough continues—as the High Saône Syncline—almost to the Vosges. South-westwards it is the west side of the trough floor that rises to the surface. First, as a continuation of La Serre structure, early Mesozoic rocks appear along the right bank of the Saône beyond Tournus, and then an easterly protuberance of the ancient rocks of the Massif Central extends as far as the river south of Mâcon.

From what is seen at the sides and known from deep borings and geophysical studies, the structure of this northern part of the trough is simple. Parallel normal faults on the west side let down the Mesozoic floor in steps and these are complemented by similar faults on the east side. That side is complicated, however, by the north-westerly push of the Mesozoic rocks of the Jura in Neogene times. The east side therefore defines the boundary between Meso- and Neo-Europa.

The history of the Bresse Basin is largely a Tertiary one. The Palaeozoic floor drops to more than 3000 m in the south, but the Mesozoic rocks cross from La Côte to the Jura without important change. The Eocene is little represented and mainly consists of fresh-water limestones with a basal conglomerate in places, composed of flints derived from the late Cretaceous Chalk. It must be remembered that the latter was left way back in the Paris Basin and is nowhere seen in the vicinity of the Rhône–Saône Trough; there is certainly no trace of it in the Jura.

Major movements along the delimiting faults poured quantities of coarse debris into the sides of the trough through the greater part of Oligocene time, while in the centre accumulated finer grained sands and clays, together with considerable thicknesses of evaporites. There were see-sawing effects along the eastern margin, tilting sometimes to the west and sometimes to the east.

Tectonic happenings to the south-east dominated the later part of the history of the

Bresse Basin, but nowhere were the Tertiary rocks deformed or displaced laterally.

Quiet lacustrine deposition at the end of the Oligocene was followed by a marine incursion in the Miocene and then molasse conglomerates poured into the trough from the rising Alps. In the later Miocene there was a return to fresh-water conditions with important lignites. These were overridden by the north-westerly moving front of the Jura. In the Pliocene came the lacustrine deposits of the 'Pontian', the coarse river conglomerates of the glaciated mountains, and the lacustrine deposits which are still accumulating in the hundreds of scattered lakes and ponds. What is called the Bressane Lake was really the last remnant of the Miocene peri-Alpine sea.

Bas Dauphiné Basin

South of Mâcon down to Valence, the metamorphic rocks of the Massif Central press close to the right bank of the river, first the Saône and then the Rhône itself after the two rivers join in Lyon. The trough is pinched in both in the north, where the Tabular Jura of the Île de Cremieu protrudes towards Lyon, and more so in the south, where the Sub-Alps try hard to reach the Massif Central near La Voulte and early Tertiary rocks are turned up on end at Crest. The low country between these two constrictions is the Bas Dauphiné or Valence Basin. It was probably here that Hannibal turned right to cross the Alps.

Unlike the northern basin, the Mesozoic rocks here show the influence of the stable land of the Massif Central. The Trias disappears completely in a north-westerly direction, while the Jurassic and early Cretaceous rocks pass from an Alpine deep-water facies into shallow-water detritic sediments. Hereabouts the 'Purbeckian' facies of the Jurassic–Cretaceous boundary appears for the first time going north. As we reach the south end of the basin and the classic section of Mont Crussol, opposite Valence, we get our first smell of the Tethys, with the feather-edge of Mesozoic limestones coming up from the warm south.

In the Tertiary, too, things were changing. The Eocene is thicker, with brackish water deposits in its upper part. Great thicknesses of sediment and salt reflect the Pyrenean-Provençal movements that preceded the Alpine contortions. The Miocene sea from the south is more evident and the whole valley foundered in Pliocene times to admit a huge ria bringing the sea almost as far north as Lyon.

Lower Rhône Basin

South from La Voulte, after a further constriction, the trough widens to form the broad lowland area of Lower Provence, with the metamorphic rocks to the west replaced by the Mesozoic limestone plateaux of Ardèche and the Tarn Gorges. The story is now complicated by a series of east–west ridges, notably the Alpilles, which reflect the Pyrenean movements of late Eocene times. These are best discussed in the chapter on Provence, since they are part of Neo-Europa. The basic divisions get strained, but the trough clearly continues, for it heads out into the Mediterranean to form the Campidano Rift within the Variscan Massif of Sardinia. The elevation of these ridges clearly had an effect on Tertiary sedimentation in the trough. Thick sandy deposits, including pebbles of quartz and volcanic rocks, poured into the basin during the Oligocene and were followed by the coarse molasse conglomerates of the Miocene from the new mountains to the east. The facies are varied and complicated and the floor of the trough continued to fall dramatically. The most abrupt change is across a north-east trending fault which reaches the coast near Montpellier and which outlines, with the Alpine front, what is now the Rhône delta.

Camargue

This is the strangest and in some ways most attractive region of France—a great watery plain formed by the delta of the Rhône. It really is delta shaped, with the point of the triangle at the Roman city of Arles, its sides the two main distributaries of the Rhône, and its base along the Mediterranean shore, west of Marseilles. The soil is salty and unsuitable for crops other than rice, and the Camargue is chiefly known for its bulls, horses, and mosquitoes, its clarity of light, its artists, and its great sense of solitude. It certainly is not known for its geology, although the high-water table presents an interesting problem of engineering geology in the burial of the dead (like that of New Orleans on the Mississippi delta, where the bodies used to be enclosed in tombs above ground level). At the perfect mediaeval town of Aigues-Mortes, the slaughtered Burgundians of a siege in 1418 had to be preserved in salt in the tower that is still named after them.

The great quantities of sediment brought down by the Rhône continuously add to the delta and threaten to close the Gulf of Fos. In places the land is gaining on the sea at a rate of 10–50 m per year, although elsewhere the reverse is happening on the land, especially at times of storms. The lighthouse at Faraman was built 700 m inland in 1840 but was destroyed by the sea in 1917. Due to subsidence, the village of Saintes-Mairies-de-la-Mer, which was several kilometres inland in the Middle Ages, now has to be protected by dikes.

9(h) Dobrogea and Moesian Platform

We leap now to the other end of Europe and to another great delta—that of the Danube. One of the most memorable geological field trips I have taken in Europe was on a luxury steamer sailing down the lower reaches of the Danube in Romania, consuming caviare and vodka in good company, and taking short excursions across the dusty, loess-covered plain to study the rocks of Dobrogea. This is an ancient massif (like others to be discussed later) that has foundered in geologically recent times so that the Precambrian and Palaeozoic rocks are largely buried under considerable thicknesses of Mesozoic and Cainozoic sediment.

Here, east of the great sweep of the Carpathian arc, we get one last glimpse of the Variscan foreland on the shores of the Black Sea. Not far to the north lies the edge of the Eo-European stable region, exposed in the crystalline rocks of the Ukrainian Massif, but part of the Dobrogea at least is distinctly Meso-Europa, for it was mobile not only in Precambrian times, but through to the end of the Palaeozoic.

Although small, the Dobrogea Massif is complex and can be divided into five distinct zones, all but the southernmost separated by reversed faults of large displacement (Fig. 9.16). The main folds trend to the north-west and the faults lie parallel to these basement structures. North and south the massif disappears completely under very young deposits and even in its central part it is poorly exposed because of a thick blanket of Quaternary loess, related to the Danube, which fills the valleys and rises like a plume behind every vehicle on the dusty roads.

Pre-Dobrogea Depression

This is the stretch of Quaternary sediments that separate Dobrogea from the Ukraine and the edge of the East European Platform. It largely consists of the old province of Bessarabia (now part of the USSR) and its most notable feature at the surface is the Danube delta and its pelicans. From borehole evidence we know that there is a thin development of Devonian red beds and some later Palaeozoic, thinning out northwards; this includes some supposed Permian 'Verrucano'-type conglomerates. Unconformable above this are some 3000 m of Middle and Upper Jurassic beds, including evaporites. Both the Palaeozoic and Mesozoic rocks differ markedly from those of the North Dobrogea immediately to the south across a major reversed fault.

North Dobrogea

The Mäcin so-called mountains in the north-western part of Dobrogea, are a metamorphic complex folded on north-west lines. The cores of some of the anticlines are formed of schists and amphibolites assumed to be Precambrian in age. They are certainly older than the thick succession of alternating sandstones and shales which flank them. These latter, rather variably metamorphosed, may well range from late Proterozoic to Ordovician. They are overlain by fossiliferous Silurian, consisting of limestones and pyritic shales, cut by basic dikes.

The Devonian is much more fossiliferous, although only the lower part is represented, as rhythmic alternations of quartzites, shales, and limestones. Granitic intrusions, dated at around 290 million years, cut all the pre-Carboniferous rocks and there seems to have been a major hiatus at this point which may represent an early Variscan event. The early Carboniferous deposits above may have been synorogenic and consist of a polygenetic basal conglomerate overlain by thick greywackes and shales like the 'Culm'. The main spasm of the Variscan orogeny then consolidated the whole massif with granitic intrusions and metamorphism enough to transform the earlier intrusions into a gneissose condition.

In the north-east the Variscan basement shows through in a few of the anticlinal cores, standing vertically beneath the Mesozoic cover, while a little Mesozoic is preserved in the synclines in the west.

Alpine-type seas flooded the massif in early to mid Triassic times leaving conglomerates, sandstones, and red limestones (locally packed with ammonites), like those of Halstatt in Austria. These were followed by flysch-like sediments and submarine lavas with late Triassic intrusions; some mineralization followed the old north-west lines. There is evidence of slight deformation and a break below early Jurassic deposits, which represent the early phase of the Kimmerian movements, important at this end of Europe.

263

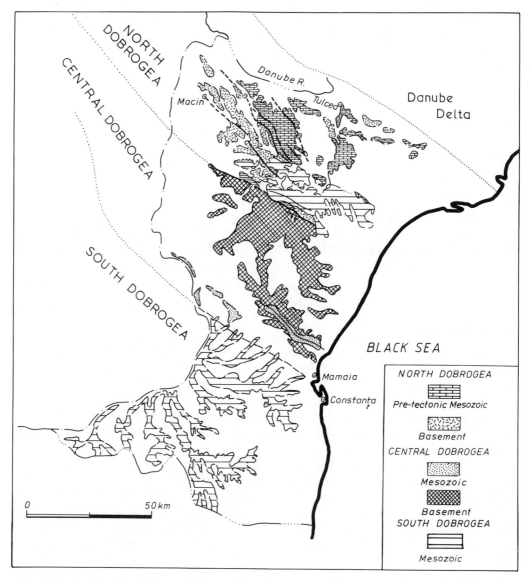

Fig. 9.16   Geological sketch-map of Dobrogea (after Burchfiel, 1976, by kind permission of the author and the Geological Society of America).

Further deformation after early Jurassic times (with faulting) led to a shift northwards of the sedimentary trough into the Pre-Dobrogea Depression.

In late Cretaceous times a trough developed within the massif, with marginal thinning and breaks. At the edges are sandy and conglomeratic littoral deposits, while in the centre the unconformable Cenomanian onwards is in a deeper water Chalk-type facies. Finally very gentle folding again followed the ancient basement lines.

Central Dobrogea

This area was uplifted relative to those to the north and south. At the surface it largely consists of presumed Precambrian rocks with a thin Mesozoic cover. Already deformed schists like those of northern Dobrogea are seen near the limiting fault and are mantled by monotonous green phyllites (the *schistes vertes*) which form most of this horst. The latter seem to have originally been flysch, with local conglomerates, and their age has been suggested as anything from Proterozoic to early Carboniferous. We now know from a boring in southern Dobrogea that they are pre-Ordovician, but they do not have any associated granites or granite gneisses such as are seen in the north. The foliation is relatively strong and generally on east–west lines, although it swings round to the north-west near the faults.

Middle and Upper Jurassic sediments lie in hollows in the old topography, especially in the synclines. Bathonian conglomerates and sandstones are followed by locally reefal limestones. Rich Alpine-type faunas pass up into others of a more north-west European aspect. Emergence followed, with late Kimmerian deformation on north-west lines. Scattered Aptian lake deposits are covered, in the south at least, by a 'Cenomanian' transgression of Albian age. This was an extension of the story to the south and the sea never got very deep.

In the north, the green phyllites are thrust northwards over the Triassic and Jurassic. In the south, at least locally, they are pushed over the Jurassic, which is in places overturned. These movements seem to have ended in the early Cretaceous since the Aptian sands are only gently warped.

South Dobrogea

Here the story has much more emphasis on the post-Palaeozoic. The basement is completely covered by gently folded Mesozoic, but boreholes show schists and green phyllites overlain by slightly deformed Ordovician and Silurian graptolitic shales and then unconformably by what looks like Lower Triassic 'Buntsandstein' (well known not very far away in Bulgaria). Again the transgressive Jurassic begins with Bathonian conglomerates but the oldest rocks at the surface are Kimmeridgian reef limestones, like those farther north.

The Cretaceous succession is relatively complete and varied, although with many breaks. Above earlier clastics, massive Urgonian limestones with rich faunas outcrop along the banks of the Danube. Slight post-Barremian movements led to palaeogeographical changes. The Aptian in the north is again lacustrine, but a more or less full marine succession is seen in the south. Albian glauconitic sandstones (like the 'Upper Greensand' of England) pass up into late Cretaceous deposits which, although locally chalky as in Bulgaria, are more frequently detrital with conglomerates, sandstones, and golden sandy limetones.

The Mesozoic generally dips gently south and only becomes complicated near faults. It is chiefly seen in the stream valleys, being covered up by flat-lying Cainozoic in between. Palaeogene seas were transgressive, depositing yellow sands and sandy limestones packed with nummulites, but the Neogene is thin and only developed in local basins. South Dobrogea passes gently and directly under the flat plains and collective farms of the next division.

Moesian Platform

While northern Dobrogea joins up with the edge of the East European Platform, southern Dobrogea disappears under the dusty Danubian loess as a platform that had a quite different geological history well known from borings. It is a direct continuation of the south Dobrogea basement with older metamorphics of amphibolite grade overlain by the lower grade *schistes vertes*. These extend westwards to merge into the Sub-Carpathian Fore-deep and south under the Danube to terminate against the foothills of the Balkan Mountains in Bulgaria. The lower grade rocks appear to disappear about 50 km west of Bucharest, but the higher grade rocks are found everywhere, cut by granites.

The Palaeozoic record makes this a part of Meso-Europa. There were several episodes of folding and block-faulting during Palaeozoic times, with metamorphism and igneous intrusions. Basal Cambrian or Ordovician sandstones deepen upwards into the graptolitic shales of the Ordovician and Silurian. These pass up through a varied sequence into a remarkable development of some 1200 m of limestone in the Upper Devonian and Lower Carboniferous with associated evaporites. The Upper Carboniferous is noteworthy for its bituminous shales with sandstones, which are followed by Permian red beds with basic intrusions. The whole Palaeozoic may amount to as much as 4500 m. There is little doubt that these were affected by Variscan movements and dips are locally steep.

The Mesozoic, on the other hand, is almost flat-lying with only gentle up-and-down warps that provide reservoirs for the abundant hydrocarbons that make this one of the most important areas economically in eastern Europe. Three distinct reservoirs can be recognized: one in the Lower Triassic, one in the Middle and Upper Triassic and one in the Jurassic and Lower Cretaceous. The Lower Triassic level is of quartzites and sandstones which pass up into dolomites and further sandstones with non-marine shales. There is a pronounced unconformity at the base of the Middle Jurassic which, in places, cuts right down to the Palaeozoic. Argillaceous sediments pass up into the usual late Jurassic carbonates, which persisted into the early Cretaceous. Karst surfaces occur at three distinct levels. Evidently there was repeated emergence and weathering and the platform was never deeply submerged at any time in the Mesozoic, although in places the total thickness reaches as much as 5 km. This thins to 2 km over some of the contemporary upwarps.

The Mesozoic is covered in turn by Tertiary sediments, mostly in the form of molasse which thickens markedly into the Sub-Carpathian Fore-deep. This also contains important hydrocarbon reservoirs in Romania, although the main oil-fields there are in the fore-deep rather than on the platform. Marine conditions spread through the area periodically during the Tertiary leaving a record only locally preserved. Thus Eocene sediments, packed with nummulites, can be well seen at the famous locality of Dikili Tash near Varna on the Black Sea coast of Bulgaria. The name means literally 'stones thrown from heaven' and refers to curious pillars that stand up from the ground here and were first described (by an Englishman, Captain Spratt, on the way to the Crimea) as man made. They are, in fact, cementation features in unconsolidated Lutetian sands. Nearby, at the port of Varna, there are low cliffs of Miocene as a vestige of one end of the belt of marine sedimentation that spread round in front of the Alpine chains at this time. At certain levels this is highly fossiliferous, notably a shelly bed in the late Sarmatian that is used everywhere along this coast as a facing stone.

The Mesozoic and Cainozoic sediments of the Moesian Platform are nowhere more than gently folded and faulted. There is a major normal fault dropping them down against the front of the Balkans and thrusting becomes more intense towards the front of the Carpathians. That something is still happening at depth is only too obvious from the earthquake that recently did so much tragic damage to Bucharest.

All along the Danube there is thick Pleistocene loess that smothers everything else over a large area and provides a fertile soil. Along the coast are dunes, lagoons, concrete hotels, and much-loved resorts such as Mamaia in Romania. It is tempting to link this low-lying country with the adjacent warm waters of the Black Sea. But because of the Alpine fold belts on the north side of the Black Sea, that is regarded here as one of the intra-Alpine basins (Chapter 15), while this is more logically included as part of Meso-Europa, albeit a rather lonely outpost.

Selected references to Chapter 9

Section 9(a)   Armorica

Barrois, C. (1930), 'Les grandes lignes de la Bretagne', *Liv. Jub. Soc. Géol. Fr.*, **1**, 83–100.
Cogné, J. (1971), 'Le Massif Armoricain et sa place dans la structure des socles ouest-européens: l'Arc hercynien Ibéro-Armoricain', in *Histoire structurale du Golfe de Gascogne*, Technip. edit., Paris, 1–23.
Cogné, J. (1974), 'Le Massif Armoricain', in J. Debelmas (ed.), *Géologie de la France*, vol. 1, Doin, Paris, pp. 105–161.
Durands, S. (1977), 'Bretagne', in *Guides géol. région.*, Masson, Paris, 208 pp.
Graindor, M. J. (1963), 'Le socle Armoricain et les contre-coups Alpins', *Liv. Mém. P. Fallot*, **II**, 187–200.
Graindor, M. J. (1968), 'Les dislocations majeures du socle Armoricain', *Bur. Rech. Geol. Min.*, mem. 52, 25–42.
Pruvost, P. (1949), 'Les mers et les terres de Bretagne aux temps paléozoiques', *Ann. Hébert Haug*, **VII**, 345–362.

Section 9(b)   Paris Basin

De Lapparent, A. F. (1964), *Région de Paris. Excursions géologiques et voyages pédagogiques*, Hermann, Paris, 195 pp.
Lienhardt, M. J. (1961), 'Etude stratigraphique, pétrographique et structurale du socle anté-permien du bassin de Paris', *Ann. Soc. Géol. Nord*, **81**, 233–241.
Lys, M. and S. P. Ellison (1965), *Geological Guidebook. Paris Basin/1965*, Amer. Geol. Inst., 13 excursions, separately numbered.
Pomerol, C. (1974), 'Le bassin de Paris', in J. Debelmas (ed.), *Géologie de la France*, vol. 1, Doin, Paris, pp. 230–258.
Pomerol, C. and L. Feugueur (1968), *Bassin de Paris. Ile-de-France. Guides geologiques regionaux*, Masson, Paris, 174 pp.

Section 9(c)   Aquitaine Basin

Alvinerie, J. (1969), Contribution sedimentologique à la connaissance du Miocène Aquitaine. Thèse, Univ. Bordeaux.

Alvinerie, J., C. Mayeux, and A. Rechiniac (1962), 'Esquisse sédimentologique de la coupe de Biarritz', *Colloq. Palaéogène, Bordeaux*, 407–424.

Bonnard, E. *et al.* (1958), 'The Aquitanian Basin, southwest France', in *Habitat of Oil*, *Amer. Ass. Petrol. Geol.*, 1091–1122.

Vigneaux, M. (1956), 'Le champ pétrolifère de Parentis', Bière, Bordeaux, 7 pp.

Vigneaux, M. (1962), 'Le Bassin d'Aquitaine', *Colloq. Paléogène, Bordeaux*, 177–226.

Winnock, E. (1974), 'Le Bassin d'Aquitaine', in J. Debelmas (ed.), *Géologie de la France*, vol. 1, Doin, Paris, 259–293.

Section 9(d)   Massif Central

Chenevoy, M. (1974), 'Le Massif Central', in J. Debelmas (ed.), *Géologie de la France*, vol. 1, Doin, Paris, pp. 162–228.

Jung, J. (1971), *Symposium: Géologie, géomorphologie et structure profonde du Massif Central Français*, Plein Air Serv., Clermont Ferrand, 610 pp.

Peterlongo, J. M. (1972), *Guides géologiques régionaux. Massif Central*, Masson, Paris, 200 pp.

Rat, P. (1972), *Guides géologiques régionaux, Bourgogne, Morvan*, Masson, Paris, 174 pp.

Roques, M., P. Lapadu-Hargues, and R. Bradshaw (1954), 'Summer field meeting in the Massif Central', *Proc. Geol. Assc.*, **65**, 278–312.

Rouire, J. and C. Rousset (1973), *Guides géologiques régionaux. Causses, Cevennes, Aubrac*, Masson, Paris, 183 pp.

Section 9(e)   Vosges, Black Forest, and Odenwald

Hameurt, J. (1967), 'Carte géologique des terrains cristallins et cristallophylliens des Vosges moyennes lorraines au 1 : 100,000 ème', *Bull. Serv. Carte Géol. Alsace Lorraine*, **20**, 117–130.

Knetsch, G. (1971), 'Der Odenwald', in *Geologie von Deutschland*, Ferdinand Enke Verlag, Stuttgart, pp. 113–115.

Theobald, N. (1963), 'Evolution tectonique post-hercynienne de la région vosgese-schwarzwaldienne', *Mem. Soc. Géol. Fr., Liv. Mém. P. Fallot*, vol. 2, pp. 159–177.

von Eller, J. P. (1970), 'Carte géologique du socle vosgien, partie septentrionale, notice explicative', *Bull. Ser. Carte Géol. Alsace Lorraine*, **23**, 5–27.

von Eller, J. P. (1976), *Vosges-Alsace. Guides Géol. région.* Masson, Paris, 182 pp.

von Eller, J. P. and C. Sittler (1974), 'Les Vosges et le Fossé Rhénan', in J. Debelmas (ed.), *Geologie de la France*, vol. 1, Doin, Paris, pp. 63–104.

Wallace, P. and D. Laurentiaux (1973), 'Summer field meeting in the Ardennes and Vosges', *Proc. Geol. Ass.*, **84**, 181–206.

Section 9(f)   Rhine Graben

Ahorner, L. (1970), 'Seismo-tectonic relations between the graben zones of the upper and lower Rhine valley', in J. H. Illies and S. Mueller (eds.), *Graben Problems*, Internat. JMP Sci. Rep. No. 27, pp. 155–166.

Sittler, C. (1969), 'Le fossé rhénan en Alsace. Aspect structural et histoire géologique', *Rev. Géog. Phys. Géol. Dyn.*, **11**, 465–494.

Sittler, C. (1974), 'Le fossé rhénan ou la plaine d'Alsace', in Debelmas, J. (ed.), *Géologie de la France*, vol. 1, Doin, Paris, pp. 78–104.

Section 9(g)   Rhône–Saône Trough

Debelmas, J. (ed.) (1974), *Géologie de la France*, vol. 2, *Les régions de transition*, Doin Paris, pp. 480–530.

Gouvernet, C., G. Guieu, and C. Rousset (1971), *Guides géologiques regionaux. Provence,* Masson, Paris, 229 pp.

Section 9(h)   Dobrogea and Moesian Platform

Burchfiel, B. C. (1976), 'Geology of Romania', Spec. Paper Geol. Soc. America, No. 158, 82 pp.

Ianovici, V. *et al.* (1961), 'Guide des Excursions. D. Dobrogea', *Ass. Géol. Carpato-Balkan*, Bucarest, 92 pp.

Shnirev, V., R. Veneva, and V. Balinov (1974), 'On the natural reservoirs of oil and gas in the Mesozoic sediments in northern Bulgaria', *Rev. Bulgar. Geol. Soc.*, **35**, 191–202 (in Bulgarian with English summary).

Chapter Ten

Southern Variscides

This chapter concerns the southern belt of Variscan massifs and basins in the Iberian Peninsula and Mediterranean area. They are characterized by a lack of definite evidence of anything that can be called 'Caledonian' and by a late Carboniferous (Asturian) climax to the Variscan story with a massive emplacement of granites, but often well-preserved Palaeozoic sequences. There were also post-Stephanian movements, but little Tertiary volcanism compared with the belts farther north.

10(a) Portuguese Lowlands

This is one of the smallest of the post-orogenic basins of Meso-Europa. There is no doubt where it belongs, since Variscan-folded Palaeozoic rocks are exposed at the surface over a large area in the south, but it is a clearly defined region geomorphologically, contrasting sharply with the rugged uplands and granite tors of the neighbouring Iberian Massif. For the most part, it is a low-lying coastal plain, rising to a low plateau in the south with a flat, vegetated interior dropping steeply at the coast to delightful bays and lively fishing ports. North of Aveiro, the massif meets the Atlantic Ocean, in the land of port wine, but southwards the coastal plain and plateau widen progressively to occupy the whole south coast of Portugal as far as the little ferry that crosses the Guadiana River into Spain and the Guadalquivir Trough (Fig. 10.1).

The Portuguese Lowlands can be divided into two areas of different character. North of the Tagus is the Portuguese part of Extremadura, with a backbone of Mesozoic rocks separating troughs of Tertiary and Quarternary. This is sometimes called 'Atlantic Lusitania'. South of Tagus is a broad plain of young sediments rising to the quiet, dry Palaeozoic plateau of the Algarve, with a further strip of younger sediments along its southern edge.

At first sight there is no geological reason for separating the Devonian and Carboniferous rocks of the Algarve from their direct continuation in the Sierra Morena in Spain. The Devonian is a shallow-water sequence of sandstones and limestones which have been quite intensely folded along north-westerly trends, as is general in the western part of the Iberian Massif. The Carboniferous succession, however, is quite different from that of the massif. The Dinantian, the Namurian, and even the Westphalian, are all in a marine

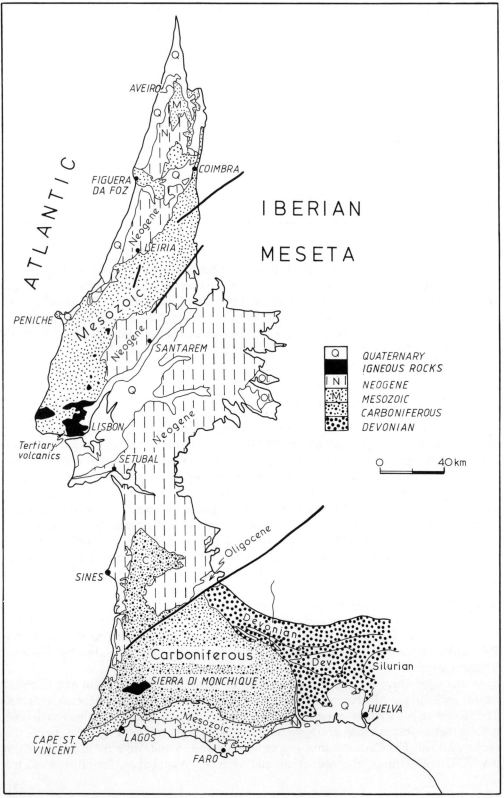

Fig. 10.1 *Geological sketch-map of the Portuguese Lowlands (based on Melendez, 1958, with kind permission of Prof. Melendez).*

facies. In the Upper Carboniferous there is a complete contrast with the monotonous 'Coal Measures' farther north. Here among the collapsed fig trees and wild pelargoniums there are greywackes and shales in a hundred thousand road-cuttings, but few natural exposures. Fortunately, there are enough goniatites for reasonable correlation. Leaving the paralic coal basins of northern Europe, with their Boreal Sea to the north, we have crossed an immense stretch of early Variscan mountains with their intermontane coal basins before at last reaching a southern ocean. This is the sort of justification we have for talking about a 'Palaeo-Tethys' in late Palaeozoic times, although its extent and significance must be debated for a long time yet. I cannot believe that it is wholly coincidental that we reach this ancient sea just when we are about to plunge into the warm waters of the entrance to the Mediterranean.

The Mesozoic rocks of the Portuguese Lowlands consist largely of Jurassic and Lower Cretaceous deposits, although some Trias is seen, especially in the extreme south, and some Upper Cretaceous in the extreme north. Triassic red beds, for example, are seen below the Jurassic on the windy headland of Cape St. Vincent (Cabo de Vicente) famous for its sea battles. The Triassic succession generally lacks the marine 'Muschelkalk' seen farther east in the Iberian Peninsula. It is dominated by sandy deposits and evaporites, the latter giving rise to many diapiric structures on the south and west coasts (e.g., north-west of Lisbon near Caldas de Rainha) and on the narrow continental shelf. These have recently attracted a lot of attention from the oil companies. The Triassic succession is very comparable, in fact, to that seen farther south along the west coast of Morocco and shows no signs of an embryonic Atlantic to the west, although there are the signs of the tension that heralded the new ocean.

However, there is no doubt about marine conditions in the Portuguese Jurassic. At Coimbra one comes off the massif on to instantly recognizable cavernous yellow dolomites of the Upper Trias ('carniolas') and then on to the limestone/shale alternations of the lowermost Jurassic that one sees over most of western Europe. The south-west corner and parts of the west coast of Portugal have some of the best records of shallow marine deposition of this age in Europe. This starts with the Lower Jurassic in splendid sections such as those at Peniche, Figuera da Foz, and Sao Pedro de Muel, which should be studied by those who want the North Atlantic to be a great evaporating dish at this time. Particularly interesting here are fossils which indicate direct marine connections with western Morocco and south-west England. A seaway was opening to the west and shallow-water benthos was migrating northwards.

The Lower Jurassic is largely thin-bedded limestones and shales. The widespread shallowing of the Middle Jurassic is reflected in thick sandy deposits (well seen along the holiday beach south of Peniche), but carbonate deposition came to a climax in the late Jurassic. In fact the term 'Lusitanian' (from the old name for Portugal) was given to a large part of the Upper Jurassic, although it must be rejected along with a lot of other superfluous stratigraphical nomenclature hereabouts. At the top of the Jurassic are the much-quarried thick carbonates seen south of the Tagus, for example on the headland west of Setubal. Around Cape St. Vincent, there is some evidence (notably in the trace fossils) that the water was getting deeper in that direction. Also, very recently, there appeared evidence (as on the west coast of Morocco) of volcanicity at this time. There are still sands farther north, however, and there may have been emergence of an island or ridge at the mouth of the Tagus.

The Lower Cretaceous shows a return to shallow-water shelly sands of vivid colours seen in the picturesque holiday-making coves of the Algarve, such as Praia da Rocha and Praia do Vau; it forms splendid cliffs at Cabo de Espichel, west of Setubal. In a more carbonate facies it is seen in the headland on the north side of the Tagus, which is adorned by the elegant resort of Estoril, including typical Urgonian at Boca do Inferno ('mouth of hell') and seen everywhere around Lisbon in pinkish rudist-filled wash-basins and park benches. North from here, however, there is a sudden change in facies. The whole Lower Cretaceous passes into fluviatile sands and clays of a 'Wealden' facies with layers of plant remains that include some of the earliest flowering plants. These form the escarpment at Torres Vedres, some 35 km north of Lisbon, where Wellington (then a mere viscount) constructed the famous defensive lines that stopped the French and saved Portugal. They extend to form the steep cliffs north of Ericeiria. Evidently the Iberian Massif continued to be a positive area through Cretaceous times, even after the usual Cenomanian transgression which carried the late Cretaceous sea much further than before, up to Aveiro and beyond. Long before the end of the Cretaceous the marine carbonates were interfingering with fluviatile deposits and there was a general regression. There is little evidence of marine conditions after the Turonian, except very locally near Aveiro. Some tuffs in Albian limestones in the Algarve indicate continuing volcanic activity and one presumes that the Atlantic continued to open to the west. Certainly Tethyan organisms must have passed this way, assisted presumably by an early Gulf Stream, to reach the British Isles, southern Scandinavia, and even Greenland.

Following the late Cretaceous regression, the Portuguese Lowlands, like virtually the whole of the Iberian Meseta, remained a land area throughout early Tertiary times. At some point there was gentle folding that affected the Mesozoic rocks of the region. Along the sharp edge of the massif, through Coimbra, this was on north–south lines, presumably controlled by the basement, but from here the main outcrop swings south-west as at Figuera da Foz. These are reminiscent of the anticlines seen on the west coast of Morocco. A much larger structure on generally east–west lines is that along the south coast of the Algarve. It is noteworthy, however, as in Morocco, that all these structures seem to terminate at the sea. This is beautifully exemplified in the cliffs at Sao Pedro de Muel, where the well-bedded Lower Jurassic dips steeply to the beach. All the folds must close within the narrow continental shelf and there is no question of such 'Alpine' structures striking out into the Atlantic as do the Variscan structures of say Brittany or Cornubia. Some of the folding is undoubtedly associated with the diapirism of Triassic salt; the rest may be minor *décollement* acting on the same deposits; none of it is truly orogenic.

Cainozoic deposits are very extensive in lowland Portugal and there is a seaward progression from a little Oligocene close to the exposed basement in the south, then Miocene (most extensive up the Tagus around Santarem), then broad spreads of Pliocene, and finally a wide coastal plain of Quaternary, also extending up the east side of the Tagus. Both the Miocene and Pliocene are particularly thick and fossiliferous. Along the south coast there is the record of the Miocene entrance to the Mediterranean, and right up to beyond the Tagus the Pliocene still has a Mediterranean-type fauna. All these Cainozoic rocks consist of soft sands and clays so that, although extensive, they make very little showing in the topography and natural exposures are few and far between. They are much excavated, however, for making bricks, tiles, and rather tasteless garden ornaments.

What are much more obvious and perhaps more significant are the late Cretaceous and Tertiary volcanics and intrusions which occur at intervals up the Atlantic coast. There are two large acid intrusions which are particularly noteworthy. One forms the lonely upland mass of the Sierra de Monichique in the south; this is the only feature to stand up from the undulating Algarve plateau; it gives its name to the light grey sparkling rock monchiquite (an alkali-rich lamprophyre). The other forms the eucalyptus-forested, palace-perching Sintra Granite north of the mouth of the Tagus with its marginal syenite which forms Cabo de Roca, the westernmost point of continental Europe. The Sintra Granite has been dated as latest Cretaceous. It alters the Jurassic limestones around it to a coarse-grained marble and stripes the associated mudstones. Later Tertiary extrusive rocks are scattered much more widely. The largest area is around Lisbon itself, on the right bank of the Tagus (surely the finest approach to any capital city in Europe—although the inhabitants of Oslo might dispute this). Local centres of lavas and agglomerates extend from Figuera da Foz in the north down to the Algarve, but are most obvious where they make features such as the promontory at Sines. Most interesting perhaps are the intrusions which occur along the north-east trending fault through Beja. These are seen mainly as a low ridge of dolerite in highly disturbed Palaeozoic sediments. This reminds one that tension and fracturing were affecting this coastline until very recently, in geological terms. In fact it was the disastrous Lisbon earthquake of 1755 (observed by Voltaire's Candide) that did more than anything to shake the confidence of the 'Age of Reason'.

10(b) Iberian Massif

The greater part of the Iberian Peninsula is made up of a strongly folded and partly metamorphosed Variscan massif. The old rocks outcrop mostly in the western part of Spain and northern Portugal (Fig. 10.2). In the eastern part of the massif, the tectonized Palaeozoic rocks are largely covered up by flat-lying or gently-folded Mesozoic and Cainozoic sediments. To the south, the Variscan structures are cut off sharply by the fault along the north side of the Guadalquivir Valley which delimits the Betic Cordillera. In the east there is the Tertiary fold belt of Catalonia and in the north-east, along the French frontier, the old Variscan structures were reactiviated during the Alpine movements to form the Pyrenees. Two major post-Palaeozoic downwarps formed on the massif, the Portuguese Lowlands in the west and the Ebro Basin in the east.

It might have been logical to divide up the great Iberian Massif into smaller units. It is very tempting, for example, to separate off the Cantabrian Mountains in the north, of which I am very fond, but for consistency with the other Variscan massifs of Europe, it seems best to keep it as a single unit. Natural divisions are elusive phenomena and many different ones have been proposed. Most attractive are the rolling and romantic regional names of old Spain: Cantabria, Galicia,* Old Castille, Extremadura, New Castille, and

---

* Not to be confused with Galicia in Poland (an alien name wished on the Poles by foreign invaders).

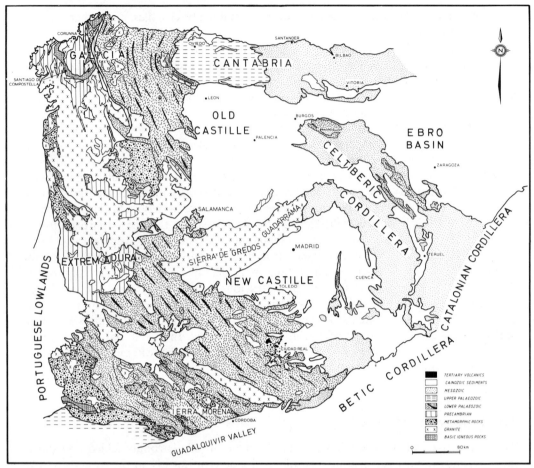

Fig. 10.2 Geological sketch-map of the Iberian Massif (based on Melendez, 1958, with kind permission of Prof. Melendez).

Sierra Morena (in order from north to south). These more or less correspond to recognizable units, but they would confuse the issue and I will proceed stratigraphically for the whole massif, separating only the basement from the sedimentary cover.

Precambrian and Palaeozoic basement

Proterozoic rocks outcrop in several areas, most notably forming much of the remarkable peneplain known as Extremadura (literally 'the land beyond'—a sort of Hispanic outback), which extends west of Madrid into Portugal. It has a sober beauty, unlike that of anywhere else in Europe, with cork oaks and scrub stretching endlessly to distant horizons. Similar rocks are seen up in the north-west corner of Spain, around Corunna (La Coruńa) in Galicia, and possibly farther south in the backbone formed by the Sierra Morena above the Guadalquivir. The rocks have been compared with the Pentevrian and Brioverian of Brittany, which makes sedimentary sense if one closes up the Bay of Biscay. Apart from a thick sedimentary sequence (mainly now mica schist but with massive quartzites), there are alleged ophiolitic sequences (e.g., around the famous centre of mediaeval pilgrimages—Santiago de Compostela), granulites and even eclogites (dated as 900 million years). The story is still far from clear but it is thought that both Pentevrian and Cadomian episodes of tectonism and metamorphism can be distinguished.

However, end Precambrian earth movements are not everywhere recognized and in places there seems to be a direct sedimentary passage from Precambrian to Cambrian. South-west of Madrid, the ancient sword city of Toledo stands dramatically on Precambrian gneiss above the Tagus. Recently it was discovered that the sedimentary sequence above the gneiss starts in the late Proterozoic and passes up imperceptibly into fossiliferous Cambrian. It is similar in the Sierra Morena, just north of Córdoba, and in the marvellous sections of Cantabria in the north where, for example along the valley through Villamanin, north of Leon, a shallow-water sequence starts in the late Precambrian and continues through the greater part of the Palaeozoic.

The nuclei of earlier orogenesis are very localized (mainly east of Corunna and around Toledo). The rather poorly defined Cadomian structures run roughly east–west and are associated with high-pressure regional metamorphism. In the north an almost circular complex of basic rocks—gabbros, norites, amphibolites, and eclogites—runs south from the coast just west of Corunna, through Santiago de Compostella and back to the coast again at Cabo Ortegal east of the city. It surrounds a dome of mica schist.

So far as the Palaeozoic is concerned, the Cantabrian mountains really provide the standard for the rest. Continuous successions of well-exposed shallow-water sequences abound, packed with abundant and well-preserved faunas and floras. Their east–west ridges form a striking (and often snow-capped) backcloth as one looks north from the edge of the meseta. They run directly into the folded Mesozoic rocks of eastern Cantabria, which pass in turn into the Pyrenees. They therefore constitute a fold belt along the north edge of Spain (Fig. 10.3) in which the Variscan effects were merely reactivated by the Pyrenean folding of the Tertiary. This will be discussed later.

Notable formations of the Cantabrian succession deserve special mention. In the Middle Cambrian there are red, nodular limestones known as 'griotte', which are a feature of the Palaeozoic in southern Europe, as are the comparable rocks known as 'ammonitico rosso' in the Mesozoic. In this succession they turn up again in the Carboniferous and not very far away in the Devonian. Their origin is still a matter of dispute, but from its fossils this particular Cambrian one was certainly shallow water, although others more characteristically only have pelagic organisms and are considered deep.

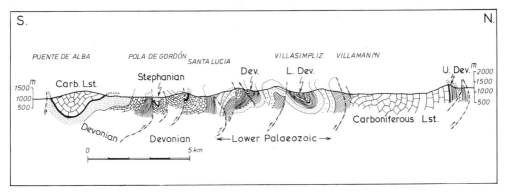

Fig. 10.3 Cross-section of the Cantabrian Cordillera (after Wallace, 1972a, by kind permission of the author and the Council of the Geologists' Association).

The most prominent formation in the Lower Palaeozoic succession of Cantabria is the Barrios Quartzite of the Lower Ordovician. It takes its name from Barrios de Luna, west of Villamanin, where it characteristically forms a wall of rock across the valley, on which has been built a dam. The craggy bastion provided by the Barrios Quartzite has played an important role in Spanish history and may, in fact, be responsible for Spain being a Christian country today. It formed a natural defence line behind which many Christians retreated during the Moorish invasion of Spain and from which they re-emerged later to reconquer the peninsula. At a subsequent traumatic moment in history it was a defence for the guerillas against the armies of Napoleon and later still for the Asturias miners against the forces of Franco in the Spanish Civil War. It is essentially the same Arenig quartzite which is seen in many other places in western Europe and was discussed in Chapter 9(a).

Westwards from Cantabria, the Lower Palaeozoic sediments pass into a deeper water facies of argillaceous flysch-like deposits (which have suffered later metamorphism) together with volcanics. These are seen in a broad belt sweeping inland from the coast west of Oviedo and reaching nearly to Leon and Zamora.

Another broad triangle of metamorphosed Lower Palaeozoic rocks extends south from Salamanca to the southern edge of the massif above Córdoba. They form much of the plateau of Extremadura and cross the border into Portugal to provide some of its famous Lower Palaeozoic faunas. Again it is dominantly a shallow-water facies with the equivalent of the Barrios Quartzite and other harder bands standing up as ridges, and thick basic volcanics in both the Cambrian and Silurian. Towards Toledo the quartzites form sizable mountains, dominating the landscape, separated by broad valleys in the intervening slates.

There is no real evidence of a Caledonian orogeny in the Iberian Massif. Certainly there are many breaks in the Palaeozoic succession and those who look hard enough for earth movements can usually find them, but the metamorphism and major intrusions seem to be Variscan, although some have been attributed to an earlier date by a few authors.

The Devonian reaches one of its greatest European glories in Cantabria, with a thick and varied shallow-water succession, rich faunas, and a magnificent development of coral–stromatoporoid reefs at the top of the Givetian, for example forming the cliff above the reservoir at Barrios de Luna. There is far less to be seen of the Devonian outside Cantabria. It does occur in patches, for example just east of Portalegre in central Portugal, and in the Sierra Morena, but these are very small in comparison with the Lower Palaeozoic outcrops and the sediments are in a terrigenous facies quite different from that of the north.

The Carboniferous was the climax in the history of the Iberian Massif as in the other Variscan massifs of Europe. In Cantabria, after the usual regression in the Famennian, there is an early Carboniferous transgression followed by the *Caliza de Montana* (meaning literally 'Mountain Limestone', like the old name for its approximate contemporary in Britain and the American Mid-West, to which it is remarkably similar). It forms the high peaks and spectacular gorges of the Picos de Europa. There is also a deeper water 'griotte' with goniatites, and then shallow-water clastics persisted in the south until the end of Westphalian times. North of the watershed, in the famous mining region of the Asturias, molasse-like coal-bearing deposits accumulated in considerable thicknesses.

Earth movements started within the Westphalian, with northerly thrusting, and then a major spasm in early Stephanian times. This is the Asturian phase of the Variscan orogeny in its type area. There is comparatively little folding, but repeated thrusting which gives the Cantabrian mountains their very pronounced east–west structure and topography. The Palaeozoic succession, although well preserved, is frequently most confusingly inverted and this is the only place I know where geopetal fillings in fossils have served to convince doubting students of the true order of things.

The Asturian spasm was followed by very coarse Stephanian. Thick conglomerates and sands filled the valleys between the new mountains, sweeping in with them plant debris from the steep slopes. This is well seen for example at Pola de Gordón, where the Stephanian deposits rest directly on almost vertical Devonian and earlier Carboniferous rocks. Rich coal deposits were formed and are extensively worked in the Asturias, but the Stephanian too was deformed (with the formation of anthracites) in a later phase of movements. The Palaeozoic succession ends with local patches of sandy 'Autunian', like that of the Massif Central, with some bituminous shales and volcanic tuffs.

Eastwards, Palaeozoic Cantabria disappears under what may be called Mesozoic Cantabria (or the Basque country). This shows the same general trends in structures that were reactivated in Tertiary movements. I suppose I should logically include that here as well, but I prefer to link it with the Pyrenees, Chapter 13(a), although my uncertainty emphasizes the contiguity of the Variscan and the Alpine structures.

Westwards and southwards the picture is very different. Compared with the vast area of Carboniferous sediments south and east of Oviedo, there are practically none at all to be seen over the rest of the massif, apart from the area of southern Portugal dealt with in the previous section and the small coal-fields of the Sierra Morena in the extreme south. That is not so say that there are no Carboniferous rocks present; in fact, they constitute the greater part of the region, but we are speaking now of the huge granite masses which were emplaced at this time.

The most remarkable feature of the Variscan events in Spain is the great 'knee-bend' south-west of Oviedo, where the westerly trending structures of Cantabria suddenly swing round in a south-easterly direction. The latter is the trend of all the rest of the massif, including that part in the east covered with younger sediments, where the old lines show through in the Celtiberic chains. The structures seem to have originated in the Asturian spasm and to reflect an earlier Palaeozoic sedimentary trough. They are sometimes called the 'Hesperides', after the nymphs who lived in a beautiful mythical garden somewhere in the west. Although more attractive than the warring tribes who provided the geological terms in Celtic Britain, another name hardly seems necessary.

The most strongly metamorphosed part of the massif lies to the extreme west in gentle green Galicia and northern Portugal. The trends there are more or less north–south, but are largely obscured by the all-embracing granites. The granite story itself is complex, with emplacements of different ages and different forms. Although they may have ranged over as much as 50 million years (from 325 to 275 million years old) this would still put them all in the late Carboniferous. There are so many granites and granodiorites that it is impossible to mention them all. The largest is that which forms the greater part of the north-west corner of the peninsula, extending from Corunna well down into northern Portugal and east almost to Salamanca. This is typical granite country with blocky 'tors' standing up from a thin soil. It is one of the wettest corners of Europe and also the country of port wine, although the rocks sometimes have to be blasted to plant the vines, which are supported on rocky posts in a countryside where wood is rare and dear.

Other famous granites are the one that stands up suddenly from the flat Spanish meseta at Toledo and—most famous of all—the Sierra de Gredos with its easterly extension, the Guadarramas, which dominate Madrid. These surprisingly wild and rugged hills, scattered everywhere with boulders, lie north-west of the Spanish capital and have played a big part in its military history. It was here that Franco drew up his four columns for the final attack in the civil war, while his fifth column (which gave its name to all such bodies) was insidiously at work within the city itself.

Along with all this granite emplacement went considerable mineralization. The name of Philip II's great palace of El Escorial, built of local granite in the foothills of the Guadarramas, refers to the tip heaps of the iron mines hereabouts. Similar iron mineralization gave Toledo its name for steel, and for swords in particular. But there is a great variety of ores everywhere, from mercury to magnetite, and the most important area is undoubtedly the Sierra Morena in the south. The cinnabar mines of Almaden are world famous; there is copper, lead, zinc, silver, and—most famous of all—the chalcopyrite of Rio Tinto, where the ore has weathered to colour the river (and so given its name indirectly to the international mining company). All the ores seem to be hydrothermal and pneumatolytic in origin.

A final phase of minor Variscan block-faulting and even a little folding may have occurred in Permian times, but that was the end of the story over the western part of the massif until the Tertiary. The later sediments will be discussed below, but reference should be made here to the Tertiary volcanicity which is found cutting through the basement rocks around Ciudad Real (the 'royal city') south of Toledo. Although not on the same scale as the Tertiary volcanicity in some of the other Variscan massifs of Europe, it is of the same general type and fits Iberia into the overall picture. There are remains of volcanic cones ('cabezos' being the Spanish equivalent of 'puys'); these are surrounded by ashes and tuffs. There are also calderas, testifying to explosive activity and now filled with lakes, together with extensive basaltic lavas which are quarried.

Mesozoic and Tertiary sediments

My general impression of the Iberian Massif is of a seemingly endless flat veneer of Tertiary continental sediments covering up everything else. Although there are patches like this right across to the west, it is the general situation in the eastern half and what may be truly called the Spanish meseta or table.

The older cover rocks are seen chiefly in the Celtiberic chains (sometimes confusingly called the Iberian chains). These are two parallel structures that run south-east from Burgos to reach the Mediterranean coast at Valencia. They are mainly composed of gently folded Mesozoic rocks, but the exact parallelism of their structures with that of the Variscan basement indicate that they are no more than a slight reactivation. It is a neglected part of Mesozoic Europe, full of many geological delights that have not yet been published.

Palaeozoic rocks show through in many places and testify to the thin nature of the cover. They are seen, for example, over a wide area south-west of Zaragoza, where a slightly metamorphosed succession includes many different parts of the Palaeozoic succession with frequent breaks and mostly in shallow-water facies. South of the quiet little town of Cañete, the basal Trias is full of boulders of Ordovician quartzite (as in England and Bulgaria) but with the important difference that the source rock is exposed just round the corner along the Rio Cabriel. The conglomerates pass up into cross-bedded red sandstones, readily recognizable anywhere in northern Europe as the 'Buntsandstein', and then into dolomites forming a ridge with a Calvary overlooking Cañete. This is presumably the 'Muschelkalk'. North and east of the town are red and green marls with salt (and the place name 'Salinas') which represent the 'Keuper' of the Germanic succession. This happens to be one area that I know, but the picture seems to be general and the evaporites in the Trias undoubtedly play a part in the structures. Although these are generally gentle, there are steep dips locally (e.g., in the ridge above Cañete), no doubt due to the slipping of the Mesozoic tablecloth on the Palaeozoic table. Actual salt-domes can be seen in places, for example at Salinas de Anaña, south of Bilbao, where the salt has been worked since Roman times, and the nearby Sobron Gorge, which provides a cross-section through a box-fold displaying the whole of the Cretaceous and early Tertiary succession. Trias salt-domes form oil traps below the surface around Vitoria.

The Jurassic outcrops over large areas of the Celtiberic chains, particularly around the Tertiary basin of Teruel. It is mainly a shallow-water sequence, highly calcareous as befits southern Europe but with faunas of a north-west European rather than an Alpine type. They contrast in this with the successions in the Betic Cordillera to the south but have strong affinities with the Pyrenees to the north.

The Cretaceous succession also is distinctly non-Alpine (in the strict sense), although it has all the characters of southern Europe. A Wealden-like facies is developed at the bottom and a shallow marine or brackish facies rapidly passes into a massive Urgonian limestone which frequently dominates the landscape. This limestone, almost without bedding, is packed with rudists and orbitoline forams. It weathers into spectacular shapes, most notably in the Ciudad Encantada ('Enchanted City') near Cuenca, where imagination runs riot for the benefit of the tourists in giving fanciful names to the strange forms. Upper Cretaceous rocks are generally lacking, although the Cenomanian—when preserved—is strongly transgressive.

To the west of the Celtiberics proper is the plateau of La Mancha, south of Madrid, where a very thin Tertiary cover allows the Cretaceous (and Palaeozoic) to show through in places. Most obvious are the little hill inliers, each carrying a windmill or two for the local gallant, Don Quixote, to charge in the dying days of mediaeval chivalry.

The Tertiary of the Iberian Massif is, for the most part, flat-lying, continental, poorly exposed, and difficult to correlate. In places evaporites within it produce dramatic diapiric structures and wide, flat, barren landscapes often prove to be largely underlain by gypsum. Locally, however, as in the Teruel basin, the scenery becomes spectacular and reminiscent of northern Arizona, with great eroded cliffs in brilliant reds and whites. The only fossils are usually local concentrations of vertebrates, for example those of the Upper Miocene near Palencia in Old Castille.

There is evidence that most of the present topographical features originated by block-faulting and upwarping in mid to late Tertiary times. Nowhere does the Tertiary exceed a few hundred metres in thickness and local thinning shows that many of the basins were original features.

There are many Quaternary terraces and at least the central part of the massif was glaciated with moraines and cirques on mountains of the Sierra de Gredos and its associated ridges. Few outsiders, who think of Spain as a hot country, realize how high is much of the massif and how cold it can be in winter.

10(c) Catalonian Cordillera

This is a peculiar range and I am not sure that this is its right place. It is clearly associated with the Iberian Massif and with the Celtiberic ranges in particular, but many would think of it as an Alpine fold belt and therefore as part of Neo-Europa. Alpine movements have given it its present form and it is clearly closely connected with the history of the Ebro Basin. But it was really the Variscan orogeny that had the major effect here and the later movements had nothing like the same intensity.

This is not a high range. It rarely exceeds more than a few hundred metres, but is spectacularly situated along the Mediterranean coast of north-east Spain and forms the back-drop to one of the most intensively touristic coastlines in Europe. It extends from near Tortosa in the south to Gerona in the north. North of Barcelona it is mainly composed of intensely folded Palaeozoic sediments and granites, while south of that city it is dominated by Mesozoic rocks at the surface (Fig. 10.4).

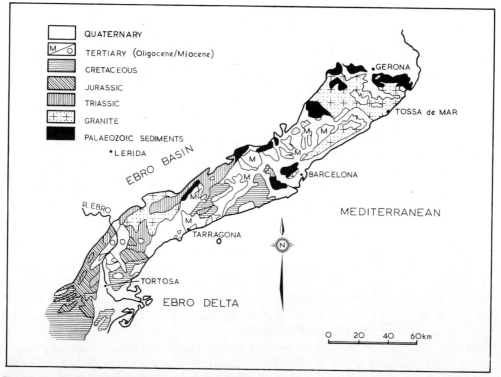

Fig. 10.4 Geological sketch-map of the Catalonian Cordillera (based on Melendez, 1958, by kind permission of Prof. Melendez).

The oldest rocks seen are Lower Palaeozoic slates (allegedly Silurian), for example around Gerona and below the weird rococo heights of Montserrat, west of Barcelona. There are small patches of Devonian limestones and then Carboniferous conglomerates and sandstones. Although mainly confined to the north, the last-named spreads out over a largish area west of Tarragona in the south, where there is also a thick development of cleaved shales with much chert. The main movements were in mid Carboniferous times and implanted a tight north-west trend on the rocks, which is virtually at right angles to the general north-east trend of the range. There is no question here of parallelism between the Palaeozoic and Tertiary structures, although the Variscan trend does conform with that of the Celtiberics, not very far away, where it affects both Palaeozoic and Mesozoic strata.

In addition to the intense folding and low-grade metamorphism, there was a certain amount of mineralization. Most important, however, was the plutonic activity with the emplacement of great masses of granite in late Palaeozoic times, cutting across the cleavage and representing a late phase of the Variscan events. Most notable is the batholith south of Gerona, which runs down the coast towards Barcelona. This rock forms the many small bays of the Costa Brava, packed with concrete hotels and sun-burned holidaymakers, where it is often embarrassing to be an over-dressed geologist. Any of the famous resorts, such as Tossa de Mar, provide numerous attractive exposures, including those of pale granites with large felspar phenocrysts (reminiscent of the Maladeta granite in the Pyrenees) and pegmatitic dikes standing out due to differential weathering. Smaller granite bodies are seen in the south in erosional windows and along fault lines, for example along the main road west from Tarragona.

Geomorphologically, the older part of the Catalonian Cordillera is divided into three, with a granitic coastal range separated by a depression filled with Quaternary sediments from a more varied inner range. The central depression takes the railway line, the main road, and most of the population in a highly cultivated valley. This northern part is wetter and the rolling hills are thickly forested. The same three-fold pattern is continued to the south of the Catalan capital of Barcelona, but the coast range becomes rolling hills of Cretaceous limestone and the central depression is mainly filled with Miocene sediments. The coast range plunges under the Mediterranean just south of Villanueva y Geltru and the depression ends in broad flats along the dull coast south of Tarragona.

The inner range continues south in its mainly Mesozoic form as bare dry hills, displaying their gently dipping limestones like textbook diagrams. A broad strip of Germanic Trias runs down the western side. Thus along the main road from Tarragona to Lerida, beyond Valls, one passes over the Carboniferous and then through the classic succession of red conglomerates and sandstone, 'Muschelkalk' limestones forming an escarpment and then red and pink 'marls' with gypsum.

The Jurassic which follows is mainly Liassic limestones. These pass directly, west of Tortosa, into the outcrops of the Celtiberics, the only difference being that the south-westerly strike swings round to north-west. The shallow-water fossiliferous Lower Jurassic limestones pass up into the Middle Jurassic, but most of the bare hillsides are made of the former.

Towards the sea, the hills are all of Lower Cretaceous limestones, mostly Aptian and Albian in the Urgonian facies of massive, white rudist-bearing 'reef' limestones. These form impressive escarpments, for example above the sea north of La Ameilla de Mar.

Where the coast road passes through this feature, you can see the gentle folding characteristic of southern Catalonia. The range ends with the broad Ebro delta, which extends up beyond the town of Tortosa.

The Alpine folding here corresponds exactly with that of the Pyrenees, that is to say, it happened in mid to late Eocene times. It does not correspond in intensity, however, and the trend is quite different, paralleling the Mediterranean coast and the range itself as a morphological feature. The relatively gentle folds become steeper inland and even overturned in places towards the Ebro Basin. There are some little thrusts of Palaeozoic and Triassic rocks overriding Eocene and dating the last push.

Following the Ebro up beyond Tortosa, one comes into a basin of Oligocene sediments which rest with marked unconformity on all that went before. Farther north, the Tertiary story is dominated by the Miocene. A remarkable trough which is, in effect, a series of graben, extends some 200 km north-eastwards from Tarragona along the central depression of the range. Around that city, the Miocene is marine. Farther north, inland from Barcelona, it is continental with a rich fauna of mammals. One could include here Montserrat, that incredible mountain that guards the approach to Barcelona from the landward side. However, for convenience that great heap of Miocene conglomerate is included here under the Ebro Basin—Chapter 13(b). The story ends here with continental Pliocene up towards Gerona and the wide wastes of Quaternary river-borne sediments in the south.

In the course of its later history, the whole geography of this region changed. In Mesozoic times and in the Eocene, the Catalonian Cordillera was closely connected with the Pyrenees. The seas evidently spread from that direction while to the south-east the granites formed part of a barrier (extending perhaps to the Balearics) against which the waters lapped. The convulsions, mild though they were, of early Tertiary times changed all that. After a brief episode in the Oligocene, with an intermontane basin along the present course of the Ebro, the Miocene saw the birth of the present landscape. Inland, all was dry apart from the rushing torrents that carried down the debris from the new mountains. To the south-east was a new sea, creeping into the area a little around Tarragona. After various vicissitudes (especially at the end of the Miocene) this was to become the Mediterranean.

10(d)   Maures and Esterel Massifs

Behind the elegant Riviera coast of Mediterranean France, between Toulon and Cannes, are these two small Variscan massifs, almost forgotton (except by the French) but important in connection with the rotation of Corsica and Sardinia away from the present mainland.

The Maures Massif, to the west, is much the larger and is continued beyond Toulon, by the slaty peninsula of Cap Sicie and Six Fours with adjacent islands. Southwards it includes the islands of Hyères, the island of Porquerolles, and the peninsula of Giens (joined to the mainland by the alluvium of Toulon airport and the salt-pans of Pesquiers). The Esterel Massif is separated from the Maures Massif by the valley of the River Argens with its disastrous dam above Frejus. This compact little massif of volcanic rocks has to the north a broader area mainly composed of gneiss, sometimes considered separately as the Tanneron Massif, the bulk of which lies directly inland from Cannes.

Although rugged, the massifs are of no great height; they nowhere reach 800 m and are mostly less than 500 m. Nearly everywhere they are thickly forested, although these forests suffer severely from summer fires which nearly every year sweep down and threaten the seaside resorts along the tortuous coastal road.

Considered as a whole (Fig. 10.5) the massifs are largely composed of gneisses and mica schist, with a slab of coarsely crystalline granite running north from Grimaud (inland from St. Tropez) towards Fayence, crossing from one massif to the other and associated with a large diorite body east of Draguignan. This is usually known as the Plan-de-la-Tour Granite, although the name refers to a little Quaternary basin within the Maures Massif north-west of St. Tropez. There are also smaller slivers and bosses of Variscan granite, notably on the broad peninsula that supports St. Tropez and its famous beach—for example, the little pale mass of Moulin Blanc, east of the town, and that of Cap Camaret to the south. The general grade of metamorphism increases from west to east, so that the older rocks around Toulon and Hyères are dominantly phyllites, those between le Lavandou and St. Tropez are mainly mica schists, while those between St. Maxime and Frejus and then on inland to Cannes are mostly gneisses. As usual in such massifs, these were formerly all attributed to the Precambrian until Silurian graptolites were found in slates on the Mont du Fenouillet west of Hyères. We must presume that much of the Palaeozoic is here represented in a metamorphosed state, as in the northern part of the Massif Central, with which these massifs are often compared. Minor mineralization is widespread, especially in the schists and gneisses of the Maures Massif, where lead, zinc, fluorspar, barytes, and other minerals, have been worked.

The main Variscan movements here, as in the Iberian Massif, were pre-Stephanian in age. They gave a generally north–south trend to the metamorphic rocks and the main faults are oriented in the same direction, although there is also another set, generally later, trending roughly west–east. The main north–south faults delimit synclinal troughs of Stephanian 'Coal Measures' which post-date the first movements although they were affected by a later phase of the Variscan (again as in Spain) before the Permian. The Permian also is affected by the east–west faults, for example near Hyères.

There are two main *sillons houillers* (to use the comparable Massif Central term). One lies right across the Maures Massif north-west of St. Tropez, where it is faulted against the main granite; the other is along the little river Reyran across the Esteral-Tanneron Massif, north of Frejus. The coals are highly bituminous cannel coals which apparently formed (as in the other central and southern Variscan massifs) in small limnic basins within the new Variscan mountains; they are dated by abundant transported plant remains.

The associated thick clastic and argillaceous deposits include post-orogenic conglomerates. All these were folded before the deposition of Permian red beds. The latter outcrop in a broad lowland area surrounding the Maures Massif from Toulon to Frejus. Much of this is poorly exposed and/or is a military zone and/or is awkwardly bisected by a railway and a motorway.

The Permian sedimentary sequence is mostly composed of red sandstones and mudstones, which have in places yielded land floras. Towards the eastern end of the Maures Massif, thick conglomerates form the splendid viewpoint of the Montagne de Roque-

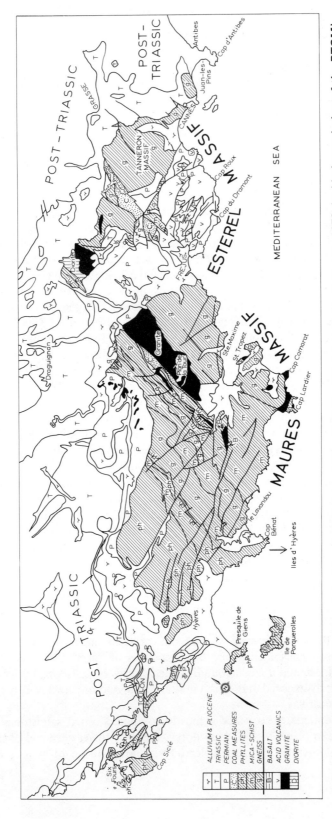

Fig. 10.5 *Geological sketch-map of the Maures and Esterel Massifs (after Glintzboeckel and Horon, 1973, by kind permission of the BTGM).*

brune, above the motorway west of Frejus, resting on a subdued granitic basement. Volcanics also appear within the Permian, going east. At about the longitude of le Lavandou and north of Frejus there is an extensive development of lavas, on either side of the motorway. They spread out like plateau basalts, although in fact they are acidic, bright red rhyolites and quartz-porphyries as we have seen (and will see) in other parts of Europe in the Permian. As is commonly the case with such rocks in such climates they support extensive (although undistinguished) vineyards. They also form the main part of the Esterel Massif (in the strict sense) between Frejus and Cannes. They culminate in the curiously named Mont Vinaigre inland and the peaks of l'Ours and Cap Roux near the coast, where they are weathered into the steep inlets known as 'calanques'. The lavas evidently flowed from an ancient land-mass to the south, perhaps now to be found in Corsica. The coarse Permian conglomerates around the little remnants of massifs that remain, pass laterally northwards into fine-grained sediments.

Although usually assumed to be of Permian age, some of the volcanics may be much later—even Cretaceous or Tertiary. The Permian conglomerates are full of pebbles of the red rhyolites, but lack pebbles of the intrusive rocks associated with the lavas along the coast. Notable among these are the dikes which form the sheer walls of Cap Roux (half-way along the Esterel coast) and the larger intrusion of 'blue porphyry' or 'esterellite' which was quarried inland from the Cap du Dramont (east of St. Raphael) to pave Marseilles. Apart from a couple of tiny basalt flows near the southern end of the Plan-de-la-Tour granite, there are no volcanics at all resting on the ancient rocks of the massifs. These differ therefore from the Massif Central and the other major Variscan massifs in lacking little graben basins of Tertiary continental sediments and extensive fault-controlled Tertiary volcanism.

The outer framework of these massifs is formed by a continuous outcrop of Triassic rocks extending from the coast west of Toulon to that east of Cannes. It displays its usual 'Bunter', 'Muschelkalk', and 'Keuper', with a general fining-upwards sequence from basal conglomerates as the Variscan massifs wore down to a uniform plain. From the western end as far as the Celtic-sounding Cascade de Penhafort, east of Draguignan, they rest unconformably on the thick Permian. The unconformity is well seen, for example, above the railway at Gonfaron, north-north-west of le Lavandou.

Around the Esterel-Tanneron Massif, the Trias rests directly on the gneisses, granites, and 'Coal Measures', and where it reaches the sea east of Cannes it completely surrounds the gneissose 'island' of Super-Cannes with its summit observatory. Offshore here, the islands of Ste. Marguerite (where the 'Man in the Iron Mask' was imprisoned) and St. Honorat testify to the proximity of Alpine-type Jurassic, as does the headland of Cap d'Antibes beyond.

10(e) Corsica

The island of Bonaparte stands up sheer and jagged from the Mediterranean. De Maupassant called it a 'mountain in the sea'. The greater part of the rugged interior is covered with the low vegatation of the *maquis* and it is one of the wildest and least man-altered parts of Europe. Superficially it appears simple in structure and (like its history) more akin to Italy than to France. It consists basically of, first, a great mass of crystalline rocks, which with some slices of poorly dated cover form the western two-thirds of the island ('Ancient Corsica'); second, a belt of *schistes lustrés* running up the northerly pointing finger of Cap Corse ('Alpine Corsica'); and third, an alluvial plain on the east coast with some other patches of alluvium and Tertiary sediments.

Plate tectonically it is a piece of continental crust (with the 'Moho' about 30 km down) and equally certainly it rotated away from the Maures and Esterel Massifs of the French Riviera. One of the curious paradoxes of European geology, however, is that (as mentioned above) French Corsica is in many ways like Italy, whereas Italian Sardinia is more like France.

The greater part of the island consists of a Variscan massif of granitic and granitoid rocks (Fig. 10.6). These form a craggy countryside, arid apart from the deep gorges, wild and forbidding, well matching its bloody history under many flags. This country culminates in Monte Cinto, with its capping of Permian volcanics, only 30 km from the sea but reaching nearly 3000 m in height. There is little to be said about this, the greater part of the island, except that (apart from the Permian lavas) it does not closely match the massifs of Maures, Esterel, or Tanneron, from which it is supposed to have escaped a close embrace. However, the massif also includes a definite slice of Neo-Europa.

Enclosed within the granite is a series of Palaeozoic rocks which serve to date the rest. These are mainly schists and gneisses, particularly in the south-east between Solenzara and Porto Vecchio (east of Ajaccio) and in the north. These are conventionally attributed to the Lower Palaeozoic, although without real evidence. They include the gneisses of Asco, some 50 km north-north-east of Ajaccio, which are thrust westwards over the Permian rhyolites of Monte Cinto. They also include phyllites such as those on the coast at Argentella, south of Calvi, which have occasional graphitic intercalations. These rocks are comparable to metamorphosed sequences in Sardinia which are better dated and conventionally attributed to the Silurian. Basic rocks, including gabbros, diorites, and even amphibolites, are known in places within the granitic massif, especially in the south, but again the age is not really known.

To the north of Porto, in the north-west of the island, are conglomerates, sandstones, pyroclastic rocks, radiolarites, keratophyres, and a capping limestone, with a fauna that crosses the Devonian–Carboniferous boundary. These serve to date the earliest Variscan granites, which cut the Argentella phyllites and which are known as pebbles in the Upper Carboniferous conglomerates of Osani, on the headland north of Porto, and dated as 329 million years (i.e., early Carboniferous). The conglomerates rest unconformably on the older rocks and are themselves dated as late Westphalian to early Stephanian by plant remains. They are followed by anthracites, tuffs, and andesitic lavas, both at Firolata, north of Porto and in an inland belt, west of Asco. Similar late Carboniferous sediments are seen elsewhere to be altered by a later series of granites such as those of Evisa, east of Porto, and Aiguilles de Bavella in the south-east, near Porto Vecchio.

It was probably at the same time (i.e., late Permian) that there were emplaced the ring dike of the Tolla and Cauro region, east of Ajaccio, and the rhyolitic intrusions of Monte Cinto. More obvious Permian rocks are rhyolites and ignimbrites which cover a large area north and east of Porto. These are dated as Permian partly by their being overlain in places by plant-bearing Triassic and partly by their resemblance to the Permian volcanic rocks of Esterel on the French Riviera. It is an easy exercise in cyclic reasoning,

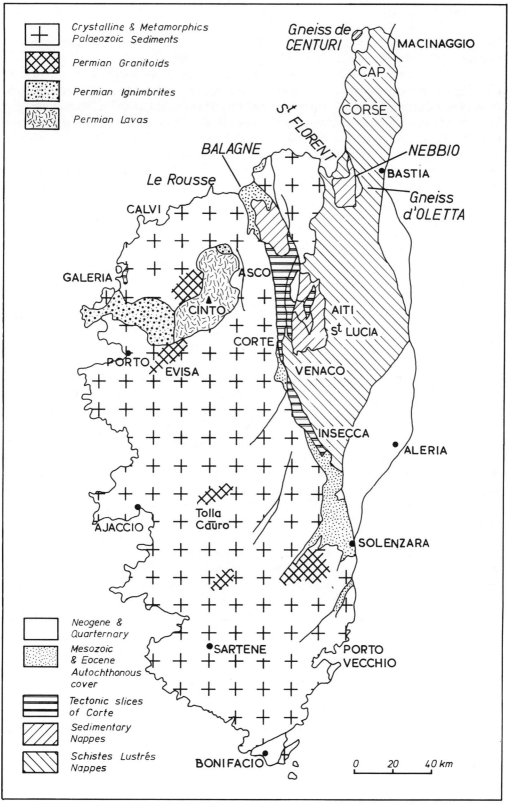

Fig. 10.6 Geological sketch-map of Corsica (based on Durand-Delga, 1974, by kind permission of Doin Editeurs and Prof. Debelmas).

however, to date them by comparison with Esterel and then postulate an anticlockwise rotation of Corsica because of the similarity of the two massifs.

Nevertheless one is obliged to say that this development of supposed Permian volcanics is the closest similarity we have as a basis for the supposed south-easterly movement of the Corsica–Sardinia microplate, and this has been confirmed most convincingly by measurements of residual magnetism in Esterel and Corsica. These show a difference of some 30 degrees, with the ancient poles in Corsica shifted to the west of those in Esterel just as one would expect theoretically from the map.

The remainder of the Corsican story (leaving aside the bloody details of human history) is very much that of the Italian Apennines. The autochthonous cover of the Variscan massif is thin but significant. A few metres of Triassic quartzites, limestones, and dolomites (seen for example on the west side of the *Desert des Agriates* in the north) are followed by equally thin Lower and Middle Jurassic limestones and dolomites. There is also a massive white limestone, more or less transformed to marble and attributed (somewhat doubtfully) to the Upper Jurassic, which in places (e.g., around Corte) rests directly on the basement. Another unconformity follows and then conglomerates and sandy limestones of the late Cretaceous which pass up into the Paleocene. At Solenzara, in the south-east, these are followed by Eocene nummulitic limestones which overstep westwards on to the basement. The whole cover usually amounts to very little, and then only on the eastern slopes of the main Palaeozoic massif.

Much thicker are the Eocene flysch deposits along the Orbo river. Like most flysch deposits these have been tectonized and even slightly metamorphosed—in at least two phases—and are thrust westwards over the contemporary deposits mentioned above. It is difficult to see what this means in terms of palaeogeography and there is the problem of a little easterly thrusting also. Later Eocene flysch is known at La Balagne, the so-called 'Garden of Corsica', east of Calvi. Here (although highly tectonized) it seems in place, since it follows directly on a remarkable basal conglomerate with boulders of granite up to 1000 m across and sandy nummulitic limestones. It is clearly an olistostrome, enclosing huge masses of limestone (possibly of Upper Jurassic age) notably the one that gives its name to Pietralba. The limestone masses presumably slid off the granite of Tenda (the *Désert des Agriates*) in mid Eocene times.

Associated with these sediments and running in a narrow belt from Ponte Leccia (north of Corte) down to the Orbo River, is a series of slices of low-grade metamorphic rocks (the *Ecailles de Corte*) also overthrust westwards on to the Variscan granite. There was more than one phase of thrusting and the slices contain a variety of rocks, including shattered granite characteristic of the eastern edge of the autochthon as well as Palaeozoic sediments, Permian rhyolites, Triassic and Liassic limestones, and Eocene sediments, like those of La Balagne.

Another allochthonous series of Mesozoic rocks overlies the autochthon around La Balagne. This is a nappe which includes the important ophiolite belt of La Navaccia which runs down, in an extremely confused fashion, from the east side of the Tenda Massif to the deep gorge of Inzecca (along the Orbo River inland from the ancient city of Aléria). This belt consists mainly of spilitic pillow lavas, with some gabbros, and is dated by associated late Jurassic and early Cretaceous sediments (including radiolarites). Here, if anywhere, we have the Tethyan ocean floor. Above comes a varied series of rocks of later Mesozoic age, including noteworthy developments of flysch and klippen of granite and Jurassic limestone. These indicate earth movements in mid Cretaceous times and are followed, with a break, by further flysch of the late Eocene.

All the above are thought to represent three separate nappes, which can be distinguished by the nature of their exotic blocks. It is plain, however, that the whole is in a complex relationship with the vastly greater nappe of *schistes lustrés*, which constitutes the greater part of the north-east corner of the island. In places the smaller nappes override the schists and elsewhere they appear to disappear beneath them.

The *schistes lustrés* here are said to be comparable with those of the Piedmont, in the Italian Western Alps, although the outsider might say that one *schiste lustré* looks very much like another! They are thought, as usual, to be metamorphosed Mesozoic sediments, although equally as usual there is not much real evidence of their age. They are conveniently seen in the northerly pointing finger of Cap Corse but southwards they strike inland to touch the east coast again at Moriani Plage, north of Aléria, and then narrow down to Prunelli di Fiumorbo, south of the Orbo River, where they finally disappear under Quaternary deposits. A crude stratigraphy can be worked out within them, with thin distinctive elements reminiscent of various Mesozoic formations of which the most obvious are ophiolites like those mentioned earlier. Probably several different tectonic elements have been lumped together in this great nappe and certainly it has been affected by several phases of metamorphism.

There are many anomalies in the relationship of the *schistes lustrés* nappe with the other units. It seems in places to have been thrust over Eocene sediments and many have suggested that it is the metamorphosed equivalent of these. Nevertheless, in the Bennio Basin, south of St. Florent (at the base of the Cap Corse finger), a tumbled jumble of rocks rests on top of the nappe and includes Mesozoic rocks of various ages, whereas at Macinaggio, on the east side of the fingernail, there is a thrust slice of Mesozoic sediments pushed on top of the *schistes lustrés* from the east. These are thought to be part of the Apennine story from Italy and to represent rocks from the eastern margin of a deep trough in which the *schistes lustrés* were deposited. The ancient massifs of Corsica and Sardinia would then represent the western margin of this sea and the thin slices below the *schistes lustrés* would be the shallow-water deposits originally deposited along its margin.

It can be assumed that the Alpine tectonism reached its maximum in Corsica at the end of Eocene times. Unlike Sardinia, no Oligocene sedimentary or volcanic rocks are known in the island and the Miocene is restricted to two small coastal areas in the north (at St. Florent and at the mouth of the Ostriconi River): one in the east (under the alluvium at Aghione, 10 km west of Aleria) and one in the south (at Boniface). There is also an inland basin of conglomerates along the Golo River, north of Corte, which may be the same age.

These are all clearly post-orogenic molasse-type deposits, sandy and conglomeratic, cemented by calcium carbonate. The most famous deposits are in the high fossiliferous cliffs of Bonifacio in the extreme south. South of this, similar sediments are seen across the water on Capo Testa, in northernmost Sardinia, and are known below the straits in between. The greater part of Corsica was already an island in Miocene times. Fantastic thicknesses of sediment, supposedly of this age, are indicated in the deeps round about by geophysical surveys, perhaps as much as 4 km in the Tyrrhenian Sea to the east and in the deep trough of ocean floor in the Ligurian Sea to the north-west, which was probably opening at this time as Corsica and Sardinia tore themselves away from the attractions of the Riviera. Eighty kilometres to the east, Miocene sediments appear again on land on the little island of Pianosa (famous for its 'dwarfed' Quaternary mammals and its 'Catch 22' airfield). Presumably, in the 'Messinian Salinity Crisis' at the end of Miocene times, Corsica was surrounded by a vast saline waste in which accumulated thick salt deposits. These later punched their way up through overlying sediments when the Mediterranean returned to the basin it had briefly deserted.

The diapirs may have been triggered off by deep-seated faulting that threw into juxtaposition the onshore Miocene marine deposits and the ancient rocks which surround them. The main outline of the island, like that of Sardinia, was blocked out at this time, although the edge of the continental crust as a whole, where it split away from the mainland France, must be placed at approximately the present-day contour 2000 m below sea-level.

Pliocene sediments are only known on the east coast between the 'ponds' of Diana and Urbino, north and south of Aléria, respectively. Sandy marine clays pass up into brackish water deposits reminiscent of those of eastern Europe. These are cut by ancient deltaic deposits of the River Tavignano, full of huge blocks from the mountains, which were used to build the ancient town of Aléria and its even more ancient Phocian (and piratical) predecessor of Alalia. Offshore, Pliocene deposits are known in submarine canyons in the gulfs of Ajaccio and Valinco, on the south-west coast, which form direct extensions of present-day river valleys, as do many other submarine canyons along this coast. These are presumably infillings of canyons cut during the catastropic drop in sea-level at the end of the Miocene.

The most obvious feature of the Quaternary Era in Corsica, apart from glaciations in the mountains, is the vast vine-growing and formerly malaria-ridden plain down the east side of the island. The sharp line between this and the mountains marks the position of tensional faults which threw down the *schistes lustrés* below sea-level and produced great tumbling masses of alluvial fans where the predecessors of the present Golo and Orbo rivers debouched from the mountains.

Corsica all but escaped the magmatic activity which rent nearby Sardinia and Italy in Pliocene and Quaternary times. There are even granite masses of this age in Napoleon's later home of Elba and in Montecristo, both less than 100 km to the east, and there was major volcanism in the island of Capraja to the north-east. All that is to be seen on Corsica, however, are a few lamprophyre sills in Cap Corse and some sulphurous springs, such as that at Aghione, west of Aléria.

10(f) Sardinia

The island of Sardinia is politically, if not geologically, part of Italy. It is an island of contrasts, ranging from the harsh mining country of Iglesiente in the south-west, across the broad, flat Campidano Rift which splits the island, to the rugged bandit-ridden granites of Nuoro and the rounded, vine-covered hills of the province of Sassari.

There is little sign of a Precambrian basement. The only possible candidates are some wedges of 'cataclastites' near Capo Spartivento at the southernmost tip of the island. These appear to have been dragged up from below by the intrusion of one of the

Variscan granites. They certainly appear to be older than the nearby Cambrian, whose base is not seen, but radiometric dates are lacking.

The Lower Palaeozoic rocks generally are seen in two contrasting facies, one in the south-west and the other in the north (Fig. 10.7). The former succession is more obviously complete and varied in character. Thus the Cambrian starts with sandstones that pass up into dolomites and limestones and then via 'griotte'-type limestones into purple and green slates like those of North Wales. The limestones are a particular feature here. They form the impressive cliff at Masua (not at all the sort of feature one associates with the Cambrian in Europe) and are dated by abundant archaeocyathids (e.g., along the

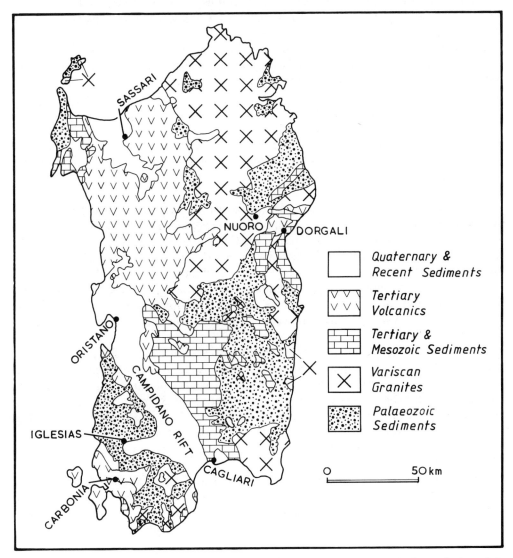

Fig. 10.7 Geological sketch-map of Sardinia (based on Moore, 1972, by kind permission of the author).

293

road north of Iglesias) as topmost Lower or lowermost Middle Cambrian. There are also stromatolites, numerous trace fossils, and enough trilobites to tell us that the record ends temporarily in the Middle Cambrian. There were movements here in mid to late Cambrian times that were named the 'Sardinian phase' by Stille in his catalogue of spasms. It is not clear if it was true tectonism or just gravity sliding off the carbonate mass.

The Ordovician in the south-west starts with a spectacular basal conglomerate, well exposed along the coast road south of Nebida (west of Iglesias). An irregular base, turned up at an angle, is overlain by flattish boulders that have been turned on edge parallel to a later cleavage. These rocks are Llanvirn to Llandeilo in age, but are in turn overlain unconformably by Upper Ordovician near Sarrabus in the extreme south-east of the island. This evident pre-Caradoc tectonic phase, so well known in other parts of Europe, was associated with acid volcanics.

A more obscure break is said to mark the Ordovician–Silurian boundary. The graptolitic shales with some limestones that follow seem to lack much of the lower part of the system. It will be seen therefore that the Lower Palaeozoic of southern Sardinia is characterized by frequent breaks, by carbonates, and other shallow-water features.

In the north of the island, on the other hand, the situation is quite different. Here the Lower Palaeozoic is distinctly eugeosynclinal in character, with a thick argillaceous succession that has been highly tectonized and metamorphosed. Thus at Cabo della Argentiera in the north-west, contorted phyllites are seen on the shore showing two distinct lineations. In the north-east the Lower Palaeozoic succession appears to be all eaten up by the Variscan granite.

Devonian rocks are only known to the north-east of the capital of Cagliari. Here an isolated patch of shales and limestones appears to represent most of the period and pass up into the early Carboniferous. The rest of the Carboniferous is only known in sedimentary terms by a few continental deposits in the centre and south of the island, but it is very well known in the form of granites. Variscan folding and metamorphism is obvious, but the granites are more so. A great granite batholith forms almost the whole of the north-east quarter of Sardinia and there are several other masses. There are also numerous dikes, valuable mineral veins, and metalliferous replacements in the limestones.

The massive Cambrian limestone referred to earlier used to be called the *Metallifero* because of its lead, zinc, copper, and other metallic ores, which were emplaced in the Variscan happening. These have been worked since ancient times, especially around Iglesias. Silver from here was particularly important to the Romans. The main problem of the mining has been the karstic nature of the limestone which allows the surrounding Mediterranean to pour in. The rival private enterprise mines cooperate in pumping it out, but it only runs straight in again. It is a matter of baling out what has been called 'the biggest sieve in Europe'.

There was emergence after the Variscan orogeny with peneplanation as in the other massifs of Meso-Europa. Scattered Permian continental deposits locally yield 'Autunian' floras and have been intruded by late phase quartz porphyries. One just south of Alghero* on the west coast may be the only porphyry copper deposit in Europe.

---

* One of the Arabic names on Sardinia that remind one of its Moorish/Spanish past; the name of the island comes from Sardu, an ancient form of Spanish which is still spoken there.

The Trias followed after a break in its usual non-Alpine form including a 'Muschelk-alk' with a poor marine fauna. This marine episode is known only in the north-west. Elsewhere there are continental basins, while the east seems to have been wholly emergent. The see-saw tipped in the Jurassic, however, and the marine deposits that follow show deep-water conditions in the east and shallow in the west with what seems to have been an early Jurassic shoreline. The easterly tilt continued and the Jurassic generally becomes more pelagic in origin that way. In between are what are called *tacchi* or isolated tabular plateaux (what the French would call *buttes témoins* and the English 'hill outliers'). These rest with marked unconformity on metamorphosed Palaeozoic sediments. (There is a splendid view of this looking south from the castle above Parador, north of Siniscola.) At the junction a lateritic soil is often developed, together with continental and lagoonal deposits (with floras) and then a transgressive conglomerate building up to Bathonian limestones. I remember climbing what I thought was an obvious volcanic 'puy' in the centre of the island to find, not Tertiary volcanics but a fossiliferous Jurassic limestone. At the top of the Jurassic succession are Tithonian reef limestones with hard grounds. Karstic weathering is again a feature and there are spectacular caves such as the Grotta di Nettuno and the Grotta del Bue Marino.

The story continues into the Cretaceous with pelagic environments preserved in the east and a shallow-water succession in the west, building up from earliest Cretaceous lagoonal facies to massive Urgonian limestones packed with rudists. These are closely related to Pyrenean and Provençal forms. The Urgonian forms the panoramic cliffs of Cabo de la Calcina, where its scarp falls straight into the sea. There was emergence with the formation of bauxites, well seen in the Cabo Cocchia, which is the main headland in the north-west of the island. An Aptian transgression brought rich new faunas into the east and the 'Cenomanian transgression' which followed is characteristically of Turonian age with peri-reefal limestones.

The Mesozoic rocks are generally flat-lying, especially in the *tacchi*, but locally they dip fairly steeply, for example in Monte Albo near Siniscola (seen from the viewpoint mentioned above), but this always seems to be related to later Tertiary faulting. There is yet another break above the Mesozoic followed by early Tertiary continental deposits. In the west, for example in the Carbonia basin, Eocene lignites are worked to smelt the nearby Iglesias ores. Long brick flues can still be seen running up the hillsides from the ovens where the lead ore was roasted. The fumes sublimated on the walls of the flues and small children were sent up to scrape off the deposits. Their life expectancy cannot have been long.

The continental deposits were followed by a marine transgression from east to west, with the thickest deposits in the former. The Eocene basal conglomerate mainly consists of pebbles of Palaeozoic age in the east, but with far more Mesozoic material in the west.

In mid Eocene times began the most remarkable feature of Sardinian geology—the north-west trending Campidano rift. This may have been along lines already blocked out in the Variscan movements, since the earlier trends are in the same direction. There can be little doubt that the rift is a direct continuation of the Rhine and Rhône structures. The faults presumably reactivated as Corsica and Sardinia started to rotate away from the Riviera. There are pockets of Oligocene sediments west of the rift, comparable with those in other massifs, but from now on the story was dominated by faulting and volcanicity. There were two great outpourings of volcanic material in the Oligocene, amounting to more than 1000 m in the north-west, much of it directly related to the faults.

The volcanicity may have lasted into the Miocene when marine invasions left thick fossiliferous deposits in deep embayments as far as the traffic-choked town of Sassari. These deposits are well seen at the bottom of the cliffs east of Porto Torres (where the ferries arrive from the mainland), overlain by deposits of a similar invasion in Quaternary times. A late Miocene sea flooded right up the Campidano rift and the whole island was submerged, apart from a few islands such as the metalliferous area in the south-west.

In the Pliocene the rift was almost filled with coarse deposits. A spectacular series of volcanoes came into existence and continued to do so through the Quaternary, almost all strictly related to the faults and most obvious up the sides of the rift. There are perfect cones and large breached calderas (such as that of Monte Funesu, south of Terralba). There were vast outpourings of plateau basalt, notably in the north-west. Faulting on north-south lines also blocked out the whole shape of Sardinia at this time and more volcanicity is related to this. Just south of Dorgali on the east coast, along the Cagliari road, one can see a Quaternary vent cutting right through a Variscan granite. A spectacular torrent of basalt from this poured down the nearby Jurassic limestone cliff to reach the beach at Cala Gonone, where it looks as though it only cooled yesterday.

Elsewhere (e.g., along the main road to Macomer) lavas are interbedded with river gravels and there are submarine flows in the Gulf of Orosei. Everywhere one has the impression that the volcanoes have only just stopped belching forth and indeed the many hot springs of the island indicate that all is not quite over. Prehistoric men may have watched the last eruptions from their caves in the Jurassic limestones. Shortly afterwards, someone built the mysterious *nuraghi* towers that are seen all over Sardinia.

Selected references to Chapter 10

Section 10(a) Portuguese Lowlands

Melendez, B. (ed.) (1958), 'Mapa geologico de España y Portugal (explicación geologica)', Paraninfo, Madrid (1 sheet with text).

Sander, N. J. (1970), 'Structural evolution of the Mediterranean region during the Mesozoic Era', in Alvarez, W., and K. H. A. Gohrbandt (eds), Petrol. Explor. Soc. Libya 12th Ann. Field Conf., pp. 43–132.

Thadeau, D. (1958), 'Carta geológica de Portugal. Noticia explicativa', Servicos geológicos de Portugal, Lisbon, 15 pp.

Wilson, R. C. L. (1975), 'Atlantic opening and Mesozoic margin basins of Iberia', *Earth Planet. Sci. Lett.*, **25**, 33–43.

Section 10(b) Iberian Massif

Brinkmann, R. (1962), 'Aperçu sur les chaines iberiques du nord de l'Espagne', *Liv. Mém. P. Fallot*, **1**, 291–299.

Comte, P. (1959), 'Recherches sur les terrains anciens de la Cordillere Cantabrique', *Mem. Inst. Geol. Min. España*, **15**, 404 pp.

Llopis Llada, N. (1966), 'Sur la structure hercynienne de l'Espagne et ses rapports avec la chaine hercynienne en Europe occidentale', *C. R. Acad. Sci. Paris, Ser. D*, **262**, 2581–2584.

Melendez, B. (ed.) (1958), 'Mapa geologico de España y Portugal. (explicacion geologica)', Paraninfo, Madrid (1 sheet with text).

Tamain, A. L. G. (1978), 'L'évolution Caledono-Varisque des Hesperides', In *IGCP Project 27, French Contrib. No. 13, Caledonian–Appalachian Orogen of the North Atlantic Region*, Geol. Surv. Canada, paper 78–10, pp. 183–189.

Wallace, P. (1972a), 'The geology of the Palaeozoic rocks of the south-western part of the Cantabrian Cordillera, north Spain', *Proc. Geol. Ass.*, **83**, 57–73.

Wallace, P. (1972b), 'Summer field meeting in the Cantabrian Cordillera, north Spain', *Proc. Geol. Ass.*, **83**, 75–94.

Section 10(c)   Catalonian Cordillera

Hahne, C. (1933), 'Ein geologischer Führer durch den nördlichen Teil des südaragonesichen-Katalonischen Mittelgebirges', *Geol. Medit. Occ.*, **3**, (133), pt 3.

Llopis-Llado, N. (1954), 'Types des chaines alpidiques du littoral méditerranéen franco-espagnol et leurs rapports avec les Alpes françaises', *24th Internat. Gen. Congr.*, vol. 14, pp. 271–279.

Melendez, B. (ed.) (1958), 'Mapa geologico de España y Portugal (explicación geológico)', Paraninfo, Madrid (1 sheet with text).

Section 10(d)   Maures and Esterel Massifs

Bordet, P. (1966), *L'Esterel et le massif de Tanneron*, Hermann, Paris, 114 pp.

Campredon, R. and M. Boucarut, (1975), 'Alpes Maritimes, Maures, Esterel', in *Guides géologiques régionaux*, Masson, Paris, 175 pp.

Glintzboeckel, C. and O. Horon (1973), *À la découverte des paysages géologiques de Marseille à Menton*, Bur. Rech. Géo. Min., Orleans, 81 pp.

Gueirard, S. (1962), *Le massif des Maures de Toulon à Saint-Raphaël*, Hermann, Paris, 78 pp.

Section 10(e)   Corsica

Brouwer, H. A. (1960–62), 'Remarques sur la tectonique alpine de la Corse', *Liv. Mém. P. Fallot*, **2**, 275–287.

Durand-Delga, M. (1974), 'La Corse', in J. Debelmas (ed.), *Géologie de la France*, vol. 2, Doin, Paris, pp. 465–478.

Maisonneuve, J. (1960), 'Etude géologique du sud de la Corse', *Bull. Serv. Carte Géol. Fr.*, **57**, 260.

Section 10(f)   Sardinia

Cocozza, T. (1975), 'Structural pattern of Sardinia', *Quad. La Ric. Sci. CNR*, **90**, 183–201.

Cocozza, T. and A. Jacobacci (1975), 'Geological outline of Sardinia', in C. Squyres (ed.), *Geology of Italy*, Earth Sci. Soc. Libyan Arab Repub., pp. 49–81.

Desio, A. (ed.) (1973), *Geologia dell'Italia*. Union. Tipogr.-Edit.-Torinese, Turin, 1081 pp.

Moore, J. McM. (1969), 'Influence of structure on the base metal deposits of southwest Sardinia, Italy', Inst. Min Metall., B135–B147.

Moore, J. McM. (1972), 'Geology and the mineral industries in Sardinia', *J. Roy. School Mines, Lond.*, No. 21, 16–22.

Vardabasso, S. (1959), 'Il Mesozoico epicontinentale della Sardegna', *Atti Acad. naz. Lincei Memoire*, **27**, 178–184.

Chapter Eleven

Uralides

11(a) Urals and Novaya Zemlya

The Uralides form a very natural eastern boundary to our continent and coincide with the generally recognized political delimitation of the European and Asian continents, although it must be realized that the Ural Mountains and their linear continuations represent, for the most part, only the western edge of the Uralides as a sedimentary and tectonic zone.

The Uralides extend for some 2500 km across the European and Asian continents, from the Arctic coast southwards to where they disappear under the thick sediments of the Caspian Basin and the Turan Basin (which contains the Aral Sea) in the low-lying western part of Kazakhstan. Northwards the Uralides twist first in a north-westerly direction through Pai-Khoi (Fig. 11.1) and then to the north-east through the long cold islands of Novaya Zemlya ('new land').

It seems likely that they are then displaced southwards to strike across the broad Taymyr Peninsula (along the Arctic coast of Siberia) and on north through the islands of Severnaya Zemlya ('north land') to be displaced again perhaps, to reappear in the western part of the 'New Siberian Islands' on the east Siberian shelf (Fig. 11.2). In other words they wrap round the north end of the Asian continent just as Palaeozoic fold belts do in North America, Greenland, and perhaps Europe.

I include the Uralides with the Variscides because, like the latter, we must think of them as mainly a late Palaeozoic orogenic belt, which developed out of the collision of the European and Asian continents. No major orogenesis has occurred here since and, unlike the Atlantic, the oceanic crust that was consumed in their coming together never reappeared. The two continents once fused remained fused, at least up to the fleeting present. But like the Atlantic, the ocean had been here before and the history of the Uralides, as an active belt, goes back into early Palaeozoic and Precambrian times. They may be the counterpart of the Caledonides and, since they came together later, it could be that they will split again later.

It is difficult to subdivide the Urals in any meaningful way without confusing both the reader and the writer, unless we go down to the details of individual ranges. The chief of these are shown in Fig. 11.1, but the generalities of the geology are summarized in Fig. 11.3.

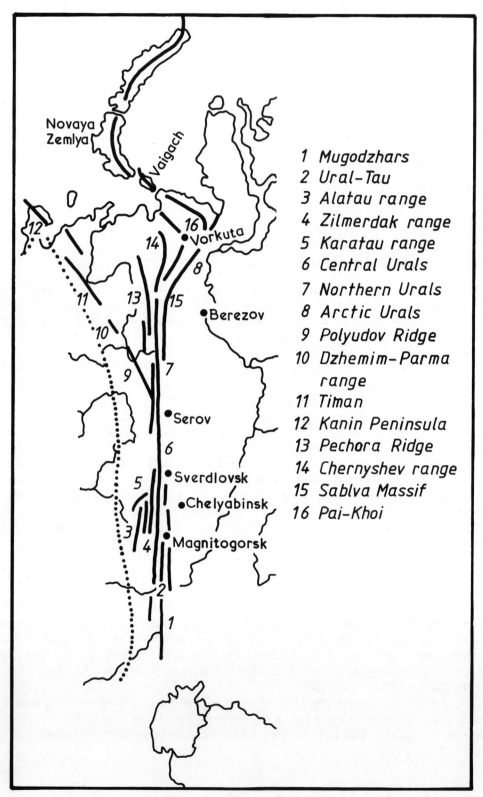

Fig. 11.1 Key to the main features of the Urals and Novaya Zemlya (after Nalivkin, 1973).

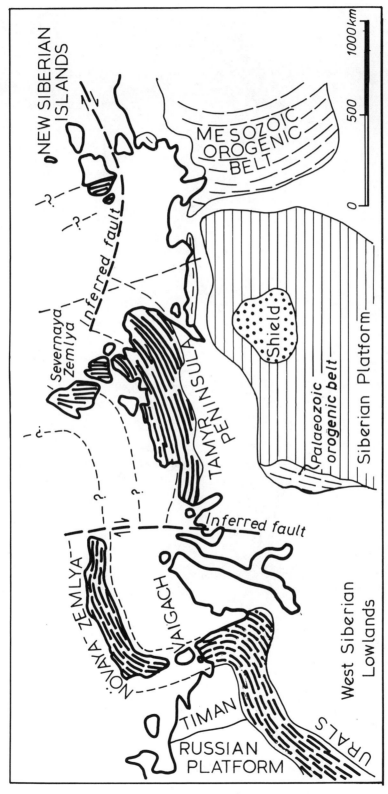

Fig. 11.2 Supposed continuations of the Uralides along the north Asiatic coast (after Hamilton, 1970, by kind permission of the author and the Geological Society of America).

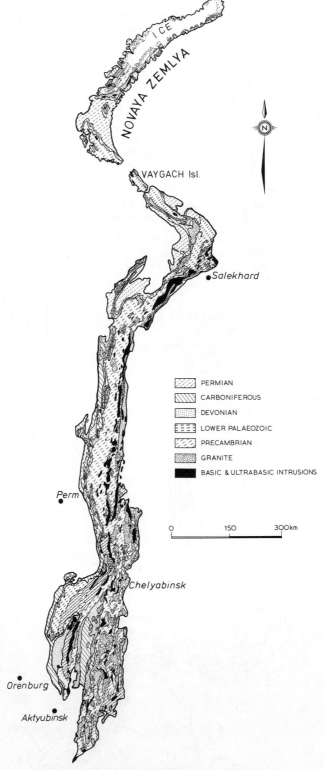

ICE

NOVAYA ZEMLYA

VAYGACH Isl.

N

Salekhard

PERMIAN

CARBONIFEROUS

DEVONIAN

LOWER PALAEOZOIC

PRECAMBRIAN

GRANITE

BASIC & ULTRABASIC INTRUSIONS

0   150   300km

Perm

Chelyabinsk

Orenburg

Aktyubinsk

Fig. 11.3 Geological sketch-map of the Urals.

Although in general terms the Urals *sensu stricto* are remarkably uniform from south to north, there are certain differences which are obvious even in a sketch-map. We may consider them from west to east. The Russian Platform with its comparatively thin cover of flat-lying Phanerozoic rocks extends almost to the foot of the mountains, especially in the north where the latter rise quite suddenly from the endless boredom of the steppes. In the south the rolling hills of the Bashkirskaya Soviet Republic soften the approach to the mountains.

Almost the whole western part of the Urals is characterized by thick Palaeozoic 'miogeosynclinal' or post-orogenic sediments. These pass laterally into shelf deposits which overlie thick Proterozoic sediments and volcanics which outcrop along the main axis of the chain, although the volcanics are mainly restricted to the north and the whole Precambrian succession is cut out in the south. All these constitute the 'Externides', which are in contact with the 'Internides' to the east along the 'Main Uralian Fault' which runs the whole length of the mainland range. One thinks of the Rocky Mountain Trench and of the North American Cordillera generally.

Immediately east of this fault is what is taken to be real ocean floor material of Palaeozoic age, thrust on to the continental crust of the western Urals. This includes a great belt of ophiolites, continuous and thick in the north, becoming broken up in the centre, and occurring as separated bodies in the south. These and accompanying volcanics are overlain by thick Palaeozoic eugeosynclinal successions which pass upwards into 'transitional' sediments, although this passage tends to be progressively later towards the east. Novaya Zemlya is composed entirely of the 'internide' eugeosynclinal rocks.

Further volcanics occur in late graben structures in the central and southern Urals and all the units are cut by later granites, although these again are mainly confined to the south. The continental collision and orogenesis appears to have been completed in Carboniferous times.

The Permian has a story of its own, as befits the region after which it was named. It is, in fact, one of the clearest stories anywhere of thin shelf sediments passing eastwards into a thick pile of carbonates, and these in turn passing into even thicker arenaceous and argillaceous deposits in the centre of a Uralian trough. They pass upwards into red beds which, as usual, conceal the Palaeozoic–Mesozoic boundary.

East of the Ural Mountains, half hidden under the west Siberian Lowlands, is the rest of the Palaeozoic story with a complementary miogeosynclinal trough, only seen clearly in the Byrranga Mountains of the Taymyr Peninsula on the north Siberian coast. It may be that there are further Proterozoic and Palaeozoic folded eugeosynclinal belts under the lowlands, as there are along the edge of the Siberian Platform farther east, along the right bank of the Yenisey River.

Any attempt to divide the Uralides further would obscure the relationships between the successions in the Ural Mountains proper and those in the lowlands on either side, which form an integral part of the story. I will therefore consider the belt in broad stratigraphical divisions.

Precambrian

The Urals were a trough of thick sedimentation in late Precambrian times. The Archaean may be represented in the varied metamorphic rocks of the Taratashian Suite at the bottom of the sequence in the southern Urals. They are mainly sedimentary in origin (including much ironstone in various forms), but there are also altered extrusive rocks, amphibolites, and migmatites. A thickness of 2000 m is recorded, but the base is, of course, unknown.

Above this come conglomerates derived from the Taratashian and a whole series of 'suites', up to eleven in number, all of which are commonly attributed to the Protero-zoic. If one adds together all the thickest developments one gets the staggering total of more than 15 km of sediments in the southern Urals (between Bakal and Kusinskian) and some 12 km in the north. They include further valuable ironstones at several levels south of Svrdlovsk, notably along the broad valley of the River Byelaya.

It could be that the upper part of this succession belongs to the Lower Palaeozoic, as some Soviet geologists believed up to fairly recently, but present opinion seems to be that they are all Proterozoic and most of it Upper Proterozoic or 'Riphean' (now an interna-tional term derived from the old name for the Urals).

Although Russian geologists have done more than any to apply classic biostratigraphi-cal methods to the Proterozoic, using stromatolites and spores, it is difficult to work out a clear story for the vast thicknesses of rocks in the Uralide belt. In the Urals proper, the latest Precambrian rocks are dominantly clastic, whereas in the Taymyr Peninsula to the east and along the lower reaches of the Lena River farther east again, they are dominantly carbonates. But we are now two-thirds of the way across Asia and this is hardly relevant to the region in hand. It has become standard practice in the Proterozoic, and more so in the Palaeozoic, to distinguish an eastern miogeosyncline from a western eugeosyncline. The so-called 'Miogeosynclinal Zone' of the Urals proper contains great thicknesses of Riphean and Palaeozoic carbonates, but they themselves cannot be called miogeosyn-clinal in the strictest sense. There are carbonates in five of the eleven constituent 'suites', but they also contain great thicknesses of poorly sorted clastic sediments and some volcanics. Associated with the latter, presumably as a result of the effect of the igneous activity on the limestones and dolomites, are important deposits of magnesite. It seems probable that a vast complexity of changing environments is contained within this broad 'Riphean' division, and it is almost ridiculous to try to cram it into one nomenclative pigeon-hole.

In recent years many stratigraphical ideas have had to be changed due to the discovery of Palaeozoic fossils in both sediments and metamorphic rocks that had previously been classified as Precambrian. Thus in the Central Urals, considerable developments of meta-morphic rocks that had always been accepted as Precambrian have been found to pass laterally into sediments with Ordovician fossils. We are now told, somewhat dogmat-ically, that there are no Precambrian rocks in the Central Urals, although there is no suggestion of oceanic crust or a hole under the visible rocks!

Elsewhere it seems probable that many adjustments in dating still need to be made. Thus a thick development on the eastern side of the southern Urals, in the vicinity of Tobol (some 650 km south of Sverdlovsk) and eastwards into Kazakhstan, is also dom-inantly clastic with volcanic rocks, but is said to be very different from the Urals proper. It is clear that the dating is still very doubtful, and the fact that the succession includes coals makes a much later age probable, at least for part of the succession.

At the top of the Proterozoic there is a thick series of clastic deposits, best developed on the west side of the southern Urals in the Sikasa Basin, but spreading over to the east side in the north and always underlying the Lower Palaeozoic. These are said to be exactly comparable to the Sparagmite of Scandinavia, although there are also very similar deposits containing Devonian plant remains.

The orogenic movements which affected only the Precambrian rocks of the Urals impressed on them a generally north-west trend, seen also in Timan and reminiscent of Eo-Europa. These were followed by the emplacement of a large number of granites, notably a number of Rapakivi type, like those of the Fenno-Scandian Shield and the Ukraine.

It is difficult to see the classical geosyncline picture in the Precambrian Urals, although it is evident that considerable quantities of clastic sediments and volcanics accumulated here while carbonates were forming on the Siberian continent. Although one is tempted to open and shut a Uralian ocean here, while a proto-Atlantic was behaving similarly at the other end of our continent, this cannot be regarded as proven and of course the palaeomagnetists would have the Asian continent far away at this time. There was a major orogenic event near the end of Proterozoic times and Lower Palaeozoic sediments commonly rest on the older successions with a marked angular unconformity.

Early Palaeozoic

With the arrival of the Palaeozoic, the picture becomes clearer. The Russians are confident about a western miogeosynclinal zone or 'externides' on the western slopes of the Ural Mountains, passing westwards into the thin flat-lying formations of the Russian Platform. The eugeosynclinal zone or 'internides' occupies the eastern flanks of the mountains and a wide stretch of the West Siberian Lowlands beyond. The main geosynclinal story lasts from the Ordovician to the Carboniferous, but it should be realized that the early Palaeozoic rocks were only recognized comparatively recently, due to their generally metamorphosed condition.

The actual time of initiation of the Palaeozoic trough is a matter of some uncertainty. Recently a 'Vendian Complex' was recognized between the classic Riphean and the Cambrian. This is characterized by certain spore-like bodies and is said to overlie the Riphean with an angular unconformity and to be overlain in turn by Cambrian rocks. One is immediately tempted to think of the so-called 'Eo-Cambrian' Sparagmite formation of Scandinavia, resting unconformably on late Proterozoic Jotnian sediments.

In the southern Urals, notably in the Sakmara Basin, the earliest Palaeozoic rocks include massive archaeocyathid limestones, indicating an early Cambrian age. Rocks of a similar age have also been recognized at the Arctic end of the range although, as is commonly the case in higher latitudes, probably lacking the archaeocyathids. Intense volcanicity already seems to have begun.

Usually the Cambrian rocks, in so far as they have been positively identified, occur along the western margin of the 'internides' and are often coarse-grained with pebbles of continental origin and volcanics of mainly alkaline type. In other words there are indications of a sialic crust in this region. In many places, notably at the Arctic end of the chain, the recognizably Palaeozoic part of the succession begins with Upper Cambrian clastics which are often of great thickness. The Middle Cambrian appears to be almost always absent and the Upper Cambrian rests either on the Lower Cambrian or the presumed Precambrian. It has been suggested that early 'Pre-Uralides' were formed in mid Cambrian times along the earlier north-west lines, with the emplacement of granites, at least in the north.

In the western 'externide' zone the Upper Cambrian sediments pass up into those of the Lower Ordovician without break and both seem to be of a post-orogenic nature. This is a miogeosynclinal belt without volcanics. The sediments thicken eastwards with no indication of a further sediment source in that direction unless it be the 'Pre-Uralides' mentioned above. The succession generally becomes finer grained upwards and limestones are developed, but nowhere can the whole Ordovician succession be seen in one place. Nevertheless, the Ordovician outcrops in many more places than the Cambrian, along the whole western margin of the Urals.

In the 'internide' zone, deeper water eugeosynclinal conditions were quickly established and there are clear indications, for the first time, of an oceanic crust with flysch-like deep-water sediments, ophiolites, and parallel dike complexes, at the bottom of the Ordovician succession. These consist mainly of ultrabasic masses, with associated basic volcanics, which are thrust westwards over the miogeosynclinal succession, forming a more or less continuous obducted ophiolite belt along the western edge of the 'internides'. This is commonly called the 'platinum belt', from the occurrence in it of that valuable metal. From geophysical evidence this belt would appear to dip eastwards at a high angle beneath the geosynclinal pile, but there is no indication of any continental crust below.

Movements occurred near the end of the Ordovician period, with considerable deformation and metamorphism, very much along the lines of the present Urals. Paradoxically, this is also described as a time of tension with widespread basic extrusions of various kinds, and the emplacement of basic and ultrabasic bodies. It has been suggested that this was the beginning of a phase of sea-floor spreading that was followed by compression and the formation of island arcs that have been recognized here in the rocks of the next period. As with the proto-Atlantic, perhaps the ocean was narrow and the period of opening brief. Through great parts of the Urals there appears to be no evidence at all of such movements.

The Silurian, Devonian, and early Carboniferous deposits go together in the Russian literature as a single cycle of sedimentation, resulting in the common usage of 'Middle Palaeozoic' for this part of the succession. In the 'externides' there is a marked unconformity below the relatively gently folded Silurian, with thick basal conglomerates resting on strongly deformed earlier rocks. Marine conditions were only re-established here in mid Devonian times. Volcanicity ended with the coming of the Silurian, as it did so widely in western Europe.

In the 'internides', on the other hand, the geosynclinal story continued; sediments and volcanicity, although temporarily in abeyance, returned in mid-Silurian times and continued until the end of that period. There was now a new mountain range to the east, providing fresh sediment to the trench. This range wore down before the end of the Silurian as volcanicity built up again. As the inflow of clastics and clays retreated to the east, so there was a build-up of carbonates, up to 2000 m in thickness, in the central Urals. Coral–stromatoporoid reefs and shell-banks grew along the western margin delimiting a complex of lagoonal deposits to the west which passed laterally into the red beds of a vast continental plain.

Late Palaeozoic

The Devonian is thickly developed and richly fossiliferous all over the Urals and has been studied in detail since the days of the famous visit by the Englishman Murchison, the Frenchman de Verneuil, and the German von Keyserling, in the 1840s. It extends from Pai-Khoi on the Arctic coast to the Mugodzhars range in the extreme south, but is highly metamorphosed in places, most notably in the central Urals.

In the 'externides' in the west, shallow-water carbonates dominate the Devonian succession and are an important source of oil around the headwaters of the Volga. They follow on the Silurian limestones and there are the usual arguments about where to draw the boundary, although the earliest datable Devonian limestones appear to be Eifelian in age. The marine Devonian spread on to the East European Platform almost as far as the Volga. Northwards the marine limestones pass laterally into typical 'Old Red Sandstone'. Important bauxites and bog iron-ores occur in the transitional facies.

Particularly distinctive is a facies which appears to represent stagnant bottom-waters within the western miogeosyncline. It occurs particularly in the north—in Novaya Zemlya, the Pai-Khoi peninsula, and Timan—but extends south in limited basins as far as the latitude of Kazan. In many ways it resembles the Permian basin facies in the Guadalupe Mountains of Texas and New Mexico, with a characteristic fauna of pelagic goniatites and pteropods, together with small bivalves and brachiopods that probably attached themselves to floating algae. The chief economic interest lies in its highly bituminous nature, which makes this facies an important source-rock for oil in the western Urals.

The miogeosynclinal limestones of the 'externides' continue into the western part of the 'internides' and at times—notably (as always) in the Frasnian—they extend right to the eastern edge of the mountains. Bauxites are again developed in the north. However, the 'internides' continued their typical eugosynclinal development with thick volcanics, siliceous shales (with manganese), and flysch-type sediments, whose sands were evidently derived from an actively eroding land-mass to the east. Rapid subsidence continued and up to 3000 m of Devonian strata accumulated in places.

Probably the last of the ocean floor between the European and the Asiatic continents met its Benioffian fate during Devonian times. The oldest sediments containing ophiolitic detritus are Visean in age and are found in the imbricate zone to the immediate, overthrust west of a zone of ophiolites running down the axis of the Urals for a considerable distance. They are particularly well seen at the Arctic end of the chain, just south of the sharp bend that takes it out to Novaya Zemlya. Here the glaciations have scraped clean magnificent exposures of everything that could be wished for (apart from pillow lavas): harzburgites, dunites, layered complexes, gabbro cumulates, and sheeted dike swarms.

After that there developed a deep sedimentary trench, the subsidence of which was interrupted by further major happenings during Carboniferous times, so the later part of the Carboniferous succession was very different from the earlier. Unfortunately the stratigraphical usage here does not tally with that commonly used in western Europe. Eight stages are usually recognized within the Carboniferous of the Urals and the East European Platform. The lower three are international, but differ from international usage in including the Namurian in the Lower Carboniferous. The Bashkirian and Moscovian,

307

which come next and must be approximately equated with the Westphalian, are called 'Middle' Carboniferous. The top three stages (formerly called the 'Uralian' and here the Upper Carboniferous *sensu rossico*) must be accommodated within the Stephanian of other countries.

The Tournaisian and Visean in the Urals are dominantly limestones and in fact were called the 'Mountain Limestone' in the early days of geology, just as they were in England and right across to the American Mid-West. They form high cliffs along several of the Ural rivers and are dominated by coral–brachiopod faunas. They are usually well-bedded argillaceous limestones associated, especially at the base, with dark, sometimes bituminous, shales. Elsewhere, as on the Ui river, north of Magnitogorsk in the southern Urals, they form massive reefs. But right in the middle of the limestones, in the Lower Visean, there comes the main 'Coal Measures' of the central and northern Urals. Murchison, not surprisingly, got this wrong and presumed that the 'Coal Measures' were later in age, as in most of Europe, although he might have remembered the situation in the Midland Valley of Scotland which has important 'Coal Measures' at this level. They represent the delta complexes of sizable rivers.

This coal sequence even persists (as coarser-grained sediments) into the eastern slopes of the Urals, as do most of the limestones, but there is still a distinctive 'internide' development with interbedded lavas and tuffs. There does not now seem to be a definite eugeosynclinal trough in this position, although the uniformity of development from north to south suggests deeper water than to the west.

It may be that the subduction—associated trench was coming to an end and that the collision of the European and Asian continents was imminent. The phases of the Variscan orogeny are difficult to distinguish in the Urals, partly due to the absence of rocks of the appropriate age and partly to the lack of sufficient studies. On the eastern slopes the succession often only begins with the Bashkirian and all stages are missing in the central region. On the other hand, on the western side of the range there is definite evidence of the Uralian orogeny only beginning in early Permian times. The probability is that the effects of the orogeny moved west with time. It was followed by the emplacement of enormous granite masses on the eastern side of the present range.

The Namurian forms a direct continuation of the limestones of the Visean throughout the area of deposition, although it may be significant that conglomerates appear for the first time in the vicinity of Sverdlovsk in the southern Urals. They shift south with time, arriving in Bashkirian times near Magnitogorsk.

It was probably at this time that the newly rising mountains started encroaching on the old trough. They probably rose first (perhaps behind a volcanic island arc) in what are now the West Siberian Lowlands. Sharp lithological breaks and changes are seen in the east, while in the west the Namurian limestones pass imperceptibly into those of the Bashkirian.

In the Moscovian, marine deposits begin to be pushed out of the eastern region altogether, being replaced by coarse clastics, red beds, and gypsum. The calcareous peace farther west was at first undisturbed but before the end of the stage conglomerates had reached the western margin, at least in the south, and distinctive sandstones are widespread. The latter are marine, but contain abundant plant debris together with volcanic material. They are the most typical feature of the 'Artinskian' facies which characterized the Ural trough at the end of the Palaeozoic times. However, they still pass into limestones on the edge of the Russian Platform.

The top three stages of the Russian Carboniferous continue the story of converging continents. Conglomerates and breccias spread to the western slopes and the old Uralian Trench disappeared, to be replaced by a new downwarp in which limestones continued to be deposited. In other words, the trough moved forward in front of the orogen, just as the Carpathian and other fore-deeps were later to form in front of the new Alpine mountains.

The Urals really came into their own in the Permian, for which they have a record second to none in the world (although this claim might be disputed in west Texas and Timor). Most 'type areas' and 'stratotypes' have but poor records of the strata they presume to typify, but this cannot be said of the old province of Perm where Sir Roderick Murchison first recognized the system while on holiday from the Anglo-Welsh Lower Palaeozoic in the early 1840s.

Murchison included much in his new 'Permian' that was really late Carboniferous, because he was not acquainted with strata of that age in a marine facies. Nevertheless, what remains is still a magnificent development, as was conveyed to English readers by Carl Dunbar in his account of a river traverse through the western Urals in 1939.

We cannot separate the Uralian Fore-deep from the East European Platform, although the developments are very different. The thin condensed succession on the platform eastwards from Moscow thickens suddenly at the Samara Bend on the Volga (where it is now almost an inland sea) into a tremendous thickness of limestones—a true miogeosyncline—at about Sterlitamak (west of Magnitogorsk). This passes upwards into red beds and salts, which so often conceal the Permian—Triassic boundary. Then eastwards, to the Sim Works, the limestones change into the arenaceous and argillaceous 'Artinskian' facies which is largely in the nature of molasse. The passage to the Trias is unknown here also, but in this case because of erosion.

It is evident from the frontal Uralian trough that active erosion of a new mountain chain was taking place in Permian times and the repeated influxes of coarse sediments imply that movements were still going on. This is particularly apparent at first at both north and south ends of the chain, that is to say in the Pechora Basin on the Arctic coast and to the east of Ufa in the south. Later, however, such deposits were far less obvious in the south, where thick evaporites were deposited as a direct continuation of those in the Caspian Depression.

All through late Palaeozoic times there was a connection between the Urals Trough and the Tethys away to the south. This is particularly obvious in the Permian because of the abundance of typically Tethyan fusulinids. These large forams serve to subdivide the 'type' Permian but are otherwise absent from extra-Alpine Europe.

Before the end of Permian times we must assume that Europe and Asia had become a single mega-continent. Coarse sedimentation continued in the Pechora Basin (perhaps implying that the collision was progressive from south to north), but the molasse-type sediments here are interbedded with workable coal-seams, already discussed. The overriding was very much of Asia over Europe. No large nappes are recognized (and such structures were long disputed in the Soviet Union) but there are plenty of high-angle thrusts and the blocks into which the Urals were very much fragmented all dip to the east. Volcanicity, which had still been important in early Permian times (with associated mineralization, including gold), had virtually ceased.

Post-Palaeozoic

By the end of the Palaeozoic the sea was pushed right out of the Ural Trough and the Triassic sediments which followed were wholly continental. Sedimentation was evidently slowing down and becoming more fine-grained with the wearing down of the new mountains. The sediments are still thickest in the fore-deep (which continued to subside for some time) but also occur in patches within the mountains. This was also the beginning of thick and extensive deposition in what are now the West Siberian Lowlands, east of the Urals. Although the Triassic includes thick red beds and evaporites, there are also coal-seams and abundant remains of land plants and animals, as there are also in the early Jurassic rocks which follow.

In places, as in the Pechora Basin, continental Jurassic sediments rest on gently folded and eroded Triassic, suggesting movements here dated as mid Triassic. Elsewhere the Rhaetian–Liassic 'Coal Measures' are gently folded, as in the Chelyatinsk region south of Sverdlovsk, so movements clearly continued, but the storm had long passed. A late Jurassic sea invaded from the Boreal Ocean at the north end of the range, but generally the Urals were an upland ridge—of no great height—throughout Jurassic times.

A Cretaceous sea also invaded in the north and a sea at times extended all the way along the Uralian fore-deep in a series of transgressions and regressions. But its deposits were nowhere of any great thickness. The Mesozoic rocks of the Urals are mostly the dark muddy sediments of the north, not the dazzling white limestones of the Tethys. Only in the southernmost part of the southerly Mugodzhars does one find the chalk and (later) the nummulitic limestones of the warm south. Here too there are the only slight indications of Alpine movements in the Urals.

Similar sediments with important phosphates (as at the far end of our continent on the Moroccan Meseta) continue into the Palaeogene through a complex series of transgressions and regressions that sound very familiar to the visitor from the far west. The deposits are not thick but they are extensive over the West Siberian Lowlands. The Urals were still there in early Tertiary times, at least as a low ridge draped with continental sediments in the extreme south. Only there did the sea occasionally swash round to the western side.

The Neogene is very sparsely represented, although the Quaternary produced a widespread marine transgression on to the grim northern wastelands of the Russian platform and Siberian Lowlands. The glaciations did their usual work and have left extensive deposits including some very interesting placer deposits of gold, platinum, and diamonds.

Selected references to Chapter 11

Section 11(a)   Urals and Novaya Zemlya

Bogdanov, N. A., B. A. Morgan, and N. J. Page (1979), 'Ophiolite complex traversed (in the Polar Urals)', *Geotimes*, **24**(2), 22–23.

Dunbar, C. O. (1940), 'The type Permian, its classification and correlation', *Bull. Amer. Ass. Petrol. Geol.*, **24**, 237–281.

Hamilton, W. (1970), 'The Uralides and the motion of the Russian and Siberian platforms', *Bull. Geol. Soc. Amer.*, **81**, 2553–2576.

Ivanov, S. N., A. S. Perfilev, A. A. Efimov, G. A. Smirnov, V. M. Necheukhin, and G. B. Fershtater (1975), 'Fundamental features in the structure and evolution of the Urals', *Amer. J. Sci.*, **275-A**, 107–130.

Khain, V. E. (1977), 'The new international tectonic map of Europe and some problems of structure and tectonic history of the continent', in D. V. Ager and M. Brooks (eds), *Europe from Crust to Core*, Wiley, London, pp. 19–40.

Nalivkin, D. V. (1973), *Geology of the U.S.S.R.*, Univ. Toronto Press, 855 pp. (English transl. by N. Rast).

Varganov, V. G. (1976), 'Time of initiation of the Uralian Palaeozoic', *Internat. Geol. Rev.*, **18**, 1319–1322 (English transl. of 1975 paper in *Sovetskaya Geologiya*).

Chapter Twelve

General conclusions on Meso-Europa

The Variscan fold belt of central Europe forms an obvious and more or less direct continuation of the Ouachita-Allegheny fold belt of eastern North America. Stand on the western extremities of Europe, such as in Munster (south-west Ireland) or Armorica (north-west France), and you can have little doubt that the old mountain ridges heading straight out into the Atlantic have been torn off from their continuations on the distant American shoreline. The Caledonian folds and thrusts run roughly parallel to the coast and the Alpine fold belts avoid the confrontation altogether (as in the spectacular *volte-face* at Gibraltar). Only with the Variscides do we have this direct cross-cutting of the Caledonide–Atlantic line and the Variscide–Alpide–Mediterranean line.

Turning to face east one can say that although, for convenience, the Variscan massifs in this book have been divided into three belts, these are not quite the same as a division on tectonic grounds. There is a northern fold belt (or 'paratectonic' zone) from Munster through Cornubia and northern Armorica, on across the Ardennes, the Eifel, and the Rheinisches Schiefergebirge to Bohemia, the Holy Cross Mountains, and perhaps Dobrogea. Throughout this belt the Palaeozoic rocks, although intensely folded, have hardly been metamorphosed (except for local contact metamorphism, as around the granites of south-west England). The sediments and the faunas are often in a remarkably healthy condition (as in the Eifel and in Barrande's localities in Czechoslovakia). Also this Variscan fold belt roughly coincides with an earlier Caledonian belt implying continued sinking of an earlier trough.

There is then a central ('orthotectonic') belt in which Palaeozoic successions have been highly metamorphosed and the original sediments and faunas largely obliterated. This belt starts from southern Armorica, down into the Massif Central, and then up again through the Vosges and Black Forest. It is perhaps seen again after that in the northern external massifs of the Alps, such as the Aar Massif of Switzerland and perhaps the ill-used Palaeozoic rocks of the Apuseni Mountains in Romania. Here the Variscan fold belt is swallowed up in Neo-Europa.

The southern belt is again comparatively little metamorphosed, starting from the Iberian and Moroccan Mesetas, with splendid Palaeozoic faunas and successions (such as those of northern Portugal and Cantabria), through the Palaeozoic massifs of the Pyrenees (affected as they are by later metamorphism), through the Montagne Noire, Corsica (with Alpine effects), and Sardinia. Perhaps one can trace this belt into the Alps also in the more southerly massifs, with Palaeozoic rocks and fossils still quite decently preserved in places—for example, near Briançon.

If one plots these belts on a map one immediately notices a sharp northerly bend in western France. It has been suggested that this, like the Spitsbergen 'knee-bend' in the Caledonide belt and perhaps the Arctic deflection in the Urals, was due to the rotation of also in the more southerly massifs, with Palaeozoic rocks and fossils still quite decently The microplate in question would have been roughly what is now the Iberian peninsula, which was to rotate again—in the opposite direction—in the Alpine movements. The folding of its leading edge is splendidly seen in the Cantabrian Mountains north of Leon, where the Asturian (pre-Stephanian) phase of the Variscan orogeny takes its name and where there was further intense folding after the Stephanian.

In my simplistic approach to structural geology (and this book is concerned with history rather than geometry) I am struck by the fact that most of the major massifs of Meso-Europa have a major 'knee-bend' in their fold patterns. This is well seen in Armorica, the Massif Central, the Iberian Meseta, and the Moroccan Meseta (Fig. 12.1). Now that the various Variscan trends can be traced, almost continuously, under the thick sedimentary cover between the massifs, we know that these sharp changes in direction are confined to the upstanding masses. It therefore becomes possible that the massifs have been more rigid and positive than the surrounding area just because of these virgations, just as a compressed syncline is more resistant than a stretched anticline.

Another structural feature of western Meso-Europa is that although the trends already discussed tend to run normal to the Atlantic line, there are still some which are parallel to it. This is most obvious in the British Isles, where the familiar east-west lines of south-west England swing round abruptly into a north–south direction in the Malvern Hills and in the Pennine backbone of northern England. On their own these little structures are perhaps of no significance, but there are plenty of others of which the most impressive perhaps (although really outside the limits of this book) are the late Palaeo-zoic folds of the Anti-Atlas in west Africa, which run exactly parallel to the present Atlantic coast. It would appear that the Atlantic influence that was so important in Palaeo-Europa was still exerting an influence at the end of Palaeozoic times, as it was to again later.

Turning to the stratigraphical matters which are my principal concern, it seems to me—as a Mesozoic specialist—that the older successions of Meso-Europa are remarkably uniform and monotonous. No doubt no specialist on the Variscides would agree with me!

In almost all the Variscan massifs there were stablized cores of metamorphic rocks long before the end of the Precambrian. Moldanubicum in Bohemia and the Auvergne Core in the Massif Central are obvious examples. There is no evidence of a widespread orogeny at the end of Precambrian times in most of Meso-Europa, in spite of the popularity of terms such as 'Cadomian' and 'Assyntian' in various parts of it. Thick arenaceous and argillaceous sedimentation seems to have prevailed over a large part of Europe through most of Proterozoic and Palaeozoic times. Certainly from Tremadoc times onwards there seems to have been what may still be called a geosyncline extending east–west across central Europe. The later continuation of this is seen in Variscan Brit-ain, although Armorica largely seems to have escaped thick sedimentation. The Caledon-ian orogeny appears to have passed without leaving a mark in Meso-Europa, except in

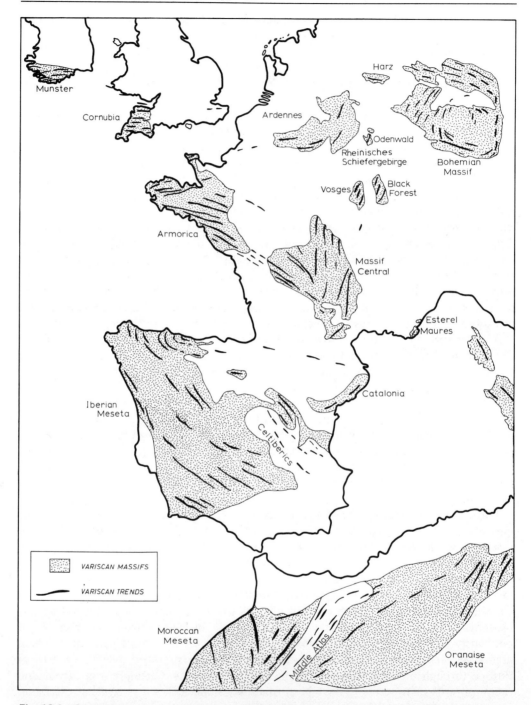

Fig. 12.1 General trends of the Variscan massifs of western Europe (from Ager, 1975, by kind permission of the Council of the Geologists' Association).

the extreme north (e.g., in the Sudetenland) where the Variscan movements may well have had Caledonian precursors on the same lines, and a possible metamorphic (but non-orogenic) event in the south.

The general pattern of muddy and clastic formations seems to extend endlessly through the Proterozoic and the greater part of the Palaeozoic, only relieved by notable carbonate developments at the Givetian–Frasnian and Dinantian levels and (in the south) more briefly in the Lower Cambrian. Some sedimentary facies are remarkably widespread, such as the white and purple quartzites of the Arenig and the black shales of the Silurian. Obviously there are differences, but the overriding impression to the outsider is one of uniformity.

Thus the early Ordovician Stiperstones Quartzite that forms a splendid scarp in Shropshire is remarkably like the Grès Armoricains which supports William the Conqueror's castle at Falaise in Normandy, which is very similar to the Barrios Quartzite barrier in Cantabria which held back the armies of Franco, Napoleon, and the Moors (who had left an identical quartzite of the same age in Morocco). The islands of Mumbles Head, which I see from my window, are made of virtually the same early Carboniferous rock as that which forms the *Roche percée* on the Moroccan Meseta. The differences are more those of fossils (and perhaps latitudes) than of sedimentary facies. Thus massive archaeocyathid limestones characterize the early to mid Cambrian in the south—in Spain, in the Montagne Noire, in Sardinia—while up here in the north we find only thin limestones with hyolithids.

The upper Carboniferous has its paralic basins bordering a sea in the north; these contrast with the intermontane limnic basins of the centre, while in the south—beyond the Pyrenees—there are marine intercalations again, but this time from a southern sea best seen in south-west Portugal. But the 'Coal Measures' are always the 'Coal Measures', whether they are worked by Welshmen singing *Cwm Rhondda*, Frenchmen with bottles of red wine in their pockets, or Moroccans swearing by the beard of the prophet.

The major palaeogeographic controversy of the later Palaeozoic of Meso-Europa is as to whether or not there was a major suture, a lost ocean, across the middle of our continent. With the first swing of the pendulum of plate tectonics, subduction zones were seen everywhere and a particularly stubborn one has been variously placed along the northern Variscan fold belt. Commonly a pair of outwardly directed zones are postulated between Cornubia, the Ardennes–Eifel–Rheinisches Schiefergebirge and Harz on the one side, and Armorica, the Massif Central and the Vosges–Black Forest on the other. The evidence is scanty, but the rocks most energetically hammered in support of this theory are the pillow lavas of Cornubia, the Rhineland, and the Harz. Really these have to be seen to be disbelieved! Little puffs of pillow lava, like those of Pentire Head in Cornwall and Chipley in Devon* are in no sense ophiolitic suites. They are almost ludicrously trivial compared with what is to be seen in the contemporaneous arctic Urals for example, or south of Skopje in 'Alpine' Yugoslavia, or even their 'Caledonian' equivalent much closer at hand on Strumble Head in Pembrokeshire. In the Rhineland one even finds conglomerates and reefs perched directly on top of the pillow lavas. Nowhere in Meso-Europa outside the Urals do the pillow lavas (which are scattered through the

---

* So over-used is this rather poor exposure that the harassed farmer now charges student parties for visiting it.

succession from Proterozoic to Carboniferous) exceed some 300 m in total thickness, and that would be exceptional. Ultra-basic masses are extremely scarce. There is nothing that could be called a 'greenstone belt' or 'ophiolite suture'; in fact there are no real linear features at all. The little bit of Carboniferous and Permian andesitic and rhyolitic extrusive activity that came at the end of the story is no kind of island arc. There are no high temperature–high pressure metamorphics. The whole Proterozoic–Palaeozoic story of this part of Europe seems to have been played out on a thick sialic crust.

In my view (and that of the relevant specialists I most respect) there is nothing in Meso-Europa comparable to the ocean floor rocks of Alpine Europe or (to a lesser degree) of Caledonian Europe either. What is more, I am not convinced that there is any great evidence of plate collision with major crustal foreshortening. One of the main preoccupations of structural geologists in the Variscan massifs in recent years has been the gradual demolition of the huge nappes postulated by an earlier generation. With rare exceptions, high-angle faults seem to be the rule rather than low-angle thrusts. If there was a plate junction, I think it was way down to the south of Europe and the northerly directed subduction zone was deep below the surface in the latitudes where it is usually postulated.

On the other hand the Urals seem to display all the classic features of plate tectonics: subduction, obduction, ocean floor, and continental collision, that are so noticeably lacking in the Variscan orogeny of Central Europe. Here surely we see continental accretion and a real suture. But even here the evidence suggests that the ocean which was destroyed at the end of Palaeozoic times was never very wide. They are the eastern (and later) counterparts of the Caledonides (although with a stronger smell of the ocean) and in their way are reminiscent of the Appalachians. They form a very natural eastern boundary to our continent.

Since we are deprived then of plate tectonics as the immediate mechanism of the late Palaeozoic orogeny in most of Meso-Europa, what are we to put in their place? One's attention is immediately drawn to the large masses of granite and granodiorite which are such a feature of the Variscan massifs. It has been shown, incidentally, that the average composition of these differs significantly from that of the Caledonian granites and must be related to differences in geothermal gradient.

The most popular view—or at least that most strongly argued—sees upward diapiric magma emplacement as the driving force of the Variscan movements. Presumably this would have started by gravity differentiation of light basic magma in the upper mantle. The granite masses involved the melting of great masses of crust and produced broad metamorphic aureoles with subsequent mineralization. As they moved upwards, narrow troughs developed in front of them and accumulated sediment. There is not the general migration of troughs as seen in the Alpine belts, although this probably happened locally, for example in the Cantabria–Asturias Troughs of late Carboniferous times in north Spain.

Later granites probably followed the same routes and much of the deformation may be directly related to these emplacements, like the disturbances caused by salt diapirs. A great deal of the folding may have been produced by gravity-sliding off the elevated centres. This makes good sense, for example, of the northward-directed structures of the Ardennes which may relate to the granites that rose in the Vosges to the south. Generally speaking the thrust and fold planes are directed outwards from the steep flanks of the plutons. Conglomerates are developed on the flanks and evidence of sediment transport indicates the same sort of directions. On top of the plutons, on the other hand, shallow-water deposits, thinning out of formations and unconformities are the rule. This is very much the pattern on the Iberian Massif, all around which there are magnificent developments of later coarse clastic deposits (I always think of Spain as a country of conglomerates). There are also thick carbonates in this position even back in the late Palaeozoic (e.g., in Cantabria). The Moravian karst limestones of Czechoslovakia may be in the same position relative to the Bohemian Massif.

Fairly early on, tensional graben began to develop within the massifs producing features such as the *Sillon houiller* in the Massif Central or even intermontane molasse-filled basins such as the Saar. This was just a preliminary warning of the great rift systems of Europe that really got going in the Triassic, although it has been suggested that they were related to a transform effect of foreshortening in the Urals and Appalachians.

At the end of the Variscan episode, tension and vertical movements became widespread, blocking out the massifs roughly as they are today. The later volcanism all relates to this. The massifs stood up as positive areas, while thick Mesozoic and Tertiary sediments accumulated around them. The Mesozoic of Meso-Europa is strictly non-Alpine. That is to say, it lacks the facies and the faunas that are particularly characteristic of Neo-Europa. Thus visiting geologists are often surprised to find the Triassic and Jurassic of Spain outside the Betic Cordillera to be remarkably like that of north-west Europe, although everything round about reminds them that this is southern Europe.

There are differences, of course, notably the flourishing of rudist bivalves and the massive Urgonian reefs in the south, but on the other hand the Triassic triptych in the Celtiberic chains has exactly the same characters as in its classic Germanic homeland. The Mesozoic seas that lapped round the Iberian Meseta and the south end of the Massif Central were just like those that lapped round the Rheinisches Schiefergebirge and Cornubia; they only differed in being more southerly and warmer and more addicted to carbonate deposition. Only locally—as in eastern Corsica—do the Alpine fold belts seem to intrude on one of the massifs of Meso-Europa.

The tension which became such a feature of western Europe in Triassic times, producing the great graben and subsiding basins between the Variscan massifs, continued right through into the Tertiary, with the production of little infaulted troughs of non-marine sedimentation, high on the ancient plateaux, such as those of the Massif Central, Maures-Esterel, and Bohemia. Veneers of continental sediment plaster the upland surfaces in places as on the Spanish meseta. The same tension played a big part in the late Tertiary trachytic volcanism which is such a feature of the massifs, with fissure eruptions and long straight lines of craters which continued to erupt into the days of early man.

The huge basins between the massifs each have their own story, although their general subsidence is also obviously a tensional effect. The marine invasions consistently come from the direction of the opening Atlantic to the west. Episodicity and oscillation seem to be the rule and the varied, highly fossiliferous sequences that resulted have provided the soil on which grew the whole science of stratigraphy.

I have included the Moroccan and Oranaise mesetas in this discussion (and in Fig. 12.1) since, although they are in Africa, they are very much part of the European story. They will be considered briefly in Chapter 16(a) where their adjacent Tertiary fold belts leave me no choice but to take an excursion outside our continent. This leads me to the point that has already been mentioned about the parallelism of Variscan and Alpine structures. In central Europe the Variscan belts plunge into the breaking waves of the Alpine fold belts. Farther south there is often a remarkable parallelism as in the way the Tertiary fold belt of the Pyrenees passes into the Palaeozoic fold belt of Cantabria, which then does a smart about-turn to march down through the Celtiberics where the Palaeozoic and Tertiary structures coincide. But I do not have to go that far. Right outside my window I can see the east–west Variscan fold belt of southernmost Wales plunging below the very gentle east–west Tertiary fold belt of the Bristol Channel. All this will be discussed further later under Neo-Europa in Chapter 17.

Selected references to Chapter 12

Ager, D. V. (1975), 'The geological evolution of Europe', *Proc. Geol. Ass.*, **86**, 127–154.

Burrett, C. F. (1972), 'Plate tectonics and the Hercynian orogeny', *Nature*, **239**, 155–157.

Dunning, F. W. (1977), 'Caledonian–Variscan relations in north-west Europe', *Colloq. Internat. Centre Nat. Recherche Sci.*, *Rennes*, No. 243, 165–180.

Hall, A. (1973), 'Geothermal control of granite compositions in the Variscan orogenic belt', *Nature, Phys. Sci.*, **242**, 72–75.

Krebs, W. (1977), 'The tectonic evolution of Variscan Meso-Europa', in D. V. Ager and M. Brooks (eds), *Europe from Crust to Core*, Wiley, London, pp. 119–139.

Krebs, W. and H. Wachendorf (1973), 'Proterozoic–Palaeozoic geosynclinal and orogenic evolution of central Europe', *Bull. Geol. Soc. Amer.*, **84**, 2611–2630.

Leeder, M. R. (1976), 'Sedimentary facies and the origins of basin subsidence along the northern margin of the supposed Hercynian ocean', *Tectonophys.*, **36**, 167–179.

Riding, R. (1974), 'Model of the Hercynian fold belt', *Earth Planet. Sci. Letts*, **24**, 125–135.

Ziegler, P. A. (1978), 'North-western Europe: tectonics and basin development', *Geol. Mijnb.*, **57**, 589–626.

Part Four

Neo-Europa

That part of Europe which was affected by major orogenic movements in late Mesozoic and/or Cainozoic times

Chapter Thirteen

Outer Arcs

I have given this name to those Alpine fold belts that seem separate and distinct from the main continuous belt. This is not to say that they are all directly related to each other in any way.

13(a) Pyrenees

The Pyrenees are simply the sudden, sharp mountain range that forms such a natural boundary between France and Spain. They are a very straight and narrow range, up to 3400 m high and extending from the Bay of Biscay some 430 km to the Mediterranean, but never more than 40–80 km wide. Geologically, they are part of a much more extensive range, extending eastwards into Provence (to meet the Alps at an angle) and westwards all along the north coast of Spain, first as Mesozoic mountains and then as the Palaeozoic mountains of Cantabria and Asturia.

They are nevertheless topographically isolated, hence their large number of endemic species left behind by climatic change (including the Pyrenean brown bear, a chamois, a lynx, and a rare ibex). Stratigraphically and palaeontologically they are not an Alpine range at all in that their facies and faunas are mainly those of extra-Alpine western Europe and are much closer to those already described in Meso-Europa than those still to be considered in most of the rest of Neo-Europa. There are also reasons for thinking that they are also not Alpine in a tectonic sense.

This orogenic belt is interesting for two further reasons. First, it is a belt where Variscan and Alpine folding appear to coincide almost exactly. Second, it is the belt along which there presumably occurred the movements involved in the opening of the Bay of Biscay, first revealed by the residual magnetism in Triassic rocks from Spain and later by geophysical evidence out on the shelf.

In its simplest terms, the Pyrenees consists of an Axial Zone of ancient rocks and large batholiths; two Internal Zones (lying to the north and south) composed for the most part of Mesozoic and Cainozoic sediments with ancient cores; and beyond these lie two External Zones or marginal troughs of thick late Mesozoic and Cainozoic sediments (Fig. 13.1). These last two are less intensely folded than those nearer the centre of the range and form two minor ridges, the Little Pyrenees to the north and the Sierras Zone

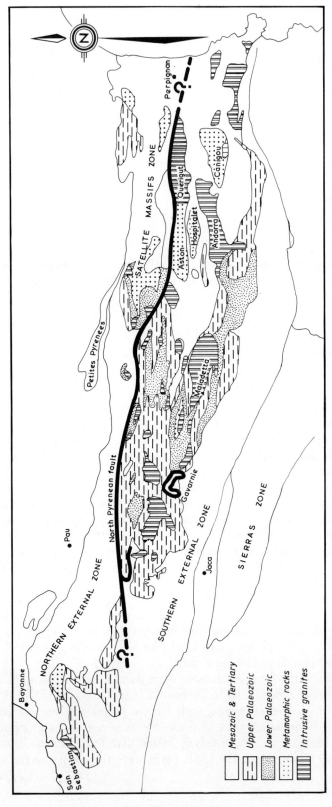

Fig. 13.1 Geological sketch-map of the Pyrenees (after Rutten, 1969, by kind permission of Elsevier).

to the south. They have been compared with the Jura Mountains in front of the Alps, but are on a much smaller scale.

The Pyrenees are almost too good to be true, both in structure and in geological history. They form an ideal symmetrical structure, with the folds in the north overturned towards the north and those in the south towards the south. What is more, the Axial Zone of most intense Variscan folding is also the central part of the Palaeozoic geosyncline, while the Internal Zones show the thickest Mesozoic sedimentation prior to the late Eocene Pyrenean folding. Finally, the External Zones have the thickest late Cretaceous and early Palaeogene sediments prior to the final earth movements and to the Neogene uplift which produced the mountains as they are today. All this, together with their smaller size and comparative accessibility, makes the Pyrenees an almost perfect mountain range for demonstration to, and study by, students.

Obviously the full story is much more complicated than this and even in the most superficial description, reservations are needed. Thus the Axial Zone thins out and becomes discontinuous to the west, while the northern Internal Zone becomes confused eastwards by the inclusion of what are called the 'Satellite Massifs'.

Pre-Devonian

The oldest fossils so far found in the Pyrenees are of late Ordovician (Caradoc) age, but there are great thicknesses of rock older than this. The oldest at the surface may well be of Archaean age. These include a thick succession of banded gneisses and mica schists which have suffered greater metamorphism than the datable Palaeozoic sediments, although it is difficult to sort out such rocks in a range that has suffered at least two major orogenies with the emplacement of numerous batholitic masses. As in the Massif Central of France, not very far away, sediments of different ages can be shown to have reached a similar grade of metamorphism, and the effects vary from one place to another.

It is generally (although not universally) accepted that the 'mantled gneiss domes' in the northern part of the eastern Pyrenees, notably the massifs of Trois Seigneurs, Arize, and St. Bathélemy, north of Andorra, have suffered early and deep-seated migmatization. The story is made more complicated by the alternation of two sequences of gneiss and two of mica schist within the same complex. This may relate to the original composition of the sediments involved or it may be that the upper of the two gneisses is the core of a nappe.

To the British visitor these ancient gneisses (seen, for example, along the main road north of Tarascon) are very much like the Lewisian of north-west Scotland. Like the latter, they contain the record of multiple early events, such as double or triple folding and the emplacement of basic dikes (now amphibolites) before their main orogenies. They include a wide variety of metamorphic rocks and are much less homogeneous than the massifs south of the North Pyrenean Fault which runs most of the length of the range. This may in itself be significant if we postulate considerable lateral movement along that line. So far, unfortunately, we have no age determinations for these northern massifs, although there seems to be little doubt that they must range far back into the Precambrian.

Above these early gneisses come further stratified metamorphic rocks and then a great thickness of arenites and argillites with some thin limestones and acid volcanic rocks.

The whole sequence seems to rest on the gneisses without obvious break and has itself been metamorphosed, with the development of iron-ores that are mined locally. This metamorphism, although of much lower grade than that just discussed, can be shown elsewhere in the Pyrenees to affect sediments as young as Devonian (as in the Massif Central). Above the metasediments in the Axial Zone comes another thick sedimentary succession of slates, sandstones, and conglomerates, that include the earliest (Caradoc to Ashgill) fossils. The coarser sediments appear to have been derived from the east and dominate the scenery of the eastern Pyrenees, especially around Andorra.

The first fossils come mostly from a prominent, thick limestone formation that occurs in reef-like lenses in the central Pyrenees. There then follows a thin development of fossiliferous Silurian limestones, interbedded with black graptolitic shales, now usually slates. These slates have played an important part in the tectonics of the Axial Zone, for they are an incompetent unit, outcropping in hollows and taking up the main sliding movements of the later orogeny. The Silurian slates are everywhere highly tectonized and form a clear break between higher and lower tectonic units, as in the vicinity of Roland's last stand at Roncesvalles, near Burguete. There is commonly a marked contrast in the grade of metamorphism above and below the black slates and it has been suggested that we have here evidence of a Caledonian orogeny with the emplacement of granites such as the Aston Massif. It would then be necessary to postulate a complete remobilization of the earlier granite during the Variscan happening. This would account for the radiometric dates. However, the general view seems to be that all the metamorphism is Variscan and that there is no certain evidence of a Caledonian event in the Pyrenees.

Late Palaeozoic

Devonian rocks cover a large part of the central Pyrenees and are varied in composition, including the red, nodular limestones, known as 'griotte', with a pelagic fauna. There has been much argument about the depth of water represented by these. In my opinion it is not enough to find special explanations for each case, and the only possible general explanation would seem to be one of latitude and climate. Nevertheless, many now seem to favour shallow water rather than the deeps previously postulated, and this may be significant in the Pyrenees, because along the central axis, the Upper Devonian passes into a flysch-like facies that may represent the centre of a trough. Shallow-water reef limestones are also developed in the Upper Devonian, as in the well-displayed monocline at the Fort de Portalet, north of the frontier col of the Puerto de Somport.

More seems to have started happening during Devonian times. There are many breaks in the succession including a notable one between the Devonian and the Carboniferous, although conodont studies suggest that this is not as important as was previously thought. The Lower Carboniferous exhibits slow sedimentation at first with 'hard grounds', chert, and layers of phosphatic nodules. This passes up into great spreads of greywacke and some plant-bearing beds. Coming south from north-west Europe in an Upper Carboniferous lacking any marine horizons, the first signs of a late Carboniferous Palaeo-Tethys are seen in the Pyrenees. This is all in the literature but it seems to me that the most significant stratigraphical features are often lost in the local detail. One must go to see for oneself. In the Pyrenees one of the most striking features one does not expect from the literature is the important development of carbonates in the lower part of the Carboniferous. They are readily recognizable as black limestones, often with intraformational breccias, and frequently showing lines of calcite-filled tension gashes (e.g., in the large quarries near Vera, at the west end of the chain). At the Canfranc hydroelectric station, north of Jaca, similar limestones are brecciated in what seems to be a storm deposit.

There is, however, comparatively little evidence of later Carboniferous sedimentation in the Pyrenees and it is difficult to demonstrate the age of the orogeny that affected the Palaeozoic succession. It must be emphasized that if there was no Caledonian orogeny here then not much happened in Palaeozoic times before the Variscan orogeny, except for thick sedimentation at times along the axis of the range. We know from much better evidence farther west along this fold belt, in Asturias, that the main movements occurred within the late Carboniferous, before the deposition of the Stephanian stage. Locally in the Pyrenees, as at Enviny near Sort (west of Andorra), one can see cleaved Westphalian shales close to uncleaved Stephanian sediments. Elsewhere—in Andorra for instance—the Stephanian too is cleaved but it is not clear if this is due to a late Variscan or to a Tertiary event.

The Variscan orogeny, with its accompanying metamorphism and granodioritic emplacement, affected the various parts of the earlier sequence in different ways. Palaeozoic sediments can be seen in many places becoming involved in the metamorphic massifs, for example along the busy international highway from Figueras to Perpignan and around the headland north of Rosas on the Costa Brava. At Bosost, close to the international border in the central Pyrenees, one can see (with perseverance) phyllites passing through progressively higher metamorphic zones, from biotite to cordierite-sillimanite, in a short walk along the road south of the village. No kyanite is recorded in the Pyrenees and steep thermal gradients are presumed, especially locally. It has been argued that at Bosost there must have been a particularly hot spot in the earth's crust, and temperatures up to 600°C have been postulated at comparatively shallow depths. Similar passages of sediments into high-grade schists can be seen in several of the other massifs.

All the pre-Stephanian sediments are cleaved as a result of the Variscan orogeny and the main cleavage, together with the main folding, is parallel to the present mountain range. There are some complications, however, for in the northern Internal Zone the folds swing to a north–south direction. There have been arguments, as in parts of Meso-Europa, as to whether or not far-travelled nappes are recognizable, and if so, in which direction they moved. The matter is still 'not proven', but the balance of evidence seems to be against them.

There is clear evidence, as in Cantabria and Asturias, of more than one phase within the Variscan movements. Probably the main spasm occurred before the Stephanian and another after it, but in places such as Candanchu, on the frontier, sediments as young as the Trias can be seen to be cleaved in the same way as the Palaeozoic. Late in the orogeny there was the emplacement of great quantities of granodiorite and then faulting of the rigid mass so produced. The major faults, such as the North Pyrenean Fault already mentioned, run roughly parallel to the range, but there are also plenty of conjugate faults at 45 degrees on either side of the main structures. These serve to break up the 'basement' rocks into angular massifs.

The emplacement of the great granodioritic batholiths towards the end of the orogeny

327

produced what are now the most spectacular of the Pyrenean mountains. A great part of the tiny mountain state of Andorra is composed of such a granodiorite, as is the great massif of Maladeta, which dominates the central Pyrenees, and Querigut-Millas, which dominates the east. The largest of these—Maladeta—stands up squarely to nearly 3500 m and is known better than the others because it is pierced by a long and uncomfortable road tunnel south of Viella. This is also a place to study contact metamorphism, which is not extensive in the Pyrenees, but marble and hornfels are seen along the junction with the Palaeozoic sediments.

Ages ranging from about 250 to 300 million years have been recorded in these massifs, fitting in with their supposed age from direct geological evidence, but a complication is an apparent Cretacous reheating, at around 113 million years ago, in the northern part of the Aston Massif farther east. This may be connected with the metamorphism seen in the Mesozoic rocks all along the north side of the North Pyrenean Fault.

The granodiorites are remarkably uniform in composition and besides producing little contact metamorphism also produced remarkably little folding in their cover. They were intruded at different levels in the sedimentary pile; some like the Valmanaya 'granite' are entirely within the gneisses, others such as Batere are entirely within the Lower Palaeozoic; a few, such as Querigut, just reach into the Upper Palaeozoic. There has been much discussion as to whether the gneisses and the granite batholiths are really separate entities or whether they are part of the same deep-seated metamorphism in the Variscan orogeny. Although many of the granites are in a highly deformed state, there seems to be no evidence of them grading into massifs such as Arize and St. Barthélemy which appear to be wholly Precambrian. There must be significance in the fact that, apart from the isolated massif of Labourd, south-east of Bayonne, the gneiss domes are all concentrated in the eastern Pyrenees, especially in the northern 'Satellite Massifs Belt'. The granites are concentrated in the same region, as might be expected from the depth of the structures revealed there, but are also well displayed in the central Pyrenees. There may be a transition from granite to gneiss in the vicinity of Andorra, or it may be a matter of distinguishing between syntectonic granites, which have been deformed and post-tectonic ones, which have not. It is also possible that the deep-seated gneiss domes have been separated from the higher granitic intrusions as a result of sliding along the line of the incompetent Silurian outcrop.

There are a few very late Carboniferous conglomerates with floras that post-date the orogeny. There was also considerable volcanic activity at the end of the Palaeozoic, especially along the southern border of the central and western Pyrenees. This was largely andesitic and probably mostly extruded as lavas in Permian times, although there are some ashes containing Stephanian plants. The most famous and spectacular of these volcanics form the Pic du Midi d'Ossau, near Candanchu.

The volcanics are followed by typical post-orogenic red beds, including thick conglomerates. These are usually vaguely attributed to the 'Permo-Trias', although the deep reds of the Permian are easily distinguishable from the paler reds of the Trias. They become finer upwards and are much thicker in the west than in the east. In the usual way of Alpine ranges, thick evaporites probably played an important part in later tectonics.

Mesozoic

The Jurassic and Cretaceous are both well developed in the internal and external zones on both sides of the range. They pass right over the central axis, as for example at Tardets (south-west of Pau) towards the western end of the range. They thin towards the centre and the Jurassic is usually missing on the axis, suggesting that this was already rising at that time. The Trias can be seen in place, only preserved as red staining and cavity fillings below the Jurassic. For the most part the Jurassic and Cretaceous are represented by shallow-water carbonate facies, often with rich faunas. An interesting point is that they do not change in facies crossing the Pyrenees. Thus the rich early Jurassic brachiopod faunas of Camarasa, north of Lerida, although containing some 'Iberian' elements, is still basically of north-west European type and quite unlike contemporaneous faunas in the Alps and Betic Cordillera.

There are several developments that are of particular interest. In the south of the central Pyrenees at Santa Maria de Mella, near the beautiful village of Ager, is a local development of lithographic limestone with a perfectly preserved fauna and flora (including an *Archeopteryx* feather and such details as beetles' eyes). This is exactly like the famous Solnhofen Stone of southern Germany in lithology and organic content and in its Kimmeridgian age. A footprint here leaves no doubt of its shallow-water origin. In the basal Cretaceous in the kippe near Coustouges, straddling the frontier south-south-west of Perpignan, are the largest algal oncoliths I have seen, probably formed in a supratidal environment. Another feature is the development of the massive Urgonian limestones in the upper part of the Lower Cretaceous. These form great limestone walls—for example in the gorge south of Tremp—and are characterized by abundant rudists, often in life position. They are usually dazzling white but at the west end of the Pyrenees it takes on locally a bright red colour, perhaps connected with the iron-ore formed at this horizon near Bilbao (and worked extensively west of that city). The red rudist limestone, packed with the thick-shelled bivalves in life position, is quarried at Arteaga, near the tragic Basque city of Guernica, and exported all over the world as an ornamental stone. It is seen, for example, in the floor of the Louvre, near the Venus de Milo.

Things started happening again tectonically soon after this in mid Cretaceous times. Spain is a land of conglomerates and breccias, reflecting its tectonically active geological history. Such deposits became widespread in Albian times. Movements occurred along the North Pyrenean Fault at this time and the Axial Zone probably rose as a ridge above the sea. These were the mid-Cretaceous movements seen in many parts of Europe. Here they gave rise to breccias at the base of the characteristically transgressive Upper Cretaceous, or at least a good marker band of brown sandstones. In the same belt, immediately north of the fault, the Mesozoic sediments are greatly altered.

Varying facies occur in the Upper Cretaceous, as in the earlier Mesozoic, but although there are obvious differences between the northern and the southern Internal Zones, the facies generally do not seem to have reflected the Pyrenean line until very late Cretaceous times when a clearly defined flysch belt became established there. In the western Pyrenees, they pass into the Cantabrian mountains, through a complex pattern of interdigitating facies. Flysch sedimentation can be seen at Deva, on the north Spanish coast, starting immediately after the black shales with ironstone nodules that represent the Albian. Along this coast, from Deva to San Sebastian, and across the border to Bidart, south of Biarritz, the magnificently exposed flysch has been the subject of classic studies. It is calcareous in its lower part, in the Cretaceous, but passes through the era boundary into the Palaeogene without a break. It shows all the characteristic features of this facies, perhaps better than anywhere else in Europe (with the possible exception of the Polish Carpathians). The characteristic trace fossils are superabundant in places (e.g., just east of the little port of Zumaya), as are the bottom structures produced by turbidity currents. Beautiful slumps are seen at Deva, at Orio farther along the coast, and at Villanua inland. Pillow lavas are well displayed up the valley of the Rio Deva towards Vergara. The source of the flysch sediment is a matter of dispute, but it may have been from the massif which is thought to have occupied the present site of the Ebro Basin.

Although flysch sedimentation crosses the Mesozoic–Cainozoic boundary, especially in the west, in much of the Pyrenees the Eocene is seen to start with massive limestones containing concentrations of nummulitic and alveolinid forams, well seen in road-cuttings between Ager and the Puerto de Ager, south of Tremp. Before the end of the Eocene, the trough was already involved in the orogeny that formed the Pyrenees as they are today. The main Tertiary folding was significantly earlier than in the other western Alpine ranges, i.e., towards the end of Eocene times. This was the Pyrenean phase of the Alpine orogeny. At the west end of the range flysch is abruptly succeeded by molasse and molasse-like sediments, as can be seen east of San Sebastian and in the cliffs of Bidart and Biarritz. Towards the east end of the range, where the flysch disappears, the movements were intimately associated with the formation of shallow-water deposits packed with large forams. At the far end of the gorge south of Tremp a rush of boulders of Mesozoic limestones is seen mixed up with nummulites and large bivalves and (again above that village of Ager) the Mesozoic limestones are thrust over the Eocene.

In a sense the 'Alpine' nature of the Pyrenees has been exaggerated, perhaps from a subconscious wish to compare this range with the other younger ranges of Europe. It may be said that the Alpine movements of the Pyrenees were only an afterthought to the main Variscan folding; they perhaps did little more than re-emphasize the lines that were already drawn firmly in the Palaeozoic. Away from the North Pyrenean Fault there is virtually no metamorphism or even cleavage in the Mesozoic and Eocene sediments and there is little in the way of contemporary volcanism or igneous intrusion.

Nevertheless, when one studies the contortions of the flysch along the motorways west of San Sebastian, one cannot deny that these were the effects of a major orogeny. Admittedly the great recumbent folds of earlier authors have now nearly all be reinterpreted as thrust slices, but this is also true of the Alps and we can still call them nappes. The most obvious of these is probably the Gavarnie nappe, on the south side of the west-central Pyrenees, north-west of Jaca. Palaeozoic rocks are also included in this structure. The klippen at Coustouges, south-south-west of Perpignan, have already been mentioned and at Bedous, north of the border crossing of Puerto de Somport, the Jurassic is thrust over the Cretaceous.

Most of the movement seems to have been to the south (Fig. 13.2), but open north-facing structures are found north of the North Pyrenean Fault, which was probably still active at this time. It is clearly very complex and marks a significant boundary in the structure of the Mesozoic rocks. The overthrusting south of the fault is up to 10 km or more and the southern Pyrenees are a classic area for the 'cascade' folds of gravity tectonics. The North Pyrenean Fault may therefore be the most important feature of the

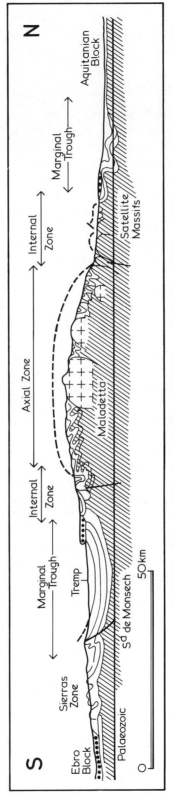

Fig. 13.2 Cross-section through the central Pyrenees (after de Sitter, 1965).

range in Tertiary times. The Axial Zone was perhaps no more than a result of later isostatic uplift.

Opening the Bay of Biscay

The idea that the Iberian Peninsula formerly occupied a position farther up in the Bay of Biscay was suggested a long time ago to improve the 'fit' of a closed Atlantic. It also made sense of palaeomagnetic observations on the Spanish Trias and of some of the Variscan patterns discussed earlier. If one thinks simply of a scissors-like movement, one might expect theoretically—speaking in the simplest terms—to find greater compression and complexity at the eastern end than at the western end. This must depend, of course, on the location of the fulcrum of the 'scissors', but one is encouraged to find that whereas at the Biscay end one passes through the Pyrenees very quickly on an almost level road, crossing nearer the Mediterranean is an arduous business of long steep climbs and rugged scenery. A whole country—Andorra—hides within the fold belts in the east.

The finding of arc-like magnetic anomalies on the floor of the Bay of Biscay led to the idea of a lateral rotation of the Iberian Peninsula and two Frenchmen suggested that this was about a centre (naturally) near Paris (Fig. 13.3). This led to the important conclusion that the parallelism of the Variscan and the Pyrenean folding on east–west lines was nothing more than coincidental.

The North Pyrenean Fault, which separates the Axial Zone from the northern Internal Zone in the eastern part of the range, is now thought to be a 'fossil' transcurrent fault. This fault can be seen to continue as a linear magnetic anomaly (and as a submarine trench) in the Bay of Biscay, as do further faults to the west: the Biscaye and Oviedo lines. On the other hand it must be said that the North Pyrenean Fault is not recognizable at the western end of the chain and there are fairly simple structural and stratigraphical arguments against the above hypothesis.

On the positive side there is the intense metamorphism and brecciation along the line of the North Pyrenean Fault, beautifully displayed on the French side near St. Béat and at Lez (north-east of Bagneres-de-Luchon). Lower Cretaceous limestones are converted into dazzling white marbles and are associated with black ultrabasic and basic intrusives. These include lherzolite (a form of peridotite), which takes its name from Lake Lherz in the centre of the range, and what the French call 'ophite', a pyroxene–plagioclase rock with (obviously) an ophitic texture. These probably come from considerable depths.

It seems therefore that the North Pyrenean Fault is a very significant structure, but its continuation in the Bay of Biscay is covered with late Cretaceous sediments. So it cannot have been responsible for the end Eocene folding. This must have been a separate and distinct coming together of Spain and Europe after the rotation (if it occurred) had been completed (see Fig. 17.2). I am still rather sceptical about the latter because of the facies patterns that seem to cross the range oblivious of any such later sideways movement.

Post-Eocene

After the main spasm in the late Eocene, there was clearly another minor phase of folding in the Miocene, but this was most strongly expressed in the External Zones where the late Cretaceous and early Tertiary sediments were at their thickest. The orogenic move-

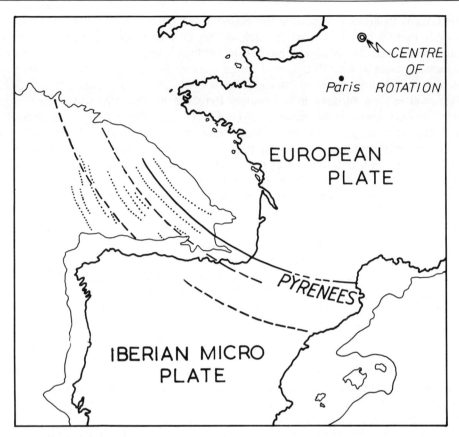

Fig. 13.3 Magnetic anomalies and rotationary faults in the Bay of Biscay and Pyrenees (after Le Pichon and Sibuet, 1971, by kind permission of Prof. Le Pichon).

ments in the Pyrenees moved outwards from the centre with time, like the troughs themselves.

The Sierras Zone, south of the Pyrenees, is comparable with, although much smaller than, the Jura Mountains in front of the Alps. It is a beautiful, but rather neglected, range of low mountains extending from west to east, north of Huesca, Barbastro, and Lerida. It is characterized particularly by Mesozoic and early Eocene limestones in open south-facing box-folds, for example the 'staircase' of folds seen along the Rio Isuela, north of Huesca. The earlier Mesozoic is thin, with many breaks. The change came at the beginning of the late Cretaceous, often after a marked unconformity, as clearly seen near Camarasa, north of Lerida. Thick foram-rich limestones are developed in the Lower Eocene. All these are involved in the Pyrenean folding. This is displayed most spectacularly in the gorge north-east of Barbastro, where post-orogenic conglomerates are seen filling a re-excavated valley in a sharp syncline of Eocene limestones. Elsewhere, the effects of the Miocene movements are more obvious, as at the Tunel de Bailin, south of Jaca, where Palaeogene conglomerates and sands, with molasse-type trace-fossils, stand on end and form a natural dam across the river. An even smaller Jura-type range are the 'Petites Pyrenees' on the French side of the mountains east of Tarbes.

The typical Palaeogene flysch of the Biscay coast does not extend far beyond Jaca. Eastwards there is a series of basins, such as that at Tremp, in which red beds pass up into the most foraminiferal clays I have seen and then a series of fluviatile deposits from the new mountains with multi-coloured conglomerates. Southwards there are nummulitic limestones and shallow-water to intertidal faunas.

High-level erosion surfaces in the central Pyrenees, at about 2400 and 2000 m, are thought to date from the Miocene or later. The last movements, which produced the present mountain range, were simply late Cainozoic isostatic uplift. There is therefore little sedimentary evidence of the last part of the story, although conglomerates and lignites with Pontian (late Miocene) pollen are preserved in an old gorge between the valleys of the Arties and the Aguamoix, high up in the Maladeta Massif above Viella. Such deposits are well over 100 m higher than the environment in which they accumulated.

To the north and south of the Pyrenees, vast thicknesses of post-orogenic sediments testify to the erosion of the mountains from Oligocene times onwards. To the west these are seen in the alluvial fans that form the Lannemezan Plateau in the south of the Aquitaine Basin. To the south they form the spectacular hills of conglomerate that stand along the north side of the Ebro Basin, for example Pena de Oroel, that dominates Jaca, the towering pillars of Mallos de Riglos, and culminating in the fantastic shapes of Montserrat, west of Barcelona. Late Tertiary volcanicity occurs in places, best seen perhaps in the cliffs of columnar basalt on which stands the village of Castelfullit de la Roca, north-west of Gerona.

The uplift was probably still going on in Pleistocene times, when the Pyrenees acquired their own mini ice-cap, and the glaciations modified the later Tertiary peneplains. Many glacial features are seen in the higher mountains and fluvio-glacial gravels form high terraces along some of the rivers (such as the Ariège at Tarascon). There is clear evidence that the valley glaciers extended much further down the cooler northern flanks than on the Spanish side. However, there are spectacular glacial gorges on the Spanish side, especially in the Ordesa National Park, where the River Arazas thunders down into a U-shaped canyon, and in the Valle de Äniscolo, where 1200 m cliffs only leave room for a small stream between them.

13(b) Ebro Basin

Linked with the Pyrenees as a frontal trough full of Tertiary sediments is the Ebro Basin. In fact the valley of the River Ebro in north-east Spain presents one of those characteristic paradoxes of European geology (like the Thames Valley in south-east England): a basin that was formerly an upstanding massif. At present it appears as a great triangular trough of young sediments, with its apex in the west and its base in the east. It is delimited by the Pyrenees to the north, the Celtiberic ranges to the south, and the Catalonian Cordillera to the east. Considered in the simplest terms, it appears rather odd even in its present form, for it is a wide river drainage system flowing into the Mediterranean, but with a mountain barrier cutting it off from the sea and the Ebro just squeezing through to make its little delta at Tortosa, south of Tarragona.

In Palaeozoic times, however, it was a rigid upstanding block, like the Aquitaine Basin north of the Pyrenees. Both are now quiet, placid, low-lying countrysides concealing their rugged past as the great millstones between which the Pyrenees were crumpled. The most positive evidence of the form of the Ebro area in Palaeozoic times comes from the thick sedimentary wedges in the Pyrenees which seem to have been derived from the south. In the Ebro Basin proper, the Palaeozoic is only seen at the surface in the little massif of Puig Moreno, north-west of Alcaniz. This is only some 5 km long by 1.5 km wide and shows an anticlinal ridge of Tertiary sediments with a core of possible Devonian striking west-north-west.

Mesozoic sedimentation is, on the whole, thin. The Trias is in its Germanic facies, as over much of Spain, with gypsiferous 'Keuper' and a capping cavernous dolomite ('Carniolas'). The salts of the Trias produce many diapiric structures which have played a part in oil and gas exploration. A typical one can be well seen west of Barbastro, along the main road to Huesca. The Trias may reach a thickness of 300 m, especially in the north, but thins southwards. So does the Jurassic, which amounts to less than 200 m and is mainly carbonates. This indicates that the Ebro was still a positive area, at least until the end of Jurassic times.

The Cretaceous picture is rather different. Something must have happened at depth (perhaps relating to the movements of the Iberian Microplate relative to the rest of Europe). The simple picture became broken up into a series of small elevations and intervening deeps. Locally, sedimentation was very thin or wholly lacking, while elsewhere there was comparatively thick sedimentation in little troughs. Speaking generally of this patchy development one can say that in the lower part of the Cretaceous it takes on a 'Wealden' facies of quartz sands, kaolin clays, and brown coals. This is followed by the usual massive Urgonian limestones, here ranging up into the Albian and dominating the Cretaceous succession. There is then a return to 'Wealden' conditions with brown coals, etc., and thin oyster banks. Fully marine conditions returned in the late Cretaceous with limestones, dolomites, and marls. The whole Cretaceous, however, only amounts to about 150 m at its maximum.

I can say nothing of the Variscan orogeny in this region, except that the older rocks were clearly already tectonized before Mesozoic times and pebbles of them first turn up in early Cretaceous conglomerates. The Pyrenean orogeny of Eocene times affected the whole region and there is a marked break above the Cretaceous. There was a general withdrawal of the sea to the north. If one drops a theoretical perpendicular from the apex of the Ebro triangle on to its broad easterly base, one can say that south of this line continental conditions prevailed throughout, while north of it the Eocene sea soon came creeping back from its Pyrenean trough. Commonly therefore, the Cretaceous is directly succeeded by the Oligocene. At this time the Ebro came into its own as a sedimentary basin. The Pyrenean movements had raised its three walls within which there accumulated great (although variable) thicknesses of Oligocene fluviatile and lacustrine deposits. These are difficult to correlate, but it is interesting to note, especially in the eastern part of the basin, that Palaeogene conglomerates are best developed to the south and not in the immediate vicinity of the frontal Pyrenean ranges. There are plenty of Oligocene conglomerates in the External Zone of the Pyrenees, but immediately south of here the succession is dominated by red and buff sandstones and marls with quite a lot of gypsum. The whole Oligocene reaches some 500 m in its thickest development and, with the end of the orogeny, probably extended far beyond the present basin over the surrounding orogenic zones. Typical flat-lying Oligocene of the Ebro Basin is seen forming the dusty scenery east of Huesca.

Although the structures of the Ebro Basin are by no means intense, it is noteworthy that the Palaeogene sediments can in places, as in the External Zone of the Pyrenees, be seen to have been folded with the Mesozoic, so indicating a later 'Alpine' phase of folding. The axial trends of the folds run parallel with the long axis of the basin and are comparable to the Jura-type folds seen within the Miocene molasse of the Franco-Swiss plain. Diapiric movements by the various evaporite bodies also play some part. It has been suggested that the greater thickness of overlying sediments in the centre of the basin caused the Triassic salt to move sideways and to break through the thinner cover at the margins with the help of the Tertiary movements.

The pattern of sedimentation is markedly different in the Miocene from what it was in the Oligocene. Although on the whole the Miocene is more thinly developed, the thickest sediments were now in the north. Thus in the Lower Miocene there are great fan deposits (e.g., at Puig Cabellé, south of Gandesa) from the newly elevated mountains. In the east, the Lower Miocene varies from some 300 m at Pinell in the north, down to as little as 10 m at Cerollera in the south. The coarser materials are mostly sharp-edged breccias and come mainly from the Mesozoic, although there are also Palaeozoic fragments which turn up again in the Cretaceous and Tertiary conglomerates and show that these older rocks were also being eroded not too far away. In the west, great walls of conglomerates stand above the Ebro at Los Mallos de Riglos and between Miranda and Haro, dipping into the basin from the north, and even more impressive cliffs tower above Casteñares, south of Logrono on the south side. The Upper Miocene consists of sandstones and marls, with some conglomerates of well-rounded pebbles. It represents basin deposition rather than the earlier scree fans.

Generally speaking, the Ebro Basin presents the visiting geologist a rather boring impression of flat-lying, pale-coloured, continental sediments of Cainozoic age, indifferently exposed in low road cuttings. Only the massive conglomerates provide a spectacular scenery, such as the incredible baroque architecture of Montserrat, on the fringe of the Catalonian ranges inland from Barcelona.

All that follows thereafter are the extensive Quaternary terrace and flood-plain deposits of the present drainage system which cover almost everything and produce an almost blank geological map.

More is now known of the underground geology of this superficially uninspiring part of the world through petroleum exploration. Seepages are common, especially in the marginal area, and there seem to be possibilities of reservoirs in the Tertiary sandstones and Mesozoic reef limestones. The rapid facies changes, sedimentary pinch-outs, and salt diapirs, all encourage this optimism, but the results have not been rewarding. The best finds have been in the Ebro delta offshore.

13(c) Provence

In the broadest sense, that glorious region of France known as 'Provence' includes six 'départements' and several distinct geological units including Variscan massifs (Maures-Esterel), part of the Western Alps proper (les Alpes de Haut Provence), and one of the 'intervening lowlands' of the Variscides (the Lower Rhône Valley and the Camargue). However, Provence as it is interpreted here, is taken to mean the distinctive region of east–west folds which was evidently part of the Pyrenean system and not primarily part of the neighbouring Alps.

It extends east and north from a point about half-way between the Rhône Delta and Marseilles, reaching nearly to Nice on the coast and up to the Alpilles ridge, north-east of Avignon. It is difficult to draw a sharp line between the Provençal fold belt and the true Alpides, for they merge where the one fold system refolds the other in the Alpes Maritimes.

The distinctive feature of Provence, as here interpreted, is the earlier folding (mostly end Eocene) displayed in the limestone ridges, and it is not difficult to imagine them continuing westwards across the Gulf of Lions to connect with the east end of the Pyrenees. There is no sign of the axial zone of the Pyrenees (unless the Maures and Esterel Massifs are interpreted as such) and we only see the higher parts of the structures.

It is a region of dazzling white limestones, fields of lavender and cicadas, Roman tiles and amphitheatres, and walls trailing with Bougainvillea. It is regular mapping country for Swansea students and one of my many favourite parts of Europe.

The oldest rocks seen at the surface are Triassic in age. These form the broad trough around the Maures and Esterel Massifs and are thought of as part of that story— Chapter 10(d). They are also seen in the cores of many of the anticlines, for example in the Baronnies, north-east of Avignon and in my favourite structures around Castellane where 'Muschelkalk' dolomites are seen, for example at the bottom of an almost complete succession on the east side of the Lac de Castillon. Towards the Alps proper the Trias seems to get more and more shattered, especially the characteristic cavernous dolomite or 'cargneules'* of the Upper Trias. There is also a considerable development of gypsum in this part of the system, which played an important part in the structures. It is well seen, for example, along thrust planes approaching the perfume city of Grasse, and there is evidence of considerable *décollement*.

The Jurassic characteristically starts with 'Blue Lias'-type limestone–shale alternations, with rich oyster and brachiopod faunas reminiscent of north-west European shallow-water facies. It passes up through *Zoophycos* beds indicative of intermediate depths, and 'hard-grounds' into deeper and more Alpine-looking sediments culminating in thick, possibly bathyal micrites of the typical Tithonian. Nowhere are these better seen than in the spectacular Grand Canyon du Verdon, south-west of Castellane. This is one of the places that, for me, typifies southern Europe with its deep gorges through seemingly endless white limestones. The Tithonian limestones yield aptychi and pygopid brachiopods, suggestive of bathyal depths, but other elements suggest that it is not as simple as that. Westwards there are reefs at this level on the Plans de Canjuers (west of the Verdon Gorge) and even dinosaurs have been found here recently.

The Lower Cretaceous of Provence is classic. Towns such as Apt and Barrême provide 'stratotypes' (if you like such things) for major stratigraphical divisions used all over the world. I have heard French geologists regretting that Tithon was a Greek deity and not a village in Provence that might have given a stratotype to the top stage of the Jurassic as

---

* These were called 'carniolas' on the Spanish side of the Pyrenees.

well, and so (theoretically) solved the tortured question of the Jurassic–Cretaceous boundary. For the most part the Lower Cretaceous of Provence consists of well-bedded limestones, contrasting markedly with the shales of the Vocontian trough to the north.

These limestones build up to a magnificent climax in the massive limestones of the Urgonian, which everywhere dominate the Provencal scenery.* Nowhere in Europe is this better seen. From Marseilles, where, surmounted by Notre-Dame-de-la-Garde, it overlooks the old port (and forms offshore islands such as the famous prison of the Chateau d'If) it extends to the frontal ranges of the Alps. Northwards its scarp rises behind Aix-en-Provence, eastwards it forms the sheer cliffs around Cassis, to the north-west it makes the spectacular escarpments of the Alpilles with the projecting cave-ridden spur of Les Baux, north-east of Arles (from which the brigand Raymond de Turenne terrorized Provence in the fourteenth century). Everywhere it is in its usual form of massive rather lensoid limestone, shallow water in origin with locally abundant rudistid bivalves and some coral reefs, such as the ones near Calissane, north-west of Marseilles, which are about 500 m across and some 20 m thick.

After this remarkable episode of shallow-water carbonate deposition there was emergence to the north-west and along a ridge right across Provence from the Marseilles–Aix-en-Provence area. This led to karstic weathering and the formation of extensive deposits of bauxite, which takes its name from Les Baux. It is still worked extensively around Brignoles, half-way between Aix and Cannes. This provides ample evidence of a warm, humid climate on land while a limy gulf persisted to the south, connected with the Pyrenees but quite cut off from the Alpine trough.

The late Cretaceous sea submerged all this with sandy glauconitic deposits and limestones packed with large exogyrid oysters or more rudists and shales full of franc-sized forams. Life was thriving in these shallow late Cretaceous seas and, as they withdrew again before the end of the period, one can see that it was also thriving on land. The final deposits of the Cretaceous contain much plant debris (including palms) sometimes forming lignites, dinosaur bones, and even—at one famous locality near Aix-en-Provence—a concentration of dinosaur eggs.

There were earth movements at this time, assisted by the Trias evaporites. Elevation produced torrential deposits, notably those seen in the weirdly weathering Cap du Bec de l'Aigle ('Eagle's Beak') halfway between Marseilles and Toulon. At the end of the Mesozoic an extensive lake extended from near Arles via Aix almost to Draguignan (south of Castellane). This lake lasted on into the Eocene, filling up with conglomerates and other deposits, but elsewhere they were the usual nummulitic limestones as in the Pyrenees. In fact the whole stratigraphical story of Provence is remarkably like that of the Pyrenees, although with a few fascinating variations. Like the Pyrenees too, the main earth movements came at the end of the Lutetian, i.e., near the end of the Eocene times.

The Provençal structures are simple for a mountain range (Fig. 13.4). The mainly east–west folds often reveal Triassic rocks in their cores that have slid and brecciated along their own weaknesses. The anticlines characteristically have steeper limbs on their north side, while the southern limbs are often completely hidden by the overthrusting of the next fold to the south. However, thrusting in the opposite direction is not uncom-

---

* Commonly, as in northern Spain, there is a double climax, with a lower white cliff of Tithonian age and an upper one of Urgonian.

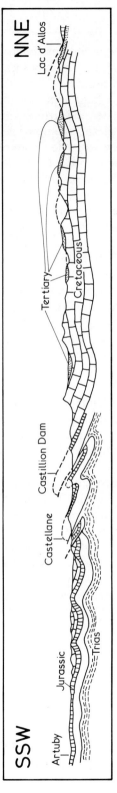

Fig. 13.4 Geological cross-section of northern Provence (by kind permission of the BRGM).

mon. *Chevauchant*—perhaps best translated as 'overriding'—is the commonest word in the literature, but it is all overriding of a strictly local nature and nothing approaching the far-travelled nappes of the Alps proper.

Eastwards the east–west Pyrenean folds approach the north-westerly trending Western Alps on a collision course, but the later and stronger mid-Tertiary folding has obliterated the contact. There is no metamorphism, there are no crossing cleavages, but there are some splendid examples of refolded folds, for example in the Baronnies north-east of Avignon. The best example I know is in the Clue* de St. Auban, 12 km east of Castellane, where an almost recumbent 'Pyrenean' fold is buckled in the middle by a later 'Alpine' fold.

The Pyrenean structures disappear into the Alps not very far from the big Argentera Massif, one of the 'External Massifs' of the Western Alps. This may be related to late transcurrent faults in the basement, and it has recently been shown that much of the deformation in this area may be connected with such movements, although gravity-sliding off the massif may also be involved.

With the rising of the new anticlinal ridges at the end of the Eocene, Oligocene conglomerates and other detrital sediments accumulated rapidly in the basins in between. The erosion and subsidence itself may have facilitated the late thrusting movements, which often involve the Oligocene detritus. A feature of the post-orogenic conglomerates here (as along the front of the Alps proper) is the way the pebbles have been driven one into the other, assisted by pressure solution, so that almost every pebble in some places is 'dented' by this process.

The Oligocene is often very thick. Under the greater part of Marseilles, for example, it is more than 800 m. Elsewhere there are lacustrine mudstones and limestones that accumulated in hollows between the new mountains. With the later movements and gravity-sliding in the Western Alps the molasse deposits are largely Miocene in age. Thick conglomerates of this time are seen, for example, around Vence (west-north-west of Nice) at the extreme eastern end of the area. Elsewhere the Miocene is very localized and there is evidence of a marine transgression in the Burdigalian across an already planed-off landscape. The Pliocene continued the same story, with a marine invasion up the Rhône and Durance as the topography approached what it is at present. Locally there were still mountains and hills to be made low, and vast thicknesses of conglomerate continued to exalt the valleys. The largest area of this kind is the basin of Valensole, south-south-west of Digne, where there are more than a thousand metres of Neogene conglomerate filling up the irregularities, while at Volonne to the west of the same delightful town, there are no less than 2000 m of conglomerate. There was a general regression at the end of Pliocene times to make this beautiful land ready for Greeks, Romans, Vandals, Goths, Franks, Moors, Popes, and tourists.

13(d) Jura and Franco-Swiss Plain

The Jura are a great arc of wooded Mesozoic mountains extending from Chambéry in south-east France to near Zurich in Switzerland (Fig. 13.5). They swell out like a breaking wave between the Massif Central in the south and the Vosges/Black Forest massifs in

---

* A deep narrow gorge, which would be a 'cluse' in the Jura.

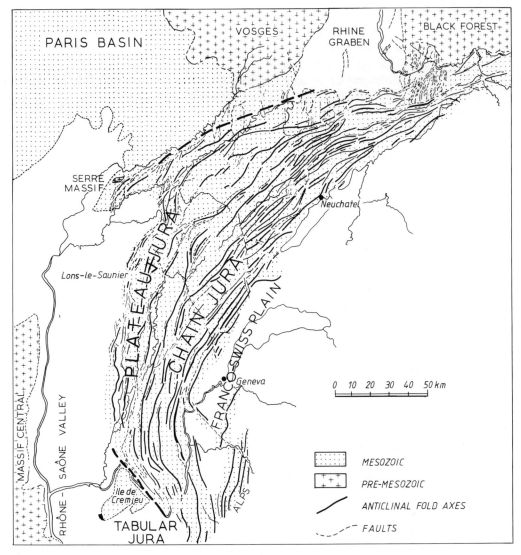

Fig. 13.5 *Sketch-map of the Jura with main structural elements (from Ager and Evamy, 1963, by kind permission of the Council of the Geologists' Association).*

the north. Traditionally they have been thought of as the bow-wave of the Alps, intermediate in stratigraphy, topography, and structural complexity, between the placid, low-lying Mesozoics of north-west Europe and the towering structural extravagances of Alpine Europe. They gave their name to the noblest period of geological time and Jurassic rocks form the greater part of their visible structure. They are also one of my favourite parts of Europe. The Franco-Swiss Plain is the undulating, largely unexposed country between the Jura and the Alps which is closer to the Jura in structure.

341

Geomorphology

The classic textbook picture of the Jura is of the anticlinal ridge and the synclinal valley, but this is usually more apparent than real. In the French Jura, only in the most easterly part of the chain can complete anticlinal structures be seen forming a ridge, for example in the ridge of the Montagne de Vuache near Bellegarde, capped by a massive limestone of mid Cretaceous age. Even when the anticlines are not broken by reversed faults (which is not often), the roofs are usually broken by erosional strike valleys or 'combes'. In some areas, for example in the Bas Bugey at the south end of the chain, the tectonic structure and the topography can be shown to be quite unrelated, probably due to major glacial modification. In the Swiss Jura, anticlinal ridges are much more common, for example in the traverse north from Neuchatel or along the motorway that crosses the range to Basle.

A particular geomorphological feature of the Jura is the presence of 'cluses'. These are steep-sided valleys which cut right through the structures and provide splendid cross-sections for the visiting geologist. Cluses provide the main routes through the mountains and one often finds river, railway, and road competing to get through the narrow defile. The mode of formation of these features is not always obvious. Some of them have been the courses of major rivers, as was probably the case with the Cluse des Hôpitaux (between Culoz and Ambérieu) which carried the Rhône itself before the glaciation diverted that river southwards across the Bas Bugey. In this example the cluse passes right through the chain and swings about relative to the tectonic structure. Most cut straight across the strike, as with the smaller cluse of La Balme, where the Rhône flows today. Others end blindly, as with the next one to the north, which enters the Jura bravely from the east at Bellegarde, but terminates abruptly at the lake of Nantua.

Another spectacular feature of the Jura are the 'reculées' or erosional re-entrants, which cut back into the western front of the Jura most notably in the central part of the chain near Lons-le-Saunier. These were produced by stream erosion, and underground waters can be seen emerging at their heads. Underground waters are a feature of the Jura, and many stories are told of disappearing and reappearing streams and rivers. One of the most amusing is that of the discovery of the true source of the River Loue. It is worth translating from the invaluable *Michelin Guide*, which should accompany every visitor to the Jura:

'One summer day in 1901, Andre Berthelot found himself on a walk at the source of the Loue. He noticed that the water had the colour and smell of absinthe. He tasted it—the Loue was truly transformed into a free aperitif! It appeared that the night before at Pontarlier, during a fire at the Pernod factory, a million litres of absinthe had fallen into the River Doubs. It therefore became obvious that the Loue was a resurgence of an underground Jura stream.'

This involved a distance of some 12 kilometres and a test with dye showed that water was escaping through a crevasse in the bed of the Doubs, which the locals immediately tried to close with cement, with resultant bitterness and arbitration. Other underground waters in the Jura probably travel much farther.

Hanging valleys and waterfalls are common, the latter characteristically forming great aprons of tufa derived from the overwhelming predominance of carbonate rocks. Everywhere there are caves, gullies, and karst surfaces. The screes are mature, stable, and vegetated, unlike some of the murderously unstable and almost uncrossable screes of the Alps. Small Quaternary basins, of varying degrees of present wetness, occur even in the highest ranges.

The general impression one gets in the Jura is of thick, but generally low, forests of fir, spruce, birch, and spiky acacia, with dense undergrowth very difficult to penetrate and, in the French part, forming ideal country for the men and women of the Resistance, who fought so bravely here during the last war. An afficionado of the Jura immediately knows he is there from the sickly sweet smell of the box bushes which cover so many of the limestone surfaces and which some Jura geologists claim can be used for tracing particular formations.

Basement

The basement is nowhere exposed in the Jura, except for a tiny pimple of metamorphic rocks in the Serre Massif near Dôle, just in front of the Jura. This is just about half-way between the great massifs at either end of the chain. Another tiny outcrop of ancient rocks is seen at the south-west corner of the 'Ile' de Cremieu, but this is nothing more than a detached fragment of the Massif Central.

Since the Second World War, the stratigraphical column of the Jura has been considerably extended through the work of the French Bureau de Recherches Géologiques at Minières. They have put down a whole series of boreholes in that part of the chain near Lons-le-Saunier known as the Ledonian Jura. The primary object was to evaluate the known evaporite deposits of the Permo-Trias there, with particular interest in possible potassium salts. They then started looking for gas and eventually found a large concealed coal-field.

Some of the boreholes reached the crystalline basement beneath a considerable thickness of previously unknown late Palaeozoic sediments. The general succession may be summarized as follows:

TRIASSIC	'Keuper' (*sensu gallico*)	Red beds with thick evaporites
	'Muschelkalk' (*sensu gallico*)	Limestones, dolomites, red beds, and evaporites
	'Bunter'	Mottled sandstones
PERMIAN	Saxonian	Red sandstones and clays
CARBONIFEROUS	Stephanian	Sandstones, shales, and coals with basal conglomerate
BASEMENT	Granite, migmatite, gneiss, and mica-schist, similar to that of the Massif Central and the Vosges.	

The strata not seen at the surface amount to some 300 m of Trias, an average of about 190 m of Permian, and an average of 600 m of Stephanian 'Coal Measures'. Individual coal-seams are up to 5 m thick. It is unlikely that these resources will ever be exploited, but more important from the geological point of view was the evidence the boreholes provided about the structural history of this part of the Jura and thence, by implication, of the Jura as a whole.

Mesozoic

As seen at the surface, the Jura consists almost entirely of well-exposed Mesozoic limestones and poorly-exposed Miocene molasse, with the former almost entirely of Jurassic and early Cretaceous age. The oldest visible Mesozoic rocks are occasional outcrops, in the cores of anticlines, of late Triassic age. These are the usual red beds and evaporites which have been blamed for most of the tectonic troubles of the range.

The Jurassic succession of the Jura is comparable with that of the rim of the Paris Basin, across the other side of the Rhône–Saône Trough. It probably reaches as much as 1000 m thick in places, but the formations vary considerably and elsewhere it is only half that thickness. The Lower Jurassic is like that of the classic areas of southern England and south-west Germany—alternating limestones and calacerous shales with the usual abundant ammonites and other molluscs. A similar story continues throughout the system, with shallow marine and richly fossiliferous sedimentation, sometimes a little deeper and sometimes a little shallower, but wholly of the shelf sea type.

Thus towards the end of the early Jurassic, deposition was clearly on the lower part of the shelf, but in mid Jurassic times shallow-water calcarenites, with frequent minor breaks, constitute the 'Dogger' of continental geologists. Coral reefs flourished locally (e.g., near Ambléon) and in the Bajocian stage crinoidal limestones are particularly characteristic. The name of a Jura village and of one of the better of the Jura wines—'L'Etoile'—refer to the star-like appearance of crinoids in the rocks.

The late Jurassic started with a major break seen in many parts of western Europe. Richly ammonitiferous calcareous mudstones of late Oxfordian age, which inaugurate this part of the succession, form a pronounced hollow between the adjacent limestones and have been worked for cement all the way from the southern tip of the Jura up through France and Switzerland into southern Germany. They also mark the start, in the region of Besançon, of a remarkable sequence of coral reef limestones, which lasted until the end of the period. Diachronous reef formation began around Besançon on the north-west or outer side of the chain in late Oxfordian times, and became progressively later in a south-easterly direction to culminate in 'Portlandian' reefs (*sensu gallico*) in the Salève ridge on the inside of the range, behind Geneva.

The faunistic diversity of the reef limestones of the Jura has often been cited as evidence of a tropical, perhaps equatorial climatic zone here on the north side of Tethys, from which maximum the diversity decreased both northwards and southwards. Certainly the faunas are diverse, although the abundance of species, especially of corals, is more in the mind of the monographers than in nature. The porosity of the coral accumulations has also, as usual, rendered them very vulnerable to dolomitization. As a result, most of the so-called 'reef limestones' prove on close examination to be featureless, unbedded dolomites or 'dedolomites' (where the dolomite has been transformed back again into calcite). It is usually impossible to prove whether the unbedded nature of these massive limestones is due to recrystallization, to bioturbation, or to true biothermal growth. Only occasionally (as in the gorge section west of Yenne in Savoie) are compound corals seen massed in life position, with their associated fauna, but they dispel one's doubts about the kilometres of barren limestone in between. Many other reef features are developed, including fore-reef breccias and back-reef algal oncolites. A particularly interesting back-reef deposit is the Cerin Lithographic Limestone only developed over a small area of the southern Jura. Like the one mentioned earlier in the Pyrenees, it closely resembles the Solnhofen Lithographic Stone of southern Germany, in age and appearance, in fauna and flora, although unfortunately no one has yet found a French *Archaeopteryx*.

The climax of reef development in the Jura came near the end of the period, and a massive Tithonian limestone is the chief feature-forming formation in the whole chain. This limestone thickens towards the Alps and forms a magnificent feature in the eastern-most ridge of the Jura. The French geologist Gignoux spoke of jumping over this reef barrier and plunging into the deep waters of the Alpine sea. Unfortunately the interesting fore-reef developments of this feature are lost in the frontal thrusts of the Alps and the next rocks one sees in that direction of the same age are deep-water *Calpionella* limestones.

One final phase of the Jura Jurassic must be mentioned. This is the development of thin fresh-water limestones with ostracods and simple plants, which have been thought of as the furthermost manifestation of the 'Purbeckian' facies of southern England. A feature of the formation is the presence of breccias, often on eroded surfaces. The fragments in the breccias all seem to be of local provenance, apart from small, black, organic pieces which might have come from subaerial deposits on Jura folds which were already emerging from the sea. Such breccias are thought to thin away from the anticlinal axes, which is difficult to prove, but if so would mean that the Jura folding began before the end of the Jurassic times.

A sequence of Cretaceous limestones follows, at first hardly distinguishable from the 'Purbeckian' below, except by a sparse marine fauna. Then shallow-water calcarenities, with erosional breaks, lead up to another climax in reef-building in Aptian times. This is again the Urgonian facies. Characteristically it contains rudist colonies in life position, but corals are probably more important reef-builders at this level in the Jura. This limestone is another feature found especially towards the inside of the range. A general truth about the stratigraphy of the Jura is that, although many formations are involved in each fold, the lower stratigraphical levels are normally only exposed towards the outside of the range and the younger formations are best seen towards the inside. As a result some Albian clays ('le Gault') are seen locally in the innermost ridge, but no later Cretaceous rocks are preserved.

Cainozoic

There next follows Miocene sands and conglomerates, with a characteristic greenish khaki appearance and a tendency to form sheer, unjointed faces in the road-cuttings where they are most commonly seen. This is the Molasse, similar to that which fills the great trough between the Jura and the Alps. The conglomerates are, for the most part, far-travelled and represent the synorogenic detritus of the rising Alps. It is a matter of dispute whether the anticlinal ridges of Mesozoic limestones were already in existence when the Molasse was deposited. Certainly the main folding movements were already completed, although in places the Molasse has been arched up along the Jura trend—for example, at Aix-les-Bains on Lac du Bourget and in the long peninsula that runs into the Bieler See at Erlach in Switzerland. There is also clear evidence in many places that the normally flat-lying Molasse was turned up and involved in late stage faulting. In deep borings one can see that the final forward thrust movements of the outer edge of the Jura carried Mesozoic limestones over the Miocene Molasse.

However, although involved in the later movements, the main folding of the Jura took place before the deposition of the Molasse or actually while it was being deposited. Although it is not my intention to say much about structures, I feel bound to expand a little in this case partly because it is such a classic region and so much cited in other mountain ranges.

The Jura take off from the front ranges of the Alps near Chambéry; north of that point they are separated from the Alps by the Molasse basin of the Franco-Swiss Plain. In front of the Jura lies the 'Bresse Plain' or 'Rhône-Saône Trough'. The Jura themselves are commonly referred to as the 'Table Jura' and the 'Folded Jura'. A better division is into three: the 'Table Jura', the 'Plateau Jura', and the 'Folded' or 'Chain Jura'. Even so, this is not satisfactory, for reasons that will become obvious later, and the usage preferred here is 'Table Jura', 'Faulted Jura', and 'Folded Jura', although it is not suggested that the Folded Jura are not faulted or that the Faulted Jura are not folded.

The Table Jura occur in two areas in front of both ends of the main range. In the north they comprise the flat-lying Mesozoic succession south of the Black Forest that spreads round south of the Vosges to pass into the Mesozoic rim of the Paris Basin. In the south they are more clearly defined as the triangular region known as the Île de Cremieu. The Table Jura, as their name implies, show very little in the way of tectonism and need not concern us further.

The Plateau Jura occupy a wide area in the central and northern parts of the outside of the chain. They consist basically of a series of plateaux, separated by reversed faults and associated overriding structures. A low-lying area showing considerable tectonic disturbance lies below the first plateau at Lons-le-Saunier. This consists of the softer Upper Triassic and Lower Jurassic sediments (following the general principle of the older rocks being exposed in the west). The area is known as the Vignoble (French for vineyard), referring to the suitability of these sediments for producing the best Jura wines.* The Vignoble rapidly disappears southwards under the first plateau, and the plateaux are usually said to pinch out in the same direction. In fact they pass directly into the western part of the southern Jura, where the box-folds of the eastern ridges are bundled together in faulted slices and the box synclines are lost altogether. This is why the term 'Faulted Jura' is preferred here for the outer part of the range.

There is a gradual passage from the Faulted Jura into the Folded Jura—the high range which is the true Jura to most geologists. This is where the anticlinal ridges and synclinal valleys are seen at their best. The whole forms a narrow fold belt all round the concave inner edge of the Jura. At the northern end it starts with a single anticline which multiplies itself by splitting and budding to as many as seven parallel anticlines in the central Jura, and then dwindles away to one again at the southern end. The ideal Jura fold is the box-fold, with flat top (or bottom) and angular bends producing steep limbs.

---

* One of my research students who worked in this area had, as frontispiece in his thesis, the label from a local wine-bottle recording that it came from vineyards on the Triassic and Liassic Marls of the Jura.

One such is beautifully displayed in the Montagne de Sérémond above Virieu-le-grand in the southern Jura, where a box anticline to the west passes into the box syncline of Valromey to the east. The next anticline beyond that is the Grand Colombier, the highest in the southern Jura, beyond which the limestones tumble steeply into the synclinal valley now occupied by the River Rhône and Lac du Bourget. Eastwards again, the last true Jura ridge before the France–Swiss Plain rises behind the Victorian watering-place of Aix-les-Bains (demurely screened from the lake by a Jura-type anticline expressed entirely in Molasse). The last ridge shows the Cretaceous—especially the Urgonian—in its best development, for we are now on the opposite side of the chain from the older Mesozoic of the Vignoble. This last ridge also shows, in the narrow cluse of the Fier Gorge near Seyssel, a magnificent example of the disharmonic folding that is such a feature of the Jura structures.

The massive Tithonian and Urgonian limestones form competent anticlines and synclines, but the less competent beds, especially the Oxfordian mudstones and the thin-bedded Kimmeridgian limestones, crumple in baroque ecstasies to accommodate the movements of the sterner stuff. Such disharmonic (or 'parasitic') folding is seen all over the Jura, often only in small exposures that serve merely to confuse the geologist, but here and there on a grand scale as in the policeman's hat ('Chapeau de Gendarme') near St. Claude. The hat referred to is of an eighteenth century shape, so the nationality of the policeman is irrelevant.

The box-folds are rarely, if ever, perfect. Commonly the tops of the box anticlines sag, as if sat upon, and commonly again the western limbs are lost or shortened in reversed faults. In the southern Jura these are accentuated westwards until the synclines disappear altogether. In the central and northern Jura, the reversed faults merely separate monotonous stretches of plateau, with the rocks rearing up locally along the fault line as in the ridge topped with a Madonna (and promises of indulgences to the tired geologist) near Verges in the Ledonian Jura.

One other feature is a whole series of tear faults cutting obliquely through the chain, especially in its central and northern parts. Each fault is in fact a bundle of faults (as are the reversed faults mentioned earlier) and some of them pass into reversed faults or thrusts as they swing across the strike of the folds. Most of them are clearly distinguished by their displacement of the folds.

The classic tectonic story of the Jura is that of *décollement* or 'unsticking'. This is the concept of the sliding and crumpling of the Mesozoic tablecloth on a polished crystalline table, with the polish provided by the Triassic evaporites. In this concept, the Jura Mountains resulted from the push transmitted from the Alpine nappes, and the Mesozoic limestones slid away tangentially, coming unstuck from the basement as they did so by reason of the incompetence and plasticity of the salts. The chain is thought to have stretched in the process, with the expansion taken up in the tear faults, but the dominant movement was outwards, away from the Alps.

All later theorizing, however, has been much more concerned with the part played by the basement. When gravitational sliding became fashionable as a tectonic process, the Jura were obvious candidates. If the Alps slid down from an upraised basement, then it is logical to suppose that the Jura were affected in the same way, so that as the Pre-Alps slid down into the Molasse Basin, the Jura slid down into the Rhône–Saône Trough.

The most popular tectonic theories for the Jura today are those which relate the structures seen at the surface in the Mesozoic rocks to structures in the basement below. For some time it has been suggested that the obvious faults of the Plateau Jura might be merely the surface expression of fault blocks within the crystalline rocks below. From that proposition it was only a step to the suggestion that the box-folds of the inner Jura might be no more than surface sediments draped over horsts and graben in the basement. In such theories, the importance of the Triassic *décollement* is very much played down, and it is relevant to note that the disharmomic folding referred to earlier is itself a form of *décollement*. With the horst and graben concept, this is little more than accommodation for sliding competent limestones. At the same time there is no doubt of the predominantly outward movement of the Jura folds and one must presume that the movements (if any) in the basement were of the same basic kind. Whether or not there was a direct relationship between each individual Mesozoic structure and one in the basement (which is highly unlikely), there still remains the question as to whether the basement was foreshortened on the same scale as the cover or whether sliding was the dominant theme and the folds are purely superficial. One important piece of information that emerged from the deep boreholes was that the Triassic evaporites are much thicker under the Jura (up to 700 m) than elsewhere in the region. There is therefore strong circumstantial evidence that the salt had something to do with the folding.

The most significant discovery, however, in several boreholes was of the Mesozoic cover resting not on the newly discovered Palaeozoic or on the crystalline basement, but on the Miocene Molasse. Mention has already been made of the involvement of the Molasse in some of the late stage faulting and it has long been known that the frontal ranges of the Alps were driven far over similar sediments. Evidence from the Ledonian Jura shows that the front of this range too has been pushed as far as 7 km over the Tertiary deposits of the Bresse Plain. The horizontal component of these movements is much more important than had been supposed. What is more, there is evidence that the movements reached their maximum in the centre of the range and were less intense towards its extremities. Thus in the Bugey region to the south, a movement of only 2 km has been calculated. Such overthrust fronts now seem to be *de rigueur* for all the European Alpine systems, even for mini-orogens such as the Jura.

Finally in their Cainozoic history, the Jura were much affected by the Pleistocene glaciations, with the diversion of drainage such as the Rhône and the scattering of nasty lumps of metamorphic rock from the Alps on the beautiful limestone hills.

13(e) Crimea

We now cross to the opposite end of our continent, where there is another mountain arc separated from the main ranges.

The Crimea is remembered by most of us in Britain for a stupid war fought long ago with great heroism and great suffering. We should also remember it for its sufferings in the last war. But apart from these accidents of military history, the Crimea is little known outside the USSR, even by geologists, although it has one of the finest records in Europe of the Cretaceous and early Tertiary periods. It is also part of the old kingdom of Scythia, which gave its name to the lowest stage of the Trias and is the homeland of the

Kimmerian movements, which are now recognized as having been so important in the Mesozoic.

The Crimea may be regarded as the narrow, north-western extremity of the Caucasian fold belt, with its southern half sunk beneath the Black Sea. It is separated from the Caucasus proper by the narrow straits of Kerch and the continuing sedimentary basin of the Sea of Azov. Physiographically, the Crimea may be divided into two parts (Fig. 13.6): the Crimean Steppes in the north and west, dry, dusty and tree-less, comprising about four-fifths of the whole peninsula; and the Crimean Mountains in the south, little more than rounded hills at first, then becoming steeper to fall in sheer cliffs to the coast around Yalta and the other spectacular holiday resorts of the south-east coast.

The Crimean Mountains are usually thought of as the direct continuation of the Alpine fold belts of the rest of Europe, providing a stepping-stone as it were, between the Balkan Mountains of Bulgaria and the Caucasus of Georgia. Certainly they are part of Neo-Europa, with their main folding in Mesozoic and Tertiary times. Soviet geologists place them firmly in their 'Mediterranean Geosyncline'. But the situation is not quite as simple as that. It is now known from geophysical studies in the Black Sea that the Balkans do not extend far from the Bulgarian coast as a topographical feature and it is arguable that stratigraphically and tectonically they terminate even before they reach the shore. The Crimean Mountains terminate even more abruptly, dropping suddenly into deep water, although this is blamed on the foundering of the Black Sea as a great graben structure during Cainozoic times. So we may say that the Crimean Mountains belong to the Alpide group of structures, but are not part of a continuous chain. This is why they are included with the 'Outer Arcs'.

Similarly, the Crimean Steppes may be regarded as a fore-deep in front of the range. The mountains are formed mainly of Mesozoic rocks, and the fore-deep is filled with considerable thicknesses of Palaeogene, Neogene, and Quaternary, sediments. In this they resemble the Balkans. What is more, the main mountain-building movements seem to have been more or less coincident with those of the Carpathians and Balkans, that is to say in mid-Cretaceous and mid-Tertiary times.

The Crimean Mountains consist essentially of three ridges:

1. The Main Ridge, reaching more than 1500 m (with Roman-Kosh, at 1543 m, the highest point).
2. The Piedmont Ridge, to the north, up to not much more than 700 m.
3. The Outer Ridge, to the north again, up to 250 m in height and with its northern slopes passing gently into the Crimean Steppes.

The whole system is a complex anticlinorium, while the steppes are basically a subsided part of the East European Platform, with a Palaeozoic and Precambrian floor buried beneath thick Tertiary deposits. The old platform below has now been reached in many boreholes, and is comparable to that of the Russian plains.

The Main Ridge in the south is formed almost entirely of Mesozoic strata, from early Triassic to early Cretaceous in age. The Russians divide these rocks into four structural units. These are units of more or less uniform lithology which, because of this, behaved similarly under tectonic stress and so are characterized by particular structural patterns.

A feature of all these units is the presence of thick conglomerates, especially in the

349

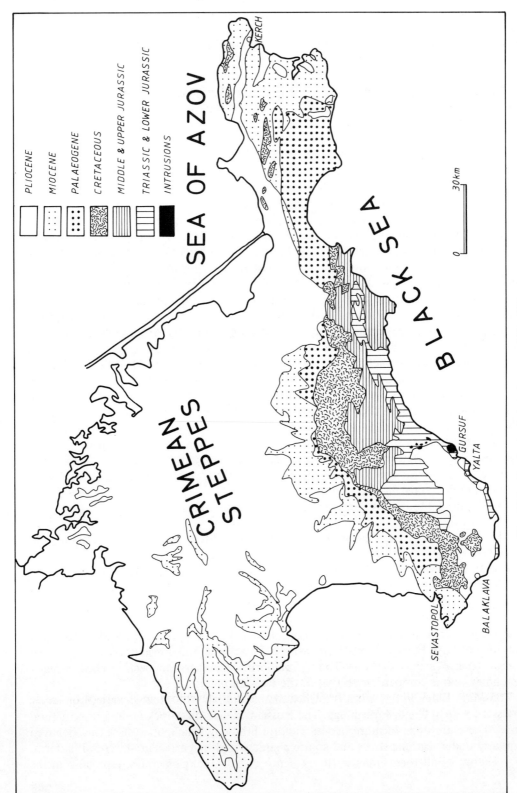

Fig. 13.6 Geological sketch-map of the Crimea.

Jurassic. These are of particular interest because when their pebbles were used to reconstruct the hypothetical southern land-mass from which they were derived, this figment of geological imagination proved to bear a striking resemblance to the Pontic Mountains of northern Turkey. This led to theories of Black Sea-floor spreading in the Tertiary.

The lowest structural unit consists mainly of late Triassic and early Jurassic deposits. Earlier Triassic sediments had been shallow shelf deposits in the south of the Crimea, with a land-mass being eroded to the north. But the late Triassic times began the first phase of the Kimmerian earth movements, with geosynclinal subsidence in the south. The whole unit is several hundred metres thick and some estimates put it as high as 6000 m. It is mainly flysch and flysch-like sediments with rare fossils, but interesting in that they include land-derived plant remains. There are enough molluscs to separate the Triassic from the Lower Jurassic in what is mainly a rather monotonous argillaceous succession. There is also a noteworthy development of pillow lavas marking the junction between these two divisions. These are the first of a succession of volcanic episodes, with associated intrusions, which characterize the Kimmerian orogeny. It is not clear that these things have oceanic significance.

The most interesting feature of the lowest structural unit is the presence of great exotic blocks, up to 90 m long, embedded in the flysch. These blocks are of Carboniferous and Permian limestones. They are now interpreted as having resulted from submarine land-slips along contemporary fault scarps. These are further evidence of orogenic movements already active which, from other lines of evidence, were exerting a direct control on sedimentation. Apart from the exotic blocks, no Palaeozoic rocks are known at the surface in the Crimean Mountains. The flysch-type rocks are, as usual with such lithologies, highly tectonized with overturned folds and intense faulting. The Crimea, in early Mesozoic times, was a region of eugosynclinal sedimentation, contrasting with the miogeosynclinal carbonate sedimentation in the Greater Caucasus to the east.

A similar picture continued through most of Jurassic times, with shallow shelf sedimentation in the north of the Crimean Steppes, an emergent ridge across the centre of the peninsula, and a deep trough in what is now the mountain region in the south. In fact the Crimean mountains are mostly built of Jurassic rocks, which encircle the cores of the complex anticlines.

The second structural unit is of mid Jurassic (Bajocian and Bathonian) shales and sandstones with associated spilites, andesites, keratophyres, agglomerates, and tuffs. The whole unit is up to 2000 m thick and rests unconformably on the unit below. South-east of Simferopol, in the centre of the Crimean Mountains, there is a thick conglomerate at the base, the huge boulders in which again suggest contemporaneous tectonic activity. However, the succession shows a progressively decreasing grain size upwards and it is presumed that the tectonism was decreasing in intensity. Major intrusions were emplaced at this time, notably the massive one near Gurzuf on the south coast.

The third structural unit is of late Jurassic age and is very thick (up to 4000 m) resting unconformably on the Middle Jurassic. Following usual Russian usage it includes all stages from the Callovian to the Tithonian, and is developed in a variety of facies, although mostly of a shallow shelf type. In Callovian and Oxfordian times, the sea was largely exluded from the south of the peninsula, and there are coal-bearing successions. But there are also marine clays, sandstones, conglomerates, and great development of oolitic and reef limestones which form the crests of many of the mountains. Volcanicity, in the form of andesitic lavas and tuffs, continued as late as the Callovian, but there was then a brief interval of quiescence before geosynclinal subsidence recommenced in the Kimmeridgian and Tithonian. Flysch deposition began again in the south, with sediment derived from the central ridge, but these deposits are atypically associated with what were evidently shallow-water sediments.

The fourth structural unit consists of early Cretaceous shelf deposits of varied lithology. The geosynclinal trough retreated eastwards and land emerged in the middle of the southern seaway. Lower Cretaceous strata extend in a broad belt north of the Main Ridge, from the beautiful land-locked harbour of Balaklava in the west to Feodosia in the east. They have been correlated in detail with the classic French sections of Provence. In the east they follow directly on the Upper Jurassic without a break, but traced westwards a marked unconformity develops until, in the vicinity of the valley of the Charge of the Light Brigade, they rest on the lowest structural unit. Sandstones predominate, together with clays, limestones and at least two conglomerates locally, which are up to 250 m thick. These conglomerates contain older rocks as well as immediately subjacent Cretaceous ones, and again the region seems to have become tectonically active. Local flysch developments reach 1500 m.

Volcanic activity recommenced in Albian times and the whole range was uplifted in the usual east European mid Cretaceous movements. Following these movements, the late Cretaceous rocks present a completely different picture. The so-called 'Cenomanian transgression' is well developed. It is necessary to move from the Main Ridge into the area of the Piedmont and Outer Ridges and into the Crimean Steppes. The Late Cretaceous rocks are best exposed in the Piedmont Ridge, from Inkerman to Feodosia. Farther north, they are largely covered by Tertiary and Quaternary deposits, although these have been pierced by many boreholes. In the mountains they attain a maximum thickness of less than 500 m, but in the steppes they reach 2400 m.

Limestones (some of them chalk-like) predominated throughout, with subsidiary sandstones. The volcanicity had ended. Flysch deposition began again in the east in Turonian times and forms part of a belt that continues into the Caucasus. It interdigitates with the carbonates and, as is the case in similar areas elsewhere, this results in what is commonly called calcareous flysch, with the coarser units largely calcarenites. A supposed island arc came into existence, extending eastwards from the south of the Crimea.

Sedimentation continued in a similar form right up to the Danian, both in the mountains and in the plain, although there is evidence of a break in places. The development of bryozoan limestones at this level is particularly interesting in view of their importance also in the 'type' sections in Denmark. Planktonic foraminifera permit a confident correlation, but the Russians on the whole have not followed most of the rest of the world in attributing this stage to the Tertiary.

Palaeogene deposits (i.e., above the Danian) are well developed, especially where they form the gentle northern slope down from the Crimean Mountains, for example near Sevastopol. Nummulitic limestones predominate in the south, for example in gorges in the Piedmont Ridge, and are used for building-stone. Farther north they pass into marly deposits. Above about 300 m of limestone come some 200 m of clay. It has proved difficult to recognize the classic west European stages in the Paleocene and Eocene. Soviet palaeontologists have therefore established their own scheme, based particularly on the section at Bakhchisarai. Their stages are as follows:

Approximate equivalents

Almian ⎫	
Bodrakian ⎭	? Bartonian
Simferopolian	Lutetian + ? 'Auversian'
Bakhchisaraian	? Ypresian
Kachian	Thanetian
Inkermanian	Montian

There are some interruptions in sedimentation, with condensed deposits, in the middle of this succession.

Compared with the earlier Palaeogene deposits, the Oligocene is poorly developed, poorly exposed, and poorly fossiliferous. Marine clays pass down conformably into the Eocene below. The deep trough in the south disappeared with the emergence of a new land-mass, and major orogenic movements clearly occurred at this time. The Alpine folds seem to have inherited many of the earlier structures. The evidence for this is much clearer in the Caucasus, where a new trough was formed to the north. An important feature of the Oligocene strata is the presence of valuable hydrocarbons. In the east of the Crimea, near Theodosia, and in the Kerch peninsula, important oil-bearing sandstones are developed as in the Caucasus. In the north too, where the Oligocene takes on a molasse-like facies, many beds are bituminous.

Neogene sediments overlie Palaeogene and Mesozoic rocks with a marked unconformity and the Lower Miocene is absent. Richly fossiliferous upper Miocene (Tortonian) outcrops over a large part of Moldavia to the west, where sandstones, clays, and limestones, yield a rich Mediterranean-type fauna, but this is not so important in the Crimea. In the late Tortonian, large reefs were developed in the eastern Crimea, forming flat-topped hills and ridges. Individual reefs are up to 4 km long and 100 m thick, distributed in a north–south belt. The main reef-builders were red algae and bryozoans, but there are very few corals, as is generally the case with reefs of this age in Europe. There is also a rich reef-dwelling fauna of bivalves, gastropods, arthropods, echinoids, and of course foraminifera. Associated with the reefs are deposits of reef detritus. The whole represents an area of shallow, warm water in high energy conditions.

The latest Miocene (approximately Messinian) deposits are very thick. At first, a variety of carbonates was deposited, including reef facies persisting in the same region as those of the Tortonian. Reduced salinity seems to have resulted in a less diverse fauna and flora of 'Sarmatian' type. The general picture seems to have been a land-mass in the south of the peninsula providing sediment for the shelf area to the north, with deeper subsidence in the north-east. A new development for the Tertiary was volcanicity, seen in the form of pyroclastic deposits and bentonites.

A barrier reef belt then developed, more than 300 km long, from Litichev in the Ukraine to Kagul in the south of Moldavia. There are also many isolated reefs and the whole region seems to have been one of shallow water, although somewhat deeper in the east and west. Uplift led to continental conditions almost everywhere. Lacustrine and deltaic sedimentation predominated by the end of the period, with fluviatile deposits that have yielded famous mammalian faunas.

The Pliocene of the Crimea also consists mainly of alluvial sediments. The sea drained out to the north-east and west (where marine conditions persist in the 'Pontian' of

Moldavia). Pliocene deposits are not thick; they are mostly clays and sands, with some noteworthy mammal localities. The later deposits are found on the higher terraces of the Dniester and Prut rivers.

Quaternary deposits are also mainly alluvial, forming up to six terraces along the Dniester, Prut, Yalpug, and other rivers of the Crimea. The rivers mainly drained into the depression to the north-east, which persists to the present day as the Sea of Azov. Until mid Quaternary times, the Black Sea is thought not to have existed at all, and the Crimean Mountains may have been twice as wide as they are today. Then large-scale foundering is though to have occurred, producing the Black Sea, the Sea of Marmara, and the Aegean. Water flooded in from the Mediterranean extending over a wider area than at present and passing up into the brackish trough that is the the Sea of Azov. With the later fall in sea-level, the Black Sea became more brackish (as it is at present) and the Sea of Azov became almost fresh.

As the Black Sea sank into a great graben it took with it a large chunk of the southern Crimean Mountains, leaving the great fault cliffs of the holiday coast that we see today. The sinking process continues and frequent earthquakes indicate that the faults are still active.

Unlike the Caucasus, the Crimean Mountains were not high enough in the Pleistocene to acquire an ice-cap. However, periglacial conditions towards the end of Pleistocene times led to the formation of the great thicknesses of wind-blown loess, which are such a feature of the dusty Crimean Steppes.

13(f)   Greater Caucasus

I was tempted to leave the Caucasus out of this book altogether, on the excuse that much of this spectacular range is not in Europe at all, but in Asia. However, I decided to compromise and just to include the Greater Caucasus (Bolshoi Kavkaz) in the north, which form (like the Urals) a natural boundary to our continent and are clearly part of the European story. They separate European Russia from the Asian Soviet Republics of Georgia (Gruzinskaya), Azerbaijan (Azerbaydzhanskaya), and Armenia (Armyanskaya) away to the south, with a cluster of tiny republics along the mountainous spine.

The Lesser Caucasus are a direct continuation of the main Alpide fold belt of northern Turkey (the Pontides). Eastwards they run without a break into Iran. They have all the familiar features of the southern Alpides, including a double belt of ophiolites, but they are wholly Asian in distribution and are no part of our concern here. They are separated from the Greater Caucasus by the North Transcaucasian Depression, which will be discussed in connection with the Black Sea—Chapter 15(e). It is a down-faulted trough filled with some 8–10 km of Cainozoic sediments and may have formed by crustal spreading at the same time as the Black Sea. Prior to that the two ranges may have converged like the Jura and the Alps at the other end of Europe, with their steeper limbs towards each other.

The wild, snowy Greater Caucasus form a direct continuation of the Crimea, dominating the touristic stretches of the north coast of the Black Sea, and then spread inland across to the Caspian. It is an asymmetrical structure, but for an Alpine range is remarkably straight (comparable in this only with the Pyrenees, another of the 'Outer

Arcs'). It stretches from west-north-west to east-south-east for some 1300 km, from the Taman Peninsula that points towards the Crimea to the Apsheron Peninsula that projects out into the Caspian above the oil town of Baku.

Georgian Block

Towards the western end of the Trans-Caucasian Depression, the Cainozoic trough is interrupted by a rigid mass, which may be called the Georgian Block (Fig. 13.7). It is therefore reminiscent of other late troughs of Europe (such as the Pannonian Basin) which seem to be similarly founded on rigid blocks rather than on mobile zones.

The Georgian Block is a portion of the floor which has not given way and is significant because it is delimited, both north and south, by convergent reversed faults. This is not in keeping with the spreading hypothesis mentioned above, but may be a very late feature. In the centre of the block is an inlier of pre-Mesozoic rocks which tells us a little about the earlier history of the region. An extension of the block extends all the way along the north side of the sedimentary trough to the Black Sea at the Georgian resort of Gagra.

The evidence from these exposed areas, and from deep borings north of the Caucasus in what is called the Cis-Caucasus (extending up to the true edge of the East European Platform), provides a new picture of pre-Mesozoic fold belts in this region. Soviet authors are convinced that the Alpine chain was preceded by a Variscan chain parallel to, although off-set from, the present range. This fits with conclusions reached by others, for example in the Eastern Alps and Carpathians.

The Precambrian rocks consist of gneisses, schists, and marbles overlain by a varied succession of Proterozoic argillaceous and clastic sediments. Within the central massif (the Dzirul Massif) on the south side of the Greater Caucasus, the Precambrian succession is overlain by a considerable thickness (about 2000 m) of slates and quartzites, with lenses of archaeocyathid limestones indicating a Cambrian age. No Ordovician is recognized, but the Silurian consists of similar sediments, similarly thick, but with important developments of volcanics. It passes up into the Devonian which is at a lower stage of metamorphism. Carbonates appear as usual in the upper part of the system and there are rich and varied faunas. Similarly the Lower Carboniferous (only seen on the north side of the range) is also in its customary calcareous form with abundant corals. 'Coal Measure' deposition began at about this time, but there are great thicknesses of slates and volcanic rocks hereabouts in the succession which have not yet been satisfactorily dated.

The main coal-bearing formations are of Westphalian and Stephanian age. They occur mainly on the north side of the Caucasus and are comparable to those of the Donetsk basin to the north. They are associated with thick red beds and pass up into the Permian in which marine and continental strata interdigitate. There are up to 4000 m of Lower Permian red beds with conglomerates containing detrital gold derived from the Precambrian. The succession is now internationally famous because Permian-type faunas here persisted into the early Triassic as they did in Greenland. The Palaeozoic succession is overlain by Middle Jurassic (Bajocian) prophyritic lavas and by Bathonian coal-bearing strata. In places, late Jurassic continental–lagoonal red beds are preserved and then everything is cut across unconformably by carbonaceous early Cretaceous deposits

355

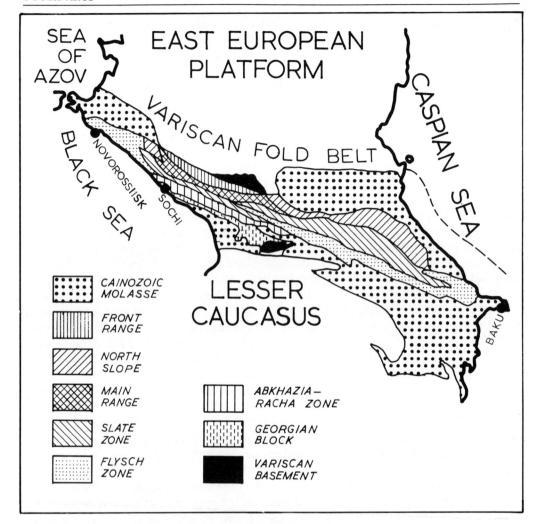

Fig. 13.7 Geological sketch-map of the Greater Caucasus (after Khain, 1975).

and by typically massive Urgonian limestones, forming a splendid scarp. In other words, it is the sort of succession one might expect on a comparatively stable, positive area almost anywhere in Europe.

Abkhazia-Racha Zone

This is the southernmost and outermost unit of the Greater Caucasus proper. It extends from the Black Sea along the northern edge of the Georgian Block as far as its eastern end. It takes the first part of its name from the tiny republic of Abkhazia (of which the port of Sukhumi is the capital) and the ridge which dominates the scenery above the Black Sea Riviera between that port and Sochi.

This zone is really transitional, so far as the Mesozoic is concerned, between the Georgian Block and the rest of the Caucasus. This is true both in stratigraphy and in structure (which consists of gentle folds and less gentle granitic intrusions). The succession starts with a thick Lower Jurassic terrigenous formation which is cut by Bajocian volcanics and then succeeded by Bathonian 'Coal Measures' like those on the Georgian Block. This is in no sense the middle of a geosyncline. The volcanism and granitic intrusions were restricted to mid Jurassic times, which seems to have been a violent episode in this part of the world and reflect the intra-Jurassic movements which were a feature of the Caucasus and the Black Sea region generally.

A marked unconformity follows and it is easy to see why Russian geologists are so anxious to start the Upper Jurassic with the Callovian. Thus at the head of the Gega River, in a beautiful Georgian National Park, one can see a subterranean river literally leaping from the basal Callovian conglomerate where the water is thrown out by the Bajocian volcanics forming a cliff below.

The river goes on to cut the magnificent Gega gorge through thick Upper Jurassic carbonates (very reminiscent of the Tarn and Verdon gorges of southern France). The Jurassic is capped with a dominating escarpment of Tithonian limestone with massive dolomitized reefs. Near beautiful Lake Ritza (where Stalin had his summer home) one can collect faunas similar to those at the classic Tithonian locality of Stramberk in Czechoslovakia.

The carbonate facies of the Upper Jurassic is only developed in the west. Farther east it passes into a red bed facies which is followed by early Cretaceous carbonaceous deposits. A later Cretaceous transgression produced a dazzling white limestone succession of which the merest tyro would instantly guess the age (in fact, he might do so easier than would a more sophisticated geologist). He would be further convinced (if he came from northern Europe) by the presence of abundant black flints. The most obvious formation, since it is widely quarried, is the Maastrichtian porcellanite which is extensively used as a building stone in Sochi and neighbouring towns. A particularly fine section through the Cretaceous is seen along the coast road west of Gagra.

Flysch Zone

As one goes westwards along the Black Sea coast of the USSR, beyond the molasse of Sochi and the narrow Akhazia-Racha Zone beyond, one comes to a long but less-visited stretch of coast, with the important ports of Tuapse and Novorossiisk, where the typically tumbled topography of flysch comes down to the sea. This extends nearly to the Crimea and can be traced, with gaps, all the way to the Caspian in the east. However, it is not really one zone but several and these are thrust southwards one over the other. It is, in effect, a narrow synclinorium of Upper Jurassic and Lower Cretaceous flysch, in part concealed beneath overthurst masses of the main range. Below the flysch is transgressive Lower Jurassic sequence that rests directly on late Palaeozoic marine sediments seen fleetingly in some of the anticlines. The low grade of metamorphism in the latter and the absence of an unconformity between the Palaeozoic and the Mesozoic led the local geologists to conclude that we are here outside the Variscan fold belt, as suggested above.

The sharp contrast in facies between the Flysch Zone and the Abkhazia-Racha Zone is particularly well marked in the Upper Jurassic. Thus on the western border of Georgia

357

(west of Gagra) the mountains to the north display huge thicknesses of flysch and the first Upper Jurassic limestone thrusting south, while at Gagra itself there are some 2000 m of autochthonous Upper Jurassic limestones in a deep gorge.

One of the finest views in Georgia is way up the Rioni River above Kutaisi, near the little town of Oni (which lays on splendid banquets for visitors). Here one can see the highest, snowiest, most angular ranges formed of the flysch with the crystalline rocks of the Main Range showing up behind and the Bajocian volcanics in front, each thrust over the other towards the south (Fig. 13.8).

Slate Zone

At the viewpoint just mentioned, between the crystalline rocks of the Main Range and the high peaks of flysch, one can see low ground formed of early Jurassic slates. This forms the south slope of the Main Range and is overthrust by it. Farther east this narrow slice widens and forms a major part of the axial zone of the eastern Caucasus between the flysch and the North Slope. Again it is probably more than one unit and the stratigraphy is obscure, but what is seen at the surface appears to be largely a thick argillaceous sequence of early and mid Jurassic age that has been somewhat metamorphosed. Nothing is seen of the rocks beneath, although deformed Permian has been found in a borehole. The slates, which include some lavas, may exceed 10 000 m in thickness. They have been intensely folded with the fold axes slightly more east-west in orientation than the main trend of the range. For this reason, mid-Jurassic movements are postulated in the Caucasus. There may have been several phases of such movements, lasting on into the late Jurassic.

Main Range Zone

The Main Range Zone of the Greater Caucasus is something of a misnomer, for other units (notably the flysch) often take the more dominating role in the topography. The Main Range consists of late Precambrian and Palaeozoic metamorphics in green schist and amphibolite facies, that have been cut by huge late Variscan granites. They occupy the major part of the axial zone of the Greater Caucasus at its western end, between a point north of Sochi and the Georgian 'Military Road' which winds through the mountains to the Georgian capital of Tbilisi (Tiflis) along the valley of the River Kura. As already mentioned, the Main Range Zone has been thrust southwards over the Mesozoic succession. In that sense it differs from the autochthonous basement seen to the north (in front of the Front Range) and to the south (in the Dzirul Massif).

The highest point in the Caucasus is Mount Elbrus (5633 m) which is, in fact, the highest mountain in Europe. This is largely formed of such Precambrian metamorphics, although assisted at the top by a Quaternary volcano. Such recent volcanicity, evidently lasted hereabouts (as elsewhere in Europe) into Man's memory, notably with the eruptions of Mount Kazbek (5047 m). This is an unusual feature to find actually within an Alpine range. Radiometric dates from the older metamorphics are anomalous, but their Precambrian age is confirmed by pebbles of them being found in Lower Palaeozoic conglomerates.

Fig. 13.8 Cross-section of the western Caucasus (after Khain, 1975).

S

LESSER CAUCASUS   GEORGIAN   G R E A T E R   C A U C A S U S
                  BLOCK
                           SOUTHERN SLOPES   MAIN   FRONT   PLATFORM
                                             RANGE RANGE

N

Mesozoic–Tertiary cover on Platform

Oligocene Miocene

Palaeocene Eocene

Cretaceous

Upper Jurassic

Lower and Middle Jurassic

Precambrian and Palaeozoic Metamorphics

Precambrian granites etc.

Paradoxically, the most interesting features of the Caucasian Palaeozoic are not in the Caucasus at all, but under the country to the north and south. Soviet geologists claim that in what they call 'Middle' Palaeozoic times (i.e., Silurian to early Carboniferous inclusive) the axial zone of the Tethyan 'geosyncline' lay to the north of the present high watershed of the Caucasus. This was in a region where earlier there had been no basins. In other words there was a down-warping of the southern edge of the East European Platform in 'mid' Palaeozoic times. This continued to the end of the era, on the evidence of the Donetsk–Dnepr trough of Carboniferous and Permian sediments. The folding and metamorphism of this belt of Palaeozoic strata between Donetsk and the Caspian, with the emplacement of granitoid bodies, indicates a Variscan fold belt close to the line of the Alpine fold belt which is so obvious today.

It is said that the Tethyan axis moved below the southern slopes of the present Caucasus in late Palaeozoic times, and by mid Jurassic times was out in the Lesser Caucasus beyond the reach of this chapter. There is, therefore, as elsewhere in Europe, an intimate association of Variscan and Alpine processes which makes it very difficult to separate the two orogenies.

Northern Ranges

On the north side of the Greater Caucasus are subsidiary ranges, usually divided (as in Fig. 13.8) into the Front Range Zone in the west and the Northern Slope Zone, mainly in the east. These ranges are delimited to the north by major reversed faults and are essentially synclinal in form. The lower slopes reveal a Palaeozoic eugeosynclinal succession, terminating in the Carboniferous and followed by late Palaeozoic molasse. This then was the site of the earlier trough and fold belt and it is significant that the Palaeozoic there differs considerably from its equivalent in the Main Range. Another major fault separates the two. So far as the Mesozoic is concerned the two ranges are very comparable, and it would seem that uniform conditions prevailed after the wearing down of the Variscan mountains. The chief difference is that the Lower–Middle Jurassic argillaceous sequence has been intensely folded in the Main Range, but only thrown into gentle open folds towards the north, approaching the stable platform.

Molasse

North from the Caucasus extends the vast East European Platform, seeming to go on for ever and looking as though the Alpine orogeny had never happened. Immediately in front of the Greater Caucasus, in the region known as Cis-Caucasia, there are two great fore-deeps filled with molasse. These are the West Kuban fore-deep in the west, forming part of the Taman Peninsula, and the much larger Terek–Caspian fore-deep in the east, which extends out under the western edge of the Caspian. Between the two, north of the highest part of the range, the edge of the basement is turned up to the surface.

There are also large areas of molasse within the mountain range proper, notably in the verdant tea-growing areas of Georgia along the Black Sea. Eastwards the whole of the

Greater and the Lesser Caucasus disappear under the molasse of the Kura and Lower Araxes intermontane cuvette. It is clear therefore that the greater part of these majestic ranges were once buried under their own detritus. It is only continued uplift, well documented in the textbook terraces of the Black Sea coast (e.g., around Sochi), that has presented this chain to us in its raw-looking state. This uplift enabled the Caucasus to have their own private ice-cap in Pleistocene times.

Selected references to Chapter 13

Section 13(a)   Pyrenees

Casteras, M. (1974), 'Les Pyrénées', in J. Debelmas (ed.), *Géologie de la France*, vol. 2, Doin, Paris, pp. 296–345.

Henry, J. (1968–71), 'Itinéraires d'initiation à la géologie des Pyrénées', *Soc. Nat. Petroles d'Aquitaine* (several different excursion guides by this and other authors).

Le Pichon, X. and J.-C. Sibuet (1971), Western extension of boundary between European and Iberian plates during the Pyrenean orogeny, *Earth planet. Sci. Letters*, **12**, 83–88.

Mattauer, M. (1968), 'Les traits structuraux essentiels de la chaine Pyrénéene', *Rev. Geog. Phys. Geol. Dynam.*, **10**(2), 3–12.

Ries, A. C. (1978), 'The Bay of Biscay—a review', *Earth Sci. Rev.*, **14**, 35–63.

Rios, J. M. (1961), 'A geological itinerary through the Spanish Pyrenees', *Proc. Geol. Ass.*, **72**, 359–371.

Rios, J. M. and J. M. Hancock (1961), 'Summer field meeting in the Spanish Pyrenees', *Proc. Geol. Ass.*, **72**, 373–390.

Sitter, L. U. de (1956), 'A cross-section through the Pyrenees', *Geol. Rundschau*, **45**, 214–234.

Sitter, L. U. de (1965), 'Hercynian and Alpine orogenies in northern Spain', *Geol. Mijnb.*, **44**, 373–383.

Zwart, H. J. (1964), 'The structural evolution of the Palaeozoic of the Pyrenees', *Geol. Rundschau*, **53**, 170–205.

Section 13(b)   Ebro Basin

Gross, G. (1966), 'Paläozoikum und Tertiär am Puig Moreno (Prov. Teruel, Spanien)', *Neues Jahrb. Geol. Paläont.*, **9**, 554–562.

Gross, G. (1968), 'Das Tertiär in südwestlichen Ebro-Becken', *Neues Jahrb. Geol. Paläont.*, **131**, 23–32.

Rios, J. M. and J. M. Hancock (1961), 'A geological itinerary through the Spanish Pyrenees', *Proc. Geol. Ass.*, **72**, 359–371.

Sitter, L. U. and H. J. Zwart (1961), 'Excursion to the central Pyrenees, September 1959', *Leidse Geol. Mededel*, **26**, 1–49.

Section 13(c) Provence

Aubouin, J. (1974), 'La Provence', in J. Debelmas (ed.), *Géologie de la France*, vol. 2, Doin, Paris, pp. 346–386.

Aubouin, J. and F. Mennessier (1960), 'Essai sur la structure de la Provence', *Soc. Géol. Fr., Paris, Liv. Mém. P. Fallot*, **2**, 45–98.

Corroy, G. (1963), 'L'évolution paléogéographique post-hercynienne de la Provence', *Soc. Géol. Fr., Paris, Liv. Mém. P. Fallot*, **2**, 19–43.

Gouvernet, C., G. Guieu, and C. Rousset (1971), *Guides géologiques regionaux. Provence*, Masson, Paris, 229 pp.

Lutaud, L. (1957), 'La Tectogenèse et l'évolution structurale de la Provence', *Rev. Géogr. Phy. Géol. Dynam.*, 103–112.

Middlemiss, F. A. *et al.* (1970), 'Summer field meeting in the south of France between Lyon and Avignon' *and* 'Summer field meeting in France', *Proc. Geol. Ass., Lond.*, **81**, 303–362 and 363–396.

Section 13(d) Jura and Franco-Swiss Plain

Ager, D. V. and B. D. Evamy (1963), 'The geology of the southern French Jura', *Proc. Geol. Ass.*, **74**, 325–356.

Ager, D. V., B. D. Evamy, and J. G. Ramsey (1963), 'Summer field meeting in the French Jura and Alps, July 1963', *Proc. Geol. Ass.*, **74**, 483–515.

Lienhardt, G. (1962), *Géologie du Bassin houiller stéphanien du Jura et de ses morts-terrains*, Mém. Bur. Rech. Geol. Min., 449 pp.

Margerie, E. de (1936), *Le Jura*, vol. 2, Mém. Carte Géol. France, Paris, 900 pp.

Section 13(e) Crimea

Anonymous (1971), *Guide Book to 12th European Micropaleontological Colloquium, USSR*, 232 pp.

Kotanski, Z. (1978), 'The Caucasus, Crimea and their foreland (Scythian Platform): The Black Sea and Caspian Sea', in M. Lemoine (ed.), *Geological Atlas of Alpine Europe and Adjoining Alpine Areas*, Elsevier, Amsterdam, pp. 545–576.

Navlivkin, D. V. (1973), 'The Mediterranean geosyncline', in *Geology of the USSR*, (English transl. by N. Rast), Univ. Toronto Press, pp. 579–707.

Section 13(f) Greater Caucasus

Khain, V. E. (1975), 'Structure and main stages in the tectonomagmatic development of the Caucasus: an attempt at geodynamic interpretation', *Amer. Jl Sci.*, **275-A**, 131–156.

Khain, V. E. (1977), 'Critical comparison of mobilistic models of tectonic development of the Caucasus', in B. Biju-Duval and L. Montadert (eds), *International Symposium on the Structural History of the Mediterranean Basins*, Technip, Paris, pp. 353–362.

Khain, V. E. and E. E. Milanovsky (1963), 'Structure tectonique du Caucase d'après les données modernes', *Liv. Mém. P. Fallot*, **2**, 663–703.

Kotanski, Z. (1978), 'The Caucasus, Crimea and their foreland (Scythian Platform): The Black Sea and Caspian Sea', in M. Lemoine (ed.), *Geological Atlas of Alpine Europe and Adjoining Alpine Areas*, Elsevier, Amsterdam, pp. 545–576.

Nalivkin, D. V. (1973), 'The Mediterranean geosyncline', in *Geology of the USSR*, (English transl. by N. Rast), Univ. Toronto Press, pp. 579–707.

Tsagareli, A. L. (1974), 'Geology of western Caucasus', in *The Black Sea, Chemistry and Biology*, Mem. Amer. Ass. Petrol. Geol., vol. 20, pp. 77–87.

Chapter Fourteen

Northern Alpides

This chapter concerns the main belt of 'north-facing' Alpides from Gibraltar to the Black Sea, although paradoxically in the Southern Carpathians they turn around and face south. They are really three ranges: the Betics–Balearics, the Alps, and the Carpatho-Balkans.

14(a) Betic Cordillera

The Betic Cordillera forms the western end of the great Alpine chains of Europe and Asia and occupies the south-east corner of the Iberian Peninsula. If one includes the Balearic Islands in the east (which are dealt with in the next section) then the Betic Cordillera extends for nearly 1000 km and is therefore about the same length as the whole of the Alps. Southwards the Betics continue in the Rif mountains of Morocco. These, although politically in Africa, are geologically in Europe and are therefore included in this book— Chapter 16(a). In many ways the Betics are Africa in Europe. The palms, prickly pear, and Barbary apes, all remind one of the southern continent, as do the scattered white farms in what (in late summer at least) is a parched and almost desert landscape.

The Betic Cordillera may be divided into five parts (Fig. 14.1): Pre-Betics, Guadalquivir Trough, Sub-Betics, Betics *sensu stricto*, and Ultra-Betics. In the diverse literature (in several languages) dealing with the Cordillera, there are several alternatives and contradictions in this general nomenclature, but the above seems to be the least open to misunderstanding. In addition to studies by the Spaniards themselves, great contributions have been made to our knowledge of the geology of the Betics by the French, Dutch, and Germans. Much of the literature is very confused and contradictory and, although great advances have been made in recent years, it cannot be said that our knowledge of the chain is as thorough as that of most of the other Alpine chains of Europe. In particular, there is little evidence from deep borings, geophysical surveys, or detailed work on metamorphic minerals and minor structures. Much of the work is still in the classic form of standing on mountain tops waving one's arms in grand demonstrations of major structural units.

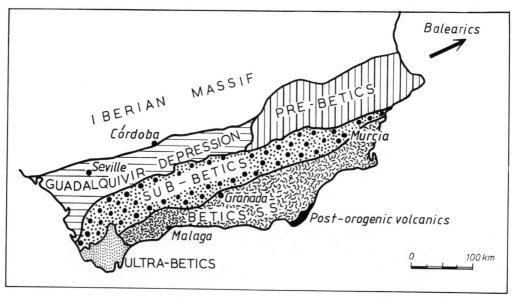

Fig. 14.1   Sketch-map showing the main elements of the Betic Cordillera.

Pre-Betics

As one drives south across the broad, swampy, rice-growing plain south of Valencia, the first sight of what may be called the 'Spanish Alps' is the isolated limestone mass in Cullera. This is typical of the Pre-Betics as a whole. Here the coast begins to swing eastwards towards the headland of Cabo de la Nao and the Pre-Betics rise up as an irregular range of limestone hills along the Costa Blanca. This is the barrier between the Mediterranean north and the arid Andalusian south.

This range as a whole consists of completely unmetamorphosed and largely autochthonous Mesozoic and Tertiary sediments trending east-north-east (with northerly directed thrusting) and heading out for the Balearic Islands which are their natural continuation. The succession is continental and shallow marine in facies (so far as is known) and contrasts with the deeper troughs to the south.

The oldest rocks to be seen are Triassic of the Germanic type, dominantly red beds with evaporites, a notable development of marine 'Muschelkalk', and intrusive dolerites with mineralization. Alabaster is common (and is used to make table lamps). As so often with these rocks, there are diapirs, but here they seem to be bigger and better than usual, forming jagged scenery. The biggest is stellate in form and is inland from Altea, about 10 km north of the famous holiday resort of Benidorm. These diapirs have imparted a local north-west trend to the basic north-easterly strike of the range.

As well as the straight punch-up structures of the diapirs there is a great deal of gravity-sliding of the massive limestones above. The best-known example is the huge rock (Punta Ifach) that dominates Calpe from the sea (and which is described in local guide books as a volcano!). Limestone masses and steep cliffs are a feature of the Pre-Betics.

Although there are Lower Jurassic rocks outcropping over large areas inland west of Murcia and at the east end of the Guadalquivir Trough, over much of the Pre-Betics and certainly near the sea the Jurassic is reduced to a single massive limestone formation which is probably Kimmeridgian or Tithonian in age. The Cretaceous is more fully developed (above a break) with a limestone/'marl' succession that ranges from the Neocomian to the uppermost stages. There is a particularly massive limestone in the Cenomanian, with chert, while the next such formation is in the basal Palaeogene (capping many of the hills) and starting a similar dominantly carbonate succession ranging up to the Miocene. This forms surprisingly striking scenery for the Tertiary—for example around Alcöy. Giant forams, which automatically make one think of the warm south, are abundant at many levels (notably among the bikinis on the south beach at Benidorm).

The main movements here were evidently of mid Miocene age with conglomerates and not much else above, apart from Quaternary gravels and calcretes along the coast. The earlier Tertiary is often intensely folded, for example west of Benidorm, and there is much 'superficial sliding'.*

The most remarkable feature of the Pre-Betics is the way they terminate abruptly inland, just west of the longitude of Almeria, where they suddenly change into the Guadalquivir Trough. They end in that direction long before the other Betic ranges but, on the other hand, extend eastwards as the Balearics. This led to an interesting recent suggestion that the Pre-Betics were shifted eastwards bodily, like sliding the bolt in a door, leaving the Guadalquivir Trough as the gap behind them. It fits!

Guadalquivir Trough

In the western part of the Betic Cordillera, the high ridges of the Betics and Sub-Betics are separated from the high plateau of the Spanish Meseta by the wide valley of the River Guadalquivir. The name is memory of a Moorish past, meaning 'Great River' in Arabic. Although parched and dusty in the summer, it is a fertile valley, somewhat reminiscent of the Sacramento Valley in California, full of groves of olives and the oranges that make its chief city of Seville so famous. Near its mouth at Sanlúcar are the vineyards of Jerez de la Frontera which gives the name 'sherry' to the fortified wine that is so popular in Britain. Eastwards, the valley passes into the Pre-Betic Chains that have already been discussed.

Like many other of the major rivers of Europe, the Guadalquivir flows in an ancient trough and the present valley is underlain by great thicknesses of Neogene sediment. In the south, the trough appears comparable with, although much larger than, the post-orogenic basins within the Betic ranges, but in the north it abuts directly the ancient meseta. The rise on to this central table-land is steep and abrupt, as seen for instance along the main road north from Granada to Jaen.

This steep escarpment, which is almost perfectly straight for nearly 400 km, cuts obliquely across the north-west trending folds in the Palaeozoic; it has long been taken as a textbook example of a normal fault. Now that the trough has received the attentions of the petroleum geologists, with geophysics and deep borings, it is known to be nothing of the sort.

---

* Childe Roland is alleged to have cut off the top of a Tertiary peak and thrown it, as an island, in the sea off Villajoyosa (south of Benidorm). Although the theory is unlikely, there is a remarkably close match in shape.

The Palaeozoic 'basement' of the meseta is delimited not by a fault but a flexure, which carries it down gently in a general southerly direction. It is down to nearly 2500 m in a borehole at Isla Mayor (about 20 km south-west of Seville) and at El Asperillo (on the coast) the base of the Trias was not reached at 3310 m. The flexure passes into small faults locally, but these are of minor importance and may represent posthumous movements along old lines in the basement. This is suggested by the nature of the Palaeozoic floor. Thus in the boring at Carmona (about 40 km east of Seville) there are granites and gneisses such as are only seen much farther north in the meseta. Elsewhere in borings there are Palaeozoic sedimentary rocks similar to those seen on the northern rim of the trough.

All along the central part of this northern rim, the Miocene is in a littoral facies transgressive on to the Palaeozoic floor. It is evident that in late Miocene times this was just about the shoreline. Eastwards, Germanic Trias comes between the two and westwards there is marine Trias. It appears that the Triassic and Jurassic shorelines in the Guadalquivir Trough were almost at right angles to the general trend of the Betics and for a very long time oscillated between Seville and the present-day sea.

Perhaps the most remarkable feature of the Guadalquivir Trough is the great olistostrome which is found in all the southern boreholes. It is best known from the borehole at Carmona (mentioned above), where it is some 500 m thick. It has been called the 'Carmona Nappe', but is certainly a gravitational rather than a tectonic phenomenon. Movements seem to have been initiated on the Triassic evaporites and a great mass slid down in a north-westerly direction. It reaches more than half-way across the trough from the front of the Sub-Betics and its leading edge is almost exactly parallel with the regional structure. It cannot be recognized for certain near the present coastline, where the Trias has changed from its Germanic gypsum-bearing facies. The olistostrome is a jumble of Mesozoic and Tertiary rocks and this situation continues into the Sub-Betics where, in the boring at Chiclana de la Frontera (about 20 km south-east of Cadiz), the Trias is passed through three times in 1032 m. Early Miocene sediments are involved in the slumping, while the later Miocene is more or less undisturbed. The movements of the olistostrome had ceased before Helvetian marine sediments overflowed the sides of the trough.

A characteristic sediment type in the Miocene here is the *albariza*; this is a mixture of white siliceous marls and hard bands of limestones and sandstone. Micropalaeontology has sorted out the Neogene stratigraphy of the boreholes and it has been deduced that the axis of the basin moved progressively north with time. After the Helvetian transgression, however, there was a general regression. The Neogene sediments are now much concealed by Quaternary alluvium and there is not much for the visiting geologist to see at the surface.

Sub-Betics

Going north across the Betic Cordillera one knows at once when one approaches the Sub-Betics by the great wall of greyish-white Mesozoic limestone, forming a dramatic skyline. The Sub-Betics extend from Alicante in the east to the Gulf of Cadiz in the west. Compared with the nappe upon nappe complexity of the Betics *sensu stricto* they appear at first glance to be beautifully simple, but their complexities are all the more difficult due to being hidden. No rocks older than Mesozoic are known but this is a glorious area for the study of the Jurassic and Cretaceous. The succession is fully marine above a Germanic Trias and is dominantly in a deep-water pelagic facies. This contrasts markedly with the equivalent sediments in the Pre-Betics to the north and the Betics s.s. to the south, where the Jurassic and Cretaceous are all of a shallow-water facies with frequent gaps.

The lower part of the Mesozoic succession almost everywhere presents a clear story of deepening water. This is well seen, for example, below the beautifully situated village of Ventas de Zafarraya, where the Sub-Betics come closest to the south coast. Above continental Trias red marls come well-bedded limestones with chert and then Lower Lias with an abundant shallow-water fauna of molluscs and brachiopods.

This passes up into pellet limestones and then into a deeper facies. Characteristically in the Sub-Betics, the Upper Lias develops a *rosso ammonitico* facies of red nodular limestones with a pelagic fauna, reminiscent of the Southern Alps. This facies is repeated in the Upper Jurassic. Higher up, more marly beds come in, providing planes of *décollement* in some of the structures. More detrital material appears in the late Cretaceous and this continues into the Palaeogene with a notable development of flysch and flysch-like rocks (also seen near Ventas).

Between the limestone cliffs of the Sub-Betics and the Betics proper, there is commonly a very complex zone. It is well seen near the town of Ronda, which stands on steep cliffs, reminding one of the formerly ubiquitous Miocene molasse. The Sub-Betics are sometimes divided into a 'Frontal Complex' which includes the dominating limestones already discussed and the 'Marly Sub-Betics' farther north. The latter have less carbonate and are generally thought of as the deepest facies. It is here that are found many spilitic pillow lavas, ranging in age from Triassic to Palaeogene. These are seen particularly in the central part of the range and are associated with mineralization, although only red ochre is worked commercially.

The structure of the Sub-Betics has not yet been fully elucidated. Everyone agrees, however, on the importance of the Triassic gypsum in their structural evolution. In fact the structure of the whole range can be summed up as more or less broken-up masses of Jurassic and Cretaceous sliding on the Trias. Whole mountains seem to be 'floating' in Triassic sediment. Thus the Sierra de Gibalbin, north-east of Jerez, has a seemingly concordant succession from the late Jurassic right through the Cretaceous into the Eocene, but is surrounded by vari-coloured Triassic marls which contain shattered fragments of later rocks.

There is also evidence in the north of the Province of Cadiz, that the Triassic salts moved diapirically and that the later sediments carried on top of them split and slid laterally. The whole structure of the Sub-Betics has been interpreted as a northerly gravitational slide on the Trias, and this sliding continues under the southern part of the Guadalquivir Trough. Northwards we know that equivalent strata are more or less autochthonous on the Palaeozoic basement, and it is unfortunate that we do not yet know what underlies the Sub-Betics.

Betics (*sensu stricto*)

The Betics in the strict sense are the highest, most spectacular, and most complex of the Cordilleran ranges. Unlike the northerly ranges they consist predominantly of Palaeozoic rocks. They stand above the tourist coast of southern Spain, from Estepona in the west (the most attractive of the many concrete resorts) to the Cabo de Palos and the 'inland sea' of Mar Menor, in the east. They display the full effects of the Alpine orogeny in a series of northerly-directed nappes, piled one upon the other.

Four major units or complexes are recognized as follows (from the highest to lowest): Malaguide Complex, Alpujarride Complex, Ballabona–Cucharon Complex, and Nevado–Filabride Complex. These complexes are recognized chiefly in the eastern and central part of the range. In the west (i.e., west of Malaga) there are further units which may or may not correspond with the above. In particular, there are great masses of ultrabasic rocks, notably in the Sierra Bermeja, south of Ronda.

The whole region is dominated by seemingly endless sequences of Palaeozoic phyllites, schists, and marbles, which it is almost impossible to date accurately because of the general absence of fossils. Some advance has been made recently with conodonts, but vast areas still remain uncertain. Most of the geologists who have worked in the region say that there is no direct evidence of Palaeozoic or earlier orogenies, although generally speaking it is obvious that these thick sequences have suffered more than the Meso-zoic limestones and associated deposits. No conspicuous unconformities have been recognized within or above the Palaeozoic, although in fleeting visits to the region I have seen great breccias below the Trias which seem to be sedimentary rather than tectonic in origin.

The effects of a regional metamorphism of Variscan age may well have been obscured by the Alpine orogeny. There are granitic gneisses—such as those in the Lubrin-Bédar area of the eastern part of the Sierra de los Filabrides—which appear to have been emplaced in Variscan times. There is also the indirect evidence of the Trias, notably the 'Buntsandstein' (e.g., on the coast road just east of Malaga) which has all the appearance of a post-orogenic deposit.

An older orogeny has been recognized in the Sierra de las Estancias, between Lorca and Baza in the west. Here there is a clear difference between the intensity of metamor-phism of a basal group of mica schists and quartzites and an overlying group of slates, quartzites, and greywackes that have been provisionally attributed to the Devonian-Carboniferous. This metamorphism has been doubtfully dated as pre-Silurian, so there is no real evidence of a Caledonian orogeny in its usual sense. So far as pre-Alpine folding is concerned, the evidence is still to be elucidated, although it may well be there, especially in the Sierra Cabrera and the Sierra Alhamilla, between the fascinating hill-top town of Mojacar and the local capital of Almeria. There is little obvious evidence of multiple fold trends such as one sees in the Alps.

Turning to the Alpine structures, there is more of a consensus about the main features. Although there are other views, there is little doubt that the general movement of the Alpine nappes was from south to north. It would be difficult to understand the general structure of Europe if this were not the case. The exact age of the movements has been more in dispute, since some authors want them way back in the Mesozoic, others equate them with the Pyrenean folding (early in the Tertiary), and the majority would put them much later in the Tertiary. It is possible, indeed probable, that there were several phases of movement, but the uncertainty results chiefly from the absence of late Mesozoic sediments in the lower nappes. It may be that the movements in the west began earlier than those in the east.

It is appropriate to consider, in turn, the main tectonic units recognized in the central and eastern Betics (Fig. 14.2).

Nevado-Filabride Complex. This lowest structural unit is displayed primarily, as its name suggests, in the backbone of the Betics, the Sierra Nevada, and the Sierra de los Filabres. As is commonly the case, the lowest tectonic unit produced the highest topographic unit, presumably as a result of isostatic readjustment after the stripping off of the overlying nappes.

The Sierra Nevada themselves stand, bare and for ever snow-capped, above the marvellous Moorish capital of Granada. The basement here consists of a thick, monotonous series of graphitic and garnet-bearing schists, with some quartzites. Above comes what used to be called the 'mixed zone'. This was once thought to be a separate Mesozoic nappe of mica shist and gneiss, quartzites, marbles, amphibolites, serpentinites, and some gypsum, which slid over the crystalline basement. Nowadays, the general view is that there is here a whole series of thrust slices, each containing elements of both units, with a slight discordance between them. The upper unit is better displayed towards the east, especially in the eastern part of the Sierra de los Filabres, above Vera. Here it certainly seems to contain several *décollements*.

Nevertheless, although such tectonic breaks are obvious, the Nevado–Filabride Complex is thought of as the relatively autochthonous, unmoved part of the Betics. This may, in part, be ignorance, for one always tends to see the lowest exposed rocks (or any rocks older than those one is actually studying) as the rigid 'basement'. The whole complex forms a vast tectonic window, entirely surrounded by higher nappes.

Ballabona–Cucharón Complex. This complex has only been recognized relatively recently in the central ranges. It is small in extent and difficult to demonstrate, but best seen in the Sierra de Lújar, near the mineral water town of Lanjarón on the southwestern flanks of the Sierra Nevada. It was formerly included with the Alpujarrides, but is said to be closer to the Nevado–Filabrides. Unlike the other higher units, this one has not yet been recognized on the north flanks of the Sierra Nevada, although it is seen north of the Sierra de los Filabres near Purchena.

The rocks of this complex consist, for the most part, of Triassic sediments which have suffered minor metamorphism. There are quartzites and conglomerates at the base (which may be Permian in age), then limestones and phyllites with intercalations of gypsum in their lower part and dolomite above. Oolitic limestones near the top of the succession may be of Jurassic age. There are important basic intrusions in the Triassic part of the succession, as in Morocco. The most far-travelled fragment of this complex, on the north side of the Sierra de los Filabres, was originally recognized as the Ballabona unit. It comprises only part of the whole unit and appears to have slid to its present position on the gypsum in the Trias. It has been compared with the 'Nappe des Gypse' in the Vanoise Alps.

Alpujarride Complex. This nappe complex is the most extensive in the Baltic Cordillera. There seems to be little doubt that it travelled up to 50 km or more over the Nevado–Filabride Complex. In the south it constitutes the greater part of the long line of mountains inland from the coast all the way from Cartagena to Nerja or beyond. It wraps round the west end of the Sierra Nevada and extends on the north side of that range and its continuation as far as Lorca.

The succession within the Alpujarrides is difficult to summarize, but includes altered

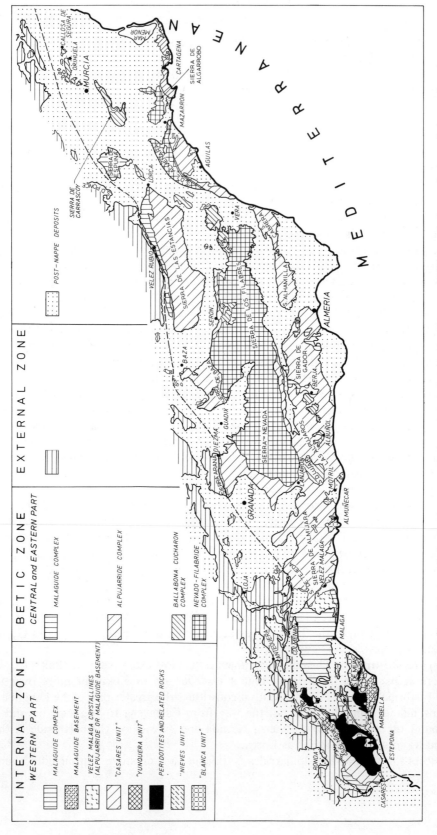

Fig. 14.2 Geological sketch-map of the Betics sensu stricto (after Egeler and Simon, 1969, by kind permission of the authors).

limestones, quartzites, conglomerates, phyllites, and greywackes, with some basal gar-netiferous mica-schists. The lowest units are referred to the Palaeozoic (possibly includ-ing some Precambrian), the next units include some datable early Trias, and the top unit consists of mid and late Triassic limestones, showing transitions to pure white marble. In many ways this top unit is the most interesting because it is Trias of Alpine type, more than 800 m thick, unlike the continental Trias everywhere else in the Iberian Peninsula. It may represent the deepest part of a miogeosynclinal trough between shallow-water and continental deposits. This is important, as in the Alps, for relating the various parts of the Cordillera to their original places of deposition. The full succession is only clearly developed in the Sierra de las Estancias. Elsewhere it is far less complete and the upper part seems to have moved relative to the lower, probably again because of a *décollement* within the Trias. The lowermost part, with the addition of basic intrusions, has a partic-ularly thick development in the Sierra Alhamilla and the Sierra Cabrera, south of Vera.

An important feature of the Alpujarrides is the development of ore deposits associated with the Triassic volcanicity. Lead and silver deposits are notable in the vicinity of Cartagena and Mazarrón in the east, while farther west (in Granada Province) there are extensive occurrences of iron ore which have become very important in recent years. Deposits of galena and fluorite are associated with the carbonates of the Sierra de Gádor and the Sierra Alhamilla, north-west and north-east, respectively, of Almeria.

A major point of disagreement about the Alpujarrides relates to the rocks exposed around Velez Malaga (just inland from Torre del Mar). A large area between here and Nerja is attributed by some authors to the Alpujarrides and by others to the Malaguides. The rocks concerned may be the 'basement' metamorphics of either complex.

Malaguide Complex. In many ways this is the most interesting of all the Betic nappe complexes, being both the highest and the farthest travelled. The Malaga 'Nappe' is very extensive, although mostly in small erosional remnants. It occupies a large area inland from the tourist capital that gives it its name and is seen in its farthest development in the Sierra de Espuña, near Lorca.

The Malaguide succession is much more complete than the others. Above the usual schists, quartzites, and greywackes (which look very much like those of the lower units), there come a variety of Permian and Triassic sediments with a basal conglomerate of breccia which, locally at least, seems to indicate a major unconformity. The Trias is in the usual continental facies with gypsum. Above are Jurassic carbonates, including oolites and pellet limestones, easily recognized by their large Tethyan foraminifera. Eocene limestones are found locally, for example in the hill topped with the neglected fortress of Velez Malaga, although these, like most of the other Betic limestones, are intensely brecciated and sparing in fossils.

At the top of the Malaguide Complex comes a sandy development of mid Eocene age, which in some areas is an obvious flysch. One presumes that this formed synorogenically and certainly it was the latest formation to be much affected by the Alpine orogeny.

One of the arguments about the Malaguide Complex is whether it moved to its present position from the south or the north. The majority would say the former, and this is certainly the more attractive hypothesis to the tidy-minded, bearing in mind the general pattern of Alpine folding in Europe. If so the Malaguides may have travelled about 50 km relative to the Alpujarrides below and therefore something like 100 km from their original place of deposition. One must bear in mind, however, that the succession near

Malaga is almost incredibly like that of the top Rif nappe in Morocco, which moved in the opposite direction.

The chief argument for proposing a movement from the north is the resemblance between the Mesozoic carbonates of the Malaguides and those of the Sub-Betics. This resemblance may be more apparent than real, but in any case the tectonic coming together of carbonates facies from the opposite sides of a trough seems to be the more likely explanation. Coupled with the postulated movement of certain units from the north was the suggestion of a great downward suction zone (*Verschluckung*) along the Betic–Sub-Betic border. This is what would now be called a subduction zone. A third explanation (which has not so far been suggested to my knowledge) might be that the Sub-Betic carbonates came from even farther south than the Betic nappes, rather in the manner of the Northern Calcareous Alps of Austria. They are thought of as para-autochthonous, but this is largely due to ignorance of their roots, and borings on the south side of the Guadalquivir Trough suggest more movement than is generally presumed.

Western Betics. West of Malaga the structure and succession of the Betics *sensu lata* is different. The Malaguides seem to be basically the same, but below them are a number of units which it may be idle even to try to correlate with the complexes to the east. Structurally they appear to come in the following order, but this may have little relationship to their true position: Malaguides, Casares Unit, peridotite and other ultrabasics, 'Rondaides' (Yunquera Unit, Nieves Unit), and Blanca Unit.

The Blanca Unit has been correlated with the Nevado–Filibrides and is unique in having an inverted succession, with high-grade Palaeozoic gneisses and amphibolites on top of Triassic limestones (which pass into marbles). These can be well seen in the Sierra de Mijas, just inland from the concrete jungle of Torremolinos. There seems to be no real reason, however, for equating them with the lowest structural unit and they are certainly not autochthonous. There is, in fact, no real reason to expect the units in the west to correspond with those in the centre and east. With a structure as complex as a mountain chain it is likely that major units of this size will have moved independently.

The 'Rondaides' have been split into two units (as indicated above) with ultrabasics between them. The Nieves Unit, seen in the Sierra of that name, has been equated with their Ballabona–Cucharón Complex. The great masses of ultra-basic rock are a feature of the western Betics and are associated with metalliferous mineralization, notably iron and lead; magnetite ore is loaded straight on to ships anchored offshore at Marbella. The largest black ultra-basic mass can be seen along the precipitous mountain road inland from San Pedro de Alcantara (west of Marbella) where it makes a steep and sharply contrasting contact with the white marbles of the Nieves Unit. The structural position of the ultra-basics is not clear, but they seem to be overlain by the Casares Unit near the village of that name, west of Estepona, where the Betics come to an end as a mountain chain. One presumes that they relate to a major suture between Europe and Africa.

The Malaguides are well seen along the coast road west from Torremolinos. One can see that the so-called Malaguide 'crystallines', easily recognized by their quartz veining, pass up into phyllites without quartz veining but with bands of shattered limestone. These are followed in the usual way by red Trias. In all these features the Malaguides in the west resemble those in the main outcrop as seen along the mountain road inland from Malaga.

A feature of the western Betics is that serpentinite seems to take the place of Triassic gypsum as the lubricant for much of the thrusting. This is well seen north of Marbella, where the serpentinite forms a marginal zone to the Malaguides where they slide over the white marbles of the Blanca Unit.

Post-Orogenic Basins. The Betic Cordillera, like Spain in general, is much concealed beneath Neogene sediments. There are three main 'interior depressions' (notably that of Granada) and many smaller basins along the south coast. The basins appear to be mostly fault-controlled synclines with great rushes of coarse sediment coming in from the sides and passing up into finer grained material. They seem to have functioned as separate basins of deposition and contain huge thicknesses of conglomerates, sands, clays, and evaporites, including both marine and non-marine elements.

Although poorly exposed and rather uninteresting to the majority of geologists, their interpretation is vital to the understanding of the Betic movements. Despite there being little in the literature about late-stage thrusting over Neogene sediments, there were late tangential movements of the nappe fronts, probably as a result of gravitational forces, as in other Alpine chains. There were also late adjustments, as can be seen along the coast road, where highly fossiliferous Neogene sands were draped over the ancient rocks, for example just west of the Rio de Velez.

One of the best areas for studying these late sediments is between the city of Granada and the Sierra Nevada. Here the Oligocene–Miocene sediments are thought by some to have been involved in the last movements. The Neogene sediments are mostly soft and easily excavated. In the past they were much dug out to form homes in the cliffs, for example in the gipsy quarter of Granada, where the caves are crowded nightly with tourists watching flamenco dancing. The marine sediments are often highly fossiliferous, with a great variety of shallow-water organisms. These show that the Mediterranean formerly opened through the Betics into the Atlantic, with evidence in the faunas sometimes of influence from the ocean and sometimes from the internal sea. Evidently the present topography of the Betics is a very modern phenomenon.

Ultra-Betics

The Ultra-Betics are also commonly known as the 'Unit of the Campo de Gibraltar' or as the 'Flysch du Campo de Gibraltar', but I prefer the less unwieldy name. They occupy a large part of the Province of Cadiz and form the not very well exposed southernmost corner of Europe. The topography is subdued compared with that of the Betics proper and the mountains end rather abruptly inland from Estepona.

The unit is composed largely of flysch and flysch-type rocks of Palaeogene age. It is undoubtedly allochthonous, hence the name 'Ultra-Betics', but the direction from which it came is still a matter of dispute. From the disposition of Triassic red beds, Jurassic–Cretaceous limestones, and Palaeogene flysch, around the 'Gibraltar Arc', it would seem that they came from the east. The present arrangement is symmetrical on either side of the Strait of Gibraltar. The 'Pillars of Hercules' themselves illustrate the unity of these parts of Europe and Africa. Looking westwards from the Spanish coast near Estepona or from the hills above Marbella, it is obvious why the ancients thought of them as the gateway to outer space. Gibraltar on the Spanish side and Jebel Musa on the Moroccan side are both formed of Jurassic limestone with the low-flying flysch belt behind.

The 'Rock', standing as it does at the end of a short spit projecting from the Spanish coast, is a mass of limestone with rare early Jurassic brachiopods, resting on later Jurassic shales and radiolarian cherts. It is therefore clear that it has been inverted and it has been interpreted as a klippe floating in a sea of flysch.

Although the whole area has been described as 'flysch' and includes great quantities of that rock type, there are several varieties of it and much else besides. There is, for example, calcareous flysch with bands of argillaceous limestone and an unusual bright red flysch. Both of these may derive from source rocks in the carbonate area to the east. Other sediments are the red Trias with gypsum on which the whole unit probably moved, Jurassic limestone as in Gibraltar, and an early Cretaceous limestone with the characteristic deep-water fauna of ammonite aptychi, belemnites, and aberrant pygopid brachiopods.

14(b)   Balearics

The sunny holiday archipelago of the Balearics forms a direct east-north-east continuation of the Betic Cordillera out in the Mediterranean. It may be regarded as an extension of the northern part of that range since it is dominated by similar Mesozoic limestones. There are three main islands (Fig. 14.3): Ibiza in the west, Mallorca (Majorca)—the largest—in the centre, and Menorca (Minorca) in the east, in addition to several smaller ones.

Menorca is the least interesting geographically and touristically, but most varied geologically. The island is flat and featureless apart from a few low hills (the highest only 365 m). Erosion here has bitten deeper than farther west and a thick Palaeozoic succession is exposed, ranging in age from Silurian to Permian. The dating on the whole is no better than on the mainland, but brown-weathering Devonian schists seem to predominate. A notable feature is the interdigitation of marine and non-marine beds with plants in the Upper Carboniferous. This then is a glimpse of the Palaeozoic basement that we could not see in the main Pre-Betic or Sub-Betic ranges.

Resting on this basement is the usual red Trias, although it is noteworthy that Alpine elements, such as megalodontid bivalves, are found in the 'Muschelkalk' here. The Trias forms low hills in the north-east and there are also a few scattered hill outliers of later Mesozoic limestones (Jurassic and Lower Cretaceous), although only enough to tell one that these rocks were deposited here as on the other islands. The island is dominated by a great slab of flat-lying, white Miocene limestone which covers the whole of the south-west and is generally dated as Vindobonian. It is clearly post-orogenic and rests unconformably on all that went before.

Menorca thus provides a summary of the geological history of the Balearics. However, unless the dull, semi-metamorphosed Palaeozoic is what stimulates you, the other islands have much more to offer. In these, as on the mainland, nothing is seen of the pre-Mesozoic and the islands are dominated by grey and white pelagic limestones of the Jurassic and early Cretaceous. In every sense—structurally, sedimentologically, and palaeontologically—these are peaks of Alpine mountains emerging from the warm waters of the Mediterranean.

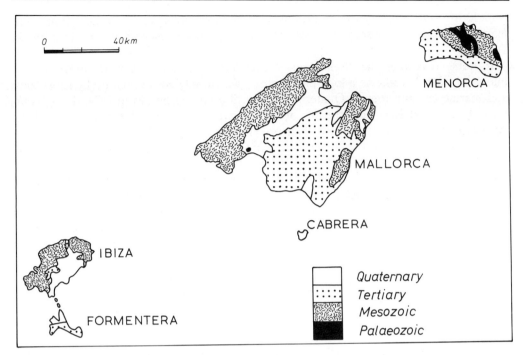

Fig. 14.3 Geological sketch-map of the Balearics.

In Mallorca, the Mesozoic succession is supposedly complete. After the usual Triassic with the volcanics of the south, it is mainly composed of a deepish water ammonitic facies. Distinctively 'Alpine' elements, such as pygopid brachiopods, turn up occasionally, but—as on the mainland—the marine succession starts with shallow-water facies and faunas in the Lower Jurassic. The platform carbonates form the famous cliffs of Mallorca with their equally famous sea-caves. In pretty little Ibiza, the succession is said to be of a generally shallower water nature, although it is difficult to see how this fits into the general palaeogeographical picture.

Structurally, the whole archipelago illustrates the general concept of a northerly 'push' of the Betics. In the low hills of south-east Mallorca and in Ibiza, there are recumbent folds, overturned to the north. The much higher northern range of Mallorca (up to 1450 m), with its spectacular cliffs, represents the steep northern limb of a major structure, which passes from a fold into a thrust. This can be traced into the tiny island of Dragonera, at the western extremity of the main island.

The youngest Mesozoic rocks are the so-called 'Gault' with pyritized ammonites (like the formation of this name in south-east England). This is dated as Albian. The sea then evidently withdrew to the south and the main orogeny may have occurred at this time. On Mallorca there is a fairly complete Tertiary succession from Lower Eocene to Lower Miocene, with intercalations of marine and non-marine deposition.

There is not much to say about the Palaeogene, except that lignites from Oligocene lakes are the island's most valuable resource after tourism, fruit-growing, and fishing. But the Miocene is very widespread. The Lower Miocene starts the Tertiary on Ibiza and the

Middle Miocene is everywhere, forming most of the table-like island of Formentera (south of Ibiza) and the south-west of Mallorca around the splendid sweep of the bay at Palma.

It seems that after the Alpine movements here, the Balearics were joined to the mainland near Alicante as a long promontory, which only got broken up by subsidence and marine erosion in early Quaternary times. Raised beaches, from 25 m down, complete the story, at least until the time when the natives' ability with the sling caused the Ancient Greeks to give the islands their present name.

Where the Balearics led to, in tectonic terms, is something of a problem. Some would turn them back to join the Celtiberics or the Pyrenees; others would project them, like one of their sling-shots, at the cliffs of the Alpes Maritimes. Neither of these alternatives seems acceptable and we must presume that something nasty happened to this line of Alpine mountains under the waters of the western Mediterranean. The recent suggestion that the Balearics slid sidewise into the Mediterranean, leaving the Guadalquivir Valley as an empty slot behind, pleases my simplistic mind, but is probably not acceptable tectonically.

14(c)   Western Alps

Of all the chapters and sections in this book, this is the one which I approach with the greatest timidity. The geology of the Western Alps is almost a science on its own, which outsiders only tackle at their peril. To many the Western Alps represent the climax of European geology, to others their structural complexity is such as to make them only suitable for the afficianado, and what is more the afficianado who is also a good mountaineer.

The Alps as a whole sweep in a single great arc from the French Riviera to the gates of Vienna, through France, northern Italy, Switzerland, southern Germany, and Austria. This arc is some 800 km long and 150 km wide. The division into Western Alps and Eastern Alps is a natural one, although at first sight it might appear to be purely political since the former lie almost wholly in France and Switzerland, while the latter lie largely in Austria and Germany. Italy has a little of each and also has the Southern Alps, which are treated as a separate unit in Chapter 16(d).

The Western and Eastern Alps are separated partly because of structural differences, partly because of different schools of thought, but mostly because of different levels of erosion. We see much deeper into the structures in the west than in the east. It is therefore all the more convenient, as well as geographically logical, to deal with the Western Alps first. They were so important in the evolution of geological ideas that it is worth while saying a little about the history of their study.

It is difficult for us to realize that it was not until the end of the eighteenth century and the beginning of the nineteenth that men started exploring the higher Alps. This was a matter of wealth, leisure, and above all inclination, with the escape from the stranglehold of library learning. Outside the casino at Chamonix stands a statue of the Swiss geologist Horace de Saussure with a guide beside him pointing to the summit of Mont Blanc (4810 m), the highest mountain in Europe west of the Caucasus. This he was the first to climb. De Saussure proclaimed that to understand ancient rocks one should study modern mountain ranges (there are still many university administrators who need that lesson).

There followed the long period when the discoveries of stratigraphy, worked out in the easier terrains of England, France, and Germany, were applied to the confusing successions of the Alps. It became obvious that the successions were often out of order, with older lying upon younger, contrary to the principles of William Smith. It was also slowly worked out that there were major facies changes in contemporaneous strata that were also mixed up together. To put it in simple terms (as once it was) Alpine geologists learned to distinguish the sediments laid down on the north side, in the centre, and on the south side of the great Alpine trough.

Only when the stratigraphy had been worked out were they able to start sorting out the complications of the Alpine structures, with their great nappes, thrusts, and klippen. In these days when tectonics (especially in some countries not very far from the Moine Thrust) are quite divorced from palaeontology, I delight in pointing out the great dependence and faith that Alpine structural geologists have in fossils. Sometimes their faith is greater than mine as a palaeontologist. As one eminent contemporary Alpine geologist said 'one bad fossil is worth more than two good hypotheses'.

So it became understood that in the Western Alps (and even more so in the Eastern Alps) great masses of material had been transported tectonically vast distances from south to north, often finishing up as completely 'rootless' mountains isolated by later erosion, like the Pre-Alps at the east end of Lake Léman (Geneva). The first nappe to be recognized, and the most spectacular, was that in the Glarus Alps of eastern Switzerland where black Permian limestones rest on light-coloured Eocene limestones full of nummulites. These things are difficult to deny.

Having accepted the large lateral displacements, the dedicated Alpinists then started a long controversy, which goes on to this day, as to their immediate cause. Basically the argument was between the protagonists of compression and those of gravity. Were the lateral movements produced by great crustal shortening, of the order of 150 km, with the nappes squeezed out of the old troughs like toothpaste? Alternatively, were they produced by a great central uplift and then the nappes sliding off (in both directions) simply under the force of gravity? As is so often the case with fiercely contested issues, both parties were probably right. There was probably considerable compression at the lower levels and much gravity-sliding in the higher structures.

Finally, we come to the era of plate tectonics, although long before this people had recognized that there were rock types in the Alpine chains that were not usually found in contemporaneous strata elsewhere. The obvious example is the so-called 'Steinmann Trinity' of pillow lavas, serpentinites, and radiolarian cherts, which we now associate with ocean floors. It was also said that the earth's crust must have been unusually thin here to allow for the intensity of the folding. Estimates of the width of the 'Tethys Trough', from which all the material came, varied from 600 to 800 km, containing up to 3 km of sediment. Deformed fossils (such as squashed belemnites) indicate a shortening of as much as 12:1. There was just not enough room for that amount of normal crust. On the other hand, geophysics have shown that there is continental crust up to 8 or 9 km thick in the ancient massifs of the Alps, although admittedly these are only in the outer part of the chain. The Alps had long been blamed on the coming together of Europe and

Africa as a result of continental drift. The new concepts merely provided for the involvement (and consumption) of ocean floor material between the two continents.

In the Western Alps we have to think of two main groups of rocks; these may simply be called the 'basement' and the 'cover'. The basement rocks are Palaeozoic (and older) and were folded and metamorphosed in pre-Alpine orogenies; they are seen in the 'ancient massifs' such as Mont Blanc. The cover consists of Triassic and younger rocks which were involved only in the Alpine orogeny. Late Carboniferous and Permian rocks sometimes seem to act as part of the basement and sometimes seem to have moved with the cover, as in the Glarus Alps.

So far as the cover is concerned, it is the distribution of the topmost unit that distinguishes the Western from the Eastern Alps. In the west this is only seen in the extreme south; in the east it sweeps northwards to cover almost everything else in the northern ranges. The line along which it turns north coincides roughly with the Swiss–Austrian border, along the upper Rhine to the Boden See (Lake Constance), although it does steal the easternmost corner of Switzerland, including St. Moritz, Davos, and that peaceful place with the lovely name—the Engadine. The 'Engadine Line' is that part of the Insubric Line (discussed below) that shows considerable (perhaps 20 km) lateral displacement along which the southern edge of the Eastern Alps moves north relative to the Western Alps. It may be largely confined to the higher structures. This at one end and the Mediterranean at the other therefore define the limits of the Western Alps (Fig. 14.4).

Within the Western Alps we can distinguish three great structural zones: Austrides, Pennides, and Helvetides. These are arranged consecutively from the inside of the range to the outside and will be considered in that order. There are many subdivisions within them, which are not to be confused with the facies belts that have their own names. It is usual with the Alps to start from the external zones and work inwards, but it is more logical, as well as consistent with the other ranges discussed in this book, to start from the mysterious roots and to move upwards and outwards into the light.

Austrides

There is not much to say about the innermost Austride or Austro-Alpine Zone in the Western Alps, although it dominates the story in the east. It is only seen in the extreme south, in the Sesia Lanzo Zone of Italy and in the huge klippe of the Dent Blanche, north-east of Aosta, with associated smaller allochthonous masses.

The steeply dipping Sesia Lanzo Zone runs from just north of Turin almost to the northern tip of Lake Maggiore. It disappears southwards under the young sediments of the Po valley and is cut out northwards by the Insubric Line, which forms its inner margin. This margin consists of a series of crushed Mesozoic slices sometimes called the Canavese Zone.

The Insubric Line is one of the great mysteries of the Alps and of Europe. It is a very important suture and is used here to separate the Northern from the Southern Alpides. It is a clearly defined line between two quite different tectonic and metamorphic provinces, and is marked either by a thick zone of mylonites or by a clear-cut post-Alpine fault. Modern thinking would have it as the front of a continent or micro-continent advancing from the south. On that side of the line, all is comparatively quiet and peaceful, whereas to the north arise the great nappes. One snag about having it as the actual site of a

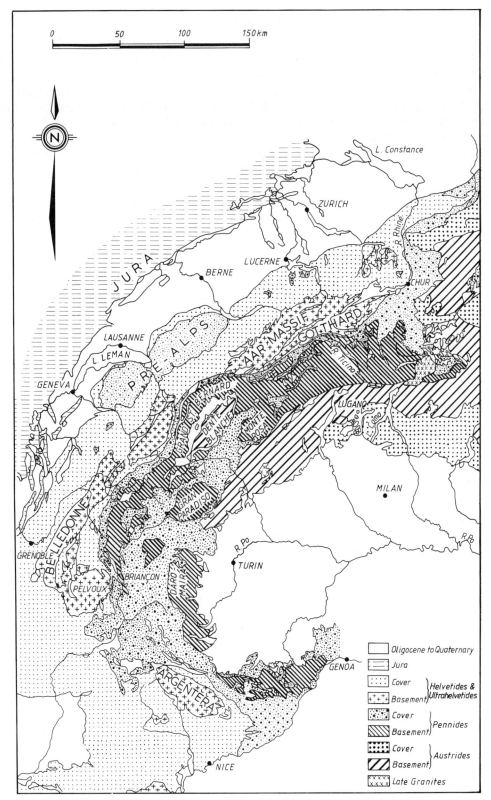

Fig. 14.4 Geological sketch-map of the Western Alps (after Trümpy, 1960, and others).

Map labels:

0   50   100   150 km

N

L. Constance

ZURICH

J U R A

BERNE

LUCERNE

R. Rhine

CHUR

LAUSANNE

P R E - A L P S

AAR MASSIF

GOTTHARD

L. LEMAN

GENEVA

GRAND ST. BERNARD

DENTE BLANCHE

MONTE ROSA

R. Ticino

LUGANO

L. Como

MILAN

BE-LLEDONNE

GRAN PARADISO

GRENOBLE

R. Po

TURIN

R. Po

PELVOUX

BRIANCON

DORA MAIRA

ARGENTERA

GENOA

NICE

Legend:

Oligocene to Quaternary

Jura

Cover } Helvetides &
Basement } Ultrahelvetides

Cover } Pennides
Basement }

Cover } Austrides
Basement }

Late Granites

subduction zone is that it lies within continental crust, while the ophiolitic ocean floor is in the Pennides to the west and north. There are squirts of ultra-mafic material along the line, however, which have been interpreted as upper mantle.

It could be argued that, stratigraphically, the Austrides are comparable with the Southern Alps and do not belong in the Northern Alps at all, but that would make life too complicated. Structurally they are very much part of the Western and Eastern Alps and so are considered here.

This zone is easiest seen while driving up the noisy Aosta Valley from the Italian plain. One soon crosses the Ivrea Zone of the Southern Alps and the Insubric Line to meet the basal part of this zone before Verres. It consists of high-temperature gneisses, marbles, and basic rocks, together with late Variscan granites, nearly all deeply altered by early and late phase Alpine metamorphism. Only locally are there unaltered remnants of the earlier part of the story. An upper unit showing only early phase metamorphism, known as the Diorite–Kinzigitic Zone, is preserved as klippen in the north and in the lower part of the Dent Blanche, resting allochthonously on Pennide elements, as in the perfect pyramid of the Matterhorn (Cervino) above Zermatt. This is thought to come from deep crustal levels in the South Alpine continent or microplate.

Cover rocks are also preserved in the Dent Blanche allochthon on the Franco-Italian border, apparently only in tectonic contact with the basement, but probably belonging here. The name of the mountain ('white tooth') immediately reminds one of the carbonates of the south. The succession starts with graphite schists and Verrucano-type breccias of the uppermost Palaeozoic and then passes into dominantly carbonate Mesozoic rocks, including familiar formations of the Southern and Eastern Alps such as the Norian 'Hauptdolomit' and the Rhaetian 'Kössener Schichten'. Great rushes of breccia appear in the Lower and Middle Jurassic at the top, implying that something important was happening in the vicinity at that time.

Pennides

These are the most extensive and most difficult of the West Alpine units. From the Italian Riviera to the Austrian frontier they form a belt of almost unbelievable complexity, not only in structure but also in nomenclature. They consist of a whole heap of nappes, each of limited lateral extent and each with its own name. The nappes are grouped in various ways, although no two authorities seem to use the same approach and whatever I do, I shall be wrong! Following the procedure so far, I approach them from the top (i.e., most interior) downwards and will consider the Piémont Zone first and then the Briançonnais and Sub-briançonnais Zones.

Piémont Zone. The Piémont (or Piedmont) Zone is often known as the *Schistes lustrés* Nappe after its most familiar rock type. Many would wish to connect it with the Ligurian Nappe of the Apennines, although it clearly faces in the opposite direction. Here, if anywhere, is the ocean floor that was squeezed out of a closing Tethys.

The Italians separate an Eastern Piémont Zone, which is entirely oceanic, from a Western Piémont Zone in which slices of a thin continental crust are preserved. In the former there are extensive Jurassic and Cretaceous ophiolites in a metamorphosed condition, associated with a small amount of metamorphosed sediments. Somewhat idealistically the sequence is thought to start with a basement of lherzolites, followed by gabbro–periodotite complexes, submarine basalts with intercalated radiolarites and detritus, plus a capping sedimentary succession of radiolarites with manganese nodules, pelagic limestones, and clay rocks.

It is suggested that the continuation of the eastern Piémont is seen in the Zermatt–Saas Zone of the Swiss Alps, which is characterized by high-pressure, low-temperature, late Cretaceous rocks of a blue schist facies with associated eclogites. But our stratigraphy has become very shaky in this zone.

The western Piémont has slabs of basement now seen as the 'Internal Massifs' of Dora Maira, Gran Paradiso, and Monte Rosa. They contrast with the 'External Massifs' of the Helvetides (to be discussed later) in being entirely allochthonous. They are essentially fold cores with Mesozoic 'cover' rocks both above and below.

The basement rocks here include both orthogneiss and paragneiss, which have suffered a lot both in the Alpine orogeny and in pre-Mesozoic orogenies. Variscan granites (ranging from 300 to 340 million years) are common, especially in the Gran Paradiso south-east of Mont Blanc (one of the oldest national parks in Europe, famous for its ibex). These cut the earlier schistosity and the whole is overlain by the usual late Carboniferous and Permian sequences found throughout the Alps, but here (e.g., in the Pinerolo area of the Dora Maria Massif) they are in a highly metamorphosed condition.

The Palaeozoic basement was covered by Triassic breccias and calcareous rocks (now marbles) ranging up into the Lower Jurassic. Then followed the remarkable formation which so much typifies this zone but which, from its few simple characters, is so easy to recognize in almost any metamorphic belt. This is the *schistes lustrés* (*calcescisti* in the Italian literature and *bündnerschiefer* in the German–Swiss). Strictly speaking these rocks consists of an inestimable thickness of sandy, calcareous schists, glittering with mica, and generally attributed (without much evidence) to the Jurassic and possibly Cretaceous. They are associated with ophiolites, sometimes in huge masses, such as that of Monte Viso (south-west of Turin) and pass upwards into radiolarites and pelagic limestones.

Because of their very plastic nature, the *schistes lustrés* are intensely deformed and this, together with their stratigraphical monotony, makes them difficult to interpret. They have been transported great distances towards the outside of the Alps in a whole series of nappes. They would seem to represent the deposits of a trough (or eugeosyncline) associated with a subduction zone, or simply a great thickness of sediment that accumulated on the leading edge of a continent before the Alpine paroxysm. Their movement may have been partly assisted by Triassic salt, but they carried with them the internal massifs, so that Monte Rosa, for example, lies in a recumbent fold on top of the Grand St. Bernard nappe of the more external Briançonnais Zone. Such are the complexities of Alpine tectonics that the Grand St. Bernard nappe is also folded back the other way into the Monte Rosa nappe (Fig. 14.5).

Later in age (late Cretaceous), but presumably coming out of the same trough, was the Helminthoid flysch nappe. This travelled much farther. The name refers to the deep-water trace fossils characterizing this flysch, which was as incompetent and plastic as the *schistes lustrés*. It rode right over the Briançonnais and Dauphinois Nappes, discussed below, and is found in the hollows between the External Massifs. In passing it scattered souvenirs in the form of klippen, such as those of Chambeyron, Peyre-Haute, and Monte Jurin, on various lower structures.

All the outwardly directed movements mentioned so far occurred early in the Alpine

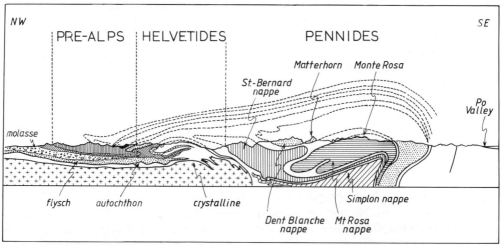

Fig. 14.5 Cross-section of the western Alps (after Trümpy, 1960, and others).

orogenesis. Towards the outside of the range, movements tended to occur later, often overriding or carrying forward overlying nappes that had already arrived. Thus in the upper part of the Durance Valley, Briançonnais Nappes of the outer part of the Pennides were pushed over the Helminthoid flysch nappe which had already been thrust from the interior. This in turn lies on autochthonous rocks of the Helvetides and displays a photogenic recumbent fold on the side of the valley below Embrun.

One of the great problems of Alpine geology has always been the Pre-Alps. This is a remarkable line of mountains that stands along the front of the Alpine chain in north-west Switzerland. They always figure, for example, as a background in the innumerable pictures of Byron's Chateau de Chillon at the east end of Lake Léman. Here you can easily see that they rest on Neogene molasse, whereas if you follow this molasse up the left bank of the Rhône to Monthey you find it resting in its turn (without tectonic break) on the ancient rocks of the Aiguilles Rouges Massif. The problem about the Pre-Alps therefore is where they came from. They have obviously been torn right off from their roots and are resting on autochthonous structures. Nearly every nappe in the Alps has been blamed for them (including several that probably do not exist) but it seems likely that, while the greater part of the pile of nappes in the Pre-Alps belong to the Briançonnais and Sub-briançonnais Zones, the topmost, farthest travelled part belongs to the Helminthoid flysch.

Another unsettled problem of the Alps is the so-called Valais Zone, which is also seen in the Valley of Aosta in Italy, around Sion in southern Switzerland, and probably on into the Eastern Alps as the Grisonides. This is trough material very comparable to that of the Piémont Zone (although relatively poor in ophiolites). The problem is whether tectonically it came from there (i.e., the innermost Alps) or whether it is closer to the Sub-briançonnais Zone and originates from a more central position. This, however, belongs more to the problems of the Eastern Alps and to the next section.

Briançonnais and Sub-briançonnais Zones.   This brings us to that great belt in the centre part of the Alpine arc which is often just referred to as the Briançonnais. Strictly speaking that term is defined by its stratigraphy, but it is also used in a purely structural connotation and for a palaeogeographical/topographical feature of Mesozoic times.

It has a poorly exposed crystalline basement and then thick uppermost Carboniferous and Permian terrestrial deposits, the former with valuable coal-seams and useful plant remains for dating purposes. In the Alps generally, normal Upper Carboniferous coal-seams can be seen passing into anthracites and then into graphite schists, but here they are often well preserved and unaltered, for example at the little village of Villard-Laté just west of Briançon itself, where tree trunks can be seen parallel oriented and uncrushed as they were when they were washed down into an intermontane basin. These are the deposits of limnic basins, cut off among the new Variscan mountains from the paralic basins of the north and receiving their plant material from the higher ground round about, rather than from *in situ* plant growth. There may be more than 3000 m of such sediments around the valley of the Arc.

Evidently this sedimentation followed the Asturian phase movements, which happened before the end of the Westphalian with metamorphism, granite emplacement, and subsequent conglomerates. Most of the coal-bearing strata are therefore Stephanian, as is usual in the Alps, but there is a break in the middle and the upper part is swamped with more conglomerates. The Stephanian is so much characterized by the flora to be expected in such dry upland environmental conditions (and by the absence of the non-marine bivalves of the paralic belt) that one wonders if ecology is not here unduly confused with stratigraphy.

The Permian is also coarse and continental, with acidic intrusions and extrusions of various kinds. It is capped unconformably by Verrucano conglomerates coming from a variety of sources. The Middle Triassic is thick and dolomitic, dominating the local scenery (e.g., on the Col d'Iseran), but thereafter the rest of the Mesozoic succession is remarkably thin with many breaks. Often the Trias is just followed by a thin Upper Jurasic marble and then by thin Upper Cretaceous. Such deposits as there are seem to be of a deep-water facies and this zone has been called a 'leptogeosyncline' or 'starved' geosyncline, formed out of reach of land-derived sediment on the north side of Tethys. Considerable lateral variations have been worked out and each nappe has its own succession.

Locally, carbonate build-ups occurred, perhaps on unstable horsts or even (in view of the earlier volcanism) on island arcs. A feature of the zone is the presence of 'hardgrounds', where sedimentation stopped for a time and a hard ferruginous crust developed on the sea-floor (a good example is easily accessible at St. Crépin near Argentière). Finally in the Eocene, sandy flysch came into the area. The Brainçonnais Zone was, in effect, a ridge between the huge trough just discussed, towards the inside of the range, and a lesser trough towards the outside.

This outer trough is represented by the Sub-briançonnais Zone in which the Mesozoic is much more completely represented. We are now on the outer edge of the internal Alps and this was evidently a place of instability throughout Mesozoic times. The crystalline basement is seen and the end Palaeozoic sedimentary succession passes up directly into the Mesozoic. This has many breaks recording the instability, together with some notable developments of breccia in the Jurassic and Lower Cretaceous (e.g., the colourful Oxfordian ones at the Col du Telégraph, north of Valloire). These seem to be submarine landslip deposits coming off the outer ridge.

Structurally we are now near the outside of the internal Alps and the front of the main over-thrusting. As already said, Briançonnais and Sub-briançonnais elements probably form most of the huge klippen of the Pre-Alps, out at the front of the chain. Triassic salt probably played a big part in lubricating the bottoms of the sliding sheets. This happened not only at the bottom of the pile, but also between nappes within it. This is well seen in the ascent from the south to the Col du Galibier (well known to Tour de France cyclists) on the north side of the Pelvoux Massif. The magnificent panorama at the top shows jagged Triassic dolomites parting company with the rocks below along the usual plane of weakness. The same structure goes on into Switzerland as the Grand Saint Bernard Nappe, although some Alpine geologists would separate here a further Vanoise Zone with a similar history to that of the Briançonnais. This slides on great wedges of Triassic evaporites. In places (e.g., at the Lac de Tignes, west of the ski resort of Val d'Isère) there are whole mountains of gypsum under the nappe.

Superficially, one of the oddest features about some of the Briançonnais structures is their tendency to reverse, that is to say to face east and south in direct opposition to the main movement of the chain to the west and north. This has already been referred to at Monte Rosa and is seen south of Briançon itself, where some of the slabs head back towards Italy and Monte Viso.

The Sub-briançonnais structures tend to be split up in thin slices, heaped one upon the other, *en echelon*. This is well seen east of the Belledonne Massif, where there are also a number of 'digitations' or bundles of folds. Northwards the Sub-briançonnais tends to be less obvious under the main mass of the Grand St. Bernard.

Helvetides

This is the external zone of the Western Alps. It consists of autochthonous crystalline basement rocks (the External Massifs) and an autochthonous or parautochthonous cover of Mesozoic and Tertiary rocks. The Helvetides take their name, of course, from Switzerland, and at the French end of the chain are known as the Dauphinoise Zone.

They form the Sub-Alps in the south, best seen perhaps along the valley of the Drôme which runs into the mountains from the Rhône Valley, south of Valence. This is the traditional route followed by Hannibal and his elephants before he was seriously misguided by locals along a track that does not even have a road today. North from here, the Helvetides form the frontal ranges of the Alps around Grenoble (with its fine Institute of Alpine Geology) and stand up above the Franco-Swiss Plain, where the Alps part company with the Jura at Chambéry. In Switzerland they swing round as some of the most glorious scenery in Europe, to terminate in the Rhine and Liechtenstein, with nearby Zurich as a great centre for their study.

Basement. The names of the External Massifs within this zone sound like a roll-call of some of the finest European mountains. From south to north they are: the Argentera Massif (Mercantour) on the Italian frontier north of Nice, Pelvoux above Briançon and its long extension—the Belledonne Massif—behind Grenoble; then there is the Mont Blanc Massif itself and, across the valley of Chamonix, the associated Aiguilles Rouges. In Switzerland there are the two great parallel massifs of the Aar (with the Jungfrau and the Eiger) and the Gotthard. Right at the eastern end is the smallest massif of all in the

Glarus Alps. The narrow synclines of younger sediments which split some of these massifs make it possible to relate them to one another structurally.

The massifs are comparable in generalities. They all lie near the inner boundary of the external zone, but are only locally affected by the Alpine metamorphism unlike the 'internal' massifs of the Pennide chains. They all have a high-grade metamorphic foundation of mica and hornblende gneisses that appear to range in age from Precambrian up to Carboniferous and which have resulted from probably more than one orogenesis during that time. The most commonly held view seems to be that there was an end Precambrian orogeny and a Variscan orogeny, but that there is no real proof of anything that could be called Caledonian.

The older metamorphic rocks include thick clastic sedimentary sequences, with a notable development of limestones at the top, and important masses of intrusive rocks and migmatites. Younger granites of Variscan age are a feature of some massifs. Mont Blanc is an obvious example, with the age of the main intrusion falling in the Westphalian, although there are older dates hereabouts and some biotites have Tertiary ages due to Alpine reactivation. The main Variscan folding is on roughly north–south lines (well seen in the Belledonne Massif), at least as it is seen now.

The massifs evidently only rose to their present dominance in late Tertiary times, as is reflected in the surrounding Neogene sedimentation. Repeated unconformities and thinning in the Mesozoic overlying the massifs indicate that they were already positive features during that era.

Although they are generally accepted as autochthonous, this is something of a relative term since in places they received a considerable shove in the Alpine orogeny. Thus the Mont Blanc Massif has pushed westwards in great slices to bury and squash the Chamonix syncline between it and the Aiguilles Rouges. At least they do not appear to have been torn off at the roots like the metamorphic masses in the inner Alps.

The continuation of the structure just mentioned is seen in Switzerland in the magnificent, much-visited Bernese Oberland above Interlaken. Here the Aiguilles Rouges may be recognized in the separate little massif of Gastern. This is virtually overidden by the huge Aar Massif (Jungfrau, Eiger, etc.) which equates with Mont Blanc. The smaller disappears under the larger near the famous and expensive resort of Grindelwald.

An important feature of the massifs, as in the other basement successions in the Alps, is the presence of thick late Carboniferous and Permian sequences resting on the crystalline basement and in a less metamorphosed condition. These post-date the main Variscan movements but are preserved in shallow synclines as a result of a comparatively gentle folding episode at the end of Palaeozoic times. The folds tend to be at a slight angle to the earlier fold axes and—in the Aar Massif for example—often remarkably parallel to the folds containing Mesozoic sediments which were formed in Tertiary times.

It may be significant, in connection with the Meso-Europa part of this book, that the best preserved, least metamorphosed, late Palaeozoic sequences in the autochthonous massifs of the Alps are in the south and west. Thus in the northernmost Aar Massif of Switzerland there was metamorphism near the end of the Carboniferous and Variscan granites penetrate the Permian. Around the Argentera Massif at the other end of the chain, in contrast, there is one of the most remarkable developments of Permian in Europe. The mountain chains of Europe are full of spectacular limestone gorges, each more breathtaking than the last, but the gorges of Daluis and Cians, south-west of the

Argenfera Massif, are the only ones known to me which cut through incredibly thick and quite unmetamorphosed Permian red mudstone.

Cover. The Mesozoic and Tertiary cover rocks of the Helvetides are usually divided into the Ultradauphinois (internally) and the Dauphinois (externally), but in the south there is an even more external unit—the Sub-Alps—and these pass into the Provençal Alps which were considered in Chapter 13(c).

The Ultradauphinois Zone is parautochthonous. It consists of the original sedimentary cover in the east, which was detached from its base (e.g., on the east side of the Pelvoux and Belledonne Massifs) and moved a short distance over the autochthon. This is well seen in the Aiguilles d'Arve Nappe, west of St. Michel in the Arc Valley.

The succession in the Ultradauphinois Zone begins with thick Trias, comprising basal quartzites, dolomites, and evaporites. These last often provide a frontal gypsiferous slide plane for the nappes. The Jurassic, where preserved, is like that of the Dauphinois (discussed below), but somewhat thinner, due to being on the outer side of the Briançon ridge. The great feature of the Ultradauphinois is the tremendous thickness of late Eocene flysch which rests unconformably on a variety of underlying rocks, due to important pre-Bartonian movements.

The Dauphinois Zone is the outer trough (not to be confused with the frontal molasse trough) of the Alps. It is seen from Nice on the Mediterranean to Grenoble, through Chartreuse of the glorious liqueurs, all along the front of the Alps into the famous Helvetide nappes of Switzerland. These are hardly nappes at all in the sense of the internal Alps, but they represent more intensive disturbance than that seen in France.

The Mesozoic succession is extremely thick and in a good state of preservation (at least for the Alps). In that much of it is limestone and none of it is volcanic, this zone has been called a miogeosyncline.

The Trias, however, is thin with a basal cross-bedded sandstone that is incredibly persistent around the Alps. This rests unconformably on the basement, usually in the latter's crystalline form, and this unconformity can be recognized in many places. It is well displayed, for example, along the narrow road 1000 m above the Romanche Valley near Bourg d'Oisans, where it rests on the metamorphic rocks of the Belledonne Massif and usually 'sticks' to them tectonically. Above the basal sandstone comes dolomite and then an evaporite-bearing sequence. These three have been compared with the triumvirate of the German Trias and remind us that we are now in northern Europe (although not forgetting that such facies go down to Spain and Morocco in one direction and Bulgaria in the other).

It was in the Jurassic, however, that the Dauphinois Trough really got going. This is beautifully seen around the just-mentioned town of Bourg d'Oisans (south-east of Grenoble). Great cliffs of thinly bedded shales and limestones are seen on all sides. This is typical 'Lias', as known far from the Alps, but is of an incredible thickness here. There are more than 1000 m of just the lowest part. In places it is flat-lying; elsewhere down the valley it is intensely folded.

In the Middle Jurassic, limestones become more general, including oolites to the west, and then after the usual muddy Callovian and Oxfordian sediments there was a build-up to massive, white Tithonian limestones. These are the deeper water equivalents of those seen with coral reefs in the Juras. They are pelagic in nature, with tintinnids and those strange Tethyan forms, the pygopid brachiopods. *Pygote janitor* takes its name from the limestone passage known as the Port de France, at the northern entrance to Grenoble, when this was not part of France. At Claps de Luc, near Die, a spectacular landslip of these rocks in the fifteenth century blocked the valley of the Drôme.

We are here in the realm of cicadas and lavender fields. From hereon southwards the facies are different and more reminiscent of the warm south. This is what is usually known as the Sub-Alps, with a much more subdued topography and comparatively gentle, non-Alpine structures. It is particularly a region for the Cretaceous. During the early part of that period there was a deep trough here, running roughly east–west, in which a great thickness of sediment accumulated. The mainly argillaceous deposits of the trough are characterized by unlikely fossils such as aptychi and nautiloid jaws (which survived the solution of aragonitic shells). Equivalent strata are missing farther north, presumably due to erosion. They culminate in a shallow-water reefal limestone, near the top of the Lower Cretaceous, which we have already met in many parts of Europe. Hannibal passed under its shadow from the great cliff of Glandasse in the Drôme Valley. This is the Urgonian, seen from Spain to the Soviet Union round the outer rim of the Alps, but here in its type locality, for it takes its name from Orgon, just south of here.

Southwards again the Mesozoic passes into what is called the Provençal facies at about the latitude of one of my favourite geological centres—Castellane. But here we are getting involved with the east–west folds of the Pyrenean system, although many features (such as the dominating Tithonian and Urgonian limestones) are similar.

Later Cretaceous rocks are found more widely and in a shallow-water, glauconitic facies with notable breaks. Late Eocene flysch spreads over the Dauphinois zone, as over the Ultradauphinois, sometimes cutting right down to the crystalline basement. In the Sub-Alps it is wholly continental, as is the Oligocene generally. The Miocene saw the inception of molasse deposition on a huge scale, with sometimes more than 4500 m of debris from the new mountains. This became very much involved in the structures of the region. There was lengthy erosion beforehand and locally the molasse is exceptionally thick and coarse, notably the conglomeratic *Nagelfluh* of Switzerland. Although the Dauphinois Zone in France is autochthonous or parautochthonous, it can be demonstrated in places that the frontal thrust of the Alps has carried a considerable distance over the molasse of the frontal trough. The pebbles in the latter are frequently driven into one another, as though by titanic forces (although pressure solution plays the chief part). This confirms the general thesis that the climax of the orogenic phases is later towards the outside of the range.

After that, the main story of the Western Alps generally was one of uplift, erosion and, of course, the Pleistocene glaciations. It can be argued as to who first produced the idea of ancient glaciations (and it is surprising with the benefit of hindsight that great early Alpinists such as De Saussure did not), but there is no doubt as to where it originated— in the Western Alps. Looking at some of the famous existing glaciers in the Alps, such as the Rhône glacier in Switzerland or the Mer de Glace in France, it is obvious to the least observant that they once extended much further down their present valleys. It is not a very big step from that to seeing everywhere the morainic deposits, the glaciated valleys, the smoothed roches moutonées, the exotic blocks, and the great heaps of outwash gravels. It was in the Western Alps that the four distinct glaciations of the Pleistocene were first postulated, then to be recognized all over the world (whether they were there or not).

14(d)   Eastern Alps

This is to me the most beautiful part of Europe, although I must admit some competition from parts of the Jura and Tatra, the west coast of Norway, the Greek islands, and the English Cotswolds. The Eastern Alps consist of rugged mountains and cultivated valleys in highly civilized country, without much of the tawdriness or overcrowding of other Alpine ranges. The people paint pictures on their houses and wear the national costume with complete naturalness, even round the remote corners that the ordinary tourist does not reach.

The Eastern Alps extend for some 500 km from the upper Rhine to Vienna and occupy the easternmost part of Switzerland, the south-east corner of West Germany, and most of Austria. The western limit was defined in the last chapter. One can stand on their easternmost end and see them disappear beneath the post-orogenic deposits around Vienna, to appear again in the distance as the first ridges of the Carpathians. Here they are constrained by the Bohemian Massif to the north (Fig. 14.6). Northwards, the main part of the range drops down through tumbled molasse country under the great northern plain of Europe. Southwards they have the razor-sharp margin of the Insubric Line.

It is impossible to deal with the Eastern Alps in the same way as the other Alpine chains, from 'internal' to 'external', because the most 'internal' are also the most 'external' and there are masses of supposed autochthon in the middle. It is more logical to climb the pile from bottom to top as follows: Pennides, Lower East Alpine Sheet, Middle East Alpine Sheet, Upper East Alpine Sheet (Greywacke Zone, Northern Calcareous Alps), Flysch Zone, and Helvetides.

Pennides

As in the Western Alps, this zone consists of strongly deformed metamorphic rocks, mainly gneisses, schists, and phyllites, but whereas in the west these are strongly allochthonous, here they appear to form the rigid base over which rode the great thrust sheets. Views differ as to their true position, but it seems to be generally accepted nowadays that they are autochthonous or semi-autochthonous. They are best known in the huge Tauern Window, which is a structural culmination in the centre of the Eastern Alps, east of the Brenner Pass. Smaller tectonic inliers are seen in the Engadine Window in Switzerland in the west and the Wechsel Window, south-south-west of Vienna in the east.

Within these windows it is necessary to separate two major units: the Central Gneiss and the Slate Cover or *Schieferhülle*.

Central Gneiss. This is seen in a series of irregular domes, mainly in the Tauern Window (e.g., in the Zillertal Alps). It chiefly consists of strongly deformed orthogneiss, including striking augen gneisses, with amphibolites and other associated rocks. The deformation and metamorphism was Variscan and the gneisses are cut by Permian-dated granites. Radiometric dates are a little confusing because of reactivation in the Alpine orogeny, and the final cooling of some of these deep-seated rocks does not seem to have occurred until the Miocene. The general coincidence of Variscan metamorphism with the centre of an Alpine fold belt is again noteworthy, especially when one considers the excellent state of preservation of the Palaeozoic succession in the Carnic Alps, not very far away to the south.

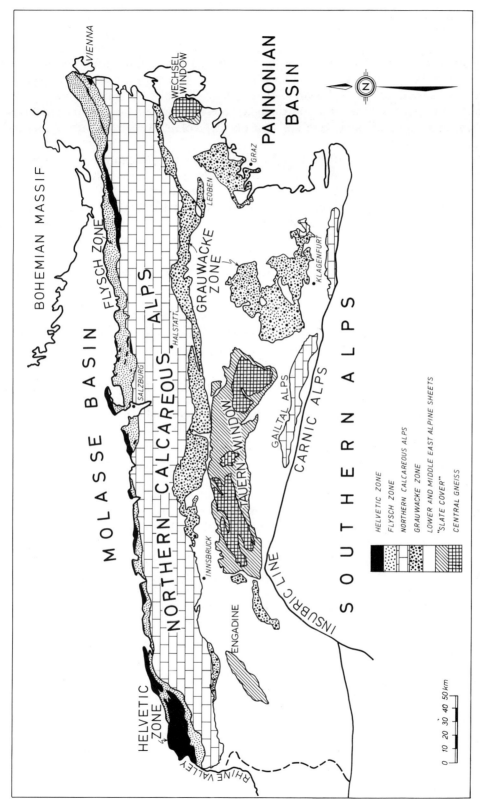

Fig. 14.6   Geological sketch-map of the Eastern Alps (after Oxburgh, 1968, by kind permission of the Council of the Geologists' Association).

Only the uppermost part of the Central Gneiss is thought to have been affected tectonically (as distinct from metamorphically) by the Alpine movements. Formerly it was thought that everything here was far travelled and that the Pennine Alps originated from a root zone down on the Italian border, squeezed out of what is here known by the general term 'Insubric Line'. It is now thought, however, that only some of the top layers of gneiss were torn off, and these are seen on the geological map as narrow tongues swinging to the north.

The Central Gneiss is usually thought to be overlain unconformably by a sedimentary cover that now constitutes the next unit. However, this is a matter of dispute and it can be demonstrated locally that the gneiss is intruded into the cover.

Slate Cover. Although for consistency I use the English translation (and prefer 'cover' to 'mantle' because of the latter's other connotations), this unit is most generally known by its German name *Schieferhülle*. As this implies, it largely consists of metamorphosed sediments but with some igneous elements, especially in the upper part. It is exposed in all three of the tectonic windows referred to earlier and is particularly well seen along the famous Glocknerstrasse, one of the highest and most spectacular passes in Europe, over the Grossglockner, where it is in its most usual form of calcareous and green schists.

The Slate Cover is usually thought of as the Mesozoic succession on top of the Palaeozoic massifs of the Central Gneiss. Nowhere has so much depended on a single fossil—an isolated Upper Jurassic ammonite—but lithological comparisons also help to confirm the general correlation and palaeogeographical reconstruction. It may be that the bottom of the succession goes down into the Upper Palaeozoic with two Variscan phases, the main early one already referred to and a later one with intrusions. Some of the older metamorphics have suffered retrograde metamorphism in the Alpine movements, making it difficult in places to distinguish them from the higher units.

The supposed Palaeozoic part at the bottom is mainly black phyllites with local quartzites (some of them graphitic) and abundant igneous rocks, now amphibolites and green schists. There are also some peridotites and other ultra-basic bodies. Significantly there is little in the way of carbonates and the whole could well be a eugeosynclinal equivalent of the greywacke succession discussed below. This is overlain by about 100 m of conglomerates and quartzites, often arkosic, with some gypsum. Conventionally this is regarded as an early Triassic transgressive deposit, but it could include the 'Verrucano' of the Permian. Above comes a carbonate sequence assumed to be equivalent to the thick Middle and Upper Triassic limestones and dolomites of the Northern Calcareous Alps, but whereas the latter reach 2 or 3 km in thickness, here there is a mere 200 m. The marbles and dolomites include some gypsiferous dolomites of the distinctive form known as *Rauhwacke*.

The rest of the succession is mainly phyllites and other formerly fine-grained sediments, but includes thin carbonate horizons such as the critical one with the late Jurassic fossil, possibly a deep-water deposit comparable with aptychus limestones elsewhere. These deposits probably represent the Jurassic and Cretaceous filling of a trough that extended through both the Western and Eastern Alps and four distinct facies belts have been recognized, parallel to the line of the trough and showing a passage from one side to the other. This was the centre of the so-called 'Alpine geosyncline'. Associated with the sediments are quite reasonable ophiolites, well seen in the large quarries at Kraubath, near Leoben, where chromite and magnesite were worked in the past. It may therefore be that we have here vestiges of Mesozoic ocean floor as in the Western Alps.

The metamorphism which affected the Slate Cover was of a low-temperature, high-pressure nature, producing blue schist grade rocks, and inevitably these rocks enter into any discussion of plate tectonics in the Alpine belt. The deformation is intense, with recumbent folds, and has not been fully sorted out. It has usually been assumed that the orogeny responsible came at the end of Mesozoic times, but there is evidence in the Engadine Window that the deposition of the Slate Cover may have continued into the Tertiary.

Lower East Alpine Sheet

Almost encircling all three of the large tectonic windows discussed above, is a group of rocks conveniently referred to by this name. For simplicity, in Fig. 14.6 they are not separated from what is here called the Middle East Alpine Sheet, discussed below. They are particularly well seen on the north-east side of the Tauern Window, south of Radstadt (Fig. 14.7), where their succession can best be demonstrated. In the form of monotonous schists and gneisses they also occupy a large area around the Wechsel Window in the east.

The Lower East Alpine Sheet consists mainly of slices of metamorphosed Mesozoic sediments thrust over the rocks of the Pennine Zone, but there are also quartz phyllites of Palaeozoic age pushed right over on top again. The Mesozoic rocks themselves are further divisible into a lower thinner unit characterized by slates with quartzites and numerous breccias and an upper mainly calcareous unit that shows strong affinities with the Northern Calcareous Alps. These two units are separated by a slab of undated gneiss.

Within the Mesozoic it is possible to distinguish a full Triassic and Lower Jurassic succession with Upper Jurassic and/or Lower Cretaceous elements above. The whole represents a series of tectonic slices that moved northwards over the axial zone and piled up on its northern side. All the structures imply movements in this direction, although it is not clear if they moved on their own account or merely as passive sufferers under the great masses of higher sheets that moved over them. They show intense internal deformation so that fossils are fantastically stretched. Elsewhere the whole unit is represented simply by a band of highly sheared rocks, but the degree of metamorphism is generally

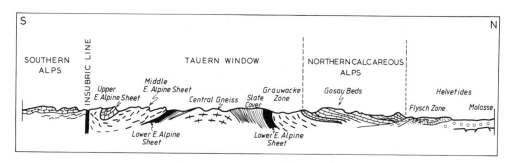

Fig. 14.7 Cross-section through the Eastern Alps.

low and most of the rocks are in the condition of slates or recrystallized limestones. Presumably they all came from the southern side of the trough represented in the Slate Cover.

Middle East Alpine Sheet

This seems to be the most suitable name for this unit, although it is usually known as the *Altkristallin* ('Old Crystalline Sheet'), which is just the sort of ambiguous field term that I discourage my students from using. Admittedly, 'Middle' is itself ambiguous, but I think it is useful for the great area of rocks in the central Alps that come between the tectonic windows with their immediate cover and the huge distinctive sheets of the upper units that went right over the top.

The *Altkristallin* in the strict sense consists of a complex series of slices of gneisses, schists, quartzites, and amphibolites, which appear to have suffered several phases of metamorphism. They are presumed to be Palaeozoic in age and intrusive granite-gneisses have been dated as early Carboniferous. In the south, near the Insubric Line, is a series of later acidic igneous bodies comparable with those of the Southern Alps (such as the Adamello intrusion). These are part of the so-called 'peri-Adriatic suite' which seems to be related to the emplacement of an errant microplate.

Above the *Altkristallin* comes a Palaeozoic and Mesozoic cover, south and east of the Tauern Window, with a fairly complete fossil record and only low-grade metamorphism. In the Gailtal Alps and neighbouring ranges the succession is dominated by Triassic carbonates like those of the Northern Calcareous Alps. In fact they are so much alike that it is appropriate to use the same ornament in Fig. 14.6. These rest directly on the *Altkristallin* with a basal conglomerate. They are close to the Insubric Line and remind one of comparable successions in the Southern Alps of northern Italy and Yugoslavia (and in fact all down the Dinarides and Hellenides to the Aegean). All of these have many points in common, especially to a student of Mesozoic benthos.

So far as the Middle East Alpine Sheet is concerned, the facts that it is slightly metamorphosed and its Mesozoic part is so discontinuous have led to the conclusion that this is a separate and lower allochthonous mass than the one which carried the Northern Calcareous Alps right over the top. The alternative interpretation is that it is the more or less autochthonous cover of the Central Alps and only the northern ranges are allochthonous.

Grauwacke Zone

We come therefore to what is sometimes called the Upper East Alpine Sheet, but which it is necessary to divide into the Grauwacke Zone below and the Northern Calcareous Alps above. *Grauwacke* (or 'Greywacke') literally just means 'grey rock'. It is an old Austrian miners' term for the monotonous grey rocks in which they found most of their ore. Whatever may have been done to the term since by sedimentologists, it is still usefully applied to the old grey phyllites and quartzites which form most of this zone. It extends in a broad, comparatively low-lying belt from near Innsbruck to the Vienna Basin with some large tectonic outliers to the south, notably west of the Tauern Window and in the mountains north of Klagenfurt and Graz. The main outcrop is limited to the south by what is called the Tauern Line and to the north by the great face of the Northern Calcareous Alps.

It is generally presumed to be a more or less complete Palaeozoic succession, although only Silurian, Devonian, and Carboniferous have been confidently proved with fossils. In terms of environment it ranges from graptolitic shales to continental deposits with land plants; there are almost certainly big breaks. There are also important developments of volcanic rocks, notably basalts and quartz porphyries.

Associated with all this are the valuable mineral veins for which the zone is famous, and which have been worked since prehistoric times. Especially important has been the copper, which is till mined today, for example at Mitterberg, near Bischofshofen, south of Salzburg. Eastwards, two distinct thrust sheets are recognized with mineralization between them. There is further mineralization at the junction between the Grauwacke Zone and the overlying Northern Calcareous Alps, with the replacement of limestone by siderite, as in the huge quarries at Erzberg ('iron mountain') north-west of the mining capital of Leoben.

The contact between the Grauwacke Zone and the Middle East Alpine Sheet along the Tauern Line is very steep and is probably a fault. Elsewhere the zone appears to have been thrust over the units mentioned above. The top contact is a complex one; there is an intermediate zone of intercalated slices of Grauwacke Zone rocks and salt-bearing Permo-Trias. It may have originally been an unconformity which was later complicated by slipping on the evaporites, although there was probably not much relative movement. Internally the zone is isoclinally folded and imbricate, with some at least of the structures probably pre-Mesozoic.

Northern Calcareous Alps

This is the great wall of limestone that one sees along the north side of the Inn Valley beyond Innsbruck. Behind are ranges of marvellous mountains full of lovely towns of happy memory like Halstatt, St. Wolfgang and Pertisau, in Austria, and (with unhappy memories for my generation) Berchtesgaden on the German side of the frontier.

Superficially it all looks simple. Stand in the Inn Valley, for example at Jenbach where the rack railway climbs up to lonely Achensee, and the Northern Calcareous Alps just look like an ordinary Mesozoic limestone escarpment, albeit vastly larger than most. The outcrop of the range as a whole seems simple and continuous all the way from the Vorarlberg in Switzerland to the gates of Vienna. Even in transverse view, for example along the Salzach valley south of Salzburg, there is no obvious intense or recumbent folding. This has led some workers, right up to the present day, to maintain a simple autochthonous succession. The majority view, however, and the one accepted here is that it is all allochthonous, having travelled a great distance from the south as a pile of thrust sheets.

Unlike the successions in the Western Alps, here the main part of the sedimentation occurred early in the Mesozoic. In the Western Alps, the 'Muschelkalk' is a comparatively thin marker band, sometimes repeated several times tectonically in a single mountainside. In the Northern Calcareous Alps, however, Middle and Upper Triassic limestones and dolomites reach up to 3 km in thickness and form a whole mountain range.

This is the Mecca of Triassic specialists. At the bottom of the succession, the Lower Trias (and perhaps some Upper Permian) are only thinly developed, but with important evaporites. Rock-salt produces lubrication for the thrusts and diapirs, of which the most famous is that at Halstatt. The name means 'salt town' and many other names in this region (such as Salzburg and Hallein) also indicate the proximity of salt. Halstatt is also famous for its Iron Age cemetery with all the craftsmanship of the early salt miners.* At the present day, huge caverns are left by the pumping in of water and the pumping out of brine.

The Werfen Beds were named from here and give an alternative stage name (Werfenian) to the Lower Trias. Their reddish thin-bedded limestone and shale alternations are distinctive. Above them come the chief glory of the Northern Calcareous Alps (and the Eastern Alps as a whole). These are the famous carbonate formations of the Middle and Upper Trias: the Halstatt Limestone, the Dachstein Limestone, and the *Hauptdolomit* ('Main Dolomite'). These represent successive interfingering facies from south to north, respectively, from offshore through reefs to lagoonal and back-reef environments. The Halstatt Limestone is a deep-water deposit of pelagic limestones and shales, full of ammonites. The Dachstein Limestone is particularly prominent, up to 1800 m thick, passing from massive reefs (mostly algal) to bedded lagoonal carbonates, and then in the *Hauptdolomit* to a special back-reef facies with patch reefs above. All these yield particularly fine faunas such as huge megalodontid bivalves and the rich and strange brachiopod faunas at Kössen in Bavaria (probably the best Rhaetian fauna in the world). Huge assemblages of ammonites, brachiopods, bivalves, and other forms have been collected and are housed in Vienna.†

There is a similar story, but by no means so spectacular, in the Jurassic, which is more variable. Argillaceous deposits in the Lower and Middle Jurassic build up to carbonates again in the Upper Jurassic with reefs once more to the south and back-reef to the north. The Hierlatz Limestone is the most famous and easily recognizable of the Jurassic formations, being reddish in colour with abundant crinoid ossicles. The variability is due to the start of tectonism, with sudden changes in thickness and facies. Coarse breccias may be related to submarine fault scarps. *Rosso ammonitico* deposits were formed on sea-mounts and can be seen to penetrate earlier karstic weathering. The Lower Cretaceous is characterized by breccias and shallow-water carbonates. Generally speaking, therefore, the Mesozoic of the Northern Calcareous Alps is of a distinctly shallow-water nature compared with the deposits in the axial zone.

Major tectonism began in mid to late Jurassic times and lasted until the mid Cretaceous. Four major structural units have been recognized and many smaller ones. Whether or not each should be called a nappe is a matter of taste, although 'nappists' from other parts of the Alpine belt are surprised to find as many as four of them postulated in a single quarry. Each of the major units is characterized by particular facies and all are thought to have travelled from the south. How far, is still a matter of dispute Some would say comparatively short distances, the majority would say right over the Tauern Window.

---

* One can (or could) still see an ancient adit, squeezed closed again by weight, with a layer of half-burnt wood spills that had been held by Iron Age miners in their teeth for light as they dug out the salt.
† Notably in the Geologische Bundesandtat, surely the only Survey in the world to be housed in a palace.

Apart from the structural evidence, what inclines me towards the far-travelled concept is the nature of the faunas. I am particularly struck by contrasts such as that between the Lower Jurassic brachiopod fauna in the Northern Calcareous Alps (e.g., on the Schafberg above St. Wolfgang) and that of the Gresten facies in the Helvetic Zone. This contrast is seen again in Hungary, where the former is, surprisingly, far to the north of the latter—see Chapter 15(b). This must mean major over-thrusting.

The thrusting can be dated within the Mesozoic by the Gosau Beds. These are seen in a scatter of late Cretaceous outliers the whole length of the Northern Calcareous Alps. One of the largest and most accessible is at Gosau itself, west of Halstatt. The outliers consists of incomplete successions, ranging from Cenomanian to Eocene, of a variable nature but including conglomerates, breccias, reefs, and even coal (locally worked). They rest in places on the thrust contacts between the sheets and their variability itself suggests continuing movements.

Although the individual thrust sheets moved relative to one another within Mesozoic times, the whole mass may have moved as a single huge sheet, Gosau Beds included, in the late Eocene. Breaks in the Tertiary succession indicate continuing movements. The evidence of tectonic windows showing the more northerly zones beneath this sheet tells us that northerly progress continued at least as late as the Miocene. It still remains to be agreed whether this was a matter of compressional foreshortening or (more likely) of gravitational sliding off an uplifted axial zone.

Flysch Zone

This forms a narrow belt below the steep northern face of the Northern Calcareous Alps but, as mentioned above, is also seen in tectonic windows below the great heap of carbonates—for example on the south side of the Wolfgangsee, east of Salzburg. Such occurrences and boreholes tell us of a forward movement of at least 20 km.

As in other Alpine belts of Europe, the main sedimentation trough moved outwards with time. It was, in the far south, perhaps, in the Triassic, whereas in the axial zone it was probably in the Jurassic. Then sedimentation began here in the flysch trough in the early Cretaceous and lasted until the Eocene. It is by no means all true flysch. It is mostly highly calcareous, but includes a variety of facies—mudstones, shales, and limestones. Only locally from late Cretaceous times onwards was there sandy flysch in the classic form 'turbidites'—for example in the cliff that holds up the castle in the tiny state of Liechtenstein. A special feature in the far west—in the Vorarlberg of Switzerland—is the 'Wildflysch', with boulders up to tens of metres across in a calcareous sandy or shaly matrix. This is probably an olistostrome and one is automatically tempted to compare it with the so-called 'klippen' of the Helvetic Zone, described below, and with the famous features of the Carpathians, described in Section 14(e).

Apart from being over-thrust by the Northern Calcareous Alps, the Flysch Zone is also buckled up by the northerly push of that calcareous mass. Some of the folding and thrusting are clearly earlier, and the final northerly push must have been very late. As in the Western Alps, this zone is parautochthonous and in its rightful position between the Helvetic Zone to the north and the Pennine Zone to the south. Deposits of all three accumulated in the same east-west trough.

Helvetides

This is a narrower belt than that of the flysch, and far less persistent. It is best seen at the west end, south of Bregenz on the Swiss–Austrian border. Its name, of course, comes from Switzerland. On the geological map it looks very odd, since just east of Salzburg its outcrop suddenly jumps from the north side of the Flysch Zone to the south and then, approaching Vienna, a belt appears down the middle. The more southerly outcrops are in fact tectonic inliers, showing up from beneath the Flysch Zone, while at the east end the main outcrop has disappeared beneath the molasse. Like the Flysch Zone, it is also seen in tectonic windows away to the south, displaying the last phase of thrusting.

The Helvetic Zone is parautochthonous as in the Western Alps. It consists predominantly of sandstones and mudstones, sometimes rich in fossils, and ranging from the Lower Jurassic (in the classic northern Gresten facies) to the Eocene without appreciable breaks. Locally, fossils such as nummulites and calcareous algae build up limestone bands, but generally the succession gets muddier to the east.

The whole zone is distributed in slightly thrust slices. It was buckled with the Flysch Zone before the over-thrusting of the Northern Calcareous Alps. A special feature of the south side of the zone, east of Salzburg, is sometimes separated as the 'Gresten Klippen Zone'. This has faulted contacts all round and contains huge Jurassic and Lower Cretaceous blocks in a matrix of late Cretaceous to Eocene age. The so-called 'klippen' are of deep-water facies and include both basic and ultra-basic igneous rocks.

There has been much argument as to whether the 'klippen' are tectonic or sedimentary in origin. It is tempting to postulate the latter by analogy with the wildflysch to the west and the Pieniny Klippen Belt in the Carpathians to the east. But the matrix of the boulders is always soft and deformed, so the whole is too poorly exposed for dogmatic conclusions.

Molasse Zone

This is a wide belt out in front of the Alps and Carpathians. It is all confusing hummocky country with few exposures, as is usually the case with the molasse. As the frontal, post-orogenic trough of the Alps it is wholly Tertiary in age, although there may be some thin earlier deposits exposed locally. The sediments are mainly Oligocene to Pliocene, with the Miocene dominating the story. They are characteristically shallow marine and brackish water deposits which thin markedly to the north as they lap against the Bohemian Massif or its underground extension.

A marine transgression in the late Eocene to mid Oligocene brought sands and clays into the trough. This was followed by the main marine deposition, up to 3000 m thick, in the mid Oligocene to mid Miocene, mostly comprising sandstones and conglomerates, such as the concrete-like rock used for building the cathedral in Mozart's Salzburg. Finally there were lake and river desposits, with some coals, in the late Miocene to early Pliocene. Significantly the first pebbles from the Northern Calcareous Alps appear at this level.

A belt of sedimentation was still moving north with time, controlled by faults in the underlying metamorphic basement. As one approaches the Alps one sees that this zone too was deformed due to the northerly thrusting of the zones to the south. We know from boreholes that it was over-thrust by at least 7 km as late as mid Miocene times, but after that there seems to have been no more northerly movement. It was then all a matter of isostatic uplift and erosion.

The glacial story was comparable with that in the western Alps and many fine glaciers are still with us in the higher mountains.

14(e)   Carpathians

The Carpathians begin in a great north-facing arc from the Vienna Basin, close to the Bohemian Massif, and pass through the eastern part of Czechoslovakia, southern Poland, and a corner of the USSR, before sweeping round the Carpathian bend in Romania to cross the Danube into Yugoslavia at the Iron Gates. The Balkan Mountains of Bulgaria form a direct continuation of the chain, which turns eastwards once more to reach the Black Sea, south of Varna. For the most part the Carpathians are rounded, thickly-forested mountains with few exposures, and may be considered conveniently in three parts: (1) the Western Carpathians of Czechoslovakia and Poland, (2) the Eastern Carpathians of the Carpathian Bend, and (3) the Southern Carpathians or Transylvanian Alps of south-west Romania and Yugoslavia.

Western Carpathians

The Western Carpathians occupy the greater part of Slovakia, Moravia, and southern-most Poland. Classic work has been done by the university and institute at Bratislava, the Carpathian Unit of the Prague Survey, and by the Krakow School of sedimentologists and structural geologists.

Although usually thought of as a mountain chain developed in the Alpine orogeny, it is evident that the separation of the geological histories of the Carpathians and the Bohemian Massif had already begun in Precambrian times. The Carpathians began to acquire their present character when the Bohemian Massif became rigid in the movements and granitic emplacements of the Variscan orogeny. They must therefore be considered chiefly on the basis of their later rocks and structures.

The Western Carpathians fall very naturally into four structural units: Internal Zone, Pienide Klippen Belt, External or Flysch Zone, and Carpathian Fore-deep. These are shown diagrammatically in Fig. 14.8.

Internal zone. Little is known about the earlier part of the record in the internal zone of the Western Carpathians, although this is more than one can say about other parts of the chain. The Proterozoic is present, but usually in a highly metamorphosed state. Some of the metamorphic rocks which were thought to be Proterozoic are now known also to include altered early Palaeozoic sequences, on the evidence of spores found in the Malé Karpaty ('Little Carpathians') of Slovakia.

The earlier Palaeozoic rocks are generally of a different facies from those in the Bohemian Massif. The Cambro-Ordovician is of a terrigenous type with much acid volcanicity, the Silurian is in a carbonate facies, and the Devonian includes great quantities of basic volcanic rocks. The largest area of these Palaeozoic sequences, now slightly

399

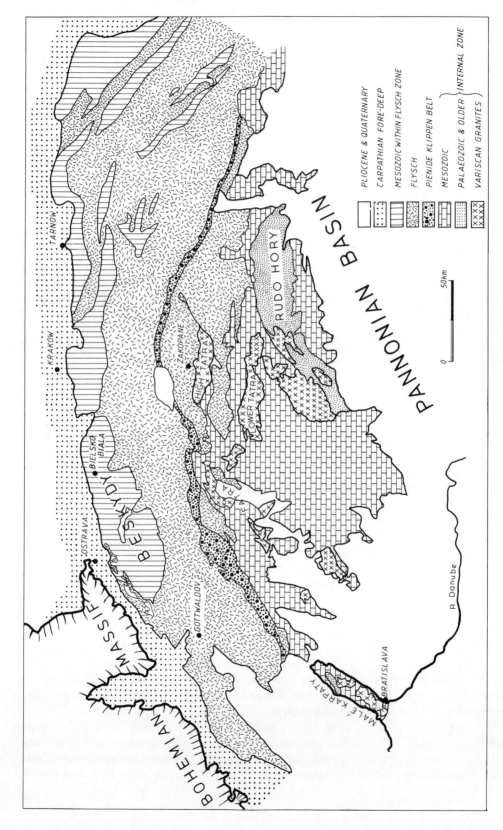

Fig. 14.8 *Geological sketch-map of the Western Carpathians.*

Legend:

PLIOCENE & QUATERNARY
CARPATHIAN FORE-DEEP
MESOZOIC WITHIN FLYSCH ZONE
FLYSCH
PIENIDE KLIPPEN BELT
MESOZOIC
PALAEOZOIC & OLDER } INTERNAL ZONE
VARISCAN GRANITES

PANNONIAN BASIN

RUDO HORY

TARNOW
KRAKOW
BIELSKO BIALA
OSTRAVA
BESKYDY
GOTTWALDOV
ZAKOPANE
HIGH TATRA
LOWER TATRA
FATRA
MALE KARPATY
BRATISLAVA
R. Danube
BOHEMIAN MASSIF

50km
0

metamorphosed, is seen in the core of the Rudo Hory of eastern Slovakia, near the Hungarian frontier.

Early Carboniferous sediments are little known, but at this time orogenic movements evidently began, accompanied by the emplacement of large plutonic bodies, mainly granitic in the wide sense, but covering a range of petrological types, including charnockites and gabbros. Probably the best known of these intrusions is the granite of the towering High Tatra mountains on the Slovakian–Polish frontier, but there are even larger masses farther south. The Hron Valley in Slovakia, (with the 'g' sound represented by the Slav 'h') is said to be the type locality of granite, but paradoxically the igneous rocks here are for the most part basic volcanics.

Although the emplacement of early Carboniferous plutonic masses in the Bohemian Massif had the effect of welding the pre-existing rocks into a stable block, in the West Carpathians it inaugurated a new phase of mobility and geosynclinal sedimentation. Clastic rocks dominate the later Carboniferous record, but include some carbonates. The latter contain deposits of magnesite and siderite produced by hydrothermal replacement. The sediments are accompanied by basic volcanics and were deformed in fairly intense folding of the Asturian phase of the Variscan orogeny. The Permian is said to be in a 'Verrucano' (continental) facies in the north, although it is marine in the south. All through Palaeozoic times there was a sedimentary trough in the Carpathian region and this was tectonized at the end of the era.

The clearest part of the history of the Western Carpathians began with the Triassic Period. An early Triassic transgression inaugurated a long episode of thick and varied sedimentation which lasted until nearly the end of the early Cretaceous. The Triassic rocks consist largely of marine limestones and dolomites in the south like the Northern Calcareous Alps with 'southern' faunas, but the Germanic 'Buntsandstein'/'Muschelkalk'/ 'Keuper' in the north. These were followed by deeper water deposits in the Jurassic: mudstones, radiolarites, and supposedly bathyal limestones such as the *Calpionella* limestones of Tithonian age, which are also well known in the Alps. Similar deposition continued in the early Cretaceous until it was brought to an end by violent earth movements which reached their maximum in the Turonian. These were in every way comparable with the pre-Gosau movements known in the Eastern Alps, and like them developed complex structures including nappes. Thrusting to the north was the dominant feature of these structures and there was comparatively little folding.

From tectonic windows within the Internal Zone it can be shown that the main mass has been moved northwards at least 10 km and from klippen in the External Zone a further 30 km can be added. Therefore a foreshortening of at least 40 km can be demonstrated by obvious structural evidence in the field, although it is difficult to separate movements of mid Cretaceous age from those of the Tertiary which followed. Using a different and more hypothetical line of evidence, Polish workers have estimated that the External Zone trough of late Cretaceous and Palaeogene age, which is now 80–100 km wide, must formerly have been at least 200 km wide. They therefore postulate a northerly movement of the outer edge of the inner Carpathians of at least 100 km.

A particularly well-displayed nappe is that which overrode the High Tatre Variscan granite and its autochthonous cover of Permian to Cretaceous age on the Slovak–Polish border. This plunges down under the nummulitic limestones and flysch of the External Zone in the national park near the resort town of Zakopane, in southern Poland.

The Cretaceous earth movements were accompanied by volcanicity, igneous intrusions, and mineralization. Noteworthy are early Cretaceous teschenite sills at the type locality of Teschen (now called Bielsko Biala) in Poland near the Czech frontier. This was the main metallogenic episode in the western Carpathians.

Pienide (Pieniny) klippen belt. The boundary between the Internal and the External Carpathians is marked by this remarkable structural belt. It is usually only 1–10 km wide (never more than 20 km) but extends for some 500 km from near Vienna to northern Romania. In effect it is a huge, chaotic, tectonic breccia consisting of great blocks of Jurassic and early Cretaceous limestone 'floating' in late Cretaceous argillaceous sediments in a complex imbricate structure. The main movements of the inner Carpathians in Cretaceous and Tertiary times probably expressed themselves and were concentrated in this belt, assumed to follow the line of a deep-seated tectonic suture. It functioned as a slide zone between the inner and outer Carpathians.

External or flysch zone. The flysch zone of the Western Carpathians has become well known to the geological world in recent years through the work of Czech and Polish palaeontologists and sedimentologists.

The pre-late Cretaceous rocks of the outer Carpathians are only known as separated masses caught up in the flysch nappes. One of the most interesting of these (to me at least) is at Štramberk (Stramberg) in the beautiful Beskydy Mountains of eastern Moravia. The Štramberk limestone has long been famous for its extremely rich fauna of corals, sponges, molluscs, and brachiopods. It has been dated as late Tithonian and has been nominated as a 'stratotype' for that division. It is generally agreed that, with other associated sediments, it has been thrust over the Cretaceous and Eocene of the External Zone, either as a single sheet or as separate masses. The interesting problem of the Štramberk limestone is its mode of deposition, coupled with its close association of late Jurassic and early Cretaceous faunas which differ ecologically as well as in age.

In some sections the relationship is superficially obvious, with Cretaceous grey marls and sandstones resting with marked unconformity on the pure white Jurassic limestone. Closer examination reveals a more complex situation. Many of the former contradictions in the recorded fauna originated from the fact that seams of marl with early Cretaceous macro- and micro-faunas penetrate deep into the Jurassic limestone, and appear as normal interbedded layers. Such are well seen, for example, in the large quarry of Koutouč, in the next hill to the type locality. The Štramberk Limestone has been interpreted by some workers as a genuine reef with massive corals in life position and associated reef detritus. Others have maintained that the limestone is wholly composed of reef detritus. The Cretaceous intercalations, when first recognized by their microfaunas, were taken to be infillings of solution pipes, perhaps descending from a karst surface which developed with emergence at the end of Jurassic times.

An alternative explanation is that much, if not all, the deposit consists of loose blocks of Jurassic limestone which tumbled down in submarine landslips to be incorporated in a deeper water Cretaceous muddy deposit. The marls are then no more than matrix between the blocks. Certainly a great part of the limestone is intensely brecciated and exotic blocks of a similar lithology are known in later Cretaceous and even Palaeogene deposits. This interpretation would imply that whole hills of Štramberk Limestone which show no brecciation are no more than single exotic blocks. This interpretation also fits in with the idea of reiterated movements through Mesozoic and Tertiary times.

From mid-Cretaceous times onward, however, sedimentation was uninterrupted. The outer Carpathians began to develop as a eugeosynclinal belt with the disruption of the inner Carpathians in the mid-Cretaceous orogeny. From late Cretaceous (Senonian) times through to the Oligocene, sandstone/shale rhythmic deposition in characteristic flysch form dominated the story, but it was evidently not a single, simple trough which received these deposits. Polish geologists have worked out a complex story of rising and falling cordilleras, with flysch troughs between. Local conglomerates are developed. Particular attention has been paid to the structures found on the under-surfaces of the sandstones in graded sequences. These are either 'bioglyphs'—trace fossils—of the typical flysch assemblage, or 'mechanoglyphs'—sedimentary structures—which indicate the direction of flow of the turbidity currents which are thought to have been responsible for the deposits. By means of the latter, it has been possible to work out the direction of flow in the various troughs for every stage of the Mesozoic. Although the sediment-laden currents evidently originated at the sides of the troughs, the dominant flow is lengthwise along them. Such a pattern has since been determined in many other geosynclinal regions, although there is an obvious danger that any lineation may be considerably modified in its orientation by later orogenic compression.

The southern zones of the flysch trough were affected by 'Laramide' folding at the end of the Cretaceous, and there were marked changes in palaeogeography at that time. But the main spasm of the Alpine orogeny came in the Miocene, probably during Aquitanian–Burdigalian times. The more plastic nature of the flysch rocks meant that they were more intensely contorted than the brittle rocks of the Internal Zone. New nappes developed, again pushing to the north, in two main tectonic units. The Magura Unit or 'Inner Flysch' to the south was thrust over the Krosno Unit or 'Outer Flysch' to the north. The latter, in its turn, was pushed forward again in Tortonian times and (as in the Alps and Jura) this last thrust rode over the Neogene sediments of the Carpathian Fore-deep (Fig. 14.9). Borings in Poland up to 15 and 18 km from the outer edge of the External Zone have revealed strongly folded flysch resting on flat-lying Miocene rocks.

Faulting in the now rigid Internal Carpathians at this time produced many of the topographical features which dominate the scenery today, notably the great south-facing fault-line scarp of the High Tatra in Slovakia. The later Neogene post-orogenic sediments throughout the Carpathians were also affected by radial faulting and are often preserved in graben structures. These contain mainly fresh-water and continental deposits, including brown coals in the centre of the Western Carpathian arc. In places, in

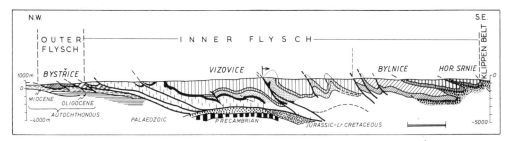

Fig. 14.9 *Cross-section of the northern parth of the Western Carpathians, showing northerly thrusting in the Tertiary sediments of the Flysch Zone.*

403

central and southern Slovakia, these are interbedded with Miocene and Pliocene volcanics (mostly andesitic lavas and pyroclastics) which are connected with gold and silver mineralization, together with some lead, zinc, copper, and mercury ores. This mineralization is less important, however, than that associated with the mid-Cretaceous orogeny.

Tertiary volcanics form a 'Volcanic Ring' around the inner boundary of the Western Carpathians and mark the outer limit of the Pannonian Basin.

Eastern Carpathians

The Eastern Carpathians constitute the great east-facing arc of the chain in northern Romania, together with a small segment in the Soviet Union (Fig. 14.10). They extend some 700 km between the Tisza and Dimbovitza rivers to form the mountain barrier between the Transylvanian part of the Pannonian Basin (to the west) and the Scythian part of the Russian Platform (to the east). Westwards they pass into Western Carpathians of Poland and Czechoslovakia, the limit between them being defined as the end of the Pieniny klippen belt and of the Transcarpathian flysch, although there is a considerable overlap, at least with the latter. South-eastwards they pass quite abruptly into the Southern Carpathians, discussed below, which face south and east over the Wallachian plain.

This great twist of the Alpine ranges in northern Romania is one of the mysteries of Neo-Europa, and will be discussed later. Apart from the Greater Caucasus (which are probably a special case) this is the only part of the Alpine system that directly abuts the old European craton of the East European Platform. What is more, they have on their inside the seemingly equally autochthonous Pannonian–Transylvanian Massif (now largely disguised as a basin) and the fold belt was trapped between the two. At the same time, much that has been said about the Western Carpathians is equally applicable here.

There is a great deal of recent literature by the active Romanian geologists, although the fact that much of it is in Romanian makes it of limited value to the outside world. The destruction in the 1977 earthquake of the institute in Bucharest which was their chief centre of activity was particularly tragic for Romanian geology, although thankfully no geologists lost their lives.

The Eastern Carpathians may be divided into three parallel zones as follows:

1. Internal Carpathians (comprising an ancient basement with a cover ranging up through the Mesozoic).
2. External Carpathians (consisting mainly of flysch).
3. Sub-Carpathian Fore-deep (in front of the mountains, as an autochthonous, molasse-filled trough).

In addition, there is a line of Tertiary volcanic mountains (most notably the Calimani Mountains) on the inside of the bend, which is here regarded as being more closely related to the Transylvanian Depression than to the Carpathians, and so is dealt with under the Pannonian Basin—Chapter 15(b).

As is usually the case, the fore-deep molasse forms low-lying country traversed by many waterways and the flysch belt consists of rolling, thickly-forested hills; neither provided many exposures nor distinctive marker horizons. The internal or Dacide Zone, on the other hand, has craggy, spectacular scenery, not yet much known to visitors from

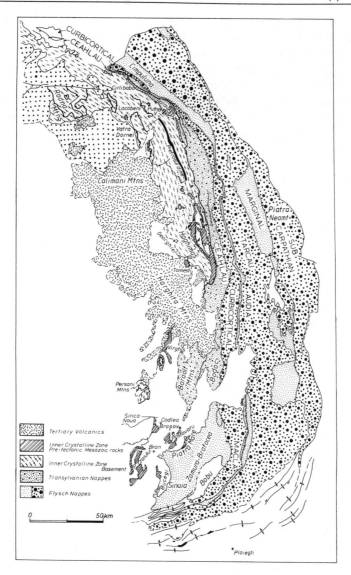

Fig. 14.10 *Geological sketch-map of the Eastern Carpathians (after Burchfiel, 1976, by kind permission of the author and the Geological Society of America).*

other parts of Europe. The mountains do not reach Alpine heights. The highest in the Eastern Carpathians are about 2000 m, but the average is much lower.

Internal Carpathians. The Internal Carpathians or 'Internal Crystalline Zone' as they are often called (although not all crystalline) were formerly divided into a Transylvanian western part and a Bucovinian eastern part. Nowadays the latter is subdivided and four units are usually distinguished from 'west' to 'east' or from 'top' to 'bottom', as follows: Transylvanian Nappe, Bucovinian Nappe, Sub-Bucovinian Nappe, and Bretila Unit.

405

Throughout the area one may also distinguish a metamorphic basement and a sedimentary cover, but all the units may be allochthonous. The zone as a whole is exposed on the inside of the Carpathian bend, with the srystalline basement chiefly seen in the northern part, from Tomeşti across the Soviet frontier. It forms the backbone of the mountain range and its most rugged scenery.

The Transylvanian Nappe is the most westerly in position and is thought to have travelled farthest. It is only seen as a string of isolated klippen, from near Cirlibaba, in the north, to the Perşani Mountains in the south. The rocks are entirely Mesozoic in age, but the complete succession is nowhere preserved in one place. Much has been pieced together from scattered klippen and from boulders in the wildflysch above.

The Trias is known this way, and appears to consist of a dominantly carbonate sequence with recognizable facies such as the late Triassic Halstatt Limestone of Austria. It includes basic volcanics which have been called ophiolites.

The Jurassic similarly reminds one of the Austride facies of the south with Adneth facies Lias, as in the Northern Calcareous Alps, although there are elements in the Persani Mountains that remind one of the northern Gresten facies. At the top of the system are massive, cliff-forming limestones like those of Štramberk. These are commonly overlain unconformably by Urgonian-type limestones, although elsewhere there are conglomerates and flysch of the same age. Clearly there is a lot of sorting out to do in these very contrasting, almost contradictory, facies and it may be that more than one zone is represented in the klippen.

The onset of flysch sedimentation as early as Barremian and Aptian times is significant, especially as much of it is of the wildflysch type, full of boulders from the earlier Mesozoic. There are important breaks within the Cretaceous, notably before the Turonian, but it is probable that the first easterly movement of the Transylvanian unit happened before this time, starting with the flysch. At first, much of it was a matter of olistoliths, up to a kilometre long, sliding into the wildflysch basin. It may be that the whole unit is nothing more than a series of huge olistostromes, impelled by gravity and sinking, in a disoriented fashion, into a porridge of Cretaceous flysch.

It must be assumed that the Transylvanian rocks come from a trough or troughs to the west of the Carpathians. On the whole they are thicker and of a deeper water facies here than their equivalents to the east. Some would like to see ocean floor here, which might be said to be confirmed by the absence of a crystalline basement, but much of the succession is not of an oceanic character. It is obviously tempting to correlate this unit with the Pienide Klippen Belt of the Western Carpathians, and so to postulate that remarkable structure extending even further than previously postulated.

The Bucovinian Nappe, in the strict sense, is thought to extend in a single sheet from beyond the Soviet frontier in the north to south of Tomeşti, with isolated klippen farther south under the Transylvanian masses. Unlike the Transylvanian unit, this nappe includes slices of basement rocks, comparable with those better known in the lower units. What is more, the overlying Mesozoic in this unit cuts across the structures, including thrusts, in the Precambrian–Palaeozoic succession below.

Mesozoic rocks belonging to the Bucovinian Nappe are exposed in the north and, less deformed, in the Perşani Mountains. Starting from a basal quartzite, the Trias passes up through dolomites to late Triassic white limestones and cherts. These were overlain unconformably, after slight movements, by Toarcian and Middle Jurassic sandy limestones followed by a varied series of pelagic deposits, characterized by aptychi, which range up into the Cretaceous.

Wildflysch sedimentation here began, at least in the north, even earlier than in the Transylvanian unit—in the Hauterivian—and the marked unconformity beneath it in places cuts right down to the crystalline basement.

The main eastward movements were pre-late Cretaceous and slightly later than those of the Transylvanian unit (which were probably completed in Albian times). Basal Upper Cretaceous conglomerates and sandstones rest on both Bucovinian and Transylvanian units, with fragments of both of them, so it is obvious that the main movements had been completed by this time. These rocks are themselves somewhat folded by later movements which seem to be directed in the opposite (i.e., westerly) direction. These later movements probably occurred late in the Cretaceous or early in the Tertiary.

The Sub-Bucovinian Nappe is thrust eastwards over the external Bretila Unit. Here the lowest element is of marble and amphibolite overlain by a thick development of mica-schists. It is presumed to be Precambrian in age but younger than the lower part of the Bretila Unit. Above it comes a thick green-schist unit, with unconformities above and below, that has been attributed to the uppermost Precambrian and Cambrian on the evidence of spores. Above again come marbles and some quartzites with poorly preserved crinoids that are thought to indicate the Devonian–Carboniferous. This would therefore seem to be a more complete succession, coming from the west, and with evidence of what could be called a Caledonian orogeny. But the evidence must not be stretched too far. All groups of metamorphic rocks are cut by granites, granodiorites, and other intrusive masses with associated dikes and contact metamorphism.

Scattered through the Eastern Carpathians generally are red sandstones and conglomerates which are commonly attributed to the Permian. These rest on both the Bretila Unit and higher units. In the Soviet Carpathians, sediments of this kind, resting on what is taken to be the equivalent of the Bretila Unit, are associated with lava flows and intrusions. In general, therefore, the pattern is comparable with that in the Alps and the climax of the Variscan orogeny here was presumably pre-Permian in age.

The Trias is as described above, except that the Upper Triassic always seems to be missing beneath unconformable Lower Jurassic sands and conglomerates. These pass up into Middle Jurassic sandy limestones and dark pelagic deposits spanning the Jurassic–Cretaceous boundary. Although comparable in general terms with the Mesozoic successions of the western units, the whole is much thinner here, probably no more than 100 m.

The Bretila Unit is best known in the Rodna Mountains in the north-west, between Bötizi and Cirlibaba, although it has now been recognized widely in the chain, including the Soviet part. It was formerly assumed to be autochthonous but is now supposed to be allochthonous. The lowest units cannot be seen detached anywhere, but there is considerable thrusting within them.

The lowest series is of clastic sedimentary rocks and basic volcanics that have been metamorphosed to amphibolite grade. It is presumably of Precambrian age, as is its metamorphism, although no radiometric dates are available. Unconformably above this is a group of clastic, calcareous, and volcanic, rocks that have been metamorphosed to green-schist grade. The volcanics are mainly in the lower part and the sediments contain rare crinoids that have been dated as Devonian–Carboniferous, so correlating with the Sub-Bucovinian Nappe.

407

It is therefore thought that we have here a late Precambrian succession meta-morphosed before being overlain by a Palaeozoic succession. The Variscan orogeny then provided a metamorphism of the younger rocks and probably retrograde metamorphism of the Precambrian. The intermediate succession of the Bucovinian Nappe which spans the Precambrian–Cambrian boundary has not been recognized here. It is of interest that structures within the Palaeozoic run sub-parallel with the Alpine trends, although the folds may close in the opposite directon.

The cover sequence on the Bretila Unit is seen in a small window through the Sub-Bucovinian Nappe near Iacobeni, south-east of Cirlibaba. Here presumed Permian sand-stones and shales are overlain unconformably by a thin, incomplete Mesozoic succession. The usual Lower Triassic quartzites pass up into dolomites (reminiscent of the 'Muschelkalk') and then, as in the Bucovinian Nappe, the Upper Triassic is cut out beneath a Lower or Middle Jurassic sandstone or sandy limestone. In the Soviet Union, the Permian includes volcanics and the Lower Jurassic is a black siltstone not seen elsewhere, except in the flysch of the 'Moldavides' (see below).

The thrusting to the east is covered by transgressive Cenomanian, but cannot be dated accurately. The whole thing is then swamped in Eocene and Oligocene flysch. All that can be said with confidence is that this is the most easterly unit and the lowest in the pile of easterly thrust blocks. Its stratigraphy suggests that we were near or actually on a positive area in Mesozoic times.

It is difficult to see a clear major suture here. If it is anywhere in the exposed rocks, it is in the Transylvanian Nappe or olistostrome. However, this was of course deposited far to the west of where we now see it and much more may be hidden under the Transcarpathian flysch or destroyed along the line of the Neogene volcanism.

External Carpathians. The External Carpathians are usually known—rather ambiguously—as the Flysch Nappes, after their principal components. Seven major nappes have been recognized, although it is not proposed to discuss them individually. The inner two are sometimes linked with the preceding zones in the 'Dacides' and the others called the 'Moldavides'. The flysch ranges in age from Jurassic to Neogene and in general is older internally (towards the west) and younger externally.

The geology of the External Carpathians is much better known than that of the internal part, chiefly because of exploration for oil. The most important difference between the two is the later date of the main movements in the region now under consideration, where they were late Cretaceous and Tertiary in age.

There is a clear picture of a main trough of sedimentation moving eastwards with time, in line with the advancing nappes. Thus in the westernmost unit (only seen in the USSR and northern Romania) thick sedimentation started in the early Jurassic and included basic volcanics. In the next nappe there are pillow lavas in the Upper Jurassic and the main thickness of flysch is Tithonian to Barremian in age, overlain by Aptian–Albian conglomerates. In the westernmost unit of the 'Moldavides', the flysch (some 4000 m of it) is Barremian to Albian, overlain unconformably by Senonian sandstones and marl. East again, everything has changed; the Barremian–Albian is very much reduced in thickness and no longer flysch; this is overlain unconformably by thick conglomerates ranging from the Upper Senonian into the Eocene.

The penultimate nappe going east covers the broadest stretch of country and shows the migration of the sedimentation belt within itself. Thick Senonian flysch passes into really massive sandstones of Eocene and Oligocene age with subsidiary flysch. These are more than 2000 m thick and dominate the scenery in the west, but wedge out eastwards. Finally in the outermost nappe the Oligocene is the dominant element; it has changed to a molasse facies and is overlain by Miocene including important developments of evaporites. There was now a considerable input of detrital material from the platform to the east.

Tectonically the picture is rather similar, with overthrusting from the west becoming later in age and fading out eastwards. The Internal 'crystalline' Carpathians are seen pushed over the westernmost nappes of the External Carpathians. In the inner part of that nappe complex, the Cenomanian rests unconformably on the older rocks, but elsewhere there is a continuous passage. Farther east, the unconformity is below the Senonian and the earlier rocks seem to have been folded with the advance of the previous nappe.

The same unconformity is seen in the next nappe, but there the Eocene is also seen to be thrust over the Oligocene and the Middle Miocene over the next nappe. Windows and borings show that the penultimate nappe (composed largely of Tertiary rocks) has moved up to 30 km or more over the outermost nappe, which is only seen in windows. This last nappe is in the form of large recumbent folds, but the forward movement was much reduced. The final unit is not a nappe at all, but parautochthonous. It moved in *en echelon* slices up to 7 km over the molasse, as in all the other Alpine chains of Europe. So we have here, perhaps clearer than anywhere else, a story of sedimentary troughs moving outwards with time and being pursued by tectonism.

Sub-Carpathian Fore-deep. The thick late Tertiary molasse, just mentioned, is known to rest on the edge of the East European Platform. This part of it (south-west of the Ukrainian Massif) is commonly called the Scythian (or Skythian) Platform after the wild tribes of mounted bowmen who lived here before the days of Alexander. Southwards the Scythian Platform becomes involved with the problems of Dobrogea and then passes on to the Moesian Platform, both of which are dealt with elsewhere. However, it is worth mentioning this great trough which swings right round in front of the Carpathians.

Extensive geophysical work and a vast number of borings, especially in connection with the famous Ploieşti oil-fields, have provided detailed information about this region, which displays almost nothing at the surface apart from the thick Quaternary loess of the Danube.

The metamorphic basement is overlain by 700–800 m of Palaeozoic sediments which are quite unaffected by later tectonism (we are therefore firmly back in Eo-Europa). The Palaeozoic includes representatives of every system except, it would seem, the Carboniferous. Triassic, Jurassic, and especially Cretaceous shallow-water sediments, contribute another 300 m or so. We then come to much greater thicknesses of Cainozoic rocks. In the north, on the Scythian Platform proper, there are up to 2000 m of Tertiary close to the Carpathians. Farther south, up to 10 000 m or more of predominantly shallow marine and continental deposits have been measured. These include great thicknesses of conglomerates which accumulated as alluvial or torrential fans in front of the new mountains. There are also thick sandstones, coal cyclothems, and evaporites, including material derived from the west as well as from the east. A remarkable series of Neogene trace fossils have been described from the Russian part of the Sub-Carpathian Fore-deep; these include such unlikely things as the footprints of ducks and cloven-hoofed mammals.

Generally speaking, the succession becomes coarser upwards, showing that the Carpathians were still rising (perhaps isostatically) in Quaternary times. The edge of the platform was also rising, for its contributions to the molasse include blocks up to more than 20 m across. Marine deposition ended with the Miocene and there began the history of the great Dacian depression which involved not only the fore-deep but also Dobrogea, the Moesian Platform, and the Black Sea itself. Some 4000–6000 m of richly fossiliferous lacustrine sediment accumulated.

The only structures that need mentioning here are the many normal faults and minor anticlines which run parallel to the Carpathian front. Some of the faults are still active, as is shown by the recent disastrous earthquakes. There are also salt diapirs, some of which reach the surface. Associated with these diapirs and with the last movements of the Carpathians, are the oil-fields of southern Romania, in particular the Ploieşti oil-field and the new ones developed since the Second World War. Most of the oil is in the Tertiary of the fore-deep, although there is some in the flysch and in the frontal Sub-Carpathian Unit. The main source of the oil seems to be highly organic Oligocene shales, with famous fish faunas; these accumulated on the bottom of poorly oxygenated lakes, not unlike the present Black Sea.

Southern Carpathians

The junction between the Eastern and Southern Carpathians is taken at the Dimboviţa River. This is a minor tributary of the Danube that passes through the range south-west of Braşov. Geologically it marks the end of the major thrust masses of the Eastern Carpathians and the beginning of an area of basement rocks forming the Fagaraş Mountains. The junction is also marked by a spread of coarse, post-orogenic sediments that break through the mountains at this point.

The Southern Carpathians (Fig. 14.11) run from east to west until they turn south to the 'Iron Gates'* where the Danube bursts through the mountains. They then pass through a corner of Yugoslavia before turning east again as the Balkan Mountains of Bulgaria.

The rocks of the Southern Carpathians fall into three simple groups: (1) the Danubian autochthonous rocks which occupy a large area in the westward-facing bend, (2) the Getic Nappe which occupies mainly the 'inner' part of the belt to the north and west, and (3) the Severin Nappe which is only seen as a few small slices on the 'outer' side of the bend.

Danubian Autochthon. The basement here is demonstrably pre-Devonian in age and is commonly supposed to be late Precambrian and early Palaeozoic. It is mainly in a green-schist grade of metamorphism and is intruded by granites that have become gneissose. Locally this basement is overlain by supposed Devonian and more generally by Carboniferous rocks in both marine and non-marine facies, reaching 1500 m in thickness. Locally a similar thickness of Permian clastics and volcanics are also preserved. These late Palaeozoic rocks were gently folded, but there is nothing that could be called a Variscan orogeny.

*I had always been fascinated by this name, but when I talked to two local girls, they thought it a very dull, ordinary place. When asked to name an exciting, exotic far-away place, they had no hesitation in choosing Liverpool.

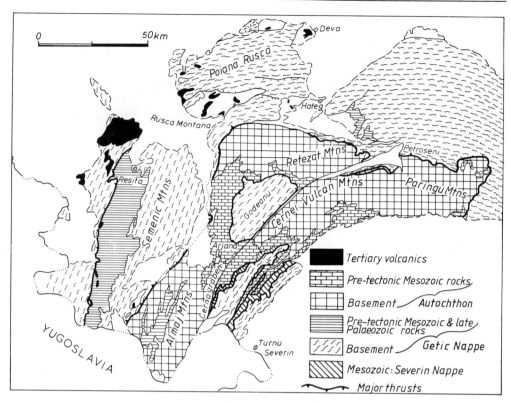

Fig. 14.11 *Geological sketch-map of the Southern Carpathians (after Burchfiel, 1976, by kind permission of the author and the Geological Society of America).*

The Mesozoic cover of the autochthon in places only amounts to some 1200 m. It starts with Lower Jurassic sediments of the northern Gresten facies, lacking in carbonates. Shales and sandstones persist up into the Middle Jurassic, and massive limestones only appear (as in so many parts of Europe) towards the top of the system. A great cliff of these stands up on both sides of the Danube at the 'Iron Gates' and contributes to the dangerous rapids at this point, which formed such a hindrance to navigation. Eastwards there is definite reef facies. There are also some basic volcanics in the Jurassic succession.

A major fault system (220 km long), the Cerna Graben, cuts through the autochthon from north-east to south-west. This important structure turns down into Yugoslavia. It appears to have influenced Cretaceous sedimentation. Early Cretaceous shales on the west side pass into massive Urgonian limestones on the east side. Again the shallowing seems to have been in that direction. Furthermore, the rocks on the west side have been folded and then cut across unconformably by late Cretaceous sediments, while on the east side the succession is complete through to shallow-water Senonian. It may be that the later rocks to the west are a wildflysch unit, containing huge blocks derived from the Jurassic. There are also basic volcanic rocks as in the Jurassic. The structure of the pre-Devonian rocks is still uncertain and the late Palaeozoic folding is very minor. But in post-Cretaceous times the autochthon was folded into two anticlinoria separated

411

by the Cerna Graben. They are over-folded to the east and south-east and the Mesozoic rocks show a weak cleavage.

Since these autochthonous rocks are only separated from the Moesian Platform of southern Romania and northern Bulgaria by allochthonous material and the thick post-orogenic deposits of the Carpathian fore-deep, one presumes that they were formerly part of the same continental unit.

Getic Nappe. These allochthonous rocks may be separated into a basement which forms the greater part of the Southern Carpathians and cover rocks which are only seen in a belt crossing the Romanian–Yugoslav frontier south from Reşita and in a tiny area near Rimnicu Vilcea, on the south side of the Fagaraş Mountains. They have also been recognized in Yugoslavia.

The basement consists mainly of high-grade granitic gneisses, often of kyanite or sillimanite grade. They are isoclinally folded but these complex structures have not yet been sorted out. Apart from the main outcrops they occur in three klippen resting on the autochthon near the Danube. These rocks are assumed to be of Precambrian age, but all that we can be sure of is that they predate the Carboniferous.

The cover rocks are best known in the Reşita synclinorium, where the basement is overlain by Carboniferous terrestrial deposits, including conglomerates and coal. These are overlain in turn by typical Permian 'Verrucano' conglomerates and sandstones, up to 1000 m thick, with intercalations of tuff. The Trias is only preserved locally and thinly in the west and it is the Lower Jurassic Gresten facies that usually rests directly on the Palaeozoic. Again there is a build-up to massive late Jurassic limestones and the Lower Cretaceous grades up into massive Urgonian reefs. There is a break at this point which is interpreted as the 'Austrian' phase of folding, but there is not much missing and Albian glauconitic sands appear above the unconformity. How often in Europe are the Aptian and Albian glauconitic! Eastwards there appears to have been shallowing and the succession becomes more incomplete in that direction.

Upper Cretaceous and Tertiary sediments are preserved locally, with andesitic volcanics at the boundary between them. But these are all post-tectonic in nature and the main displacement clearly occurred in mid-Cretaceous times.

It is clear from the klippen on the Danubian autochthon that the Getic rocks were transported eastwards a considerable distance in the neighbourhood of the Danube. In the Reşita synclinorium, Mesozoic and Palaeozoic rocks are folded together, with the axes overturned to the east and many thrusts and reversed faults inclined in the same direction. A major westerly-dipping thrust delimits the west side of the synclinorium. The same thrust may continue right around the north side of the autochthon and under the Fagaraş Mountains, possibly as far as the Eastern Carpathians. The nappe must have moved at least 60 km, but it did so with little disturbance at its base.

Severin Nappe. There may be other structures, but this is the only one that has been recognized, and then only in a limited area. It is a highly tectonized sheet quite unlike those just described. It consists of very late Jurassic and early Cretaceous shales and cherts with associated basic volcanics and serpentinites, followed by later Cretaceous flysch-like sediments up to Aptian in age. It would be tempting, but going beyond the evidence, to say 'ophiolites'. Conglomerates contain pebbles from the Getic basement.

These rocks can only be seen easily along the Danube west of Turnu Severin, from which they take their name. They may be the equivalent of part of the Eastern Carpathian flysch nappes, but their precise structural position is still a matter of dispute. They may come from a trough to the west of the other units, although since they only occur east of the Cerna Graben they may have been squeezed out of that structure. These very incompetent rocks are highly deformed, but the evidence suggests transport from west to east to lie in a position always between the autochthon and the Getic Nappe.

The main movements here have been dated as very late Cretaceous, although some movements may have occurred earlier in that period. Post-orogenic deposits of early Oligocene age overlie thrust masses near Petroşeni. Considerable thicknesses of similar post-orogenic sediments, often in the form of chaotic conglomerates, extend over large areas of the Southern Carpathians, both internally and externally. They are seen, for example, along the front of the Făgăras Mountains on the south of the range and along the Mureş Valley, west of Deva, which separates the north side of the mountains from the Apuseni Mountains of the Pannonian Basin.

Finally in connection with the main tectonism, mention should be made of the intense andesitic volcanicity which occurred on the inner side of the range, notably north of Reşita, at the very end of the Cretaceous and early in Palaeogene times.

14(f) Balkanides

I prefer to avoid the word 'Balkans' (which refers to the whole south-eastern peninsula of Europe) for this range. The Balkan Mountains, or Balkanides, form the direct continuation of the north-facing Alpine–Carpathian belt running west to east through Bulgaria. They reach well over 2000 m in the central part of the range but drop down markedly to end abruptly at the Black Sea north of Burgas (Fig. 14.12). They lie between the Rhodope Massif to the south and the Moesian Platform to the north. The former is shared with Greece and the latter with Romania, but the Balkan Mountains are wholly Bulgarian and the geologists of that country have made tremendous advances in recent years in unravelling the stratigraphy and structure of this chain. One of its chief fascinations is its comparative neglect, so that new discoveries are constantly being made and this account will probably be out of date before it is published. For the palaeontologist, the Balkanides are a constant source of delight, for the fossiliferous exposures have not suffered the depradations of centuries of fossil collectors as they have in the more frequented parts of Europe.

After the complications of the Alps and the Carpathians, the Balkanides are gloriously simple in structure. This presumably is the result of their position relative to the moving microplates (see Fig. 17.2). The Rhodope Massif will be considered in Chapter 15(c), while the Moesian Platform has already been considered under the Variscides—Chapter 9(h). The Balkanides can be usefully divided into three belts. These are, from north to south:

1. The Pre- or Fore-Balkans, in the north, which have comparatively gentle, open structures.
2. The Stara Planina or Balkan Mountains *sensu stricto*, which form the central, highest ranges and have more complex, almost Alpine structures.

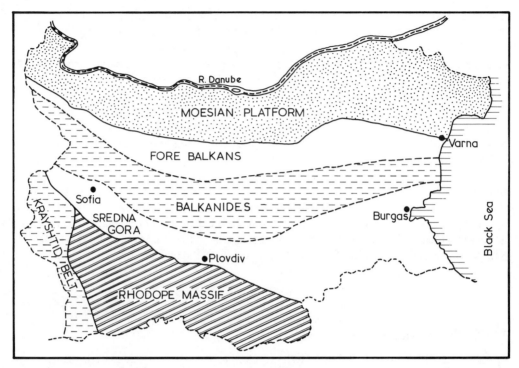

Fig. 14.12 Geological sketch-map of the Balkan Mountains (after Ager, 1972, by kind permission of the Council of the Geologists' Association).

3. The Sredna Gora, in the south; the name means literally 'Middle Mountains' and refers to their position between the high ridge of the Balkans proper and the Rhodope Massif.

Nevertheless, they are best considered together stratigraphically. The Pre-Balkans may be compared with the Jura, coming as they do between the main fold mountains and the rigid platform. The Balkans *sensu stricto* were not thought of as really 'Alpine' until comparatively recently and certainly the lateral displacements are nothing like those in the Alps or Carpathians. There are, however, overthrusts, large overturned folds, and some small nappes of traditional type. Older rocks appear in places through the dominating Mesozoic sediments. Thus near the historic Shipka Pass,* in the centre of the range, an ancient granite has been pushed from the south 14 km over Mesozoic sediments. Paradoxically, the Sredna Gora are usually not mountains at all, but rounded hills, and in some places they are almost completely planed off and covered with Quaternary sediments. Where exposed, the structures in Sredna Gora show a characteristic pattern of steep folds broken by reversed faults. The structures include a variety of ancient, including metamorphic, rocks. Eastwards, the Sredna Gora swings southwards and runs down through Turkey to the Bosphorus as the 'Anti-Balkans'. The former idea

---

* Here, in 1877, a small force of Bulgarian patriots was saved at the last moment by a Russian army from annihilation by the Turks, an event which led to the liberation of the country from five centuries of Ottoman oppression.

that the Balkanides continued under the Black Sea to the Crimea has already been discussed—Chapter 13(e).

Precambrian and Palaeozoic

Precambrian rocks are mainly confined to the Sredna Gora. They consist of a complex of granites, gneisses, migmatites, etc. An Upper (less metamorphosed) 'Crystalline Series' has been distinguished from the highly metamorphosed Lower 'Crystalline Series'. The lower part of the latter, referred to locally as Archaean, is confined to the southern part of the Krayshtid Belt in the west where the Balkans swing to a north–south trend. It is nowhere seen in the Balkan Mountains themselves. No dependable radiometric age determinations are as yet available. A mixture of diorites, gabbros, and granodiorites turns up in the core of many structures and may belong to the top part of this sequence. In places there are pillow lavas and serpentinites, so it probably represents fragments of an ophiolitic suite and it would be of particular interest to know its true age. It is certainly pre-Ordovician and most Bulgarian geologists regard it as Proterozoic, although it could be Cambrian.

Cambrian rocks have not yet been proved in Bulgaria, but archaeocyathid limestones are known in similar rocks in Yugoslavia. Ordovician and Silurian sediments are known chiefly in the Krayshtid Belt on the Yugoslav border and in an inlier within the Stara Planina seen in the gorge of the Isker River, just north of Sofia. Ordovician and Silurian graptolite faunas are now moderately well known and a few trilobites have also been described. These two systems are chiefly represented by shales, but the usual Lower Ordovician white quartzites are present.

Devonian rocks have not been proved with certainty, but an extensive formation in the west Balkans, mainly volcanic in origin, may be of this age. There are also a series of what in north-west Europe would probably be called 'Caledonian' granites, although they may be as late as early Carboniferous in age. It is thought that the main Variscan movements took place hereabouts at that time.

They were followed by late Carboniferous continental deposits, not very extensive, but containing valuable coals including anthracites, for example around Svoge in central Bulgaria. Good floras are known, but no marine horizons. They may therefore be compared with the limnic basins of western Europe. Permian rocks are similarly continental in facies with some coals, thick conglomerates, and breccias, which are inevitably referred to the ubiquitous but certainly diachronous 'Verrucano' of southern Europe. Typical Permian breccias, like those of the English Midlands, are seen at Falcovetz in north-west Bulgaria, immediately overlain by Lower Triassic conglomerates, again like those of the English Midlands. The Permian includes tuffs and lavas which are useful for correlation, for example in the classic Isker Gorge.

The detailed effects of the Variscan orogeny have not yet been worked out in the Balkan Mountains. The Rhodope Massif was already in existence as a positive feature at the beginning of Mesozoic times. It is thought to have supplied the clastic sediments which accumulated in the Balkan Geosyncline, as it has been called, between the Rhodopes and the Moesian Platform to the north. It must be borne in mind, however, that the greater part of the post-Variscan Balkan sediments is carbonate, as in many other Alpine belts of Europe.

Mesozoic

Mesozoic sediments form by far the greater part of the visible Balkan Mountains, and they need to be considered in more detail.

Triassic sediments occur in three distinct regions of Bulgaria: the west Balkanides (and the Krayshtid Belt), the east Balkanides, and the eastern part of the Rhodope Massif—considered in Chapter 15(c). Lower, Middle, and Upper Trias are present in all three areas, but in somewhat different form.

In the west, the Triassic begins in the usual Germanic facies of northern Europe, with typical 'Buntsandstein', well exposed for example in the passes through the mountains immediately north of Sofia. It is even better displayed in the fantastic pinnacles of Belogradchik in the north-west corner of the country. Near here, at Falcovetz Bridge, there is the basal conglomerate mentioned above, just like that of the English and Spanish Trias, full of boulders of purple quartzite coming from the Ordovician. The stratigraphical record is at times very odd!

In the east Balkans, on the other hand, the Trias starts off in the usual Alpine facies, and the two facies apparently meet in central Bulgaria. The Alpine sea evidently spread from the east, and higher up the column Anisian and Ladinian strata of Alpine type are found, interdigitating with the Germanic facies of western Bulgaria. The Upper Trias is of the Alpine type throughout the country, forming magnificent white limestone cliffs, for example in the Isker Gorge.

The sea retreated eastwards again at the end of Triassic times. The Rhaetian stage is entirely continental in western Bulgaria, but of normal Alpine limestones (with a fairly rich fauna) in the east. This regression presumably represents the early Kimmerian orogenic phase, which is also suggested by local unconformities.

In the Jurassic there is similar paradoxical evidence of the persistence of the Alpine facies, with its characteristic faunas in the east, not the west. Although it does not solve the palaeogeographical problem of an Alpine sea coming from the east, the surprising juxtaposition in the Balkans of markedly different 'faunal provinces' has been explained in tectonic terms, since the rocks of Alpine facies have been shown to be allochthonous, having been transported a considerable distance from the south in an olistostrome.

Like the Rhaetian, the Lower Jurassic is again partly continental in the western Balkans, sandy in facies with local coals developed in small basins. The Lower Jurassic is, however, strongly transgressive and cuts down through the Trias on to the crystalline basement. Middle and Upper Triassic are only preserved locally. As the detailed zonal stratigraphy of the Lower Jurassic is being worked out, remarkably exact parallels are being found with the zonal schemes recognized in western Europe, especially Britain. If one fights one's way through the undergrowth of proliferating taxonomy and human idiosyncrasies one finds that many species are remarkably constant right across Europe. However, although the bulk of the Lower and Middle Jurassic faunas are like those of north-west Europe, there is a small area, once more in the extreme east, with red limestones of the Alpine Hierlatz type and a Hierlatz-type fauna as in Austria and Hungary. From the Callovian onwards it takes on a general 'Mediterranean' aspect.

Much of the Jurassic is very condensed (e.g., the Bathonian is locally down to only 3 m), but all the stages have now been recognized as well as many of the north-west European ammonite zones. The only exception to this general thinning is the Tithonian stage at the top of the Jurassic, which is exceptionally thick. It occurs in two facies. In the north it is the usual white massive limestones (as at Štramberk in Czechoslovakia) up to 400 m thick. It is well seen at the narrow gorge known as Vratsata ('small door'), near Vratsa in north-west Bulgaria, scene of a tragic dam disaster in 1966.

To the south and south-west it passes through a gradual, diachronous transition into a flysch facies which may reach more than 2000 m thick, well seen along the Struma Valley in south-west Bulgaria. These two facies pass up into the Cretaceous without break, and a large area of Bulgaria is underlain by Cretaceous rocks.

The Urgonian facies of massive white limestones with corals and rudists appears at the usual Barremian to Lower Aptian level. As always, it dominates the scenery, especially in the central Balkans (e.g., near the old capital of Turnovo and above the monastery at Cherepish). It is characteristically in great lenses and is followed by sandstones and marls of late Aptian age, but the Urgonian 'reef' facies is almost certainly diachronous.

Perhaps the most remarkable and interesting deposit in Bulgaria is the olistostrome (mentioned earlier) that extends from the Kotel area in the eastern Balkans almost to the Black Sea coast. This has only been recognized comparatively recently. It is of 'mid' Cretaceous age (Albian to perhaps Turonian) and consists of a shaly matrix containing exotic blocks up to the size of hills. The latter mostly originate from Triassic and Jurassic source rocks that are not known *in situ* in Bulgaria. It also contains granitic boulders at the west end of the outcrop and has yielded Carboniferous spores. The Mesozoic limestone blocks in the olistostrome are of 'southern' aspect with faunas (and facies) like those in the Northern Calcareous Alps of Austria and quite different from the Mesozoic succession in the Balkan Mountains generally. The material must have been transported a considerable distance, either from the Black Sea to the east or (more likely in my opinion) right over the Rhodope Massif from the south.

The emplacement of this olistostrome was presumably part of the important movements in late early Cretaceous times. These probably started in the Aptian and indeed the Upper Aptian sands are often called the 'Lower Molasse' by Bulgarian geologists, due to their resemblance to the post-orogenic deposits of Tertiary age so familiar in the Alpine ranges.

After all had settled down again there was a transgression into the Balkan Mountains area from the east in Cenomanian times. Calcareous deposition thereafter dominated the Cretaceous story, with massive limestones in the Maastrichtian, such as those that form the famous beauty spot near the Kotel olistostrome known as the *Tchudnite steni* ('wonderful walls'). Particularly interesting is the development at the east end of the range of a chalk facies with all its characteristic features. This is well seen near Shumen (Kolarovgrad), where it is rich in fossils that remind the visitor from north-west Europe of home.

Volcanic activity broke out in late Cretaceous times and lasted until the end of the period. In particular, the extrusion of andesitic tuffs and lavas in the Sredna Gora marks a belt that extended to the Bosphorus and out of our continent. Also, at the end of the period there was the emplacement of a series of major acidic intrusions in the Sredna Gora which are usually known as the 'South Bulgarian Granites'. Around Plovdiv (Philippopolis) in the south are monzonites (plagioclase syenites). Near here a valley in the granites is famous for its roses, grown only here to produce 'Attar of Roses' for perfume (one of Bulgaria's odder exports, along with the bacterium that produces yoghurt).

A sharp dislocation known as the Maritza Line separates the Sredna Gora from the

Rhodope Massif and it is worth noting that geysers still eject boiling water from considerable depths roughly along this east–west line.

Mineralization accompanied the Mesozoic volcanicity, and ores of lead, zinc, copper, and silver are found, notably in the Triassic limestones. An important discovery for the economy of Bulgaria was metasomatic iron-ore, almost within sight of the capital, leading to the development of the large iron and steel industry of Kremikovtsi.

Cainozoic

Tertiary earth movements began at the end of the Mesozoic and Sredna Gora became land. An east–west trough developed in front of them to the north, in which were deposited Eocene nummulitic limestones and sands.

The main Alpine folding seems to have occurred after the Lutetian, when the Balkan Mountains were formed with overthrusting towards the north. Granites and syenites were also emplaced at this time, for example the complex intrusion that forms the local beauty spot and recreational area of Mount Vitosha, just outside Sofia.

The structures produced in these movements were basically simple with only limited overturning and thrusting (Fig. 14.13). There was no cleavage produced or metamorphism, except as contact effects around the intrusions.

Oligocene marine deposits are only known in the east. There was further folding at this time and extensive volcanicity within the Rhodope Massif. Elsewhere there were continental deposits including valuable brown coals, for example around the industrial town of Pernik (Dimitrovo) in the west, which depends on these deposits for its fuel.

Further marine transgressions occurred in Miocene times, both from the east and the north-west. In the west, the deposits are like those of the Vienna Basin, but in the east (as might be expected) they have much closer affinities with those of the Crimea. The latter are seen in the Varna Basin on the Black Sea and form low cliffs on the north beach at Varna. Only the Upper Miocene is present here, but it is extremely fossiliferous in places and is quarried locally for building purposes, especially for facing stones for the many new hotels along the Black Sea coast. Farther south there are lake deposits with valuable lignites.

Quaternary glaciations apparently affected only the highest mountains in Bulgaria. The most noteworthy Quaternary deposit is the thick series of loesses along the Danube in the north. The spread of these southwards was stopped by the Balkan Mountains.

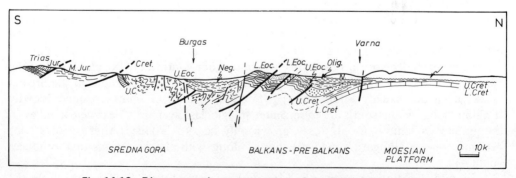

Fig. 14.13 Diagrammatic cross-section of the Balkan Mountains.

Selected references to Chapter 14

Section 14(a)   Betic Cordillera

Bailey, E. B. (1953), 'Notes on Gibraltar and the northern Rif', *Quart. Jl Geol. Soc. Lond.*, **108**, 157–176.

Chauve, P., J. Didon, J. Magne and Y. Peyre (1964), 'Mise au point sur l'âge des phenomènes tectoniques majeurs dans les Cordillères bétiques occidentales', *Geol. Mijnb.*, **43**, 273–276.

Colom, G. (1967), 'Sur l'interprétation des sédiments profonds de la zone géosynclinale Baléare et Subbétique (Espagne)', *Palaeogeog., Palaeoclimat., Palaeoecol.*, **3**, 299–310.

Egeler, C. G. (1963), 'On the tectonics of the eastern Betic Cordilleras', *Geol. Rundschau.*, **53**, 260–269.

Egeler, C. G. and O. J. Simon (1969a), 'Sur la tectonique de la zone bétique (Cordillères Bétiques, Espagne)', *Verh. Nederl. Akad. Wetensch. Naturk.*, **25**(3), 1–90.

Egeler, C. G. and O. J. Simon (1969b), 'Orogenic evolution of the Betic zone (Betic Cordilleras, Spain), with emphasis on the nappe structures', *Geol. Mijnb.*, **48**, 296–305.

Fallot, P. (1948), 'Les Cordillères Bétiques'. Consej. sup. Invest. Cient, *Inst. Invest. Geol. 'Lucas Mallada', Est. Geol.*, **8**, 83–172 (a summary of many earlier papers).

Hoeppener, R., P. Hoppe, H. Mollat, S. Muchow, S. Dürr and F. Kockel (1963), 'Uber den westlichen Anschnitt der betischen Kordillere und seine Beziehungen zum Gesantorogen', *Geol. Rundschau.*, **53**, 269–296.

Perconig, E. (1962), 'Sur la constitution géologique de l'Andalousie occidentale, en particulier du bassin du Guadalquivir (Espagne méridionale)', in M. Durand Delga (ed.), *Mém. Soc. Géol. Fr., Liv. Mém. P. Fallot*, **1**, 229–256.

Torres-Roldán, R. L. (1979), The tectonic subdivision of the Betic Zone (Betic Cordilleras, southern Spain): its significance and one possible geotectonic scenario for the westernmost Alpine belt. *Amer. J. Sci.*, **279**, 19–51.

Section 14(b)   Balearics

Colom, G. (1950), *Más allá de la prehistoria; una geologia elemental de la Baleares*, Cons. Sup. Inves. Cient. Inst, San José de Calasany, New York, 285 pp.

Colom, G. and B. Escandell (1962), 'L'évolution du géosynclinale baléare', in M. Durand-Delga (ed.), *Mém. Soc. Géol. Fr., Liv. Mém. P. Fallot*, **1**, 125–136.

Melendez, B., ed. (1958), 'Mapa geologica de España y Portugal. (explicacion geologica)', Paraninfo, Madrid (1 sheet with text).

Section 14(c)   Western Alps

Ager, D. V., B. D. Evamy and J. G. Ramsay (1963), 'Summer field meeting in the French Jura and Alps, July 1963', *Proc. Geol. Ass.*, **74**, 483–515.

Aubouin, J. (1972), 'Chaînes liminaires (Andines) et chaînes geosynclinales (Alpines)', *24th Internat. Geol. Congr., Montreal*, sec. 3, pp. 438–461.

Badoux, H. (1967), 'Géologie abrégée de la Suisse', in A. Lombard (ed.), *Geologischer Führer der Schweiz*, Schweiz. Geol. Geseel., pp. 1–44.

Dal Piaz, G. V., J. von Raumer, F. P. Sassi, B. Zanettin and A. Zanferrari (1975), 'Geological outline of the Italian Alps', in C. H. Squyres (ed.), *Geology of Italy*, Petrol. Explor. Soc. Libya, pp. 299–375.

Debelmas, J. (1974), 'Les alpes Franco-italiennes', in J. Debelmas (ed.), *Géologie de la France*, vol. 2, Doin, Paris, pp. 387–442.

Gwinner, M. P. (1971), *Geologie der Alpen*, Schweizerbart Verlag, Stuttgart, 477 pp.

Ramsay, J. G. (1964), 'Stratigraphy, structure and metamorphism in the Western Alps', *Proc. Geol. Ass., Lond.*, **74**, 357–391.

Trumpy, R. (1960), 'Palaeotectonic evolution of the central and western Alps', *Bull. Geol. Soc. Amer.*, **71**, 843–908.

Trumpy, R. (1973), 'The timing of orogenic events in the central Alps', in K. A. DeJong and R. Scholten (eds), *Gravity and Tectonics*, Wiley, London and New York, pp. 229–251.

Section 14(d)   Eastern Alps

Anon. (1964), 'Geologischer Führer zu Exkursionen durch die Ostalpen', *Mitt. Geol. Gesell., Wien*, 57 pp.

Exner, C. (1966), 'Geology of Austria', in *Erläuterungen zur Geologischen und zur Lagerstätten-Karte 1 : 1,000,000 von Österreich.*, Geol. Bundesanstalt, Wien, pp. 77–84.

Gwinner, M. P. (1971), *Geologie der Alpen*, Schweizerbart Verlag., Stuttgart, 477 pp.

Heissel, W. and C. Exner, ed. (1951), *Geologischer Führer zu den Exkursionen*, Verh. Geol. Bundesanst, Wien, A. 130 pp.

Lombard, A., ed. (1967), *Geologischer Führer de Schweiz*, Schweiz. Geol. Gesell., pt 1 Allgemeine Einführungen, pp. 1–44.

Oxburgh, E. R. (1968), 'An outline of the geology of the central Eastern Alps', *Proc. Geol. Ass.*, **79**, 1–46.

Oxburgh, E. R. (1968), 'The Eastern Alps—a geological excursion guide', *Proc. Geol. Ass.*, **79**, 47–127.

Schönlaub, H. P. (1979), *Das Paläozoikum in Österreich*, vol. 33, Abhandl. Geol. Bundesanst., 124 pp.

Tollmann, A. (1977), *Geologie von Österreich*, vol. 1, Franz Deuticke, Vienna, 766 pp.

Section 14(e)   Carpathians

Andrusov, D. (1964), *Geologie der tschechoslovakischen Karpaten*, Akad Verlag, Berlin, 263 pp.

Andrusov, D. (1967), 'Aperçu général sur la géologie des Carpathes occidentales', *Bull. Soc. Géol. Fr.*, **7**, 1029–1062.

Bleahu, M., D. Patrulius, D. Radalescu, E. Saulea and H. Savu (1967), 'Carte géologique de la Roumanie, échelle du 1/1,000,000 (note explicative)', *Roman. Geol. Inst.*, Bucharest, 33 pp.

Burchfiel, B. C. (1976), 'Geology of Romania', *spec. paper, Geol. Soc. Amer.*, No. 158, 82 pp.

Codarcea, A. *et al.* (1968), 'Geological structure of the south-western Carpathians', *Guide to Excursion 49*, 23rd Internat. Geol. Congr., Prague, 49 pp.

Contescu, L. R. (1974), 'Geologic history and paleogeography of eastern Carpathians: example of alpine geosynclinal evolution', *Bull. Amer. Ass. Petrol. Geol.*, **58**, 2436–2476.

Książkiewicz, M. (1956), 'Geology of the northern Carpathians', *Geol. Rundschau*, **45**, 369–411.

Książkiewicz, M., J. Samsonowicz and E. Rühle (1968), *An Outline of the Geology of Poland*, Sci. Publ. foreign Coop. Center, Central Inst. Sci. Tech. Econ. Inf., Warsaw, 414 pp.

Mahel, M. *et al.* (1968), *Regional Geology of Czechoslovakia*, pt II, *The West Carpathians*, Geol. Surv. Czechoslov., 723 pp.

Patrulius, D., M. Stefanescu, E. Popa and I. Popescu (1968), 'Geology of the Inner Zones of the Carpathian Bend', *Guide to Excursion 50*, 23rd Internat. Geol. Congr., Prague, 50 pp.

Section 14(f)   Balkanides

Ager, D. V. (1972), 'Summer field meeting in Bulgaria, 1971', *Proc. Geol. Ass.*, **83**, 239–268.

Boncev, E. (1971), *The Tectonics of the Fore-Balkans*, Izdatel. Bulg. Akad. Nauk, Sofia, 584 pp. (in Bulgarian with English summary).

Boncev, E. and C. Dimitrov (1965), 'Exkursionsführer, Sofia–Belogradcik–Sofia', 7th Congr. Karpato-Balkan. Geol. Ass., Sofia, 97 pp.

Dimitrov, C. (1965), 'Exkursionsführer B, Sofia–Plovdiv–Burgas–Varna–Tarnovo–Kasanlak–Sofia', 7th Congr. Karpato-Balkan. Geol. Ass., Sofia, 91 pp.

Dimitrov, S. (1959), 'Kurze Ubersicht der Metamorphen Komplexe in Bulgarien', *Freiberger Forschungs.*, **C57**, 62–72.

Tzankov, V. and E. Boncev (1965), 'Exkursionsführer A, Sofia–Pleven–Plovdiv–Tarnovo–Varna–Plovdiv–Sofia', 7th Congr. Karpato-Balkan. Geol. Ass., Sofia, 124 pp.

Yovchev, Y. (1965), 'Notion sur la géologie et la richessc minerales du territoire de la République populaire de Bulgarie', Sofia.

Chapter Fifteen

Intra-Alpide massifs and basins

This chapter concerns the major massifs and basins within the Alpine chains which had lives of their own but which were directly related to events in the adjacent fold belts. In most cases the existing basins can be shown to have been upstanding massifs at an earlier stage in their history.

15(a)   Po–Adriatic Basin

Since it is part sea and part sedimentary basin, it is appropriate to take this as the first of the series of negative areas which form the civilized lowlands and waters between the wild excesses of the Alpine mountains. We must not be over-influenced by what has happened in the last few moments of geological time, since it can often be shown that what is so placid and geophysically negative today was violently disturbed and uprising in the past. Nevertheless, these basins are similar in many features of late Cainozoic history, and all still contain something in the way of an enclosed sea or puddle in which sediments are accumulating.

Nowhere is this more obvious than in the Po Basin, between the Alps and the Apennines, and its direct continuation the Adriatic Sea between the Italian Apennines on the one side and the Dinarides–Hellenides of Yugoslavia, Albania, and Greece, on the other (Fig. 15.1). It is tempting to compare this basin with the classic picture of a geosyncline. It has the correct form and it seems to be filling with sediment from one end. At its north-west end, the readily available debris of the new Alps and of the eugeosynclinal northern Apennines made infilling inevitable. Farther south-east, a more reduced neighbouring topography and miogeosynclinal source rocks starved the trough like the oceanic deeps of Indonesia. However, the fact that the trough does pass from one regime to another is at least a hint that everything is not quite that simple.

Po Valley and the frontal Apennine Trough

The Po Valley (or Padan Plain), with its mixture of intense industrialization and almost Asiatic rurality (thinking of the paddy-fields) overlies the complexities of both Apennines and Alps. It has been called a 'fore-deep' to the first and 'hind-deep' to the second and

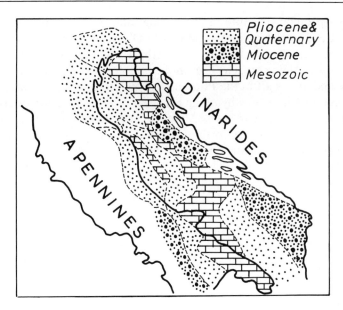

Fig. 15.1 Geological sketch-map of the Adriatic (after Celet, 1977, by kind permission of Plenum Press).

clearly it post-dates the main over-thrusting, but its earlier sediments were affected by the Alpine movements. This is seen particularly well west of Bologna (the site of Europe's oldest university), where Miocene sediments are much affected by the last compressional movements of the Apennines. Nevertheless, the southern edge of the Po Basin is sharp and straight, seemingly made straighter by the motorway from Milano via Bologna to Rimini on the Adriatic, whose low-lying placidity contrasts sharply with the sudden steepness inland of Monte Titanus, holding aloft the tiniest, if oldest, republic in the world—San Marino. The western and northern borders of the basin are less sharp due to the effects of later marginal transgressions.

East of Romeo and Juliet's Verona the basin opens out to the north-east into the Venetian plain. Geometrically this is the direct continuation of the rectangle of the Adriatic, and although that most glorious and neglected of cities stands on 'her hundred islands' of mud, and all around are great thicknesses of young sediments, there is clear evidence of stable, flat-lying Mesozoic limestones beneath. Not very far away, across the Gulf of Venice (Venezia) is the Yugoslav holiday peninsula of Istria, protruding into the Adriatic, and similarly built of autochthonous flat-lying Mesozoic limestones. But that is the Dalmatian Zone of the Dinarides, which extends nearly all the way down to the Yugoslav coast and its multitude of elongated islands. With the Gavrovo Zone of the Hellenides, it is the concern of the next chapter. On the Italian side, one has to go all the way to the Gargano Peninsula and Apulia at the other end of the Adriatic to see these limestones at the surface.

So far as Tertiary sediments are concerned, the filling began in late Eocene times, although marine deposits of this age only seem to be present in the east and centre of the Po Valley. In Oligocene times the sea spread westwards and southwards, spilling over the edge of the Apennine structures and flooding into the Piedmont part of the Italian Alps at the west end of the basin. In mid to late Oliogocene times it spread up into the lake country of the Lombardy Alps to the north, resting unconformably on the Eocene flysch sequence of an Alpine trough. The story continued with detritus from the new Alps in the Miocene and above all in the Pliocene and Pleistocene, when fantastic thicknesses of sediment accumulated, especially along the front of the Apennines, where the floor of the Pliocene drops to 6000 m below sea-level between Reggio Emilia and Bologna, and even exceeds 7000 m on the coast north of Rimini. This floor was disturbed by a series of reversed faults paralleling the Apennine front and diminishing in extent and throw towards the north-east.

The deep trench along the front of the Apennines, known as the Pre-Padan Fore-deep, continues all the way down the east side of the Italian peninsula as the lowlands of the Adriatic coast, in front of the farthest travelled ridges of the Apennines. South of Ancona, it is known as the Adriatico–Bradanic Fore-deep, but it continues on into Apulia, discussed below. Whether this is treated as the fore-deep of the Apennines or as part of the Adriatic story is of no importance, but it appears that the Adriatic trough has been subsiding for a very long time.

Gargano Peninsula and Apulia

Apulia is easily recognized as the 'heel' of the Italian boot and the Gargano Peninsula is the 'spur' that projects into the Adriatic farther north. They would normally be considered with the Apennines rather than the Adriatic, but it seems to me more logical to include them here.

This region has been called the 'foreland' of the Apennines, for at the surface are seemingly autochthonous carbonate sequences beyond the farthest travelled allochthonous sheets of the southern Apennines. That limit can be traced in the subsurface running from north-west to south-east down into the middle of the Italian 'instep'. To the east lies a broad lowland belt, famous for its wool and wheat and centred on the old market town of Foggia. This is the Pede-Apenninic trench, filled with post-orogenic Plio-Pleistocene, reaching up to 2000 m in thickness.

Farther east again are the hot limestone plains of the 'heel' proper, running up past the ancient ports of Brindisi and Bari to the Gargano Peninsula. This belt continues up north under the sparkling Adriatic to the Venice Basin and in the opposite direction to the Hyblaean Mountains of south-east Sicily to form a foreland, not only of the Apennides coming from the west, but also of the Dinarides and Hellenides coming from the east.

This is not a foreland in the usual sense of a massif of crystalline rocks, although such may be hidden beneath the thick Mesozoic carbonates, but the rocks here have not been affected by any of the tectonic violence that deformed the rest of Italy. The succession in general resembles that of the southern Apennines, but even more it resembles that on the opposite side of the Adriatic. Boreholes have proved more than 10 000 m of Mesozoic carbonates, all of shallow-water and often reef facies. Characteristically the Upper Triassic includes thick gypsum and anhydrite and many of the extensive Jurassic reef limestones have been dolomitized. There is a rim of reefs down the east side, cutting across the middle of the Gargano Peninsula and separating the succession just described from a markedly thinner development only seen in the eastern part of this headland. Here there are cherty Jurassic and Cretaceous limestones that amount to less than half their equivalents to the west and very much like the succession in the Ionian zone of Albania and the Epirus. They appear to be of a deeper water facies, including sediments such as *rosso ammonitico* and *Scaglia* of the Apennines.

The Tertiary sediments which patchily cap this succession are, in contrast, very thin. Palaeogene and Miocene limestones, again with reefs, amount to less than 200 m in thickness, and rest transgressively on the Upper Cretaceous. Unlike the Mesozoic, however, the Tertiary formations thicken somewhat eastwards on the Gargano Peninsula.

The palaeogeographical interpretation of the Apulia–Gargano belt is disputed, but those on the spot (i.e., chiefly geologists from Naples) think in terms of an outer subsiding platform, separated by a trench from an inner platform on the west side of the Italian peninsula. The two platforms differ in stratigraphical detail, but also in that the inner platform has been highly disturbed tectonically while the outer platform has remained pretty much as it was when formed in early Mesozoic times. The succession in eastern Gargano suggests another trough to the east, sunk beneath the Adriatic, implying a history for that classic seaway vastly older than the Doges of Venice, the Roman galleys, and the Greek colonists who passed this way.

Eastern Margin

On the opposite side of the Adriatic are the similarly autochthonous rocks of the Dalmatian Zone of Yugoslavia and the equivalent Gavrovo Zone of Albania and Greece. These are described in the sections on the Dinarides and Hellenides, respectively (Chapter 16), since they belong so intrinsically to those ranges. However, they are clearly related to the history of the Adriatic, as the stable platform on its eastern side. Even more relevant are two further westerly zones in the Hellenides—the Ionian Zone down the west coast of Epirus and neighbouring islands, and the Pre-apulian Zone only seen in the westernmost Greek islands. These last two zones belong to a sedimentary trough in Mesozoic times that shows the transition from the flysch of the Hellenides to the organic debris interpreted (as the name of the westernmost zone implies) as having come straight off the Apulian platform. This is reasonable in that it lines up with what would be a direct southerly extension of Apulia, although separated from it by the beginnings of a deep trench (of presumably recent ancestry) that runs south-east towards modern Africa.

The Adriatic therefore seems to be a stable block so far as Alpine tectonism is concerned, although with a tendency to subside since way back in the Mesozoic. Faulting, often on a large scale, is usually parallel to the present seaway and continuing vertical instability is suggested by the deep-sea trench, earthquakes, and possibly the magmatism in the outermost Yugoslav islands. Whether or not it represents the battering ram of a northerly moving African continental plate will be discussed in Chapter 17. I only comment here that, long before the days of plate tectonics, I recorded the distinctiveness of the Mesozoic brachiopod faunas around the Adriatic, although I did not say then (and I would not say now) that they are particularly 'African' in character.

425

Adriatic Sea

Of all the post-orogenic basins of Neo-Europa, the Po-Adriatic Basin is certainly the wettest, if one excludes the Mediterranean itself. Sedimentologists can tell us a great deal about what is going on today, for example, in terms of sediment movement. A general anti-clockwise circulation produces the mud on the east coast of Italy and the sandy beaches of Yugoslavia. But these are the fleeting facies of historic time and there is far less to say about the earlier history of this remarkable seaway.

More evidence has become available in recent years, both from drilling and geophysics, but there is no real indication that the great wedge of Tertiary sediment in the Po Basin continues down the Adriatic. This may be partly a matter of supply, like the starved deeps of Indonesia, and partly a matter of insufficient subsidence to accommodate such material. The islands and the mainlands on either side do not suggest any great thickening of Tertiary sediments this way, nor is there any sign of a passage to deepwater facies. Indeed in the Pre-apulian Zone of the outermost Greek islands one already seems to have waded across the deeper part and to be paddling out on the far side.

Only when one reaches the western part of the Ionian Sea, south of Italy and right outside the Adriatic, does one find great thicknesses of Tertiary sediment. As much as 14 km has been estimated here as a direct prolongation of the Sirte Basin of eastern Libya. The crust below is very thin.

15(b)   Pannonian Basin

The Pannonian Basin is the largest of the sediment-filled post-orogenic basins of the Alpine system. It fills a great hole in the centre of Europe, contained within the glorious sweep of the Carpathians with its base on the Dinaric Alps (Fig. 15.2). It covers the whole of Hungary, extends westwards as the Vienna Basin into Austria, southwards into the peaceful, unvisited, north-east part of Yugoslavia, and eastwards into Count Dracula's Transylvania in Romania. Anyone who has driven across the Great Hungarian Plain or, in particular, along the 'autoput' from Ljubljana to Belgrade, knows how dull this vast area can be geologically. But it is much more than just a late Tertiary basin. Paradoxical though it may seem at first sight, it is more of a massif than a basin. For most of its history it was an upstanding region of ancient rocks, comparable with the Variscan massifs of Meso-Europa.

The ancient floor shows up through a thick carpet of Neogene sediment in the Apuseni Mountains of Romania, which separate Transylvania from the main basin. The main basin is also divided in two by a line of Mesozoic hills running from north-east to south-west across Hungary as the Bükk, Gerecse, Vértes, and Bakony 'mountains'. These separate the Little Hungarian Plain to the west (continuous with the Vienna Basin) from the Great Hungarian Plain to the east (famous for its horses, Magyar horsemen, and asparagus). These are *Zwischengebirge* ('between mountains') of classic Alpine theory, lying between the north-facing Carpathian and south-facing Dinaric fold belts as a central crumple. It is not as simple as that, as is revealed by a further group of hills around Pécs in the extreme south of Hungary (the Mecsek and Villány hills) which are surprisingly northern in character.

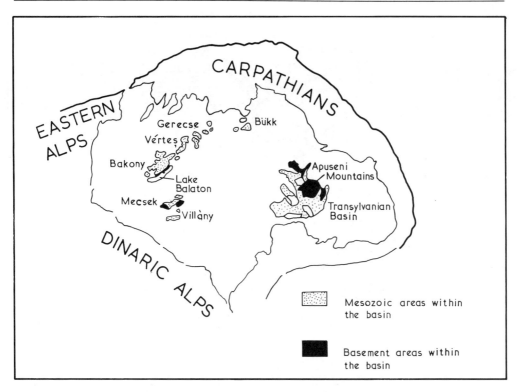

Fig. 15.2 Sketch-map of the Pannonian Basin.

Apuseni Mountains

The floor of the Pannonian Basin consists of some 20–25 km of continental crust, which makes it a good candidate for a microplate. As mentioned above, the basement is seen at the surface in the Apuseni Mountains of Romania and also in the hills around Pécs in southern Hungary. On their basis this section could be called the 'Pannonian–Transylvanian Massif'.

The basement is most clearly autochthonous in the northern Apuseni Mountains, more specifically in the Gilău Mountains, west of Cluj, and in the Plopiş Mountains to the north-west (Fig. 15.3). The rocks are chiefly medium- to high-grade metamorphics, dated by spores as late Precambrian to early Cambrian in age, and intruded in the central Gilău region by granites that have been dated as Variscan, but may be older.

Up the west side of the Apuseni Mountains, ancient rocks are seen in a series of nappes that form ridges running out into the Tertiary basin (Highiş, Codru Moma, and Pădurea Craiului). The ultimate is seen in the Bihor Mountains (immediately west of Gilău), where seven distinct tectonic units have been recognized above the autochthonous basement. The oldest unit is the highest, and together with the usual amphibolite grade schist and gneiss includes tremendous masses of marble. Lower units are of a green-schist grade and include considerable developments of igneous rocks, while sediments range up to Permian in age, with Mesozoic sequences involved in the Codru nappe system.

427

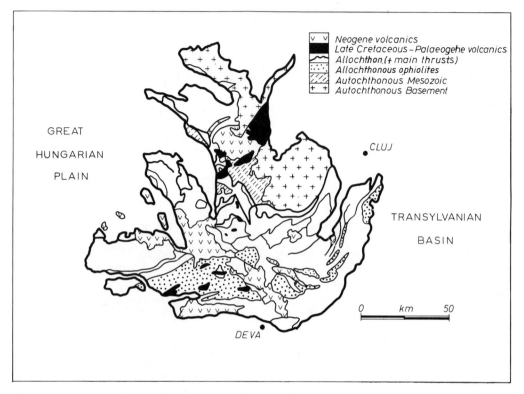

Fig. 15.3 *Geological sketch-map of the Apuseni Mountains (after Burchfiel, 1976, by kind permission of the author and the Geological Society of America).*

The autochthonous basement of the northern Apuseni is overlain by post-orogenic late Permian sands and conglomerates which pass up into Werfenian-type Lower Triassic and then a calcareous Middle and Upper Triassic plus Gresten facies Lower Jurassic, all reminiscent of the Eastern Alps. Shallow-water carbonates with stratigraphical breaks, bauxites, massive Urgonian limestones, and discordant Senonian Gosau molasse complete the distinctly Alpine story, although of a northern rather than a Tethyan theme.

In the allochthonous sequences there is also much to remind one of the Austrian Alps and the western Carpathians. Although there are many complexities of facies, there is an overall tendency towards more marine and deeper water conditions to the south once the nappes are 'put back in place'. The nappes all came from that direction, with those containing both Precambrian and Palaeozoic metamorphics overriding those composed mainly of Mesozoic and Palaeozoic sediments. The present form of the northern Apuseni Mountains, however, is not determined by the form of the nappes which had completed their travels before the deposition of late Cretaceous Gosau-type sediments. Perhaps some moved earlier, but the evidence is incomplete. Certainly there was some post-Gosau folding before the Tertiary volcanism and faulting which shaped the mountains as they are today.

In the southern Apuseni Mountains the situation is very different. Here we are in a classic Mesozoic 'eugeosynclinal' situation, with thick developments of flysch and basic igneous rocks. One thinks immediately of the ocean floor and marginal trenches with the usual east Mediterranean ophiolites of early and mid Jurassic age, followed by cherts, aptychus beds, and flysch. These are all poorly seen in the thickly wooded Mureş Mountains. The main part of these, occupied by ophiolites, are also known as the Metalliferous Mountains because of their ores. Again there are fascinating complications notably the presence, in the Trascau Mountains to the east, of shallow-water, reef limestones like those of Štramberk in Czechoslovakia. These fossiliferous late Jurassic limestones are mixed up in a flysch sequence and the whole thing is probably an olistostrome (as at Štramberk), but it is not clear whence it came. There are noteworthy developments of later Mesozoic volcanic rocks, including calc-alkaline suites, which may have come from reef-crowned island arcs.

Although there is thrusting along the northern edge of the Mureş Mountains and a nappe has been postulated in the east (which may only be a giant olistostrome) the main structure of the southern Apuseni Mountains is an east–west trending anticline that swings north-east at its eastern end. Although there were some intra-Cretaceous movements, the main deformation came at the end of that period.

As the orogenesis ended with the Mesozoic, so began Tertiary volcanism, faulting, and sedimentation. Normal faulting produced the graben and tilted blocks that are the present river valleys. Basically these are north-west trending in the west and north-east trending in the east, so once more we have a 'knee-bend' as in the Variscan massifs of western and central Europe and, again, Tertiary volcanism is often centred on fault lines. The faulting controlled early Cainozoic sedimentation and it blocked out the Apuseni Mountains as they are today. The big difference, however, is the involvement of the Mesozoic nappes in the virgation.

The Mesozoic hills

For the Magyar horseman of the Hungarian Plain, these hills were no doubt mountains, as they are still called locally, but to us they must be just a line of lovely hills, of no great height, but impressive in the way they stand up suddenly from the plain. Nowhere is this suddenness more obvious than in the Hungarian capital of Budapest. Here the old city of Buda, with its rebuilt mediaeval buildings and its all-dominating Russian war memorial, stands on top of a fault plane that drops straight into the River Danube. From the top one looks out over the modern city of Pest and the seemingly limitless Tertiary plain. Below the war memorial are genuine Turkish baths, built when this was a frontier town of the Ottoman Empire. The people used, and still use, hot springs that come up the fault plane and have coated the hanging wall of Triassic limestone with a layer of travertime. This could well be a reflection of a deep-seated fault in the basement, as could many of the other faults which delimit the Mesozoic outcrops.

It is necessary to separate the Bükk and Transdanubian Central Mountains, as the Hungarians call them, from the Mecsek and Villányi Mountains of the south. The Bükk Mountains, near Miskolc in northern Hungary, are rather isolated from the rest, and their Mesozoic rocks are almost entirely Triassic carbonates, but there is also a most interesting development of Triassic basalts and porphyries, which set a pattern of igneous activity that continued in the Cretaceous and—most energetically—in the Neogene. The

Tertiary volcanism is part of a much wider picture, but the persistence of such activity here should be remembered before we start postulating plates moving over scorching hot-spots.

When one crosses the Danube from the east at Budapest, as did the Magyars, one is immediately in the Transdanubian Mountains, extending from the Gerecse Hills to the west of the capital, down through the Vértes Hills to the more extensive Bakony Hills, standing on the north shores of Lake Balaton. The gentleness of the hills and their structures gives no hint of the violence their position must imply. Tectonically, they are gently folded on a north-easterly trend, with minor tensional faults at right angles to this. There are some thrusts, notably along the north-west flank of the anticiline that dominates Lake Balaton, and the modern interpretation is that they are wholly allochthonous.

Although quite unlike the Alpine ranges topographically, the Transdanubian Central Mountains are completely Alpine, in facies and fauna. At the bottom, right on the shore of Lake Balaton, are Devonian and Carboniferous shales and phyllites, altered and deformed before they were covered, with marked unconformity, by coarse late Permian continental deposits. These are overlain unconformably by Alpine Trias. Some 2500 m of carbonates, with minor developments of other sediments (plus some volcanics), yield giant megalodontid bivalves and other fossils typical of the Northern Calcareous Alps. In Vértes and Gerecse there is evidence of early Kimmerian movements before the Jurassic. In Bakony, Dachstein-type limestones are followed by Hierlatz-type limestones as one passed up into the Jurassic, and there is said to be no break, although I have seen what seems to be intra-Triassic folding near the resort town of Balatonfüred.

There are also numerous breaks within the Jurassic, and the faunas are some of the best of Tethyan type in Europe, perhaps because they are concentrated in comparatively thin developments. The Liassic brachiopods are particularly splendid! The most important breaks are where valuable manganese deposits have formed, infilling a contemporaneous karst topography. This is well seen at Urkut, near the old capital of Veszprém. Unfortunately, the gentle curves and luxurious forest of these hills do not usually provide many natural exposures for the frustrated geologist. However, great imagination and hard work by the Hungarian geologists (particularly the Magyar Foldtani Intezet) has led to the digging of many long, wide trenches across critical parts of the succession and the preservation of their best sections. The most remarkable locality (and an example to the geological authorities throughout the world) is at Kálvária-domb (Calvary Hill) on the outskirts of Tata, below the Gerecse hills. This displays splendidly the condensed Mesozoic succession, ranging from late Triassic to early Cretaceous, in a complex of preserved quarry and natural exposures. There are also early archaeological remains and, not far away, the elegant lakeside castle from where the Eszterházy family ruled a large part of Hungary and patronized Haydn.

Limestones and marls with Tethyan faunas such as pygopid brachiopods, tintinnids, and reef-forming rudists, form most of the Cretaceous succession, but at the top there was shallowing and emergence. Immediately above the Turonian in the Bakony area come brackish and fresh-water deposits, with an interesting story of gastropods changing rapidly in response to the salinity. At Ajka, west of Veszprém, there are 100 m of 'Coal Measures' at this level, while in the south-west of Bakony, in the castle-capped outlier of Sümeg, there are terrestrial sandstones and conglomerates. Shallow marine conditions returned with rudist reefs and extensive oyster beds, but there was general uplift at the end of that period and probably a long break before the commencement of Tertiary sedimentation.

At Sümeg (just across a fault from the castle) an Eocene conglomerate plus nummulitic limestone rests with a marked unconformity on an Upper Cretaceous reef complex. Elsewhere, for example at Bagolyheg in the Vértes Mountains, there is a thick development of bauxite at the Cretaceous–Eocene junction. Bauxites are developed at various levels in the Cretaceous and are a speciality of Hungarian geology. At this particular locality bauxites rest in a doline in a karst surface of Triassic limestone, but elsewhere they occur one above the other within the Cretaceous succession. They are extensively worked here and in the Bakony hills.

The main folding and displacement of the Mesozoic hills is dated as end Cretaceous ('Laramide'), with asymmetrical folds and reversed faults directed to the north. Everything is smothered in soft Tertiary with only comparatively minor faulting affecting both the Mesozoic and the cover. The more spectacular effects, such as Gellért Hill in Budapest, are demonstrably normal faults setting down the Mesozoic in a series of steps under Palaeogene sediments. Such faults delimit most of the Mesozoic hills.

Mesozoic rocks are presumed to continue southwards under the Tertiary sediments of the Great Hungarian Plain to appear again in the Mecsek and Villányi Massif in the extreme south of Hungary. It is more doubtful if they continue to the north-west. It was thought that these southern hills constituted the southern limb of a great synclinorium, especially in view of the fact that Palaeozoic rocks, including Variscan granites, outcrop along their southern margin. However, the Mesozoic succession in southern Hungary is very different from that in the north. This was brought home to me very forcibly when I found a completely unexpected Lower Jurassic brachiopod fauna of north-west European type in the supposed Bathonian of Villányi. Unknown to me, it was obvious long before that in the well-developed Liassic 'Coal Measures' of Mecsek (which have been worked for some 200 years). This is the northern Gresten facies of Austria here in the south. In fact it reminds us of equivalent strata as far north as Sweden.

It might be said that the Mesozoic succession in the south represented the southern shore of Tethys, but this does not fit in with our general knowledge of facies distributions around Alpine Europe. It is more likely (indeed it is an inescapable conclusion) that the Transdanubian Mountains, like the Northern Calcareous Alps which they so closely resemble, are allochthonous from the south, while the Mecsek and Villányi hills are more or less autochthonous.

This distinctive distribution of facies is most marked in the Lower Jurassic rocks. Later spreading of carbonate-depositing seas brought uniform conditions and implies that the two areas were not all that far apart. If the Transdanubian Central Mountains have to be carried right over the southern hills, one has to look again at the Apuseni Mountains of Romania, where both the autochthonous and allochthonous sequences seem to be of a northern type and the ophiolites, with their presumed suture, are in the extreme south. The absence (or at least ignorance) of a Mecsek–Villányi succession *under* the Transdanubian Mountains makes one suspect a major lateral displacement, but this is part of a much broader problem involving both the Eastern Alps and the Carpathians and will be considered in Chapter 17.

The basin proper

There is a basic (but often forgotten) truth in geology that quarries are always atypical (that is why they are worked where they are). The same is true of boreholes (which are customarily sited on geophysical anomalies). It may also be true of natural exposures on a regional scale when, as in the Pannonian Basin for example, glimpses of the floor are seen at the surface in the various upland areas just discussed. Do we see the older rocks of the Apuseni Mountains because their nature and structure are atypical or are they a random sample of the basement?

The floor over the main part of the Pannonian Basin has been reached in a few boreholes, but for the most part is only known from geophysical investigations. It is mainly granitic in nature but a strong positive magnetic anomaly in the centre of Transylvania suggests something more basic, perhaps connected with the Tertiary volcanism. The crystalline floor shows a horst and graben structure related to known Tertiary faulting. It has been reached in the horsts by borings down to 3000 m, while in the graben it may drop to as much as 7500 m below the surface. In the southern Vienna Basin, where it is best known, the Tertiary fill is about 3000 m thick. In the centre there is a longitudinal trough filled with about 150 m of late Quaternary gravels which coincides with an active earthquake zone. So the movements and the basin filling are still going on. Generally speaking, datable Palaeozoic and Mesozoic sediments seem to be thin (hence the probable atypicality of the hills) and the whole has been positive rather than negative through the greater part of its Phanerozoic history.

Palaeogene sediments are also thin, but are well known where they outcrop around the Mesozoic hills. Normally they begin with non-marine sequences often resting on Cretaceous bauxites, as at the Bagolyheg locality in the Vertés Hills. Here fresh to brackish water clays and marls, with abundant large gastropods, are overlain by more bauxites and brown coals of early Eocene age. These are overlain in turn by the first definite marine horizon—a foraminiferal limestone. This seems to be typical of the general picture. The Palaeogene coals (here and elsewhere) are important to the Hungarian economy and have been worked (and studied) extensively. The facies story is complex, but the incoming of foraminiferal limestones of Lutetian age is particularly widespread. Limestones full of giant nummulites are as good as in the Pyramids or anywhere. They cap the section at Sümeg in Bakony, already mentioned, and are particularly well developed around Zirc in north-west Bakony where loose nummulites form the paths of the famous monastery (where the monks used to run a cheese factory and where the cheese factory now runs the monastery).

By the end of the Eocene, volcanic activity was becoming more and more apparent and is associated with a general withdrawal of the sea at this time. The Oligocene shows a comparatively minor development and includes conglomerates full of nummulitic limestone and other Eocene pebbles. The Miocene began a new story and the main part of the infilling of the Pannonian Basin is by Miocene and Pliocene sediments. In Romania, great thicknesses of coarse Neogene molasse deposits are seen in the vicinity of the Carpathians and the Apuseni Mountains. In Hungary, where the mountains were farther away and perhaps lower, this is less obvious. A sea spread round in front of the Alpine chains and broke through the newly risen mountains into this subsiding centre of Europe. The Miocene sea planed off the rocks below, as in the pronounced surfaces around Veszprém.

By Middle Miocene (Tortonian) times, the marine transgression was at its maximum, with algal reefs and a rich and diverse marine fauna including such unusual forms (at least for the Tertiary) as large brachiopods together with thick-shelled molluscs, implying shallow, high-energy conditions. At Herend, west of Veszprém, more than 400 species of mollusc have been recorded in the Lower Tortonian alone. The easily cut Miocene limestones are much used for building stone. At St. Margarethen, between Vienna and the Hungarian frontier, they are worked in a big quarry for repairs to the cathedral and other older buildings of the city. The same quarry shows the next phase in the story, when the sea again began to retreat.

There follows what has always struck me as one of the most exciting episodes in European palaeontology. The Pannonian Basin became an evolutionary hothouse, with the most unlikely fossils evolving with incredible rapidity in response to changes in salinity within what was now an enclosed basin. Curiously enough it had happened earlier in the same area, with rapid evolution of some of the gastropods of Bakony with the change from marine to fresh-water conditions at the end of the Cretaceous. Perhaps it was already an enclosed basin at that stage, with no opportunities for migration in or out.

At the top of the St. Margarethen quarry, Sarmatian (uppermost Miocene) boulder beds rest on Tortonian reefs. The fauna has become 'brackish' with the disappearance of most, but not all, of the marine fauna. This is the equivalent of the now-famous Messinian salinity crisis in the Mediterranean, when the whole of that great sea may have dried out. Due to its unusual facies the Sarmatian Stage is associated particularly with this region and with the Dacian Basin to the east. This causes some confusion in international correlation.

The Pannonian Stage of the Lower Pliocene which follows, and which takes its name from this basin, is even more peculiar, with clays and sands of brackish to fresh-water environments characterized particularly by strange bivalves. The shells are easily washed out of the soft sediments around the shores of Lake Balaton and small children sell visitors specimens of *Congeria ungulacaprae* which, as its name implies, bears a superficial resemblance to a goat's hoof.* The later Pannonian is generally completely of a fresh-water nature and was progressively colonized by fresh-water molluscs very similar to those living today, while the mammals browsing and hunting along the shores of the great lake became more and more familiar. Conditions continued to change, however, in that the lake, completely cut off by new mountains, had no drainage and therefore again became progressively more saline. Ordinary-looking fresh-water snails such as *Lymnaea* (which are notoriously conservative) evolved rapidly into a strange limpet-like form, *Valenciennessia*, while the theoretically much faster evolving horse, *Hipparion*, grazed unchanged along the borders of the lake.

Lake Balaton is the last vestige of the great Pannonian inland sea which must have filled most of the basin for the greater part of Neogene times. It is the largest lake in Europe, shallow and rapidly evaporating, but only a puddle compared with what it was. Elsewhere in the basin there are extensive fluvial and fluvio-glacial deposits, travertines,

*The children tell the story of a goatherd who dared to love the same lady as the god of the lake who, in revenge, spread his waters and drowned the foolhardy lover and his flocks. This is a much nicer story than the real one, but serves to illustrate the unusual forms taken by the molluscs under these conditions of changing salinity.

and severe weather screes, all bearing witness to the Pleistocene glaciations of the surrounding mountains. Most important, however, especially in a broad belt along the Danube and Tisza rivers, are thick loess deposits which cover up a great deal of the beautiful geology and palaeontology.

Tertiary volcanics

Although not well-known outside Hungary and Romania compared with the touristic volcanics of the Auvergne, the Eifel, and Italy, the Pannonian Basin includes the most extensive Tertiary volcanism in Europe east of the Atlantic margin. The volcanic rocks extend in a broad belt from the Calimani and Harghiţa Mountains on the inside of the Carpathian bend in Romania westwards via the Apuseni Mountains to the Bükk area of northern Hungary. From there it is not a great step to the comparable volcanism of the Bohemian Massif and on into West Germany. But it cannot be said that there is a stratigraphical progression as one might expect from a plate moving eastwards across a static 'hot spot'. What is more, as has already been mentioned, there is much older volcanism (e.g., in the Triassic of the Apuseni) and there is volcanism outside the belt shown in Fig. 9.10.

Tertiary volcanicity started, paradoxically, in the late Cretaceous, at least in the Apuseni Mountains. Following from the oceanic volcanism of the allochthonous Jurassic and early Cretaceous, the later stage is characterized by a range of intrusive rocks, from granite to diorite, and only minor volcanism in the form of andesites, dacites, and rhyolites. These lie in a north–south belt through the west-central part of the Apuseni Mountains and continue down into the southern Carpathians where they head into Yugoslavia. They pass through the Cretacious–Tertiary boundary and may be associated with the last phase of the 'Laramide' folding. Eocene volcanism is also known, mainly in the form of tuffs interbedded with sediments, in the Transdanubian Mountains of Hungary.

However, the main volcanism started in the Miocene with the extensive magmatic rocks which mark the boundary between the Pannonian Basin and the Carpathians. The Calimani and Harghiţa Mountains form part of the Carpathians topographically, as do similar rocks of the Baia Mare area in the extreme north of Romania. Indeed in the latter area they spread into the Carpathians proper, in that small part of the range that lies in the Soviet Union. However, they seem to form part of the Pannonian story and are best considered here.

This broad belt round the inside of the eastern Carpathians is one of the largest single areas of Tertiary volcanic rocks in Europe. It consists of a long series of lava flows and pyroclastics which began in late Miocene times and lasted (as in so many parts of Europe) into the Pleistocene. Although predominantly andesitic, there is a progressive change in the eruptives, from rhyolites in the Upper Miocene, to dacites in the lowermost Pliocene, to andesites through the rest of the Pliocene, and finally to basalts in the Pleistocene. There is associated mineralization, including gold and silver, besides more commonplace zinc, lead, and copper ores.

The volcanism appears to emanate from deep fractures round the inside of the Carpathian bend and must be connected with the relationship between the Carpathians and the Pannonian–Transylvanian Massif at the time of the Carpathian orogeny. The volcanism started at the same time as the great intermontane basin and, at this point on its boundary at least, there appears to be an abrupt break rather than a gentle flexure. The comparable andesitic volcanism of the Apuseni Mountains is aligned along north-east and north-west trending tensional faults, in the same area as the earlier volcanism. It has been suggested that they are in the nature of an island arc with intracratonic back-arc spreading.

In Hungary, late Tertiary volcanism is concentrated in the Bükk Mountains in the extreme north, notably in a broad belt passing through the town of Eger. This is chiefly famous for *Egri bikavér*, the dark, full-bodied 'Bull's Blood' wine whose vine prospers on the local volcanics as do grapes on Neogene volcanics in many parts of Europe. Cellars are cut in the soft tuffs below the town. This is the most mountainous part of Hungary with jagged volcanic peaks, the youngest of which still preserve their original form, as they do in many places in Romania.

The famous area for volcanic geomorphology, however, is the southern part of Bakony, which has been called the Hungarian Auvergne. The most spectacular feature there is the Tihany Peninsula which projects into Lake Balaton. A great heap of tuffs and travertine (or 'geyserite') dips outwards from a central hollow which holds two small lakes 60 m above Lake Balaton. It has been interpreted as a collapsed caldera, which is what one would like it to be, but more probably it is just an erosional effect. Hot springs abound here as they do elsewhere in Hungary (e.g., supplying the Turkish baths in Budapest), so magmatic activity has not entirely ended. This and occasional minor earthquakes tell us that this stable centre of Europe still has some life in it.

15(c) Rhodope Massif

The Rhodope Massif occupies the southern part of Bulgaria and stretches down through Grecian Thrace to the Aegean and on to the beautiful island of Thasos. Eastwards it extends into the Turkish part of Thrace. It is probably the least well known of all the ancient massifs of Europe, although a great deal has been found out about it in recent years and there is much in the Bulgarian literature particularly, which is hardly known outside that country.

It is a mountainous, densely forested region and includes Musalla (formerly Stalin) Peak which, at 2925 m, is the highest mountain in the Balkan Peninsula, being slightly higher—although less holy—than Mount Olympos. A northern extension of the Rhodope Massif is seen in the delightful little Rilla Massif to the south of Sofia.

It has become customary to separate from the Rhodope Massif, as the 'Serbo-Macedonian Massif', those metamorphic rocks which lie west of the River Struma. These continue up into Yugoslavia and perhaps connect with those of the Pannonian Basin. The theory is that the Serbo-Macedonian Massif was much involved in the Alpine orogenesis (and is therefore considered here under the Hellenides), whereas the Rhodope proper was thought of a stable Variscan block. This is not altogether correct.

The massif in general was certainly considerably affected by orogenesis, include high-grade metamorphism, towards the end of Palaeozoic times and probably rose as a feature in the late Carboniferous. Most of the rocks are thought to be of Precambrian age, with the oldest rocks confined to the east and west and comparatively younger rocks down-faulted between them. In Bulgaria these old rocks have been divided into an Upper and a Lower Crystalline Series. The latter is more highly metamorphosed and is a very complex unit of high-grade gneisses and migmatites. The older part of this lower series is confined to the most easterly part of the massif and is commonly called 'Archaean' although no reliable dates are yet available.

The Upper Crystalline Series includes considerable thicknesses of metamorphosed sedimentary rocks, such as the marbles of western Thrace and Thasos; these are usually attributed to the Palaeozoic. They are cut by many supposedly Variscan granites (although some may be Precambrian) and there is a great deal of valuable mineralization, which is much better known than the academic geology. The most important ores are those of lead, zinc, silver, copper, manganese, chromium, and iron. Tremendous developments in the exploitation of these natural resources have taken place in Bulgaria since the Second World War, thanks to a geological survey and institutes of the Bulgarian Academy of Sciences that seem almost incredibly large compared with the population of the country. The Greek part is perhaps less well known in this respect, although it is connected in the classical mind with less prosaic matters, such as legends of Orpheus and his music and of Dionysus and his wine. Different countries have different priorities!

After becoming emergent with the Variscan orogeny, the massif suffered periodic flooding by Mesozoic seas, especially on its south-west side. Nevertheless, it seems to have remained a barrier between the Hellenide and the Balkanide troughs. In the past twenty years or so it has become apparent that it was something more than a peaceful breakwater. Like so many of the metamorphic terrains of Europe, it has proved younger than it looks.

Palaeozoic fossils are known in various places, notably around the Bosphorus, dealt with under the Thracian Basin. Triassic bivalves were found in Strandja Mountain in south-east Bulgaria, within a sequence of amphibolites, phyllites, calcareous schists, and marbles. Similarly, Jurassic ammonites were found near Alexandropolis at the easternmost end of Greece, in a sequence that seems to rest discordantly on a more highly metamorphosed basement. What is more, some of the granitic intrusions are datable as Jurassic and Cretaceous. It seems, therefore, that sizable areas of the Rhodope Massif were affected by the Alpine movements and magmatism, although the general picture is still far from clear.

Later still, Eocene deposits spread on to the metamorphic basement. These were mainly of a coarse, detritic nature and contain, in their upper part, pebbles of nummulitic limestone showing that elevation and erosion were still going on. In fact some of the granites have been dated as Paleocene and even Miocene.

On the other hand, the Rhodope Massif resembles the more 'normal' Variscan massifs of Europe, such as the Massif Central and Bohemian Massif, in having little down-faulted basins of Neogene continental sediments and volcanic eruptions of Pliocene and Quaternary age along the fracture lines. The little Thracian Basin to the east is certainly a continuation of this massif under a thicker load of Tertiary sediment. One must ask therefore the meaning of this strange massif. It was formerly thought of as one of the classic *Zwischengebirge* of Europe, coming as it does between the outwardly directed Hellenide and Balkanide ranges. This concept implied that the massif remained stable and inert during the folding phases that affected the terrains on either side. We now know that this was not the case. Nevertheless, whether it be a *Zwischengebirge* in the classical sense or a microplate in the modern sense it is hardly reasonable to expect that the full-back between the two converging rugby forwards will not suffer something in the encounter.

As the two continents crashed together or (more likely) the Adriatic microplate collided with Eurasia, the two fold belts of the Balkanides and the Hellenides spewed outwards. The Rhodope Massif must have been squeezed upwards, metamorphosed, and cooked to magma point. It is important to remember that this did not happen just once in some apocalyptic coming together of plates, but repeatedly from Precambrian times till as late as the Miocene.

15(d) Thracian Depression

The great mass of Turkey, with all its fascinating geology, is in Asia and is therefore sadly outside the terms of reference of this book. There remains, however, the small area west of the Bosphorus, which is known as 'Turkey in Europe' and forms the greater part of the Thracian Depression. This extends into the north-east corner of Greece. It is, in effect, the smallest of the Tertiary basins of Europe as here defined and does not need lengthy description, although it has oil and gas potential.

The depression opens into the Aegean and Sea of Marmora to the south and is delimited to the north by the metamorphic rocks of the Rhodope Massif, which extend into this part of Turkey. Apart from these ancient rocks, the only appreciable areas of pre-Tertiary sediments seen at the surface are in the vicinity of the Bosphorus, the narrow drain from the Black Sea which separates Europe from Asia. At the south end of the Bosphorus, forming the foundations of the fabulous city of Istanbul and around the inlet of the Golden Horn (which runs through the heart of the old city), there are Palaeozoic rocks.

These have all been attributed to the Silurian and Devonian, and although being somewhat tectonized, have yielded abundant shallow-water fossils. The Silurian successions consist for the most part of felspathic quartzites, surprisingly interbedded with limestones in the upper part and containing corals. The prominent feature of Çamlica Hill, on the Asian side of the Bosphorus, was formerly thought to be a klippe of these limestones resting on greywackes and shales, but this has now been shown to be an interbedded succession. A special feature hereabouts is the development of a chamosite oolite with a distinctive fauna of orthoceratid nautiloids and conulariids.

The overlying Devonian is predominantly shaly in the vicinity of the Bosphorus, but becomes more calcareous to the east, as in the Princess Islands in the Sea of Marmara, where richly fossiliferous Devonian limestones and shales rest on Silurian quartzites in an atmosphere strangely reminiscent of the Isle of Wight. The faunas are everywhere of a shallow-shelf type, even in the greywackes which occur in both the Lower and the Upper Devonian.

The Palaeozoic rocks form the narrowest part of the Bosphorus, where in 1453 the Ottoman Turks crossed to Europe, captured Constantinople (as it was then), and accidentally triggered off the Renaissance of Learning. North of here, looking across the Bosphorus at Kavak Castle, one can see the Devonian succession thrust north over Cretaceous tuffs. The Palaeozoic rocks are cut by andesites of presumed Cretaceous age.

North of the thrust as far as the Black Sea such Cretaceous volcanics, with some sediments, dominate the two shores. All this is part of the northerly thrusting of northern Turkey. The junction between Palaeozoic and Mesozoic is one of a series of such thrusts, one of which runs the length of the Sea of Marmara and slices off the Gallipoli peninsula at the far end. All this shows that, as with the other Tertiary basins of Neo-Europa, underneath the younger sediments is a Variscan massif. In this case it is, in fact, the eastern extension of the Rhodope Massif, dealt with in the previous section.

But our main concern here is with the Tertiary sediments that fill the Thracian Depression. It has been estimated that there are some 3000 m of pre-Pliocene Tertiary. Where late Cretaceous sediments are preserved they are in a flysch-like form and these pass up into the Paleocene. They are notably calcareous. They are followed (as in the other Tertiary basins of eastern Europe) by transgressive Eocene. This includes several conglomerates and limestones packed with nummulites. It may be more than 1000 m thick. Barrier reefs were developed along the northern margin of the basin and form possible oil reservoirs on basement 'highs'. The Oligocene and Lower Miocene are even thicker, with a flysch-like facies in the lower part and both brackish and fresh-water facies above, recording more than one regression. The uppermost Miocene, on the other hand, is clearly post-orogenic. It is dominantly clastic, with thick conglomerates and sandstones (amounting to some 900 m altogether) spreading into the basin from all sides. Conglomerates and sandstones continued into the Pliocene, but very much thinner and probably not amounting to more than 100 m altogether. The main movements therefore took place in late Miocene times with the formation of broad folds on east–west axes, with step-faulting and some local overturning towards the north, especially along the southern margin.

Not very far to the north lay the great Euxenic Basin of the Black Sea, which may be regarded as the very large remnant of the Dacian Basin of Romania and northern Bulgaria. In the same way, the Pannonian Basin lasts on to the present day in Lake Balaton in Hungary and the huge Caspian Depression of Tertiary times as the Caspian and Aral Seas. Similarly, the Thracian Depression may be extended to include the Sea of Marmara (which gives its name, incidentally, to marble, although this comes from much older rocks). The Thracian and Euxenic Basins differ from the others, however, in that the sea that had been pushed out of them in the Pliocene came back again in the late Quaternary. The Mediterranean breached the Dardanelles (more successfully than the Allies in the First World War) to resalinate the Sea of Marmara, and then pushed on through the Bosphorus to reach the Black Sea. With it came a Mediterranean fauna of perceptibly reduced diversity. All the rocks described here continue into the main hinterland of Turkey, so this seemingly natural boundary for Europe in the south-east is geologically a very recent phenomenon.

15(e) Black Sea

Once more the present is a very misleading guide to the past. The Dacian depression—that big trough of young sediments in front of the Southern Carpathians and Balkan Mountains—slopes gently eastwards under the warm, brackish waters of the Black Sea (Fig. 15.4). It is reasonable to think of it all as one big basin. So far as recent geological history is concerned, this is true, but so far as earlier history is concerned, the Moesian

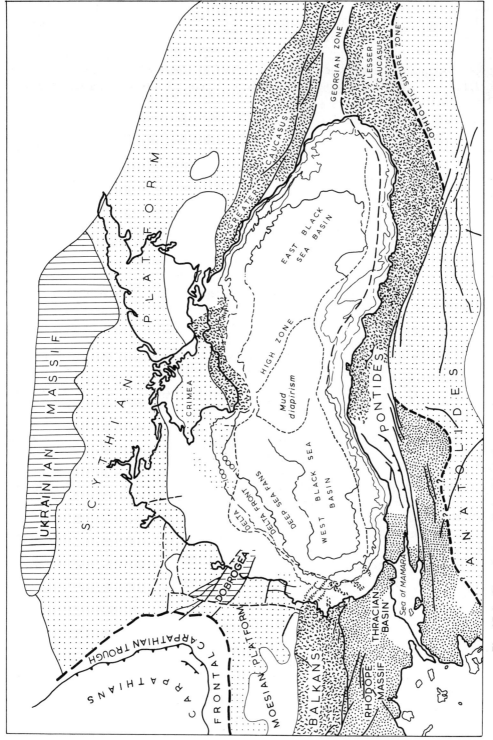

Fig. 15.4 Sketch-map of the Black Sea (after Letouzey et al., 1977, by kind permission of Dr Letouzey).

Platform on land is very different from what lies offshore. It is also tempting to think of the Balkan Mountains of Bulgaria heading off under the waters to reach the Crimea, and then on to the Caucasus as a northern mountain rim to the Black Sea, while the Pontic Mountains of northern Turkey guard it from the south. This certainly is not true. If the Balkan Mountains go anywhere, it is south-east to the Bosphorus and on into the Pontides themselves. The Crimea and Caucasus do not seem to connect with the main Alpine chains of Europe.

I am concerned here with the Black Sea as a geological entity and not as a body of water. I will therefore disregard those areas, such as the very shallow Sea of Azov, where the onshore geology just gets a little wet. The sea as a whole covers some 450 000 km^2, with a broad northern shelf (extending nearly 200 km west from the Crimea) and a narrow southern shelf. It appears to have evolved quite independently of the Mediterranean and was only connected to that sea, via the Bosphorus, in Quaternary times. The flat floor in the centre is between 2000 and 2200 m deep.

The geology of the surrounding areas is discussed elsewhere, but it is possible only to guess how their older rocks behave under the Black Sea, if they are there are at all. Geophysically the north and south shelves are continental, while the abyssal plain is called 'sub-oceanic'. Magnetic 'striping' has not been observed, although there are some positive anomalies on the north side which appear to relate to structures in the Crimea and Caucasus.

Like many good things, the Black Sea appears to have started in the Jurassic. Russian geologists studying conglomerates in the Jurassic of the Crimea deduced that they had been derived from the south. They then reconstructed an imaginary land, out in the Black Sea, from which their pebbles must have come. Rather to their surprise, the geology of this imaginary land turned out to be very like the pre-Jurassic geology of the Pontides in northern Turkey. In other words, the Black Sea was not there! I said this before, but it is worth repeating.

Tectonism and magmatism in the late Triassic and early Jurassic of the Pontides and of the Crimea–Caucasus probably inaugurated the formation of what was to be the Black Sea as a marginal sea behind an island arc. There may have been two basins, for a basement high seems to separate an eastern basin from a wider and deeper western one. A subduction zone is generally accepted across northern Turkey through the greater part of Mesozoic time. This may be regarded as the southern margin of Europe, putting the Pontides in our continent, but that is another discussion (about which I have strong views).

Distensional volcanism probably continued through to the end of the Cretaceous, but it was only in the early Tertiary that sediments began to accumulate thickly on a cooling and subsiding ocean floor. The Tertiary deposits appear (from seismic profiles) to bury a pre-existing topography on both the northern and southern shelves. This topography was presumably produced in the end Cretaceous ('Laramide') folding.

The main opening probably came in Palaeogene times, with the ending of subduction under the Pontides. This conclusion has been reached from various lines of evidence including onshore work in Georgia, which is strictly 'Asia' and beyond the terms of this book. Here, at the east end of the basin, between the Greater Caucasus and the Lesser Caucasus, is a wide east–west graben filled with Tertiary sediment. This is a direct continuation of the Black Sea and it evidently opened at this time.

That the Black Sea was separated from the Mediterranean during the Tertiary is indicated by the complete absence in this basin of any record of the traumatic episode known as the 'Messinian Salinity Crisis' which was such a feature of Mediterranean history. The rich marine faunas of the coastal Miocene around Varna in Bulgaria presumably indicate that all was well here, and there are no records of evaporites. However, the Dacian Basin was cut off like the Pannonian Basin and the inflow of fresh water from rivers soon changed it into a vast inland lake.

Subsidence and sedimentation speeded up considerably in the late Cainozoic, and tremendous thicknesses of Pliocene and Quaternary deltaic deposits are known, especially in the vicinity of the great rivers such as the Danube and the Dnepr. The visible Danube delta on the Romanian–Soviet border, with its pelicans and other fascinating wildlife, is quite a small affair in view of the size of its drainage area. Under water, however, the combined delta fans of the Danube and Dnepr cover the whole western basin with some 2500 m of sediment. Mud diapirism was a feature of the central 'high'.

The Black Sea is probably best known to the majority of geologists for the black, anaerobic muds which accumulate in its deeper parts and which give the sea's Greek name (i.e., euxenic) to such facies everywhere. The present fauna of the Black Sea is an interesting one (well seen in the splendid aquarium at Constanţa in Romania) but is of low diversity, due to the low salinity, and is wholly derived from the Mediterranean via the narrow channel that opened in Quaternary times through the Bosphorus. This chance of geological history allows me to finish my book at that channel and excuses me the still unsolved complexities of Turkish geology.

15(f) Mediterranean

The Mediterranean, cradle of European civilization, was also the cradle of much that has happened in Europe's geological history and still holds within it the omens of much of Europe's geological future.

This must be a rather different section from the others, since although the great 'Middle Sea' is its chief concern it cannot omit reference to all the lands that surround that sea or avoid consideration of grander themes in the realms of plate tectonics and sea-floor spreading. It must supplement the general conclusions of Chapter 17. Intimately involved with the Mediterranean is the whole history of the Tethys, in its many different connotations. When I helped to organize a symposium on Tethys some years ago, it soon became obvious that the term meant quite different things to different people. To one it had a purely geographical meaning, to another it meant a particular faunal realm, and to another it was entirely a matter of tectonics.

It is important to realize here, that in talking of the Mediterranean I am talking of two seas of fundamentally different structure (Fig. 15.5). In the west we have a sea completely surrounded by Alpine mountain chains, much of which has been a positive area in the geologically recent past. In the east the Alpine chains drive straight into the sea, where one finds troughs and arcs and a possible mid-ocean ridge; in other words, everything is still happening.

Of the early history of the Mediterranean/Tethys, in the Palaeozoic, all is uncertain

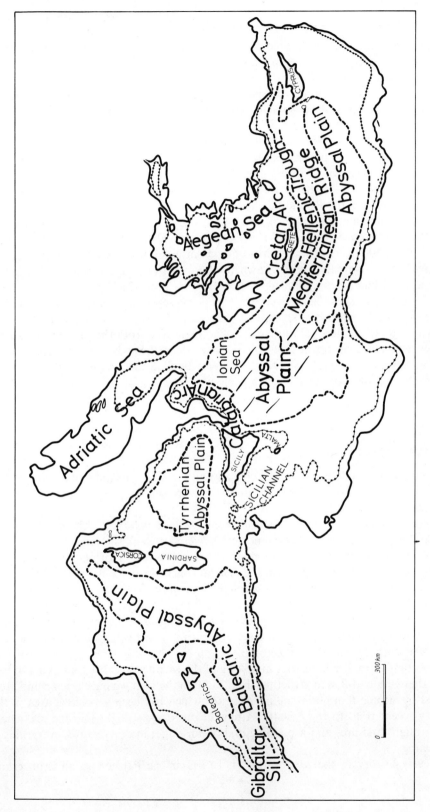

Fig. 15.5 Sketch-map of the Mediterranean.

and full of controversy. Many palaeogeographers postulate a 'Palaeotethys' dominating the southern European record, at least in late Palaeozoic times. Almost all geologists would accept a seaway of some sort in the area, separating a northern 'Laurasia' from a southern 'Gondwanaland', although there are considerable differences of opinion as to its width and extent. Even as far back as the Cambrian there seems to be strong evidence of an east–west marine connection here. Thus redlichiid trilobites in the Lower Cambrian of Spain have been taken as evidence of a connection with similar faunas in the Middle East and onwards into south-east Asia. Similar conclusions have been reached about Ordovician shelly faunas. There is no suggestion of a deep geosynclinal sea at this time, although it was already tectonically and volcanically active.

By latest Palaeozoic times there is no doubt of a separate and distinctive marine realm in the Tethys area. Thus one enters such a realm as one crosses Europe from north to south pursuing the rocks of late Carboniferous age. In the north, in the paralic coal basins, one sees the marginal incursions of a Boreal sea with marine faunas of limited diversity. One then passes through the intermontane limnic basins within the Variscan orogenic belts that the sea never reached, and finally one gets a deep draught of the warm south as one approaches the Mediterranean with intercalations (e.g., in north Spain) of diverse and distinctive marine faunas. In southern Portugal, all is marine. In the Permian, this is even more obvious. The Boreal Zechstein Sea lacks many of the most distinctive elements of the world-wide Permian marine faunas, notably the richthofeniid brachiopods and fusulinid foraminifers (especially those belonging to the family Verbeek-inidae) which flourished in the Mediterranean area.

The Tethyan faunas are always different from those of the ephemeral northern seas. But how far can we really take this 'Palaeotethys' back in time, and was it an intercontinental sea like the modern Mediterranean or was it just an open southern ocean? Recently, certain palaeomagnetists have sent the Palaeozoic continents scuttling about the earth's surface and put Africa far from Europe in early Palaeozoic times. I am far from happy about this, for some of the earliest Palaeozoic facies and faunas (e.g., the basal quartzites and trilobites of the Ordovician) seem to remain remarkably constant as one traces them down across south-west Europe into North Africa.

Most authors, however, think of the Mediterranean as starting as the western part of the Old World Tethys in early Mesozoic times after the widespread development of the 'Verrucano' conglomerates (perhaps the Palaeotethys at its smallest extent). There was probably continuous sialic crust from Europe to Africa after the Variscan movements. The earliest Triassic transgressive epicontinental marine deposits everywhere rest unconformably on these older acid rocks. One must think of the Mediterranean area at this time as quite different in configuration from what it is now. Corsica and Sardinia were closed up to the French Riveria, in close juxtaposition with the similar but smaller massifs of Maures and Esterel. Similarly, the 'leg' of Italy was close up against their eastern side and Greece was probably tucked partly into the Gulf of Sirte in what is now Libya. Spain was rotated into the Bay of Biscay and Africa as a whole was displaced considerably to the west relative to Europe. All this is founded on palaeomagnetic evidence, but does not seem to contradict anything we know from stratigraphical or other evidence.

Certainly the Triassic rocks of the Mediterranean area could not, in any sense, be called oceanic. Although thick in places, they are all dominantly continental or shallow-water carbonates, with shallow-water faunas. Sediments such as flysch only appeared much later. Westwards, though Spain and Morocco, red beds and evaporites indicate that the Triassic Mediterranean was not open to the west, although it probably opened eastwards into the world ocean.

The initial separation of the European and African plates may, however, have started as early as Triassic times although the bilateral symmetry of the western Mediterranean does not seem to allow for the two continents ever to have been far apart. The basic mechanism was presumably the opening of the Atlantic, especially the growth of the east flank of the Mid Atlantic Ridge south of the lateral ridge that runs off from the Azores in the direction of Gibraltar. This ocean spreading had the effect of carrying Africa eastwards in an anticlockwise direction, probably about a rotation pole that was close to the 'best fit' pole postulated for both Africa and North America. This rotation happening in early Mesozoic times would also account for the early Mesozoic compression at the other end of Europe—in the Caucasus and Crimea—where the Kimmerian movements are best developed.

At the same time there may well have begun the rotation of microplates all going in the same direction. Thus Spain rotated out of the Bay of Biscay, Corsica and Sardinia away from the Riviera, Italy in turn away from them, while Yugoslavia and Greece left their close proximity to North Africa. All these moved independently of the European plate to which they are now so firmly attached. The resultant tensions presumably led to fissure eruptions in the Triassic continental sequences, which have been mentioned in this book in several of the Mediterranean lands.

It was in Jurassic times that the Tethys really came into its own. It is worth remembering the words of W. J. Arkell, who summed up the Jurassic deposits of the world, to which he had devoted his life's work, as: 'little more than relics of marginal lappings of the sea around the edges of the continents; *the sole exception being the Tethys ...*.' The italics are mine. The Jurassic Tethys dominated southern Europe and at times its influence was felt as far north as Britain and Sweden. Although commonly spoken of as a geosyncline, much of it was obviously a shelf sea and it only opened into a true ocean to the east. There also appeared the Jurassic ophiolite suites of pillow lavas, ultra-basics, and radiolarian cherts. Although best known in the western Alps and the northern Apennines, their greatest development was through the Dinarides and Hellenides and on into Turkey. We can presume that the lavas and intrusions broke through the crust of the Jurassic Mediterranean, where the tension was greatest, and formed its own mid-oceanic ridge. The resultant high silica content of the water above the split led to the proliferation of radiolaria which formed the characteristic cherts. It is noteworthy that chert first appears in the Mesozoic (to any significant degree) in the very late Jurassic and then remains with us all through the Cretaceous.

The Alpine, Apennine, Pyrenean, and Betic–Rif eugeosynclines came into being, but the openings were probably never very wide and most of the movement was probably lateral. Many would say that there was left-lateral movement of the European and African plates (i.e., that Europe moved to the west and Africa to the east). At the same time the new sea opened westwards into the Atlantic and we can begin to distinguish the facies and distinctive faunas of the two shores of Tethys. Thus by middle to late Jurassic times we can recognize particular elements in the shallow-water benthos (particularly brachiopods) which persist from Malagasy, through Tanzania, Kenya and Somalia to

Saudi Arabia and Sinai, across to southern Tunisia and the south-west corner of Morocco, and some elements possibly as far as Mexico. These are significantly different from the equivalent faunas on the European side. At the same time other forms can be seen spreading from Morocco up to Portugal, thence to western Britain and eventually to east Greenland as the Atlantic split open and the early Gulf Stream warmed its way to the north.

The basification of the crust which began in Triassic times continued and even upper mantle material has been claimed in the Rif Mountains and in the Betics (such as the black ultra-basics of the Ronda region). At first there was general submergence of the continental plates on either side, so that the early deep-sea basin formed in this way received calcareous and siliceous ooze rather than terrigenous detritus. Later, in Cretaceous times, troughs formed which received great thicknesses of flysch. Some of these, such as those on the north rim of the Alps, probably represent plate boundaries, others—such as the Ultra-helvetic flysch of Switzerland—may have formed behind island arcs, and yet others—such as the Pennine flysch—may have accumulated on broad abyssal plains.

It may be significant that the earlier Cretaceous flysch, for example in the western Pyrenees, is often highly calcareous, while the more 'typical' flysch is Palaeogene in age. By late Cretaceous times, the east end of the Mediterranean/Tethys appears to have been closed. The anticlockwise rotation had opened up wedge-shaped 'sphenochasms' which now constitute the down-faulted abyssal plains south of the Balearics and in the Tyrrhenian Sea. By late Cretaceous times there was probably a reversal of this movement and the microplates moved in a clockwise direction, closing up the gaps and eventually coming to an end with the main spasms of the Alpine orogeny. These movements, as has been repeatedly stated in this book, started in mid Cretaceous times and reached their final stage, throughout most of Europe, in the Miocene.

By the end of the Miocene the shallow sea which had extended round in front of the rising Alps had been squeezed out into basins in which the brackish Sarmatian and the fresh-water Pontian deposits accumulated in eastern Europe. Salinity gradients produced strange and rapid sea-changes in the invertebrate faunas of these basins. Just as the Mediterranean is no more than a shadow of the former Tethys, so the Pannonian Basin of Hungary now only survives as Lake Balaton, the Dacian Basin of Romania and Bulgaria is fossilized as the Black Sea, and the Caspian is all that remains of the great Caspian Depression of Tertiary times.

The fantastically fossiliferous, flat-lying sands and limestones of the Miocene around the Mediterranean, for example in southern Spain, Sardinia, and Sicily, all testify to shallow, high-energy marine conditions of normal salinity, but contrast markedly with the overridden molasse in front of the Alps. These places have already been discussed elsewhere in this book. There is, however, one little country that is wholly Mediterranean and cannot be dealt with elsewhere. This is the history-packed island of Malta, south of Sicily, which has a record, unique in Europe, of late Oligocene and Miocene marine deposition with abundant life. The only place I know like it (and still 'Mediterranean', although outside the area covered by this volume) is the Sirte Basin of eastern Libya, where the flat-lying Miocene, the echinoids, and the bivalves, go on and on in hundreds of kilometres of continuous escarpments. A special feature of Malta and its neighbouring island of Gozo is the development of circular faults marking huge collapse structures in the golden limestones. One of these carried the village of Maqluba down into the underworld in the fourteenth century, due to its wickedness, leaving only the holy church untouched on its rim.

The limestones (and subsidiary clays) are undisturbed and provide a splendid record of peaceful marine sedimentation with abundant life, troubled only by the abundant sharks. But towards the end of Miocene times, the early Mediterranean was getting distinctly uncomfortable for its inhabitants. Salinity built up and evaporite deposition set in all round the Mediterranean; thick salts were laid down (e.g., in Sicily). This was the much-discussed 'Messinian Salinity Crisis' which affected all the faunas of the region and many other things besides. All connection to the west, as well as to the east, had been cut off, although much of the area was below sea-level. Parts of what is now the floor of the Mediterranean were probably elevated in relation to the rest, and what are now submarine canyons and the lake-filled trenches of the Italian Alps may have been cut subaerially at this time.

Evidently something rather fundamental happened in mid-Tertiary times. Perhaps the 'hot spot' in the earth's interior that had produced the basification of the crust and the splitting had cooled off. With the change to clockwise rotation, expansion was replaced by compression, producing the last forward movements of the Alpine chains as Africa drove forward against Europe in the west producing the Betic and Rif ranges. In the eastern Mediterranean, the compression produced island arcs, notably the one through Crete at the south end of the Aegean, with its unusually thin crust.

It also produced the Hellenic trench that lies beyond the above arc. This is a compressional subduction structure. Beyond that again is the important structure that includes the island of Cyprus. Whether Cyprus is in Europe or Asia is a political decision. For the purposes of this book, Cyprus is very much part of the Europe story. In its Troodos Massif, we have what seems to be (from both petrological and geophysical evidence) a piece of oceanic crust pushed up in the form of a mid-oceanic ridge. It includes an ultrabasic, plutonic complex plus tholeiitic pillow lavas and diabase dikes. In front of it, to the north, are the Mesozoic carbonates of the Kyrenia Range, which structurally and stratigraphically are part of the Taurus Mountains of southern Turkey (and are now—perhaps symbolically—occupied by Turkish troops).

We must remember that Cyprus gave its name to copper and was one of the starting points of our metallic civilization. The association of porphyry copper mineralization with plate margins is well known and Cyprus forms the centre point of a belt of such deposits. Perhaps the most notable feature of Cyprus geology is the high gravity anomaly over the Troodos Massif. Such anomalies, together with seismicity and the volcanism along this zone, are all characteristic of opening plate margins. A study of seismicity in this region through historic time has shown how the activity has tended to change its loci with time. Evidence comes from written records and from changes in architectural styles (i.e., whether or not buildings were designed to minimize earthquake damage).

Volcanicity is concentrated in the Aegean on the inner side of the Cretan island arc, and was dominantly andesitic in mid-Tertiary times (with granitic plutonism) becoming more basaltic by the Quaternary. One of the last great events here was the caldera forming eruption in the island of Santorini which some think destroyed the Minoan civilization on Crete.

Beyond the island arc to the south, following the normal pattern, is the Hellenic trench and beyond that again the broad compressive belt of relative shallows known as the Mediterranean Ridge. This appears to be uplifted abyssal plain. The story in this part of the Mediterranean is not simple. The Aegean Sea, much of Greece, Crete and western-most Turkey belongs to one microplate that is still moving south-west and underthrust-ing the Mediterranean, while most of Turkey, together with Cyprus, is moving westwards against Greece. Fortunately, the complexities of Turkish geology are outside the concern of this book, but it is obvious that things are still happening in this corner of Europe.

A second island arc, at the western limit of the eastern Mediterranean, may be repre-sented in what is called the Calabrian Arc. This passes through the 'toe' of Italy and north-east Sicily and is again an active seismic zone (recalled by the disastrous Messina earthquake of 1908). It has the associated volcanism of Stromboli, Etna and others (including numerous sea-mounts in the southern Tyrrhenian Sea). These deserve a separ-ate section to themselves and are dealt with in Section 15(g) below.

Nevertheless, it must be emphasized that the greater part of the crust in the eastern Mediterranean (and for that matter in the western Mediterranean too) is continental in nature, with low gravity readings except in compressive arcs. One feature of the Mediterranean that has worried geophysicists is the complete absence of the magnetic 'striping' that so much characterizes spreading ocean floors.

Returning to the western Mediterranean, it is worth recording that in the centre part of the Balearic Abyssal Plain there are seismic velocities and high heat flow comparable with those of the mid-Atlantic Ridge. At the same time the Tyrrhenian Sea has an abnormally thick crust with no trace of anything oceanic. It may be that the eastern Mediterranean is now passing through a phase of ridges and trenches that the western Mediterranean passed through in late Mesozoic times. Perhaps the eastern Mediterranean has not long to last (geologically speaking) as a sea, for even unconsolidated sediments there are evidently being compressed. One can imagine this area as the site of the next European orogeny.

The dividing line between east and west Mediterranean lies in the shelf or sill that extends between Sicily and north Africa. This is covered with a thick Mesozoic–Cainozoic sedimentary sequence of a shelf nature; seismic reflection surveys show it to be a direct continuation of the African plate.

The western Mediterranean, on the other hand, has gone through a phase of expansion and of inversion, whereby the old positive areas have become depressions (as in northern Europe). The western Mediterranean is now active sedimentologically rather than tecton-ically. The sharp contrasts in depth, due to the down-faulting of blocks, together with the building-out of deltas (most notably by the Rhône), produce great slumps on the sea-floor and modern turbidity currents. The extensive Miocene evaporites are punching up through the overlying sediments as diapirs that show up clearly in the geophysical records of the Ligurian Sea (off the French Riviera) and the Balearic Abyssal Plain.

So far as the present Mediterranean is concerned, this is thought to have started with a splash in early Pliocene times, with the Atlantic bursting through the Strait of Gibraltar and producing a huge cataract that filled the low-lying desert basin. Being surrounded by warm dry climates, where evaporation exceeds run-off, the Mediterranean is still largely fed by the Atlantic. The faunas and floras of the Mediterranean are relatively poor, especially on the African side, because there is little in the way of nutrients coming from the land and the inflow from the Atlantic is lighter surface water that is already depleted.

447

Finally the Mediterranean acquired the triremes and the amphora, the dead Carthaginians and the Knights of Malta, the Roman eagles and the German Stukas, that constitute the record of man's brief history in the area.

15(g)   Tyrrhenian Volcanic Region

Late Cainozoic volcanic activity occurred in three distinct areas in the Mediterranean which are not directly related to one another. They are: the Tyrrhenian Province of Italy, the Aegean Province of the Greek islands, and the Iberian Province of southern Spain and Portugal. The last two are dealt with elsewhere in this book, but the first is so important that I think it deserves separate treatment.

A great arc of young volcanoes extends from the French Riviera bordering the Ligurian Sea in the north, down the edge of the Tyrrhenian Sea via Rome and Naples through the Aeolian Islands to eastern Sicily and beyond (Fig. 15.6). This arc includes some of the most famous volcanoes in the world, although most of them (apart from Etna) have been neglected in recent years compared with the work that has been concentrated on oceanic volcanoes such as those of Hawaii. They will be considered from north to south.

Liguria and Tuscany

There are a few small centres of extinct volcanicity inland from St. Tropez on the French Riviera and a more extensive area on the coast east of Antibes.

In Tuscany, late Cainozoic volcanicity is much more obvious; in fact, some of it is still steaming. There are some old explosive centres and some distinctive late Tertiary extrusives, but the most important and interesting volcanic phenomena are the steam vents of Tuscany around the industrial centre of Lardarello, south-east of Pisa. Here steam comes to the surface in constantly shifting fumaroles or *soffioni*, which have been known since the eighteenth century as a source of boric acid. The commercial possibilities were recognized and developed by the Comte de Lardarel, a refugee from the French Revolution, who gave his name to the chief town. Nowadays, instead of using natural vents, the steam is obtained from deep borings and conveyed directly to power stations for the generation of electricity (notably for the Italian railways). The borings are put down through the *argille scagliose* of the Liguria Nappe, which provides a good impervious capping, and have to hit faults in the autochthon below. The steam comes up at great pressure and high temperature; its relatively high radioactivity suggests a deep-seated origin.

Rome area

There are four main volcanic centres north of Rome, aligned in a north-westerly direction and a fifth one to the south of the eternal city along the same lines. Smaller centres occur to the west of this line, but are of different composition. All are extinct and are more famous for their crater lakes than for the denuded cones themselves. Only the most northerly of them, Monte Amiata, preserves its beautiful cone shape. The others are probably collapsed calderas. These volcanoes, like the others of Italy, are dominantly alkaline. There has been much argument as to how much of the material extruded was

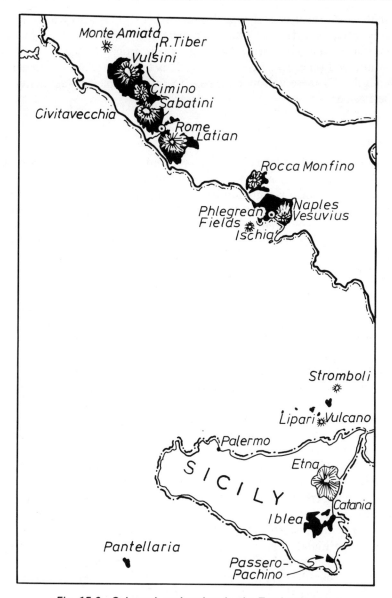

Fig. 15.6 Cainozoic volcanism in the Tyrrhenian area.

truly laval in form and how much was ash. Much of the latter may have been in the form of ignimbrites, as in Sardinia and elsewhere. There is evidence that the rising magmas assimilated material from the Mesozoic carbonates through which they passed, so that gradations occur within the extrusions of a single volcano. In general the smaller eruptions contain a higher proportion of assimilated material than the larger.

The extensive ash falls around Rome provide a very fertile soil for agriculture, which was one of the factors that made it possible to support a large city population (and

449

perhaps made it more successful than barren Athens). It is also worth noting that the volcanic soils here, as in Hungary and elsewhere, grow the best vines. Most notable in this area is the strong white wine Frascati, which grows on the slopes of the Latian volcano, south of Rome, just across the caldera from the Pope's summer palace, the Castel Gandolfo. All these volcanoes appear to have completed their activity within the Pleistocene Period.

Naples area

Here, on the other hand, volcanicity is still very much with us. The most famous of all volcanoes, Vesuvius, broods across the bay from Naples with its thin plume of smoke always reminding the local population of its terrible potential. The first of all volcanological treatises may be said to be Pliny the Younger's account of the eruption on 24 August A.D. 79, although it is curious that he did not mention the destruction of the cities of Pompeii and Herculaneum on that occasion. Before that date, perhaps for a thousand years, Vesuvius had appeared to be extinct. It was surmounted by a caldera of which the deep Valle dell'Inferno and the low arcuate ridge of Monte Somma, on the north and east side of the mountain, are all that remain. The present perfectly circular cone and crater were produced in the eruption that destroyed the south and west walls of the earlier crater, burying Pompeii under ash and Herculaneum under mud. Smaller eruptions have occurred at regular intervals since, including the one in 1944 that destroyed the famous funicular railway.

The usual pattern of the eruptions goes through three stages in the course of a few days. First there is the 'Vesuvian stage', with the fracturing of the cone and the pouring out of lava; then there is the 'Plinian stage', with violent explosions blasting the lava into a cloud of fine ash, scattered with volcanic bombs; finally, there is the 'Vulcanian stage', when the uprush of gases has diminished allowing the sides of the crater to fall in, resulting in further blockage of the pipe and more violent explosions. Throughout its life, Vesuvius has extruded remarkably uniform products, mainly leucite basalts (often displaying clear 'ropy' textures) and ashes with phenocrysts of leucite and augite. One can readily collect perfect crystals of the latter around the summit crater. Occasional lavas have been more sodic.

Vesuvius is only the eastern end of a broad belt of volcanism that stretches westwards past Naples to the island of Ischia. West of Naples, on the mainland, are the Phlegrean Fields which include a remarkable assortment of volcanic phenomena. This is the centre of the volcanism, but the whole area is floored with Cretaceous and Tertiary rocks. Subsidence began during the Pliocene and the trough so formed filled up slowly with lavas and pyroclastic rocks. There are several large extinct craters including the one filled by Lake Avernus, which was thought by the ancients to be the entrance to the underworld. It was said that birds flying across the lake died—this was presumably due to noxious gases. Just east of here is the perfect cone of Monte Nuova, which formed in two days in 1538, and was later described in detail by Sir William Hamilton (husband of the famous Emma) in one of the first scientific works on volcanology. The cones and craters are superimposed on older collapsed caldera, which must have produced huge quantities of tuff. Two other famous localities in the Phlegrean Fields show us that volcanic activity here has not entirely stopped. In the cave known as the Grotta del Cane, carbon dioxide accumulates at floor level and is sufficient to asphyxiate dogs, although human tourists with their air intake at a higher level are not affected. At Solfatara, gas still bubbles violently through muddy pools in the crater which last erupted trachytic lava in 1198. Sulphur is much in evidence.

Farther west again are several volcanic islands in the Tyrrhenian Sea. The largest is Ischia, which has a complex horst-like structure. An early phase of volcanism was followed by block faulting which allowed smaller extrusions to take place along the fault lines. This brings one's attention to the up and down movements which have been such a feature of this region even in historic times.

On the coast in the centre of the Phlegrean Fields is the town of Pozzuoli, where there still stand the Roman columns of the so-called 'Temple' of Serapis. These columns (actually part of a market-place) were made famous by Charles Lyell as a frontispiece in his *Principles of Geology.* They show the borings made by marine bivalves when they were submerged in sea water. Lyell used them as irrefutable evidence of past changes in sea-level. Observations at a geophysical station here have shown some correlation between local volcanic activity and sea-level, although the precise cause is still a matter of dispute. I am always struck by the absence of borings lower down in the masonry, which suggests to me that the sea-level changes were sudden rather than gradual.

The only connection between the Naples volcanic area and the Rome area to the north is the large but isolated extinct volcano of Rocca Monfino near Gaeta. Southwards, there is an even bigger gap between Naples and the Aeolian Islands, which look like fragments that the toe of Italy has kicked off the angular block of Sicily.

Aeolian Islands

These islands, sometimes called the Lipari Islands, include several famous volcanoes. One of them is the island of Vulcano itself, which gave its name to the whole phenomenon. In classical times this was the home of Vulcan, the god of fire, although he was also said to have had a smithy under Mount Etna in Sicily. The island of Vulcano, like several of the other islands, is a composite volcano, consisting of three distinct craters, the last of which erupted in 1892. It is also typical of all the islands in that its products are of varied composition, from basalt to rhyolite. Its lavas have on the whole been rather acidic (especially dacites) and their viscous nature has resulted in violently explosive eruptions. This is the 'Vulcanian' type of eruption.

Stromboli, at the north end of the group, is characterized by 'Strombolian' slight but continuous activity, with occasional paroxysms. It has been behaving in this way for at least 2000 years. It may contain a great fissure, kept open by the continuous subsidence of the area and the inward seepage of sea-water. It is one of the most beautiful of all volcanoes, rising steeply from deep water in a perfect cone. Its products are largely basaltic and it is famous for the continuous shower of basaltic spray and bombs tumbling down its north-west side towards the sea. It may also be remembered as the volcano up which Jules Verne's travellers returned from the interior of the earth.

Lipari itself is the largest of these islands and again has three craters with a complex history, although all of them now appear to be extinct. Its main products have been acidic lavas, notably rhyolites (including spherulitic types) and obsidian. These produced steep-sided cones. It also produced great quantities of pumice, covering the north-east part of the island and extensively quarried.

Sicily and Pantellaria

The Calabrian Massif extends into north-east Sicily between the Aeolian Islands and the volcanic region of eastern Sicily. This is one area where the history of the volcanicity can be traced far back into geological time. The ophiolitic suites of the Jurassic in the west do not concern us here, but at the south-east corner of Sicily, at Capo Passero-Pachino, there are submarine basic lavas and submarine glassy tuff accumulations of late Cretaceous age, while in borings at Ragusa to the north-west, similar rocks have been found interbedded with Triassic and Jurassic sediments.

In the Iblean Mountains, between Catania and Syracuse, there is an extensive area (some 250 km^2) of volcanics ranging in age from late Tertiary to early Pleistocene. They are again mostly submarine basaltic lavas and glassy tuffs, sometimes showing pillows. The activity probably took place in fairly shallow water, near the shore. Some volcanoes evidently built up as islands. The whole area is cut by a fault system trending north-east, with a second system at right angles. The volcanism seems to have moved north with time, eventually in early Pleistocene times moving north of the present city of Catania to form the noble mass of Etna, although recently a prehistoric and a fourteenth century pillow lava were described between the city and the mountain.

Etna is the largest active volcano in Europe and reaches some 3300 m in height. Like Stromboli it is continuously active, but is liable to express itself in periodic destructive violence (as it did recently). In 1696, a lava flow from Etna reached and breached the city wall of Catania and flowed round its western side to reach the sea.

Activity here seems to have started in early Pleistocene times, when the story farther south was continued with submarine eruptions on to a shallow muddy sea-floor. These early stages are recorded in the much-photographed pillow lavas on the east coast. Since then the vast volcano has built up with a succession of great caldera collapses. The most obvious and oldest of these is the Valle del Bove on the east side of the present summit. The usual fate of such caldera is to be filled by later eruptives. This is what has happened to the large summit caldera, which filled up in the seventeenth century and is only seen now as a bevel around the central cone. Eruptions now come alternatively from the central crater, notably the terrifying kilometre-deep hole known as the 'Chasm', and from smaller cones and fissures on the side of the mountain. The 'lateral' eruptions must originate from the same pipe as the central crater. But there are also 'eccentric' eruptions, which appear to arise quite independently from the central system. The most destructive of all Etna's eruptions came from an eccentric cone (Monti Rossi near Nicolosi) in 1669.

The dominant north-east trending faults, mentioned in the Iblean Mountains, also control most of the eruptions on Etna, although there are others along the second fault system at right angles to this. Progressive movement of the eruption centre on such lines has been observed in recent bursts of activity. The basaltic lavas and ashes of Etna, like those around Rome, give rise to a very fertile soil. Hence, in spite of the danger, the lower slopes are densely populated with farmers raising vines, citrus, and other fruits. Higher up, the slopes are densely forested. Throughout history, destructive lava flows have coursed down all sides of the mountain, blazing their way through forests, orchards, and vineyards, often leaving cylinders of solidified lava around charred tree-stumps. On average there are about fifteen eruptions per century, although there is no sign of any regular periodicity. Evidence suggests that the centre of activity is moving westwards, away from the coast.

Finally I should mention the lonely island of Pantellaria, halfway between Sicily and Tunisia. This was a more acidic volcano than most of the others, being characterized particularly by rock-type 'pantellarite'. This is an acidic lava, ranging from rhyolite to trachyte in composition. The volcanic suite here is often compared with that of Mount Kenya, although the significance of this observation is not apparent, except for the proximity of a major rift. There is some evidence of activity on the sea-floor in the Sicilian Channel, although Pantellaria itself is extinct.

In conclusion it must be commented that although the Tyrrhenian volcanic activity is so varied in detail, it does present a fairly uniform picture of caldera-type volcanicity, related to fault lines, starting in late Tertiary times and persisting, albeit in a declining form, to the present day. The volcanicity, at least so far as the main part of peninsular Italy is concerned, obviously parallels one of the major sutures of the Mediterranian. It is not clear how the volcanicity of eastern Sicily fits into this picture and it may be that the remoter islands of the Aeolian group, notably Ustica, north of Palermo, are following the main trend. It must also be remembered that we are also following a major seismic line, of which the disastrous Messina earthquake of 1908 provided an awful warning.

Selected references to Chapter 15

Section 15(a)   Po–Adriatic Basin

Celet, P. (1977), 'The Dinaric and Aegean Arcs: the geology of the Adriatic', in A. E. M. Nairn *et al.* (eds.), *The Ocean Basin and Margins*, vol. 4A, Plenum Press, New York, pp. 215–261.

Fallot, P. (1959), 'La geologie profonde du Bassin du Pô et le mystère de celui du Guadalquivir', *Est. Geol. Madrid CSIC*, **15**, 155–162.

Vandenberg, J. and A. A. H. Wonders (1976), 'Paleomagnetic evidence of large fault displacement around the Po Basin', *Tectonophys*, **33**, 301–320.

Section 15(b)   Pannonian Basin

Burchfiel, B. C. (with contributions by M. Bleahu) (1976), 'Geology of Romania', *spec. paper, Geol. Soc. Amer.*, **158**, 82 pp.

Deak, M. H. (1969), 'Explanations to the Geological Map of Hungary: Veszprém', Hungar. Geol. Inst., 60 pp.

Fülöp, J. (1969), 'Geology of the Transdanubian Central, Mecsek and Villányi Mountains', Hungar. Geol. Inst., 67 pp.

Gavăti, I., D. Ciupagea and S. Airinei (1970), 'Rapport entre la structure profonde et la structure des complexes sedimentaires de la depression de Transylvanie', *Rev. Roumaine Geol. Géophys. Géog., Ser. géol.*, **14**, 153–159.

Gécszy, B. (1973), 'Plate tectonics and paleogeography in the east-Mediterranean Mesozoic', *Acta Geol. Acad. Sci. Hungar.*, **17**, 421–428.

Giuşcă, D. *et al.* (1968), 'Neogene volcanism and ore deposits in the Apuseni Mts.', Guide 48AC, 23rd Internat. Geol. Congr., 51 pp.

Heissel, W. and C. Exner, eds. (1951), *Geologischer Führer zu den Exkursionen*, Verh. Geol. Budesanst, Wien, A. 130 pp.

Kertai, G. (1968), 'Geology of the Pannonicum', Guide 42C, 23rd Internat. Geol. Congr., Prague, 58 pp.

Trunko, L. (1969), 'Geologie von Ungarn', in *Beitr. Regional Geol. Erde*, vol. 8, Borntraeger, Stuttgart, 257 pp.

Section 15(c)   Rhodope Massif

Ager, D. V. (1972), 'Summer field meeting in Bulgaria', *Proc. Geol. Ass.*, **83**, 239–267.

Brunn, J. H. (1960), 'Les zones helléniques internes et leur extension. Réflexions sur l'orogenèse alpine', *Bull. Soc. Géol. France, Ser. 7*, **2**, 470–486.

Dimitrov, S. (1959), 'Kurze Übersicht der metamorphen Komplexe in Bulgarien', *Freiberg. Forschungs.*, **57**, 62–72.

Petraschek, W. E. (1953), 'Magmatismus und Metallogenese in Südosteuropa', *Geol. Rundschau*, **42**, 128–143.

Section 15(d)   Thracian Depression

Campbell, A. S., ed. (1971), *Geology and History of Turkey*, Petrol. Explor. Soc. Libya, 511 pp.

Doust, H. and Y. Arikan (1974), 'The geology of the Thrace Basin', in H. Okay and E. Dileköz (eds.), Second Petroleum Congr. Turkey, Assoc. Turk. Petrol. Geol., Ankara, pp. 119–134.

Erentöz, C. (1956), 'A general review of the geology of Turkey', *Bull. Min. Res. Explor. Inst. Turkey*, Foreign edn., No. 48, 40–54.

Ivanov, R. and K. O. Kopp (1969), 'Zur Tektonik des thrakischen Alttertiar-Beckens', *Geotekt. Forsch.*, **31**, 117–132.

Section 15(e)   Black Sea

Balabanov, V. F. (1975), 'Tectonics of the pre-Black Sea basin', *Geotectonics*, **9**, 34–39.

Balavadze, B. K. *et al.* (1969), 'Tectonics of the Black Sea and Azov area', *Geotectonics*, **4**, 238–246.

Letouzey, J. *et al.*, (1977), 'The Black-Sea: a marginal basin. Geophysical and geological data', in B. Biju-Duval and L. Montadert (eds), *Internat. Symp. on the Structural History of the Mediterranean Basins*, Editions Technip., Paris, pp. 363–376.

Muratov, M. V. (1972), 'History of the development of the deep-water trough in the Black Sea as compared with those of the Mediterranean', *Geotectonics*, **5**, 269–278.

Ross, D. A. (1974), 'The Black Sea', in C. A. Burk and C. L. Drake (eds), *The Geology of Continental Margins*, Springer-Verlag, Berlin, pp. 669–682.

Ross, D. A. (1977), 'The Black Sea and the Sea of Azov', in A. E. M. Nairn, W. H. Kanes and F. G. Stehli (eds), *The Ocean Basins and Margins*, vol. 4A, Plenum Press, New York, pp. 445–481.

Section 15(f)   Mediterranean

Auzende, J. M., J. Bonnin and J. L. Olivet (1973), 'The origin of the western mediterranean basin', *J. Geol. Soc. Lond.*, **129**, 607–620.

Bijn-Duval, B. and L. Montadert, eds. (1977), *Structural History of the Mediterranean Basins*, Editions Technip, Paris, 448 pp.

McKenzie, D. P. (1970), 'Plate tectonics of the Mediterranean region', *Nature*, **226**, 239–243.

Nairn, A. E. M., W. H. Kanes and F. G. Stehli, eds. (1977), *The Ocean Basins and Margins*, vols. 4A and 4B, Plenum Press, New York, 503 and 407 pp.

Ryan, W. B. F. *et al.* (1969), 'The tectonics and geology of the Mediterranean Sea', in J. C. Maxwell (ed.), *The Sea*, vol. 4, Wiley, London and New York, pp. 387–492.

Sander, N. J. (1968), 'The Premesozoic structural evolution of the Mediterranean region', Petrol. Explor. Soc. Libya, 10th Ann. Field Conf., pp. 47–70.

Sander, N. J. (1970), 'Structural evolution of the Mediterranean region during the Mesozoic Era', in W. Alvarez and K. H. A. Gohrbandt (eds.), Petrol. Explor. Soc. Libya, 12th Ann. Field Conf., pp. 43–132.

Smith, A. G. (1971), 'Alpine deformation and the oceanic areas of the Tethys, Mediterranean and Atlantic', *Bull. Geol. Soc. Amer.*, **82**, 2039–2070.

Stanley, D. J., ed. (1973), *The Mediterranean Sea. A natural sedimentation laboratory*, Dowden, Hutchinson and Ross, Stroudbsberg, Penn., 765 pp.

Van Bemmelen, R. W. (1972), 'Driving forces of Mediterranean orogeny', *Geol. Mijnb.*, **51**, 548–573.

Section 15(g)   Tyrrhenian volcanic region

Ager, D. V. (1955), 'Summer field meeting in Italy', *Proc. Geol. Ass.*, **66**, 329–352.

Barberi, F. *et al.* (1974), 'Evolution of Aeolian arc volcanism (southern Tyrrhenian Sea)', *Earth Planet. Sci. Lett.*, **21**, 269–276.

Bellon, H. and J. Letouzey (1977), 'Volcanism related to plate tectonics in the western and eastern Mediterranean', in B. Biju-Duval and L. Montadert (eds.), *Structural History of the Mediterranean Basins*, Editions Technip., Paris, pp. 165–183.

Desio, A. ed. (1973), *Geologia dell'Italia*, Union Tipogr.-Edit.-Torinese, Turin, 1081 pp.

Squyres, C. H., ed. (1975), *Geology of Italy*, 2 vols., Earth Sci., Soc., Libyan Arab Repub., 402 and 392 pp.

Chapter Sixteen

Southern Alpides

Finally we come to what may be called the 'south-facing' Alps (even though—paradoxically—the Apennines face north). Like the Northern Alpides this belt falls basically into three parts: the ranges of north-west Africa, the Apennines and Southern Alps, and the long Dinaride–Hellenide chain down into the Aegean.

16(a) Maghreb

Maghreb is an Arabic word meaning literally 'the land where the sun sets'.* It is used for the countries of Morocco, Algeria, and Tunisia, in north-west Africa. We are here concerned with the northern part of the Maghreb—roughly the Mediterranean lands that were formerly known as 'High Barbary', chiefly famous (in European eyes) for their pirates.

It may well be asked what business I have including a chapter on part of Africa in a book on the geological history of Europe, but to me north-west Africa is geologically part of the European continent. Southwards the great Saharan Shield, with its platform extensions, are a plate apart. But it is reasonable to include here most of Morocco, a large part of northern Algeria, and half of Tunisia, to complete the European picture. Having seen its close similarities with southern Europe I am all the more tempted to include it, although the already overstrained covers of this book force me to condense this chapter even more than the others. In fact I will include three different major units together (Fig. 16.1), even though it can well be argued that they belong in three different places:

1. The Rif (which is undoubtedly part of the Southern Alpides).
2. The Maghreb Massif (which is a Variscan massif).
3. The Atlas (which is an 'Outer Arc' in the sense used herein).

These form a mirror image of the major elements in the Iberian Peninsula.

---

* 'Europe'—in the form 'Ereb'—meant the same in ancient Assyrian, which emphasizes the point I made in the Introduction about Europe being no more than a peninsula at the end of the Asian continent.

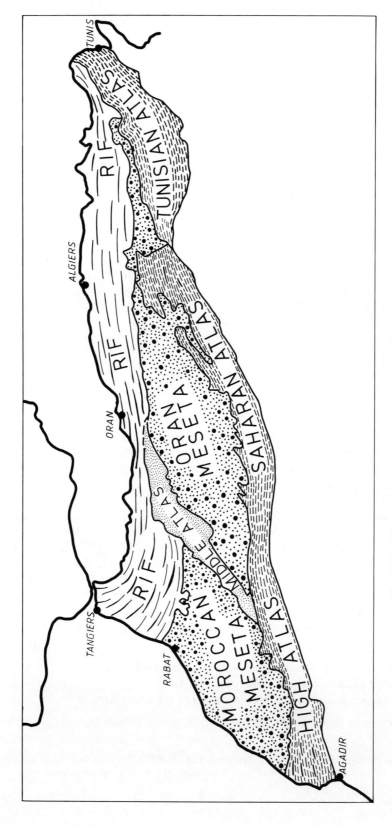

Fig. 16.1 Sketch-map of the main structural elements of the Maghreb.

Rif

The Rif chain is a direct continuation of the Betic Cordillera of southern Spain, differing from it in having been pushed the other way and so forming the first link in the Southern Alpides. The resemblance is almost ridiculously exact and makes it unnecessary to describe the Rif separately. The 'Gibraltar Arc' is a tight geniculation with an almost due east–west axis that passes through the Strait of Gibraltar. The Rif is delimited to the north by the Mediterranean and to the south by the *Sillon prerifain* (Pre-Rif Furrow). The folds and thrusts of the Rif are more or less concentrically arranged, with the inner units pushing south over the outer and these in turn overriding the Pre-Rif Furrow. They will be considered in turn from 'inside' (i.e., north) to 'outside'.

Kabylides. These are a complex unit including the Sebtide Zone of Morocco, the Kabylie Zone of Algeria, and the Galitide Zone of Tunisia. At their western end they are thought to be the continuation of the inner zones of the Betic Cordillera, and at their eastern end they pass naturally into the Calabride Zone of north-east Sicily and the 'toe' of Italy.

In Morocco, the Betic trend swings north–south and then east–west. The lowest complexes of the Betics have not been recognized, but the extensive Alpujarride Complex continues as the Sebtide Zone of the inner Rif. This is the deepest structural unit seen at the surface and is characterized by a low degree of metamorphism and by peridotites. For the most part it consists of Palaeozoic argillaceous rocks and is exposed in a broad belt along the coast south of Ceuta (Sebta) as far as the Pointe des Pêcheurs (Punta Pescadores). The lower part comprises gneisses and schists up to the garnet grade; these are seen in the north around Ceuta and the Cabo Negro. They have not been dated, but are thought to be Cambro-Ordovician, as the beds above are definitely Silurian to early Devonian shales and greywackes with fossiliferous limestone intercalations. These pass up into greywackes that have yielded rare plants and are probably early Carboniferous in age. There is no sign of a Variscan orogeny but they are overlain by Permo-Triassic red beds which, north of Tetouan, pass up into the late Triassic and early Jurassic carbonates of Jebel Haouz. The succession is cut by dikes that are assumed to be Triassic in age because of the presence of Triassic intrusions and extrusions elsewhere in Morocco and southern Spain. Small patches of nummulitic late Eocene, sandy Oligocene, and Miocene molasse, resting unconformably on the older rocks, complete the story.

In Algeria this zone is represented mainly by three massifs: the Grande Kabylie to the east of the city of Algiers, the Petite Kabylie west of Philippeville, and the Edough Massif forming part of the broad peninsula west of Bône. This is a great geanticlinal structure which then strikes out to sea and is only seen in Tunisia as the offshore Galite islands. These rocks were long regarded as an undatable crystalline basement of metamorphic rocks, but enough fossil evidence has now been accumulated—especially in the Grande Kabylie—to be sure that Ordovician, Silurian, Devonian, and Carboniferous rocks are represented in a marine facies. Thrusts from the north carry Cretaceous and Palaeogene flysch over the Palaeozoic.

Dorsal Zone. This is sometimes called the Ghomarides and is certainly equatable with the Malaguide Complex of the Betic Cordillera in southern Spain. In places the resemblances are almost too good to be true. The Palaeozoics, reduced Mesozoics, calcareous Eocene, and detrital Miocene are all the same. It is known by various names, of which the *Châine calcaire* is the most commonly used. As this implies the zone forms a comparatively high, axial zone of dominantly carbonate rocks, but it is very narrow and impersistent. The deeper facies are towards the exterior (as in Spain).

It is seen chiefly on the south side of the massifs of the Grande and Petite Kabylie. It resembles the Malaguides in its distribution as tectonically isolated masses of Mesozoic limestone. The faunas—as in the Rif generally—are of a distinctly 'Alpine' character, with groups such as the rhynchonellinids and pygopids well represented.

Flysch Zone. This may be regarded as a direct continuation of various high Spanish nappes including the Gibraltar flysch or Ultra-Betics of southernmost Spain. Jebel Musa in Morocco which, with Gibraltar, forms the 'Pillars of Hercules' is part of the same allochthonous unit, sometimes called the Tariquides. The zone culminates in the famous Numidian flysch of Algeria and the Fortuna Sandstone of eastern Tunisia. These are the highest and most extensive thrust slices. It is all clearly allochthonous, with large exotic blocks and a variety of sediments (not all flysch by any means) all seemingly Cretaceous or Palaeogene in age. In the Khourmirie and Mogods area, in the extreme north-west corner of Tunisia, the flysch is seen thrust over the foreland. There are Miocene and Quaternary volcanics in several places from one end of the range to the other.

Pre-Rif Zone. This zone (also known as the 'Tellian Furrow') is the characteristic frontal trough present in every Alpine chain. It may be compared with the Sub-Betics of Spain, although here the mirror cracks a little. It is characterized by the usual red bed Trias with thick evaporites that have produced diapir structures (e.g., in the north of Tunisia) and also by Jurassic, Cretaceous, and Eocene sediments that become progressively thicker towards the north. In Tunisia the so-called 'furrow' takes the form of largish mountains of Lower Cretaceous reefs and Eocene limestones.

In general the Rif is an Alpine chain in structure and stratigraphy and contrasts markedly in these characters with the Atlas Mountains to the south. The first important movement that can be called Alpine was the uplift and emergence of the Dorsal Zone at the end of early Jurassic times. The usual marine transgression started in late Cretaceous, accompanied by some slight local folding. The transgression continued in the Palaeogene with the main folding occurring during or at the end of the Oligocene, especially at the western end of the chain. Farther south the movements may have been slightly later, persisting into the Neogene, but before the late Miocene transgression. Finally there were slight local movements in the Pliocene tilting the whole structure gently to the south.

Maghreb Massif

The term 'Maghreb Massif' is coined here for the Moroccan Meseta and its easterly continuation into Algeria and Tunisia as the Oran Meseta and the 'High Plateaux', together with the Middle Atlas range which forms the boundary between them (Fig. 16.2). Westwards, considerable uplift has brought large areas of Precambrian and Palaeozoic rocks to the surface, especially in the south, but the whole area is essentially a plateau. The meseta is dominantly of older rocks and can be compared directly with the Variscan massifs of Europe. On the whole it is not well exposed, even in European terms.

Moroccan Meseta. As here defined, this is delimited by the Atlantic to the west (with

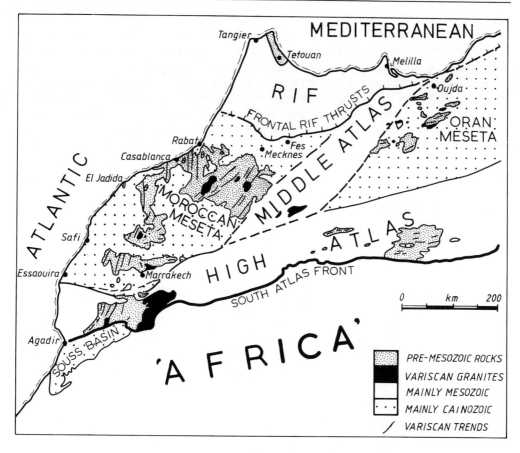

Fig. 16.2   Sketch-map of the western part of the Maghreb.

its narrow continental shelf), by the frontal furrow of the Rif to the north, by the Middle Atlas to the east, and by the High Atlas to the south.

Although we think of the meseta as being made, like other European massifs, of Precambrian and Palaeozoic rocks, over great areas there is little to see of them beneath Mesozoic (in the south) and especially Tertiary sediments (Fig. 16.2). The resemblance to the Iberian Meseta is quite remarkable and (if one avoids camels) photographs of the one can perfectly easily be taken for photographs of the other.

Precambrian rocks are not known for certain on the Moroccan Meseta. The only rocks which have been attributed to the Precambrian are the rhyolites and dacites of El Jadida (Mazagan), pebbles of which are found in the Plio-Pleistocene raised beaches between Essaouira and Agadir. It is presumed that the main source of these pebbles foundered offshore, but this has not shown up in the geophysical surveys of the continental shelf. Much larger areas of metamorphic rocks and granodiorite inland are thought to be metamorphosed Palaeozoic sediments.

Cambrian rocks are best known in the Jbilet (Jebilet) range, which rises behind Marrakech. North of Chichaoua, in Jebel Irhoud (with its barytes mine), there is a great

461

archaeocyathid reef. Lower Cambrian limestones are overlain by shales and sandstones of mid and late Cambrian age. Similar rocks appear from time to time below their later cover, for example along the Oued Oum* inland from El Jadida, in a general anticlinal trend that runs north to the sea at Casablanca, where it outcrops on the touristic beaches on both sides of the town. The Cambrian is not known for certain farther east and the general picture is of thickening to the west and south-west, i.e., towards the Atlantic.

Graptolitic shales and arkoses of Ordovician age are found in synclines on either side of the Casablancan anticline. In the central part of the Moroccan Meseta, the Ordovician succession starts with a massive sandstone, reminiscent of the Arenigian quartzites of the Iberian Massif, Armorica, and western Britain. Shales and sandstones, sometimes ferruginous, characterize the Ordovician throughout Morocco. The general absence of carbonates is probably significant in view of the major Ordovician glaciation now recognized in the Sahara. Sands in the Ordovician appear to derive from the south, as do those of the Cambrian, in which there seems to be a whole series of alluvial fans (reminiscent of the Devonian 'Catskill delta' of New York State) coming from the direction of the Sahara.

The Silurian is similarly shaly and graptolitic with minor sandstones, and its outcrops are much more widely distributed than those of the older systems. They are seen in the north-east trending anticlinorium that runs from Khouribga (south-east of Casablanca) to Oulmès, south-east of Rabat (which supplies half the bottled drinking water of Morocco). It is also seen farther east, in the anticlinorium between Ziar (north of Khenifra) and Azrou, which is perhaps continued to the north-east in Jebel Tezzeka (east of the fascinating city of Fez). The line runs exactly parallel to the trend of the Middle Atlas and clearly demonstrates the parallelism of Palaeozoic and Tertiary folding. At the very top of the Silurian, carbonates begin to return with brachiopod lenses which accumulated on algal substrates on submarine rises within the muddy basins. The benthic faunas of both the Silurian and Devonian are, however, very lacking in diversity compared with the rich assemblages now known to the south.

In the Devonian there was a great change in sedimentation. Whereas the Ordovician and Silurian had been times of monotonous muds, in the Devonian there was a differentiation of shallow and deeper water deposits. There was evidently submergence of a basin to the north-west, centred on what is now Casablanca, while there was uplift and erosion to the south, towards the High Atlas. Although there is no real evidence of a Caledonian orogeny of the Moroccan Meseta, something was already happening along the High Atlas line, as there was through the rest of Palaeozoic times. Between Khouribga and Oulmés there are thick shale and flysch-like formations, with only minor limestones, and there seems to be an unbroken passage through from the Silurian. Eastwards, however, a basal unconformity is recognizable and the Devonian rests on the Ordovician in places. The usual development of reef limestones in the Frasnian is found on both sides of the basin, for example near Casablanca and near Azrou.

Carboniferous rocks outcrop over a larger area of the meseta than those of any other Palaeozoic system, although they are almost entirely confined to the 'Central Hercynian Massif', extending all the way from the coast between Rabat and Casablanca to the sudden front of the Middle Atlas east of Khenifra and Azrou.

* *Oued* is the equivalent in 'French' Arabic of *Wadi* in 'English' Arabic.

The Lower Carboniferous is particularly extensive and includes notable developments of shallow-water coral-produced limestones reminiscent of north-west Europe. They are seen, for example, in the long dip slopes of Khenifra and at 'Roche perćee' near Khenifra, where the track formerly went through a natural tunnel in the rock (forming an almost impregnable defensive position against the colonizers until the present road was blasted through the valley).

Of special interest in this region are olistostromes, with limestone masses (often full of Devonian fossils) 'floating' in a clay formation of early Carboniferous age. Nappes have been postulated in the past to explain these, but they are almost certainly all of sedimentary origin. In fact the idea of major nappes among the Variscan structures here has now been generally abandoned, as it has in other Variscan massifs.

The main deformation of the meseta appears to have occurred in early Westphalian times. The folds show a simple virgation, as in the other large Variscan massifs of Europe (see Fig. 12.1). In the west they are generally north–south and the same trend is seen continued in the Tichka Massif in the High Atlas south of Marrakech. On the east side of the meseta, the trend is to the north-east and parallel to the line of the Middle Atlas.

As the north–south trend is followed south it swings gently to parallel the present Atlantic coast, and is seen following the same lines down through what used to be Spanish Sahara and on into Mauritania. It is then a simple stretch of the imagination to see it continued in the Appalachians and Ouachitas of North America. This emphasizes the unity of 'Pangaea' up until the end of Palaeozoic times, and the importance of the Atlantic line.

One feature of almost every reassembly of these continents is a lateral displacement of Africa relevant to Europe and the necessity to postulate sinistral strike-slip movements. These can explain the pattern of faulting which dominates the Moroccan Meseta and which was evidently operative as far back as the Ordovician. It may be that the main movement was at first along the South Atlas Front (what is now the Agadir seismic line) and the main displacement only later moved to the Azores–Gibraltar Line which figures in most plate diagrams. The main strike-slip movements could then have produced the *en echelon* tension faults, in two sets normal to each other. Sedimentation, especially in the Carboniferous, was controlled by this faulting in a fashion comparable to that of the 'pull-apart' basins that have been described from California.

Mesozoic rocks make little showing on the meseta proper, apart from the usual Cenomanian transgression, which spread carbonates on to the southern edge of the meseta as far north as Casablanca. The later Cretaceous sea was more limited and was of an unusual kind in which were inaugurated the remarkable series of phosphatic deposits which are the chief source of Morocco's wealth.

The deposits are mainly worked in the 'Plateau des Phosphates', in the region between the main eastern mass of the 'Central Hercynian Massif' and Rehamna. They are best known around Khouribga. That they range down into the Cretaceous is shown by the presence of a conglomerate containing bones of marine reptiles. Oysters near the top of the phosphates are attributed to the mid to late Eocene. Evidently the deposits were laid down in unusual conditions with winnowing and concentration of vertebrate remains as in many other (less productive) phosphate deposits. Presumably they were laid down in embayments along the margin of the young Atlantic.

Late Tertiary deposits are of a minor nature. The phosphates are covered by an overburden of up to 100 m of further Eocene sands in the south of the main basin, but generally speaking the only later deposits are some Miocene clays and sands with lignite in the extreme north of the meseta and scattered Plio-Pleistocene marine deposits along the coast, including a splendid series of raised beaches, for example south of Safi. Even the beach rock, which seems to have formed only yesterday, is often disturbed. Thus at the seaside resort of El-Harhoura, south of Rabat, it can be seen to be tilted quite steeply inland, forming a lagoon.

Like the Iberian Massif, Cainozoic volcanism here was local and late but quite intensive. There was a little Miocene volcanicity in the Rif but Pliocene volcanicity was limited to a little rhyolite (albeit a flow 300 m thick) near Khenifra. In Quaternary times extensive basalt flows spread across the countryside, mostly along the margins of the Middle Atlas, where they can be related to late tension along the fault-lines. They form steep-sided flat cappings to the topography, notably over a wide area south of Azrou, and are associated with fluvial sediments between there and the twin ancient cities of Meknes and Fes. Many separate volcanoes have been recognized including phonolitic, dacitic, and other domes reminiscent (in their multitude of rock-names as well as their form) of the puys of the Massif Central, and strung out, like them, along the faults. Lava flows follow the valleys and overlie river deposits as they do in the Auvergne. Near Meknes there are perfectly preserved cinder cones with complete craters.

From the sediments and vertebrate fossils it is clear that periods of much heavier rainfall than are known today in this arid land accompanied the glaciation of the High Atlas mountains to the south.

The Middle Atlas. These are dominantly composed at the surface of Mesozoic rocks which were folded, albeit gently, in the Alpine movements. However, they are no more than a crumpled tablecloth on the solid table of Palaeozoic rocks which are the Meseta. They are comparable with the Celtiberic Ranges of eastern Spain, where no great thickness of Mesozoic rests on the Iberian Massif, and like them show a close parallelism between Alpine folds of the tablecloth and Variscan warps in the table. Like them, too, the Middle Atlas run at an acute angle to the main Alpine fold belts to the north and south, but conform to the Palaeozoic structures beneath. Although it is logical to describe the Middle Atlas with the Moroccan Meseta, it is almost equally unnatural to separate the Middle Atlas from the High Atlas to the south. Thus the Mesozoic stratigraphy of the two is closely comparable and the Palaeozoic structures on the meseta continue into the Tichka Massif in the High Atlas.

The north-west front of the Middle Atlas is clearly marked by a major tensional fault, which last moved in Quaternary times and shows as a prominent escarpment. This 'accident' is most spectacular south-east of Ifrane (which has all the appearance of a French provincial town). Here the fault evidently controlled shallow-water deposition in Jurassic times, with small patch and pinnacle reefs still standing up as knolls. One can also see great floods of Quaternary basalts and volcanic cones all seemingly originating from the fault fissure.

The Triassic sediments of the Middle Atlas are as red as one expects anywhere in Europe outside the Tethys. Thus, at Kerrouchin, south-east of Khenifra, the system starts in the usual way with conglomerates, then red sandstones, and then red mudstones with salt. This last has been worked at many places in the Middle Atlas, notably at Bekrite, east-north-east of Khenifra, in the Massif de Tichchoukt, east of Azrou and to the south of Taza. It is almost unbelievably like the Trias of extra-Alpine Europe, and one cannot conceive of this part of Africa having been far away at this time.

As in the High Atlas and parts of Spain there is a series of basaltic lava flows and/or sills in the Trias, especially near the top. These are famous for their geodes, some of which are colourful amethyst (although much of what is sold by small boys at the roadside is luridly painted ordinary quartz). One cannot help but associate this magmatic activity in Triassic times with the tensions of the first opening of the present Atlantic, especially as it can often be related to faults and one can match both the sediments (themselves fault-controlled) and the volcanics with the Newark Group on the east coast of North America.

A spectacular feature of the Lower Jurassic in the Middle Atlas are the beautifully exposed coral reefs. Even a cursory visit is enough to satisfy oneself that they were growing on a shallow shelf, with lagoonal deposits behind them and facing (with their more massive compound corals) an open sea to the north-east, along the line of the range.

The western edge of the Middle Atlas is sometimes called the 'Causse' by analogy with the dry, cave-ridden limestone plateaux of central France. Here also the early Jurassic is clearly of a shallow-water facies, lacking ammonites and correlated mainly by means of brachiopods. A deeper, muddier, ammonite-bearing facies was more extensive in Toarcian times, as is so often the case in Europe. This was particularly so in the central and northern parts of the Middle Atlas, where there is hardly any evidence of a marginal facies.

Although the Jurassic story of the Middle Atlas is mainly that of the Lias, the same situation did continue into Mid Jurassic times, but the marine influence was waning. Mudstones and muddy limestones of Bajocian and Bathonian age yield rich brachiopod and bivalve faunas along the margins and there is still a cephalopod facies in the centre of the chain, particularly south of Taza. One of the best places is around El-Ksiba (east of Kasba Tadla) which is well named the 'Pearl of the Atlas'. However, from mid Bajocian times onwards the marine deposits began to shrink. Plant debris from nearby land-masses becomes abundant in the Bathonian, together with fresh-water vertebrates and, most notably, the famous dinosaurs of El Mers, 70 km east of Azrou. We do not, however, find the footprints that occur in rocks of the same age at the High Atlas end of the range at Demnate. It seems, therefore, that although their bloated corpses floated to the centre of the basin (leaving disarticulated bones) dinosaurs did not set foot in the Middle Atlas. The trough came to an end. It is therefore all the more difficult to accept this line as an oceanic suture between microplates in the Alpine history of the Mediterranean as some of the 'megathinkers' would have us believe.

Late Jurassic and early Cretaceous sediments are completely absent from the Middle Atlas unless one follows some authors in continuing the range as far as the Mediterranean north-west of Oujda. Here there are shallow-water deposits of late Jurassic age, but these seem to be more a part of the Tethys/Mediterranean/Rif story, for the sea came in from the north.

The great spread of the Cenomanian sea over the Moroccan Meseta carried shallow-water deposits also over the Middle Atlas, but was separated by a belt of continental deposits from a similar transgression to the east. The sediments abound in oysters of various kinds, and the smallest fragment of an oyster shell is an almost certain indicator of a Cretaceous age in this region. Red beds and gypsiferous deposits indicate oscillating conditions and there are obvious breaks in the succession. The last record of the Cretaceous is in the form of polygenetic conglomerates, only preserved in major synclines. They often produce a startling topography such as 'la Cathédrale' south of Beni-Mellal. Some continental deposits lingered on to the end of the period, but by then the sea had virtually withdrawn from the Middle Atlas and was never seen there again but for some doubtful Eocene deposits. From then on it was a positive area lacking deposits of any kind.

The Tertiary movements here were on a gentle scale and closely related to the structures of the underlying Palaeozoic. In this too they resemble the Celtiberic chains of eastern Spain. Like them also there are nevertheless places where dips become near vertical and even overturned. There are low-angle thrusts and even supposed nappes— for example near Timahdite south-south-east of Azrou. Here, early Mesozoic rocks have been pushed westwards over the late Cretaceous and early Tertiary succession. As usual, however, Triassic red beds with evaporites are at the bottom of the succession and are also doubtless at the bottom of the tectonics too.

The High Plateaux. The *Haut Plateaux* match the Moroccan Meseta in generalities on the other side of the Middle Atlas. They extend eastwards from north-east Morocco into Algeria but are pinched out between the converging Rif and Atlas ranges. The small, scattered outcrops of Palaeozoic rocks east of the Middle Atlas are comparable with those of the Moroccan Meseta in being surrounded and all but covered with Tertiary and Quaternary continental deposits. This may be treated as a separate massif and, indeed, some have made it a separate 'Oranaise Microplate', but in the absence of evidence of a major suture under the Middle Atlas, this need not be taken very seriously.

The most important of the inliers is that of Djerada (Jerada) south-west of Oujda, where Morocco has its one productive coal-field. A succession of lavas and tuffs range up to the end of the Tournaisian. They are dated mainly by included radiolarites, which show remarkably close affinities with those of the Montagne Noir. These and a flysch succession above may be thought to be evidence of a lost ocean, but it passes up into a Westphalian delta complex that includes the valuable coals. The latter are remarkably persistent over scores of kilometres and testify to a very stable situation. This is also suggested by the fact that the Variscan folding is much less pronounced in the High Plateaux than in the Moroccan Meseta. The folding is slightly later in age, coming at the end of the Westphalian and followed, above an unconformity, by red bed deposition of Stephanian and Permian age.

The trend of the folding is distinctly different, being essentially east–west and parallel to the Mediterranean coast to the north and the High Atlas ranges to the south. The Palaeozoic rocks within the easternmost High Atlas of Morocco (the Monts des Kcour) show a similar trend, as do their enclosing Mesozoic sediments. It may be said, therefore, that while the fold trends of south-west Morocco (and the countries to the south) have a clearly Atlantic trend, these swing round in the Middle Atlas and have attained a Mediterranean trend before the Moroccan–Algerian border. As in Europe, we are getting away from the influence of the Atlantic.

The Mesozoic record of the High Plateaux is scanty and related to the Rif and the Mediterranean rather than the Atlas and the Atlantic. Triassic rocks are virtually unknown and the earliest Jurassic is represented only by poorly fossiliferous dolomites, south of Oujda in the *Pays des Horsts*. The Middle Lias is better developed in a shallow marine facies with species reminiscent of northern seas and notable for remarkable molluscan reefs, notably in Jebel-el-Abed, just over the Algerian border south-south-east of Oujda.

The Upper Lias is most extensive and as usual of a deeper water facies, especially in the north. Southwards, towards the High Atlas, there were signs of emergence and in Middle Jurassic times a monotonous dolomitic facies spread over great areas of the Plateaux, although with enough marine fossils to provide a framework of dates. By late Jurassic times the sea had withdrawn completely from the main part of the High Plateaux and marine deposits are only known in the northerly *Pays des Horsts*. Here they are shallow-water limestones passing eastwards into Algeria as sands.

Thereafter no deposits are known until the transgressive Cenomanian lapped on to the southern edge of the plateaux from the High Atlas trough, as it did in the Jbilet farther west. This soon withdrew again and there are no later marine deposits. So Algeria lacks the valuable phosphates of Morocco, but does have oil-fields. Continental deposits, mainly red sands and conglomerates, extend over large areas of the High Plateaux resting unconformably on the Cretaceous and earlier formations. The sands contain huge concretions, sometimes 200 m long, which weather out to form fantastic shapes, such as the 'towers' of Chott Tigri in the extreme south, where these deposits spread onto the margins of the High Atlas. There are associated multicoloured marls but no evaporites, and there are enough fresh-water gastropods to date the beds as probably Miocene.

There are also Miocene lava flows around Oujda, but the Plio-Pleistocene volcanics of the Moroccan Meseta and Middle Atlas are almost completely absent on the High Plateaux. Presumably the tensional strains here were less farther away from the Atlantic. There are just a few Pliocene basaltic and phonolitic centres. More important is the blanket of Pliocene and Quaternary sediments which cover vast areas of eastern Morocco and central Algeria. Some are Pliocene lake deposits, such as those along the Oued Moulouya between Guercif and Midelt, but most are the sands and wind-blasted stones of this arid countryside and the deposits of the ephemeral rivers and lakes.

Atlas *sensu stricto*

The term 'Atlas' is used for various mountain chains within the Maghreb. Thus the 'Tellian Atlas' of Algeria and Tunisia and the 'Middle Atlas' of Morocco are quite different from the 'true' Atlas as here interpreted. I am concerned with the 'High Atlas' of Morocco (with which I have been intimately and hotly involved) and their easterly continuation which is sometimes known as the 'Saharan Atlas' in Algeria and the 'Tunisian Atlas' in Tunisia; but they are also known by other names. Quite different again are the 'Anti-Atlas' of southern Morocco which are outside the limits of this book.

The Atlas, as here defined, are the range of high mountains and high plateaux which the ancients thought held up the sky along the southernmost edge of what I regard as 'Europe in Africa'. As one heads south across the eastern part of the Moroccan Meseta and suddenly sees a great wall of rock stretching from horizon to horizon along the frontal 'accident', one can understand why the early semi-civilized people of Europe thought this was the end of the world, with nothing beyond. At the eastern end, the barrier is much less clearly defined, although there is still a line of isolated mountains, of which Jebel Zaghouan is the most impressive, swinging north to meet the Mediterranean in the Gulf of Tunis, just opposite ancient Carthage.

To the south the Atlas are delimited by the Agadir fault-line and its continuation, backed by the 'Pre-African Furrow'. At the Moroccan end one quite suddenly passes from the glorious reds and buffs of the folded Mesozoic rocks into gloomy, flat-lying Palaeozoic and Precambrian sediments and volcanics (but perhaps my prejudices are showing). At the Tunisian end the Mesozoic sediments continue south of the line, but whereas in the 'Atlas' they are sharply folded and mineralized, southwards they seem to go on for ever, down the long escarpments south of the Mareth line to the Libyan frontier and—one might imagine—all the way to the Cape of Good Hope. Everywhere they are as flat as the proverbial pancake.

The Atlas do not constitute an Alpine range in the strict sense. Although often high, they are comparatively simple in structure with large open folds and high-angle faults. They have none of the great overthrusts and nappes of the true Alpine chains and no not belong within the twisting fold belts that dominate Mediterranean Europe. If one pursues the 'mirror-image' comparison of Morocco with the Iberian Peninsula, then the Rif are the Betics, the pre-Rif trough is the Guadalquivir Valley, the Moroccan Meseta is the Iberian Meseta, and the Atlas would then have to be the Pyrenees–Cantabrian Chain. Up to a point this last comparison holds good, although the tectonic situation is quite different since France to the north of the Pyrenees is not the Saharan Shield! One point of possible parallelism here is the coincidence of Palaeozoic and post-Palaeozoic troughs.

Within the western part of the Atlas ranges there are Variscan massifs, of which the largest is the Tichka Massif, south of Marrakech. Here a thick complex sequence of Palaeozoic sediments has reached the grade of slate and is cut by Variscan granites. The trends in this, the most westerly of the Atlas massifs, are a direct continuation of those in the Moroccan Meseta and are roughly parallel with the present coastline. Farther east, away from the Atlantic influence, the trends in the Palaeozoic coincide almost exactly with that of the Mesozoic mountain range itself. What is more, there is evidence in the Palaeozoic sediments, as far back as the Cambrian, of both negative and positive features operating in the Atlas area. So it has been postulated that this was a Variscan fold belt before it was a Mesozoic one. The fact that Devonian limestones in the Tichka Massif appear to rest unconformably on the slaty Lower Palaeozoic, with a basal conglomerate, has been taken as evidence of a Caledonian orogeny.

West of the Tichka Massif is a rather separate area of Mesozoic rocks between Essaouira (Mogador) and Agadir which is directly related to the adjacent Atlantic. Near the massif, in the arid Argana Basin, basement structures clearly contolled red bed sedimentation in the Triassic and earliest Jurassic. Farther west there is salt in the upper Trias that has punched its way up forming domes, and these are also known on the narrow continental shelf offshore. The most obvious example is Jebel Amsitten, cut by the coast road south of Essaouira. Basic intrusions and extrusions in the Trias in the western Atlas, as throughout southern Morocco, are part of a radiating pattern of remarkably similar rocks of this age all round the North Atlantic, centring on the Blake Plateau north of the Bahamas. A minor marine invasion from the west in the early Jurassic was followed by a major one in the late Jurassic that left a fringe of coral-algal reefs around the western High Atlas, one of them at least oil-bearing. After an episode of storm-torn lagoons, the sea withdrew at the end of the period to be followed by a renewed transgression from the west in the early Cretaceous. Later in that period the sea smothered everything, lapping on to the Meseta to the north. All these sediments thin away from the coast and change into a less marine nature. In this they are the mirror-image of the Cretaceous and Tertiary down the east coast of the USA. Although there is nothing oceanic to be seen, there was clearly something going on out there in the Atlantic at this time. This coast continued to be unstable until recently as is shown by the staircase of raised beaches along the coastal cliffs, the tilted beach rock, and the movements on the Agadir fault which destroyed that town on 29 February 1960.

The Mesozoic story in the larger part of the Atlas chain that lies east of the Tichka Massif is similar, but in reverse. Palaeozoic rocks are exposed in places* and a largish massif is seen near the Moroccan–Algerian frontier. But the Atlas are largely composed of Mesozoic rocks, which in turn are slowly submerged under the Cainozoic as one goes eastwards towards the Mediterranean. A tiny patch of Permian, with fusulinids, is exposed near Medenine, below the Mareth scarp in Tunisia.

At first a trough filled with Triassic red beds of the usual type with considerable thicknesses of salt, especially in the middle (Algerian) part. These were important to the economy in the days before refrigerators and are still worked in many places, for example near the decaying palace of the Glaoui family (the 'Lords of the Atlas') at Telouet. The salt gave rise to many diapiric structures. Then a long narrow marine gulf extended across the Maghreb from the east. Geologists have made comparisons with the Red Sea, encouraged by some intrusions down the middle that push up into Jurassic strata. I am not convinced! In its deepest parts the Lower Jurassic passes into a 'turbidite' facies of a distal type, but this is just where we know there is Palaeozoic below. On either side and at the western end there is a transition into shallow sub-tidal environments with reefs developed at several levels and behind them lagoonal and supratidal carbonates. Generally speaking the later Jurassic strata are better developed towards Tunisia, culminating in the massive Tithonian limestones that form, for example, the sheer top of Jebel Zaghouan.

There was then a general break-up of the Jurassic carbonate shelf, as in Sicily, and the Cretaceous story is far less clear, with many local facies changes. There was uplift first on the south and then in the north, until the whole of the 'Kasserine Island' at the eastern end of the trough was uplifted in late Cretaceous times and there is no record of the highest stages. However, whereas at the western end of the Atlas there are no Mesozoic sediments immediately south of the Agadir Line, at the eastern end both Jurassic and Cretaceous marine and continental strata spread far to the south into what is Africa by anyone's definition. Much of this sediment derives from the south, as is particularly evident in the Cretaceous. The other important point is the contrast in faunas between the Atlas and the Rif on the one hand and between the Atlas and the Saharan Shield on the other. In general the Atlas faunas are remarkably north-west European in aspect, lacking many (but not all) of the 'Alpine' elements of the Rif. In the south there are significant elements identical with those of East Africa.

Tertiary sediments spread over the Mesozoic of the Atlas in places, especially in the east, and serve to date the movements. After several minor incidents there appears to

---

* Such as the small outcrop of shales by the *Tunnel des Legionnaires* in the Valley of Ziz in eastern Morocco, where the driver found graptolites while the geologists were studying the local Mesozoic.

have been a major phase of movement at the end of the Eocene and a second immediately before the Miocene. These therefore correlate with the happenings in the Pyrenees, and strengthen the parallel between the two ranges. There is even a 'North Atlas Fault' to match the 'North Pyrenean Fault', which had a considerable influence on sedimentation. Perhaps here too there was lateral movement. The folding here is not as intense as along the French–Spanish border and there is no regional metamorphism or even cleavage in the Mesozoic rocks. The open Jura-type folds were undoubtedly helped by slipping along and pushing by the Triassic salt. They tend to be steeper and pass into reversed faults on the northern side, although the opposite seems to be true in the extreme west. The sharp bend in the range at its eastern end, to turn up to the Gulf of Tunis, appears to be related to the functioning of 'Kasserine Island' as a stable massive in Mesozoic times and then as a positive feature in the early Tertiary. Subsidence to the south of this produced the deep Gabes Basin which is wholly in 'Africa' but nevertheless connects with the Tertiary basin of southern Sicily.

16(b)   Sicily

Sicily conforms to the pattern of the rest of Italy in generalities, but at the same time is very different. This is true whether one is speaking of history, society, tectonics, or sedimentology. All its main geological features (apart from Recent volcanicity) can be traced into Tunisia across the narrowest part of the Mediterranean. The island consists of a number of tectonic units, each with a distinctive stratigraphical succession. Unfortunately Sicily has suffered from a multiplicity of terms, partly due to the variety of geologists who have worked there. If I wished to be nationalistic I might say that students of Sicilian geology belong to an Italian school, a French school, a German school, and a small British school. It is not that these schools have disagreed completely about the fundamentals of Sicilian geology, rather they have adopted different approaches, different emphases and different terminologies.

The only decision I can reach is to be slightly prejudiced in favour of the home team, but to try to use both common terminologies. On this basis, the successive units from 'internal' to 'external', that is from north to south, may be named as follows:

Sicilian unit	Tectonic interpretation
Calabride Complex	Internal Massif
Sicilide Complex	Eugeosyncline
Panormide Complex	Miogeanticline
Basal and Ex-Basal Complexes (Himerese facies)	Miogeosyncline
Bradanic Massif (Trapanese and Hyblean facies)	Foreland.

The alternative terminology is used in Fig. 16.3. It must be realized that even the most up-to-date studies have not finalized the structural solution—the history of the earth

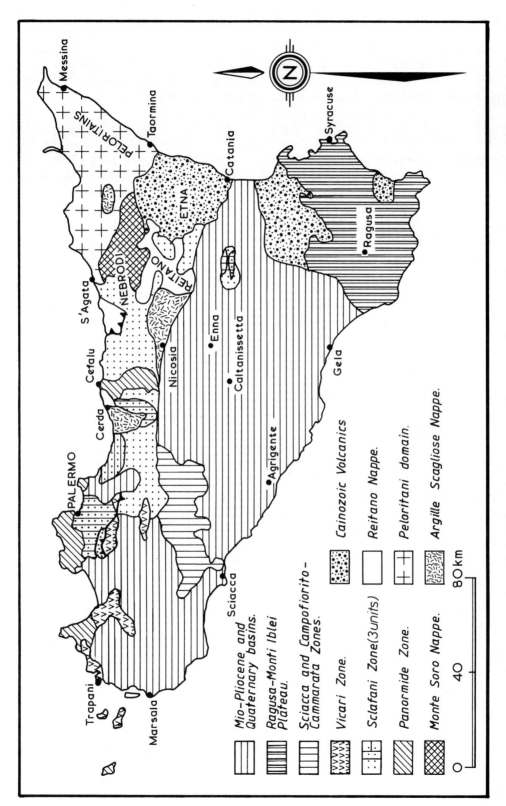

Fig. 16.3 Geological sketch-map of Sicily (after Caire, 1961, in Nairn, Kanes and Stehli, 1978, by kind permission of Plenum Press).

Legend:

- Mio-Pliocene and Quaternary basins.
- Ragusa-Monti Iblei Plateau.
- Sciacca and Campofiorito-Cammarata Zones.
- Vicari Zone.
- Sclafani Zone (3 units).
- Panormide Zone.
- Monte Soro Nappe.
- Cainozoic Volcanics.
- Reitano Nappe.
- Peloritani domain.
- Argille Scagliose Nappe.

0   40   80 km

cannot be rewritten overnight. We may presume that the Internal Massif is the edge of the European continental plate, that the eugeosyncline is the marginal trough with all that we have of Tethyan oceanic crust, and the rest are the trailing edge of the Atlantic-type margin of the African continental plate. But this may be forcing facts into a theory.

Calabride Complex

The Calabride Complex may simply be expressed as a metamorphic basement overlain by Mesozoic carbonates and Tertiary flysch. It constitutes the 'Peloritani domain' of Fig. 16.3. The basement is a direct continuation of the Calabrian Massif in the 'toe' of Italy and increases in metamorphic grade from south to north. These rocks outcrop over a large area of the Peloritani Mountains in north-east Sicily, occupying the greater part of that end of the island north of Etna.

The basement consists largely of gneisses and granites in the west and of schists in the east, but both developments include relics of folded phyllitic material and both pass southwards into phyllites. The succession includes andestic and rhyolitic volcanics and an altered limestone that has yielded Devonian fossils. The granites have been dated as Variscan and although slices of Mesozoic sediments are caught up in late stage movements, the main metamorphism must have occurred at that time, with structural trends running just south of east. The curious superposition of high-grade on low-grade metamorphics implies a major Variscan recumbent fold or thrust pushing down from the north, paralleling the general Sicilian trend of north–south movements in the Alpine orogeny. Thus the Calabride Basement, or 'Peloritani Basement', may be interpreted as the Internal Massif to the Sicilian Mesozoic geosyncline, and was pushed over the trench sediments in mid-Tertiary times.

The post-Variscan succession in the Calabride Complex begins, as usual, with 'Verrucano' sandstones and conglomerates, but the Mesozoic part consists mainly of carbonates that were presumably deposited on a northern shelf. The story is said to be complicated by early phase northerly thrusting of eugeosynclinal material before the main southerly movements. This may, however, now be interpreted as obduction of ocean floor prior to the overriding of one continental plate by another.

The Mesozoic carbonates are generally thin, with stratigraphical breaks and hard grounds. They also display numerous solution pipes in the limestones which carried down younger sediments into the older, often through considerable thicknesses. Although there are great structural complexities due to Variscan, early Alpine and later Alpine folding, the main movements and metamorphism of the basement took place before Mesozoic times, on the evidence of numerous Jurassic and later outliers resting on the metamorphic rocks. The most famous of these is the outlier of richly fossiliferous Jurassic limestones at Taormina on the east coast, where the faunas were described in the classic monographs of Gemmellaro. Here we are near the southern edge of the 'massif', and the sediments and faunas are both of a deeper water facies with radiolarites, aptychus limestones, and—in the upper part of the Cretaceous—mottled *Scaglia*-type sediments as in the Apennines.

The *Scaglia* persists into the Eocene, but the Alpine orogeny proper started here in Ypresian–Lutetian times, perceptibly earlier than in the Apennines. Something was evidently happening from the beginning of Palaeogene times, for large exotic blocks of

Mesozoic material are caught up in the Tertiary sediments as seen, for instance, just north of Taormina. The Ypresian–Lutetian phase of folding, which was restricted to this part of the island, was followed by considerable erosion and then the deposition of late Eocene conglomerates containing (for the first time) pebbles from the high-grade metamorphics of the basement.

The whole mass of the Peloritani Mountains was thrust southwards in the main Miocene phase overriding the flysch of the trench. The block appears to have ridden as a single unit, with only slight shearing of the Mesozoic cover. This was followed by general uplift and the formation of large synclines in which late Miocene (post-orogenic) conglomerates, sandstones, and marls are preserved. A further transgression brought Pliocene and early Pleistocene marine sediments into the area, as in most of the Mediterranean region. The story is complicated by the outbreak of volcanicity to the south, which is described elsewhere.

Sicilide Complex

In this complex the early parts of the story are unknown, but we have flysch sedimentation starting in late Jurassic times and the whole is interpreted as the 'eugeosyncline' of the Sicilian 'geosynclinal couple'. This complex is particularly well developed in the eastern part of the Madonie Mountains in the north–central part of the island. A mainly carbonate succession is taken to represent an autochthonous median shelf deposit. This ranges from Triassic to Eocene in age with some terminal, possibly Oligocene, conglomerates. Immediately overlying these is the Panormide Complex, discussed below, and then the allochthonous, eugeosynclinal Sicilide Complex which is the subject of this section.

The complex is seen in two nappes, the Monte Soro Nappe below, comprising the upper part of the sequence, and the Reitano Nappe above with the lower part itself partly inverted. The succession starts with late Jurassic to early Cretaceous flysch, a later Cretaceous to early Eocene argillaceous formation that has been separated as the *argille scagliose* in central Sicily, and then some Eocene to Oligocene marl–limestone alternations that might be called carbonate flysch, with andesitic volcanics. At the top there is Oligocene to Lower Miocene flysch with ample evidence of derivation from the internal massif. Placed as it is, between the Calabride Complex and the Panormide Complex, the palaeogeographical position of the Sicilide Complex has only been deduced, in the classic Alpine manner, from its facies.

Panormide Complex

Again the earlier parts of the story are unknown, but the mainly carbonate succession extends back to the Late Triassic. It is best developed in the eastern Madonie Mountains in the centre of northern Sicily. Here the complex is caught up within the 'Numidian flysch' (discussed below), but in its distinctive succession cannot belong within that tectonic unit. The carbonate sequence represents the greater part of the Mesozoic Era, from late Triassic to late Cretaceous. All is in a shallow shelf facies, sometimes with reefs, and is followed by further shaly carbonates extending up into the Eocene and finally by calcereous conglomerates of Oligocene age.

The same sequence, similarly allochthonous, is found in the white Palermo Mountains around the Sicilian capital and in the Capo San Vito (or Trapani) Mountains. These two form the northerly projecting peninsulas of north-west Sicily. Since this succession does not match the autochthonous miogeosynclinal succession to the south and lacks deep-water elements, it is interpreted as the deposits of a median shelf or miogeanticline.

Basal and Ex-Basal Complex (Himerese facies)

This complex is exposed in north-central Sicily and inland from Palermo. Its complexities are lumped together as the Sclafani Zone in Fig. 16.3. It is again predominantly composed of carbonates in its Mesozoic part, but these are of a deeper water type and include important developments of radiolarian cherts and of basic volcanics in the Middle Jurassic. This is followed by a transgressive Palaeogene marly limestone which passes up into a tremendous development of Oligocene–Miocene flysch. This can confidently be called the 'Numidian Flysch' as in north-west Africa, for the resemblance is very striking, and the derivation of the constituent polycyclic sands and lateritic clays was clearly from the continental deposits of the Saharan Shield to the south. The flysch passes up into more normal marine deposits of later Miocene age, which are thought to have come from the north.

The Italians interpret this sequence as a miogeosynclinal one, although the flysch and volcanics hardly fit in with the conventional picture. The thick Mesozoic carbonates certainly contrast with the contemporaneous flysch and variegated shales of the Sicilide Complex.

Bradanic Massif

In the highlands of south-east Sicily (the Ragusa–Monti Iblei Plateau of Fig. 16.3) and in the Sicani Mountains in the west (the Sciacca, etc., Zones), there is a final tectonic unit which is interpreted as the 'foreland' of the above geosynclinal development. This is almost entirely carbonate, from very thick Upper Triassic dolomites to Lower Miocene calcarenites, but again includes basic volcanics in the Middle Jurassic. The story is complicated by the deepening of facies from shelf carbonates with reefs in the main part of the Jurassic, to pelagic limestones from Tithonian to Eocene. All this is referred to as the 'Hyblean facies' to distinguish it from the 'Trapanese facies' near Trapani in the west (the Vicari Zone in Fig. 16.3). The latter only differs in the development of glauconite in the Oligocene and basal Miocene, which is taken as a transition to the miogeosyncline.

The Jurassic carbonates of west Sicily were deposited on a rapidly subsiding platform. An unusual complication is that the platform became broken up by faults, producing blocks that subsided at different rates within Jurassic times. This led to a topography of sea-mounts and intervening basins. All the features of modern sea-mounts have been recognized, including ferruginous crusts and ferromagnesian nodules.

Finally in the geological history of Sicily, the major part of the centre of the island and a great part of the western end subsided to form large Neogene and Quaternary basins. The Miocene is 'classic' with, for example, the 'type' section of the Messinian near Etna in the centre of the island. The Neogene consists of soft 'marls', with thick gypsum horizons marking the 'salinity crisis' at the end of the Miocene times. The late Caino-zoic basins form a direct continuation of the great basin of eastern Tunisia across the Sicilian Channel. In fact, since much of what is geographically north-west Africa is here classified as Europe, it can be said that nowhere else in the European continent do we come so close to Africa. Sicily, which has suffered so much throughout its geological and human history, took the full impact of the colliding continents.

16(c) Apennines

The Apennines extend south through Italy from the Sestri–Voltaggio Line in the north, where the south-westerly facing Alpine folds change suddenly into the north-easterly facing Apennine structures. This line marks a sinistral wrench fault that runs straight inland from the bend in the coastline just north of Genoa and operated throughout Palaeogene times. This line, however, may seem to be more important than it really is. In places the 'Alpides' seem to be thrust over the 'Apennines' and stratigraphically the northern Apennines are very like the southern Alps.

The Apennines constitute the greater part of Italian geology. They form the topographic backbone of the Italian peninsula (although 'leg-bone' would be more appropriate anatomically). From the forested slopes and mediaeval hilltop towns of Tuscany in the north, they extend as a bundle of parallel ridges down to the barren sun-blasted mountains of the Abruzzi and Campania in the south. It is then only a step across the Straits of Messina to Sicily.

This region is both classic and revolutionary. In the past twenty years or so, Apennine geology has passed through three upheavals of thought to match the disruptions of the rocks to which they relate. First there were the revolutionary ideas of the Firenze school in the late 'forties and early 'fifties which made the Apennines a mountain chain quite unlike any other in Europe. Then there was the counter-revolution which put them back into a more conventional framework. Finally there was the revolution of plate tectonics, which had them receiving the full impact of the African battering-ram. This too needs further thought.

In view of the direction of our peregrinations, it is logical to deal with the southern part of the chain first and omit the geologically recent volcanicity which was dealt with in a previous chapter.

Southern Apennines

These are the bleached and baking hills of southern Italy with their flocks and vineyards, the fertile basins in between, and the autostrada marching over all (Fig. 16.4). They are the old provinces of Abruzzi, Campagna, Lucania, and Calabria. Their dazzling white limestones are hard on geologists' eyes in the summer and contrast with the gloomier ridges of the north.

The boundary between the northern and southern Apennines is defined at the Anzio–Ancona line, running inland from the bloody beach-head of 1944, south of Rome, in a north-north-easterly direction to the Adriatic coast. This line, between the 'eugeosynclinal' north and the 'miogeosynclinal' south, functioned successively as a flexure, a

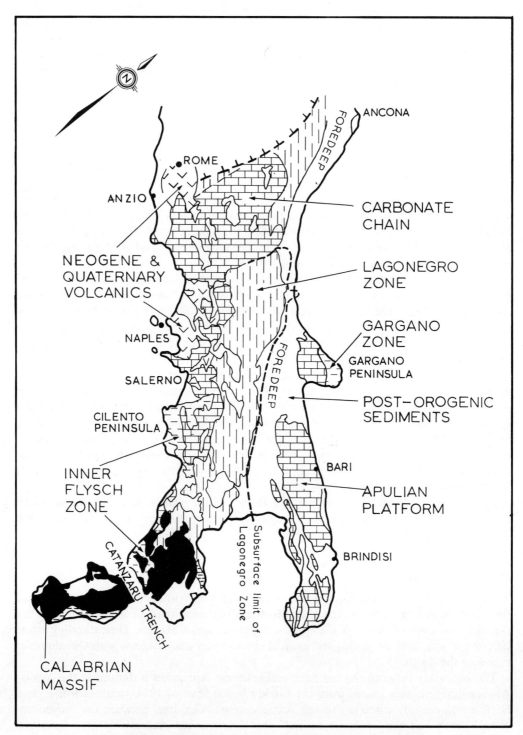

Fig. 16.4 Geological sketch-map of the southern Apennines.

normal fault, a wrench fault and—at least in the south—as a thrust, where the *Marnosa arenacea* flysch of the Umbrian arc is pushed over the limestones of the Abruzzi.

The northern part of this region is sometimes separated as the Central Apennines, but this terminology does not seem particularly useful. In effect, the moment you cross the Anzio–Ancona Line you are in a different world. Just as a northern Italian will tell you that south of Rome is another country with a different people, so it is with the geology. We have entered a great sweep of outwardly facing tectonic arcs, centred on the Tyrrhenian Sea and curving through the southern Apennines into Sicily and then into Tunisia. However, this is a somewhat superficial impression, overemphasized by the last tectonic movements.

Inner Flysch Zone. If we proceed from west to east across the lower part of the Italian 'boot' we see several successive zones. The first matches the Ligurid nappes of the north, but is largely hidden under the Tyrrhenian Sea. The general pattern down the west coast of Italy is the progressive cutting out of structural units by the coastline. Although known as the 'Internal Flysch Zone', there is little in it that can truly be called 'flysch', even if that term is used in its broadest sense. The succession is complex and in a state of structural confusion, but basically seems to consist of three succeeding sequences:

1. Cilento Sequence (mid or late Jurassic to early Cretaceous or later).
2. Variegated Shale Sequence (late Cretaceous to late Eocene or ? Oligocene).
3. Gorgoglione Sequence (Miocene).

The Cilento Sequence takes its name from the broad Cilento Peninsula on the south side of the broad, flat, Quaternary invasion bay of Salerno. It extends from here southwards, down into Calabria. The Jurassic consists of tiny, confused outcrops of limestones (including the deep-water *Calpionella* type) associated with ophiolites and siliceous rocks. The Cretaceous is much thicker, with a variety of sediments, all somewhat metamorphosed and again associated with ophiolites. There are later rocks which may or may not belong to the same tectonic unit. Detrital material started arriving in the early Cretaceous, and the later Cretaceous–Eocene formations above are truly flysch-like in nature.

The Variegated Shale Sequence is comparable to the *Scisti policromi* of the northern Apennines and consist of shales, sandstones, and cherty limestones, with volcanic material in its upper part and ranges from as early as Albian to as late as Oligocene. It is again dominantly a deep-water facies although with notable conglomerates and breccias indicating significant 'happenings'.

The Gorgoglione Sequence is a post-orogenic deposit which rests unconformably on the earlier units and is basically composed of molasse-type sediments with conglomerates, all of mid Miocene age.

The main part of the Internal Flysch Zone is a 'eugeosynclinal' trench deposit in nature, with important developments of ophiolites, and like most such zones it is clearly allochthonous, coming from an ocean floor to the south-west, although there are many structural complications. It also contributed material to the external zones to the north-east.

Carbonate Chain. The second zone of the Southern Apennines, which is vastly more extensive than the first, is the 'Carbonate Chain' or 'Calcaro-dolomitic Shelf'. This is the huge area of Mesozoic limestones that outcrops in the Gran Sasso d'Italia (the

'Great stone of Italy'); this is the high range above Aquila, north-east of Rome. From there it extends southwards to form all the rolling hills of the Abruzzi and down the Campagna (Campania) to the toe of Italy. Its best known development is its western extension to the coast of Salerno, where it forms the romantic, traffic-jammed peninsula of Amalfi and Sorrento, with a detached fragment in Tiberius's blue-grottoed island of Capri.

The carbonate sequence ranges from late Triassic to Cretaceous, with more varied Tertiary sediments above. The Triassic part, known chiefly in boreholes, is largely dolomitized with evaporites and Verrucano-type conglomerates. The main part, however, consists of a monotonous sequence of shelf limestones of Jurassic and Cretaceous age, with few recognizable horizons apart from an *Orbitolina* clay and bauxite developments (both reminiscent of Provence) in the Lower Cretaceous. There are probably many concealed breaks in this succession, for it all seems to be of shallow-water origin, although the 5000 m or more of Mesozoic limestones imply that it was subsiding as fast as the supposed troughs on either side. Although seemingly autochthonous, Italian geologists postulate a considerable thrusting of this zone to the north-east (presumably once more on a Triassic evaporite polish) and a series of major thrusts have been recognized, running roughly parallel to the present coasts, the outermost of which forms the scarp of the Gran Sasso itself. The limestones are cut by a series of dextral wrench faults, occurring very late in the tectonic story. These trend north or north-east, parallel to the Anzio–Ancona Line.

Thin limestones and other sediments of Palaeogene age are only found along the margins of the carbonate area, mainly towards the north-east. The Mesozoic is again generally followed by transgressive Miocene which includes flysch and olistostromes full of blocks of earlier material. Tectonism was continuing. But—as in so many parts of the Mediterranean—the Miocene ended with the thick evaporites of the Messinian, when the western Tethys, which was to be the Mediterranean, dried out, with disastrous results for its organic population.

Lagonegro Zone. Finally, mainly on the east side of the Apennines, comes what has been called the 'External Flysch Zone' where we are back in a largely eugeosynclinal facies along a belt that runs south from the Abruzzi limestone hills to the west part of the 'instep' of Italy in Lucania. How this belt is related to the others already described is still a matter for dispute, but the succession is distinctive; it is commonly called the 'Calcareous–Siliceous Sequence' but is best defined geographically rather than lithologically as the *Lagonegro Zone*. It is highly allochthonous, overturned and sliced, with developments of olistostromes to confuse the situation further.

Its allochthonous nature complicates our view of what went before, since there is evidence (although this has been disputed like everything else in the Apennines) that this zone has been overthrust by the rocks of the Carbonate Chain described above. Much of it, however, is comparable with the rocks of the Inner Flysch Zone and may be tectonically continuous with the inner belt. This includes developments of *argille scagliose* type of olistostromes, many of which may have been redeposited (possibly several times).

It is the easternmost manifestation of the Apennines proper and, with its underground extension, immediately borders the Pede–Apenninic Trough, filled with post-orogenic sediments, which probably rest on an autochthonous carbonate platform. This was discussed in Chapter 15(a).

The term 'Lagonegro Zone' is just a convenient shorthand (probably disapproved of by the locals) to include both the allochthonous successions mentioned above and what may be called the main succession of this zone, which is equally allochthonous, but different in character. This is basically a carbonate sequence and has been called a 'miogeosynclinal trough' as distinct from the 'miogeosynclinal platform' of the Carbonate Chain. It contains abundant chert and other siliceous sediments of a deeper water facies.

Dolomitic Middle Trias with chert passes up into possible Jurassic, although the greater part of that system consists of siliceous shales and radiolarities. These pass into flysch which persists to the top of the Lower Cretaceous. Shallower water deposits come in in the Upper Cretaceous, including rudist reefs comparable with those in the previous zone. Then, in the Tertiary, this became a region of sandstones, conglomerates, olistostromes, and further flysch deposits, right up into the Miocene, indicating the continuance of active tectonism.

We are left therefore with a confusing picture, which is too complicated to put into a few words here. Attempts have been made to recognize succeeding ridges and troughs as separate palaeogeographical entities across a mobile belt where almost nothing seems to be in place. The only certainties are that, as in the northern Apennines, there is more ocean-floor type of material in the west, coming from that direction. Unlike the northern Apennines, there was an extensive carbonate platform farther east and also a carbonate trough, tectonically interwoven. We known that, farther east again and possibly overridden by the above elements was an autochthonous carbonate platform (the Apulian Platform) which is part of the Adriatic story. Whether we are entitled as some geologists would wish us, to postulate several platforms and several troughs is much less certain, although I prefer Occamian simplicity in the absence of definite evidence to the contrary.

Scattered through the southern Apennines, as in the north, are Plio-Pleistocene basins filled with post-orogenic sediments and fossils that some find particularly exciting but most geologists unfortunately prefer to ignore. Also not to be forgotten is the volcanism of the Rome and Naples regions (and the islands to the west) which were described in Chapter 15(g).

Calabrian Massif. The 'toe' of Italy—the province of Calabria and southernmost Lucania—is largely occupied by a disturbed Variscan massif. It is a little-visited corner of Europe, full of hot beaches and forested hills, with man chiefly in evidence from his vast olive groves and his high-perched fortified towns and Norman castles.

The massif is a direct continuation of the Peloritan Massif, across the Straits of Messina in north-east Sicily. The fault that separates the two is probably less important than the sinistral wrench of the Catanzaro Trench which cuts across the 'toe' and separates the two main outcrops of ancient rocks.

There is a pre-Variscan basement of granulites that were re-altered along with late Palaeozoic sediments at the end of that era. The greater part of the exposed basement seems to be metamorphosed Devonian and Carboniferous sediment, with just enough fossils to make it respectable, together with late Carboniferous granitoid intrusions of which the most important is that which forms La Sila, nearly 2000 m high and the highest point in Calabria.

The Calabrian Massif is just one of a series of 'highs' in an arc around the Tyrrhenian Sea and there seems to be no reason to regard it as a special entity or as a 'microplate' that went its own peculiar way. Many of the great massifs of Europe are nothing more than bare patches in the Mesozoic carpet, but in this case it is not just the floor showing through, it is a splinter of a floorboard that has been kicked up to rest on top of a very worn floor-covering. In other words it is allochthonous and a series of nappes have been recognized here, as in the rest of the Apennines, distinguishable by their degrees of metamorphism.

This is not to say that Calabria has not been a positive area for a very long time. This is testified to by the thin and scattered cover of Mesozoic and Cainozoic rocks that surround and overlie the large areas of Palaeozoic metamorphics. There is no Trias here and the rest of the Mesozoic is thin and continental or very shallow marine. In Eocene times the oldest, granulitic rocks were thrust east over the late Palaeozoic sequence and that in turn (with its thin carbonate cover) over the Mesozoic confusion of the Inner Flysch Zone. It was overthrust in turn by *argille scagliose* type sediments coming from the west.

In the south, the Calabrian Massif borders the pre-Apennine fore-deep and the main impression when driving along the coast road is of hills draped in late Tertiary soft white marls, famous for their microfossils. Late uplifting of the area made it what it is today and Quaternary sediments are more than 1000 m thick. The Catanzaro Trench is also a geologically recent feature, reminiscent of the similarly trending Campidano rift of Sardinia.

The distinguishing features of Calabria are, first, the presence of ancient rocks in the Apennine story (a feature that continues into Sicily and North Africa); second, the lateness of the Mesozoic transgression here (not until early Jurassic times); and third, the early date (i.e., Eocene) of the start of Tertiary thrusting.

Northern Apennines

This section covers the old provinces of Tuscany, Liguria, Umbria, and Latium and constitutes the northern Apennines with their legacy of remarkable ideas, in civilization as well as in geology (Fig. 16.5). Here Leonardo da Vinci noted marine creatures on mountain tops and here were developed the geological schools of Florence (Firenze), Pisa, and Bologna, with their very original ideas.

No doubt a modern Italian geologist would tell me to forget the heady delights of tectonic wedges and submarine landslipping, but I would like to mention them here at least briefly. Partly this is because I was particularly influenced by these ideas at an impressionable stage in my geological development and partly because they had so much influence on geological thought in the rest of the world. It would be a pity to throw out the baby (whose name perhaps is *argille scagliose*) with the bath-water of successive tectonic ridges.

These ideas may be introduced through the words of an American reviewer who worked in the area himself: 'To a geologist educated in the United States, the Apennines would seem to be made of improbable rocks, arranged in improbable structural forms, and explained by utterly improbable hypotheses'. Nevertheless, the writer concerned seemed to be convinced of the validity of the interpretation.

The oldest rocks seen at the surface are of late Palaeozoic age with rare fossils (mainly plants) and usually more or less metamorphosed. The highest of these rocks is a distinc-

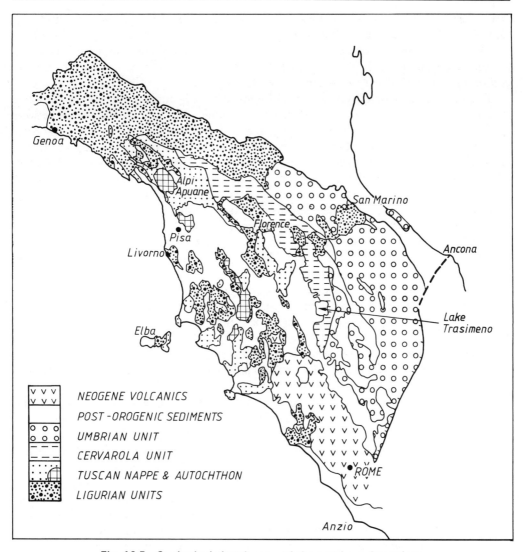

Fig. 16.5 Geological sketch-map of the northern Apennines.

tive pebbly grit or conglomerate—the Verrucano—which is thought to be of Permian age. The term 'Verrucano' is used all over southern Europe for conglomerates at about this level, but here we can be sure of it, because we are in the type area. It takes its name from Mount Verruca (or 'wart'), where the conglomerates stand up steeply as an isolated hill, south of Pisa. The Verrucano is taken as a convenient marker for the top of the Palaeozoic and may represent the Palaeozoic Tethys at its minimum extent before the renewed transgressions of the Triassic.

The main Mesozoic succession began with thick late Triassic carbonates containing a sparse marine fauna. Gypsiferous beds are only seen at one or two places at the surface, most notably above the village of Sassalbo, near Collagna on the way up to the Cerreto

Pass. The original deposits probably took the form of alternating bands of dolomite and anhydrite. The latter was hydrated to gypsum and then commonly dissolved away to produce a collapsed dolomitic breccia, the *Calcare cavernoso*. This distinctive lithology is readily recognized all over the northern Apennines and may be compared with the *cargneule* of the Alps and *carniola* of the Betics.

The Triassic carbonates were followed by massive early Jurassic limestones without a break. It was long maintained that there were virtually no stratigraphical breaks between the Norian transgression of the late Triassic and the sudden change in sedimentation at the end of the Oligocene. Many stratigraphical breaks had been postulated in the past and to me a succession without breaks is as rare as a man without faults. But these breaks were all reinterpreted as tectonic in origin. Massive limestones dominate the top of the Trias and the lower part of the Lower Jurassic. Near the west coast, notably in the Alpi Apuane, metamorphism has transformed the Triassic limestone into the dazzling white Carrara Marble, which for many years supplied the world with statues, tombstones, and now obsolete wash-stands. Around Carrara and Massa, on the west front of the beautiful Alpi Apuane range, the marble gives many mountains a snow-capped appearance.

Above the massive and supposedly shallow-water limestones of the earliest Jurassic come more thinly bedded limestones with chert nodules that range up through the Middle Jurassic. The sea was deepening. By late Jurassic times the succession had graded up into radiolarian cherts (the *Diaspri*) and siliceous limestones which are thought to have been deposited at considerable depths. This story is continued into the Cretaceous with varicoloured shales, the *Scaglia* or *Scisti policromi*, which have all the characteristics of many Tethyan deposits that are alleged to have been deposited in deep water. *Scaglia*-type deposition was thought to have continued all through the Cretaceous, the Paleocene, the Eocene, and the greater part of the Oligocene. One of the outstanding features of this story is the small amount of sediment that was thought to have accumulated, without breaks, through a considerable period of geological time. Nevertheless, fossils are surprisingly rare, no doubt testifying to its deep-water origin.

The great event in the history of the Apennines, according to this interpretation, was the sudden change in sedimentation that occurred in mid Oligocene times. This was heralded by a thin, but very persistent bed, the *Brecciole nummulitiche*, which is a brecciated limestone full of the broken tests of large formas. This was followed by the most famous formation in north Italy, the *Macigno*. It is chiefly famous because it was in the Macigno that Migliorini first clearly recognized and described deposition by turbidity currents, leading to the famous joint paper with Kuenen who had arrived at the same idea by a different route. The formation consists of coarse feldspathic greywackes, sometimes conglomeratic, occurring in thick graded beds. Single units in the Macigno are said to exceed 20 m in thickness in places and the whole formation may amount to more than 3000 m. This is in spite of the fact that the whole Macigno was deposited within late Oligocene and earliest Miocene times. It must be compared with little more than 100 m in places for the whole record from the late Jurassic to the early Miocene. Obviously something fundamental happened at this point in time, with the change from gentle, slow, fine-grained deposition to turbulent, rapidly deposited, coarse-grained sediments. What had happened, of course, was the beginning of the Alpine orogeny.

As a source of this sediment, the Italians postulated a major land-mass in the Tyrrhenian Sea, west of the present coastline. This land-mass was not thought to have subsided until Quaternary times, leaving perhaps as its only remnant the Napoleonic island of Elba. It should be noted that the metamorphism mentioned above is confined to a narrow strip along the coast, including Elba and a few other islands and the north-east edge of Corsica, which was discussed earlier. The metamorphism of the Carrara Marble has been blamed simply on sedimentary overburden, but elsewhere—for example in the Monti di Campiglia—similar marbles are seen within the contact aureole of an intrusive, fine-grained granite. It seems that a more general cause must be sought for the alteration of great thicknesses of sediment.

Fairly early on in the Oligocene, therefore, there began the main orogeny of the Apennines. It went on with decreasing force until at least as late as the early Pleistocene. During that time, starting with the Macigno, great thicknesses of synorogenic and post-orogenic sediments accumulated in the Apennine region. These go under various names and include huge thicknesses of molasse-type deposits.

Now we come to the much more controversial part of the story. According to the Migliorini–Merla school, the orogeny expressed itself in the successive uplift of six or seven ridges. These run roughly from north-west to south-east, parallel to the present coastlines of peninsular Italy, and several of them remain as topographic features. It is important to remember that they are thought of as *successive* tectonic ridges; the oldest (i.e., the one that came up first) was that in the south-west, nearest the Tyrrhenian Sea. The others are progressively younger to the north-east, and are numbered accordingly. It is possible that there may have been an even earlier ridge than No. 1, but offshore and now sunk with the old land-mass in the Tyrrhenian Sea.

Each ridge was thought to be based on a special structure, known as a 'composite wedge'. These are essentially bundles of faults, converging downwards, and in each case steeper on the south-west side of the ridge. They were compressional structures and emerged as topographical features as a result of later isostatic readjustment.

All the sediments described so far were regarded as autochthonous. However, with the orogeny there arrived in the region that is now the Italian peninsula an allochthonous series of sediments and associated volcanics that had travelled, by purely tectonic agencies, far from their original place of accumulation. These rocks were said to be completely unknown within the autochthon. Now this allochthon had, of course, long been known to Italian geologists. At one time it was thought merely to be a peculiar series of Tertiary rocks, resting unconformably on all that went before. The usual interpretation, however, was that these highly disturbed rocks constituted a great nappe—the 'Ligurid Nappe'—comparable with those of the Alps.

The Migliorini–Merla school produced a new type of interpretation, which did not involve great overthrusts and foreshortening. They suggested instead a great series of submarine landslips, starting in the south-west and carried forward by the rise of successive tectonic ridges. Only a slight elevation was needed for slipping to begin in both directions, but it would be mainly forwards, i.e., towards the north-east. So the allochthonous material went switchbacking across Italy from ridge to ridge, until it finally stopped beyond Leonardo's Firenze.

The other important concept involved in this hypothesis is the nature of the allochthon. The greater part of it is the *argille scagliose* ('scaly clays'). It consists of the shattered remains of an argillaceous formation that has tumbled and slid along from ridge to ridge until it has lost almost all trace of its original form. Contained within it are exotic blocks, ranging in size from pebbles to mountains, and all carried far from their original situation. Most of them cannot (or so the hypothesis says) be recognized within the autochthon, and it is assumed that they came from unknown outcrops where there is now the Tyrrhenian Sea. The age of the exotic blocks varies considerably, hence the long uncertainty over the age of the *argille scagliose*. Some, such as the Alberesi Limestone, are as young as Eocene; others, such as the Pietraforte Sandstone, contain Cretaceous fossils. Most significant are the suite of pillow lavas, serpentinites, and associated rocks, which are certainly of Jurassic age. It can be shown that these allochthonous blocks decrease in size and abundance towards the north-east. This shows up particularly well for the ophiolite suite. If one drives along the coast road south of Livorno (Leghorn), one cannot fail to see the great masses of serpentinite close to their Tyrrhenian source. But to the north-east the mountains become blocks and the blocks become pebbles.

As the allochthon moved onwards as submarine landslips, more sediment was deposited on top. So this later sediment was itself transported progressively shorter distances. Thus Oligocene sediments are thought to have been carried up to 120 km, Miocene sediments about 50 km, and Pliocene only about 5 km. At one place in the north Apennines, the *argille scagliose* is said to rest on Lower Pleistocene deposits. This is the latest datable horizontal movement. It must not be forgotten that vertical movements also played an important part in the process and only the last Pleistocene glaciation appears to have affected the Apennines. Since this last glacial advance was a comparatively minor one, it can be assumed that it was only in the last phase of the Pleistocene that the Apennine mountains reached a sufficient height to carry their own glaciers.

As the ridges rose isostatically, so the valleys between became filled with late Cainozoic lake deposits. Pliocene land floras and faunas are widespread and the Geology Department at the University of Florence is filled with a magnificent collection of the Pleistocene elephants and other large mammals that lived in the area before the Medicis.

The importance of these ideas lies not only in their local application, but in their worldwide implications. Even if much of the hypothesis is not now thought to be tenable in the Apennines, there are aspects of it which are certainly universal. Most important perhaps is the idea that mountain chains can be produced without very much in the way of crustal shortening. This must be awarded the convenient Scottish compromise verdict of 'not proven'. Submarine landslipping, with the production of *argille scagliose* type of deposits, however, are now recognized everywhere, literally from Peru to Timor.

Much was written in the 'sixties and 'seventies that takes us back to a more conventional interpretation of Apennine tectonics in terms of nappes. Before considering that, it is worth commenting on the contrast between the autochthonous sediments described above and the allochthonous rocks, whatever their mode of transport. These fit in very clearly with pre-plate-tectonic geosynclinal theory.

The autochthon, with its thick Triassic and Jurassic carbonates and its complete lack of contemporaneous volcanicity, would be an 'external miogeosyncline'. The subsequent thin deposition through late Mesozoic and early Tertiary times reminds one of the 'starved' geosynclines of the Alps ('leptogeosynclines'), as in the Briançonnais Zone in south-east France. The allochthon, with its thick argillaceous successions, its few limestones, and its well-developed ophiolite suite, would clearly come from an 'internal eugeosyncline' in the Tyrrhenian Sea. This interpretation makes sense when one relates the northern Apennines to neighbouring regions.

The structural nature of the allochthon is another matter, and recent thought has reinterpreted the whole, not as a single 'Ligurid Nappe', but as a pile of nappes as in most of the other Alpine chains. The general picture is of the highest nappes being the most 'internal' in origin (i.e., to the south-west) and having moved first. The main units are as follows, from top to bottom. Ligurian Units, Tuscan Nappe, Tuscan Autochthon and Parautochthon, Cervarola Unit, and Umbrian Unit.

The *argille scagliose*, although now regarded as an imprecise sack term, would seem to apply to chaotic olistostrome-type deposits belonging to either the Ligurid or Tuscan nappes. They are still thought of as landslip deposits of predominantly argillaceous sediments and there is still an acceptable story of progressive displacement and redeposition towards the north-east, sometimes carrying less deformed units on top of the sliding masses.

The Ligurian units generally include much of this *argille scagliose* type of material, but they are basically a series of allochthonous slices of eugeosynclinal material, including great quantities of ophiolites. These are of Jurassic age, as in so many other places, and must be taken to be a wedge of ocean-floor material thrust up from the Tyrrhenian Sea to the west. Associated *schistes lustrés* type of sediments, flysch, cherts, and *Calpionella* limestones range up into the Cretaceous.

The Tuscan Nappe is overriden by the Ligurids (which evidently moved last) but came apart itself at the level of the Triassic evaporites. It lies generally within the extensive Liguride country, on the south-west side of the range, but disappears completely below the Ligurian nappes up towards Genoa. The succession ranges from the late Triassic to the *Macigno*, but its general thinness seems to indicate a starved ridge to the north-east of the Ligurid trough. Nevertheless, material from the Ligurids is incorporated in the top of the succession, although the main sediment source seems to be from the Alps to the north-west. A ridge may have moved with time towards the north-east, as in the older theories, so that the Tuscan Ridge of late Triassic times is buried beneath a much thicker Jurassic and Cretaceous succession.

This is not to be confused with the more or less autochthonous sequences of the Alpe Apuane and Monte Pisano, which have been called the 'Tuscan Backbone'. This forms a solid dominating ridge, near the west coast, which comes up as a window through the Tuscan Nappe and includes the famous metamorphic rocks of Carrara and neighbourhood. It has its granitic basement with a Variscan lineation, and passes up into Tertiary flysch. The succession generally is similar to that of the allochthonous unit above, but is metamorphosed as a result of its hard life under the main weight of the Apennines. On either side of the main autochthonous block, notably around Massa, there is a zone of parautochthonous, low-grade metamorphic rocks which have been carried over earlier units.

The comparatively small Cervarola Unit takes its name from Monte Cervarola in the centre of the range, where a broad arc of mountains above Arezzo forms the outer rim of the Tuscan Nappe. It is seen around Lake Trasimeno (where Hannibal's elephants were so successful), although the Tertiary flysch which constitutes most of the unit tends to form irregular, densely wooded country. The sediments were probably originally deposited on the outer, north-eastern side of the Tuscan autochthon but moved in their turn to overlie the outermost Umbrian Unit, at least at its innermost edge.

Although the term 'Umbrian Arc' is used, rather confusingly, to cover the whole of the Northern Apennines, the Umbrian Unit refers just to the broad arc of country east of Perugia, forming the Umbrian and Marchigiano Apennines and the front of the whole range. Again detachment seems to have occurred at the Upper Triassic level. The succession generally is shallow water in origin and has probably not moved far, for it belongs near where it is found, on the north-east side of the great wedge of Apennine sediment. At the top there is developed the sandy flysch known as the *Marnosa arenacea*, of Miocene age, passing into molasse and part of the great infill of the front furrow of the Apennines. This is the last expression of the wave of thick sedimentation that moved across the Apennines through Mesozoic and Tertiary times, although, as with the other units, sediment transport seems to have been longitudinal, from the north-west, rather than normal to the rising ridges. That the Umbrian Unit is not itself autochthonous is shown by the way, at its southern edge, it overthrusts the units which are part of the Southern Apennines.

The above is a gross oversimplification of a complex story, which involved (for example) some backwards movements as well as the general thrusting to the north-east. But perhaps the best demonstration of the whole story is provided by the huge detached slab of Ligurian rocks which rests on the latest Umbrian Unit at the front of the range and includes the whole of the oldest and smallest republic in the world—San Marino.

Finally, concerning the Apennines as a whole it is worth repeating a general comment on their similarity (if one ignores age) to the Scandinavian Caledonides. In both cases we have to postulate ocean floor being destroyed to the west and being pushed eastwards on to a rigid basement. No one, however, has found it necessary to postulate anything like the present Atlantic Ocean out in the Tyrrhenian Sea. This suggests to me that such an ocean is not needed either west of early Palaeozoic Norway.

16(d)   Southern Alps

The Southern Alps are defined as that part of the main Alpine chain that lies south of the major suture known as the Insubric Line (and also by such aliases as Canavese, Tonale, Giudicarie, Pusteria and Gailtal Lines). 'Lines' are a great feature of Italian geology, like 'accidents' in France and 'disturbances' in South Wales. This line, one of the most important sutures in Europe, can be seen at many places sharply separating very different geological regimes. Thus along the valley of the River Adda (which flows into Lake Como) it separates low-grade mica schists of the Southern Alps from high-grade gneisses which are thought to be the roots of the Austro-Alpides. It is well seen from Aprica Pass. Not far away, near Delebio, white Triassic dolomites provide a clear marker in the hillside for the south side of the razor-sharp line, which is probably a very ancient structure.

The Southern Alps lie east and south of the Pennine Alps in the west, and south of the Austro-Alpine Alps in the east (Fig. 16.6). They are not synonymous with the 'Italian Alps' because that country also possesses a fine sweep of Western Alps along its frontier with France and because the Southern Alps also creep into southern Switzerland and Austria.

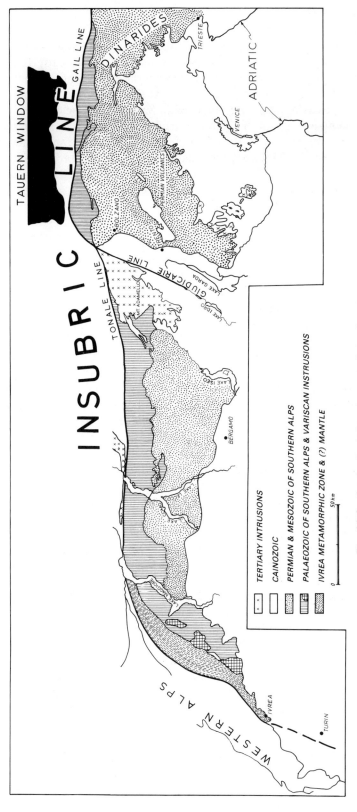

Fig. 16.6 Geological sketch-map of the Southern Alps.

They are theoretically separated from the Apennines by the Sestri–Voltaggio Line, but in fact they disappear under the young sediments of the Lombardy Basin long before reaching that feature, which is only seen at the surface throwing into juxtaposition the opposite-facing Pennine Alps and Apennines. At their opposite end they pass into the Dinarides of Yugoslavia, which are discussed in Section 16(e) below.

The outstanding features of the Southern Alps, compared with the sterner Alps to the north, are their ramifying lakes, their well-preserved Palaeozoic succession, the unmeta-morphosed state of the Mesozoic with its distinctive faunas, and the turnover of the Alpine structures from north-facing to south-facing. They may be divided into the regions west and east of the Giudicarie Line, which branches off from the main Insubric Line and runs down west of Lake Garda.

West of the Giudicarie Line

Basement. Metamorphosed basement rocks are seen in an 'external' position, close to the Insubric suture and also in the most 'internal' of the structures of the Southern Alps. In the first category came the rocks of the Ivrea area, which one sees as soon as one hits the mountains west of Milan (Milano) or north of Turin (Torino). From here they run in a broad belt northwards to near Locarno in Switzerland (at the north end of Lake Maggiore). They consist of high-grade gneisses, granulites, and amphibolites and have been interpreted as deep continental crust. Slices of periodotite come up between them and the Canavese Line (as it is here called). These are seen, for example, in the Ossola Valley, near the frontier town of Domodossola, and are thought to have come from even deeper—in the mantle itself. There is a considerable gravity anomaly—the 'Ivrea body'—just south of the mountains, which is thought to represent such mantle material. The line here is complex and the rocks on the far side are also high-grade gneisses, although of the Austro-Alpine unit which also travelled far to the north. The granulite metamorphism is said to be Caledonian in age, although the magmatism represented by the amphibolite has been dated as Variscan.

Metamorphic rocks are also seen more 'internally' around the lovely lakes of Maggiore, Lugano, and Como in the form of mica-schists and paragneiss up to amphibolite grade. These also are thought to be Caledonian, although they are cut by Variscan intrusions of which the most famous is that at Baveno on Lake Maggiore, which gives its name to the system of crystal twinning. They are accompanied by Permian rhyolitic lava flows and some andesite.

Similar rocks are seen in the Strona–Ceneri area, where Caledonian metamorphism is more provable, since its orthogneisses, migmatites, and granites, were re-affected by amphibolite-grade metamorphism in the Variscan orogeny.

Cover. The cover rocks in this western region range through Triassic limestones and dolomites with shallow-water faunas and floras, black Rhaetian like north-west Europe, Lower Jurassic *rosso ammonitico** and massive limestones, Middle and Upper Jurassic radiolarites to Lower Cretaceous pelagic limestones. Much of this is displayed at the roadside above the village of Sogno, south-east of Lecco. Although the latter part suggests deep water, there is rapid lateral thinning over 'palaeo-highs'. Thus 5000 m of Lias

---

* As we are now in Italy it is time to explain that, since this is an Italian expression, it should be given in the correct Italian grammatical form, *rosso ammonitico*, and not transposed as has so long been the custom.

in Monte Generoso is down to less than 100 m a short distance to the east. There is also no sign of ophiolite-type magmatism, although there is a little volcanic material within the Triassic limestones.

The cover rests unconformably on Permian rhyolites or on what are taken to be late Palaeozoic continental deposits. It is completely unaffected by Alpine metamorphism and has magnificent fossils such as the huge megalodontids around the ski resort of Cortina d'Ampezzo. In its healthy state it contrasts markedly with the *schistes lustrés* and associated rocks of the adjacent Pennine Alps.

These cover rocks outcrop generally in a broad belt south of the metamorphics, from about the centre of Lake Maggiore across the southern, forking part of Lake Como to the Giudicarie Line, which runs down the valley holding Lake Idro, heading directly for Brescia. Southwards is a narrow belt of molasse which marks the southern edge of the Alps.

A Tertiary pluton forms Mount Adamello in the north-east corner of the region. This vast instrusion, covering some 550 km^2, gives its name to the granodioritic rock *adamellite*. It terminates against the Tonaale Line to the north, also recognized by the related rock-type *tonalite* which, along with ordinary granodiorite, forms the major part of the intrusion. The Adamello batholith also terminates against the Giudicarie Line to the east, so it predated both branches of the Insubric Line, at least in their present representation. It has been dated radiometrically as 30–45 million years and is probably related to extensive Oligocene volcanism, which can also be dated by fossiliferous tuffs. Similar intrusives, such as that of Masino Brigalia (with a sheer face popular with rock-climbers), are found immediately on the north side of the Insubric Line.

Structurally, as the broad distribution of outcrops imply, this is a southerly dipping succession. A great flexure is seen all along the Southern Alps, for example behind Donizetti's home town of Bergamo, with the succession turning over to the south in a steep monocline (known as a *piaga a ginacchio* or 'knee-fold'). Geophysical surveys show that there are further such folds buried under the plain, for example below Milan.

The earlier Caledonian and Variscan trends are difficult to determine but the main Tertiary folding is undoubtedly directed towards the south. This can be seen in the recumbent folds of Monte Generosa on the east side of Lake Lugano. Farther east a major southerly thrust is beautifully displayed on the east side of Lake Como (Fig. 16.7).

In the southernmost structures there is Cretaceous flysch, but this disappears again in borings south of Milan, going back to the usual limestones. There is an almost perfect match stratigraphically between the Lombardy Basin, at the west end of the Southern Alps, and the first successions in the northern Apennines. An important difference is the absence of anything that can be called ocean floor in the Southern Alps. There are plenty of radiolarites and such like, which most geologists there still accept as deep-water deposits, but this was a marginal basin rather than an ocean. Only in the western part of the northern Apennines do real ophiolite suites appear.

Special mention should be made of the lakes, long famous for their beauty, their glaciated sides, and the moraines damming their southern ends. What has only been recognized comparatively recently, however, is that they are far too deep to be blamed wholly on glacial down-cutting. The floor of Lake Garda, for example, is as much as 100 m below present sea-level. It is now thought by some Italian geologists that they were deeply entrenched at the time of the Messinian drying out of the Mediterranean in late

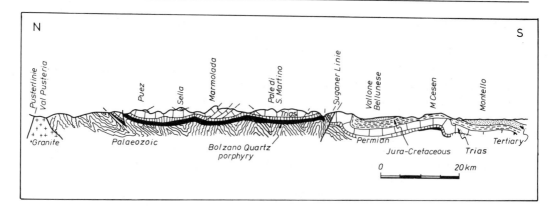

Fig. 16.7 *Cross-section of the Southern Alps through Lake Como (after Gwinner, 1971, by kind permission of Schweizererbart'sche Verlag).*

Miocene times. It still remains to be proved if the deep rocky trenches contain Pliocene as well as Pleistocene material. Scenically they would outrank the Grand Canyon of Arizona, if it were not for the geologically recent debris that has accumulated in their bottoms!

East of the Giudicarie Line

Although the lakes of the western part of the Southern Alps have their attractions, they can hardly compare with the scenic (and geologic) marvels of the Dolomites, the Carnic Alps, and the Julian Alps, in the east.

Basement. Metamorphosed basement rocks are known chiefly in two areas: 'externally' along the bend in the Insubric Line (here called the Pusteria Line) north of Bolzano (Bozen), and 'internally' east of Trento (Trent). They also underlie the known Palaeozoic in the western part of the Carnic Alps. They consist of schists and gneisses of various types, amphibolites, quartzites, and crystalline limestones. As in the west, an early 'Caledonian' metamorphism has been claimed in some areas (e.g., at Bressanone, north-east of Bolzano), but the main phenomenon was end-Palaeozoic, at least in the areas where there are no overlying Palaeozoic sediments to deny it. The effects were mainly dynamic and low-grade thermal in nature.

In the Carnic Alps, the problem is more difficult, since the oldest unmetamorphosed sediments are late Ordovician in age. It has been assumed that the Caledonian came early in these parts, in early Ordovician times. However, there are close resemblances between some of these sequences and proven Silurian in Austria and the basal contact of the fossiliferous Carnic succession is always tectonic.

A problem that does seem to have been solved is the age of the vast quantity of quartz porphyry that one can hardly miss after crossing the Brenner Pass and heading towards Bolzano, especially in the vertical-sided gorge between that bilingual city and Auer (Ora) to the south. At least it was always called quartz porphyry and it looks like quartz porphyry to me (as a palaeontologist), but we are told now that we should call it 'rhyolitic and rhyodacitic ignimbrite'. This 'Bolzano Porphyry Plateau' (as I shall still call it) covers 4000 km², the lavas and associated tuffs are said to reach 1500 m in thickness. They were formerly thought to be late Ordovician to early Silurian in age, by analogy with Austria, but (to be rather unscientific) they certainly look much younger than that! It has now been shown that they cap the Variscan metamorphism and are probably correlatable with late Carboniferous or Permian continental deposits in the fossiliferous sequence of the Carnic Alps. I cannot resist commenting again on the coincidence of very similar porphyries of Permian age occurring in the Oslo Graben.

Palaeozoic and Triassic of the Carnic Alps. This unique area of well-preserved sediments lies immediately south of the Insubric Line (now the Gailtal Line) right along the Austrian–Italian frontier west of Villach. The succession is remarkably complete, from the Upper Ordovician through to the Upper Triassic, the only significant break being in the middle of the Carboniferous. Thus on the Gartnerkofel, just inside the south-east corner of Austria, I have seen the only section I know in Europe with marine Permian passing up into marine Triassic.

Apart from an episode of graptolitic shales in the lower part of the Silurian, the succession from the Caradoc through to the Dinantian is almost wholly shallow marine limestones, with rich shelly faunas and a notable development of reefs in the usual place in the Middle and Upper Devonian. There are variations, from thin developments over 'palaeo-highs' to thicker, more thin-bedded developments in between. The whole succession is thought to pass eastwards into a deeper water, shaly facies in the Karawanken range, south of Klagenfurt on the Austrian–Yugoslav border.

The break in the middle of the Carboniferous may account for a large part of the Dinantian. Only in the eastern Carnic Alps and in Karawanken is the Dinantian preserved, in a shaly, conglomeratic facies. The uppermost Carboniferous may include some Westphalian, but is largely Stephanian in the usual Alpine pattern. It is dominantly of a non-marine facies with plant remains, coal-seams, and many levels of conglomerate, giving clear evidence of an Asturian phase of the Variscan orogeny.

Similar beds alternate with marine limestones in the lower parts of the Permian, but then massive limestones and dolomites return to dominate the story through to the Norian, with large fusulinid forams in the uppermost Permian and well-known formations such as the *Dachsteinkalk* in the Trias, all reminding us of the warm waters of a southern Tethys.

Cover. The main 'cover' rocks in the Alpine sense, i.e., the Mesozoic (apart from the Trias just mentioned), have to be sought elsewhere, notably in the fantastic scenery of the Dolomites. For anyone who has not seen them they are hard to believe, with their skylines of finials and buttresses that outdo the local baroque style. This topography develops on the Triassic carbonates which dominate the succession, especially the Norian *Dolomia principale* (the familiar *Hamptdolomit* of the Eastern Alps).

However, the succession starts down in the Permian, with conglomerates and breccias, naturally called *Verrucano*, resting on the quartz porphyry. These are followed by sandstones with plants, and a mixed bag of shales, gypsum, *Rauhwacken*, and thin marine limestones, in the Upper Permian. Conditions continued variable through early and middle Triassic times with marine and non-marine deposits, local conglomerates, evaporites, and a remarkable build-up of organic 'reefs' in the Middle Trias of the 'Adige ridge' in the Dolomites. Conditions only really became stable and uniform with the development of the massive *Hauptdolomit*. Instability returned with the Early Jurassic, although a prominent feature on the 'palaeo-highs' was Austrian-type *Hierlatzkalk*. Thicknesses vary up to six-fold on and between the 'highs'. Then at last, evidently, conditions became deeper with *rosso ammonitico* and cherty *Scaglia*-type deposits through to the later Cretaceous, although banks of rudists were not far away and notable organic build-ups occurred in the vicinity of the Carnic Alps.

Farther south, notably in the Giudicarie Alps, on the west side of Lake Garda, massive dolomites persisted through from the Anisian to the Rhaetian and there are terrestrial deposits with plants in the Lower Jurassic. It would seem, on the whole, to have been shallower this way. But from mid Jurassic time onwards the situation was more or less the same. Flysch deposition began everywhere right at the end of the Cretaceous and continued until nearly the end of the Oligocene, when it was followed by molasse.

East of the Venice meridian, and most notably in the Julian Alps on the Yugoslav frontier, the stratigraphy becomes more and more comparable with that in the Dinarides, described in Section 16(e) below. The palaeogeographic trends swing to a north-westerly direction in keeping with that range. The Italians would say that the Southern Alps extend to Ljubljana and (as inliers) to Zagreb.

The volcanism, which was such a feature of the northern part of this area at the end of the Palaeozoic times, returned in the Middle Triassic with acid intrusions and extrusions along the 'Adige ridge'. There was more intense magmatic activity in the Palaeogene and earliest Neogene, comparable with that in the region west of the Giudicarie Line. It is most obvious in the hills west and south of Vicenza, and close to Padova (Padua), almost on the Venetian plain.

Structually the region is simple (for the Alps), apart from the many nappes that have been postulated (and mostly disproved) within the crystalline basement. Broad open structures are the rule for the cover; these resulted from rather weak folding episodes from early Triassic times onwards. The major structures are mainly late Tertiary in age and are in the form of gravity-sliding phenomena. Many features in the Mesozoic succession that were formerly thought to be tectonic in origin are now recognized as sedimentary slumping effects along the steep sides of troughs between the 'palaeo-highs'.

The most interesting structural feature of the eastern part of the Southern Alps is that in the north (in the Carnic and Julian Alps and around Belluno) the folds and associated faults are directed towards the north and north-east, whereas in the south (from Brescia eastwards) there are gravity-impelled overthrusts directed towards the south and south-west. Some of these thrusts have moved several tens of kilometres, but all in geologically recent times, mainly in the Pliocene, and even in the early Pleistocene. All this is in keeping with the general pattern of mountain-building movements through the southern Alpine belt.

16(e) Dinarides

The Dinarides or Dinaric Alps are defined here as that part of the Alpine system which extends south-eastwards along the east coast of the Adriatic, linking the Southern Alps of northern Italy with the Hellenides of Albania and Greece. They take their name from Mount Dinara in Croatia, northern Yugoslavia, and occupy almost the whole of that country, apart from a corner of the Pannonian Basin in the north, a narrow strip of the Carpathians in the east, and the province of Macedonia in the south, which is best linked with the Hellenides. The term 'Dinarides' was originally used by Suess to include also the Hellenides, but as used here the dividing line is taken as the transverse structure that runs from Shkoder (Scutari*) near the coast in northern Albania, inland to Péc, on the edge of a little Neogene basin, just north of the Albanian border in Yugoslavia.

In a structural sense the Dinarides are a mirror-image of the Apennines of Italy, just as the Betics are a mirror-image of the Rif, but whereas the latter face outwards from each other, the Dinarides and Apennines face inwards and the structures in the Dinarides are all directed towards the south-west. In both cases the broad thrusts and folds are cut by late faulting on mainly north-west and north-east trending lines. Lithologically and stratigraphically the chains are very different, most obviously in the tremendous development of carbonates in the Dinarides, which give rise to their famous karst scenery.

Considering the chain in my usual way, from the 'inside' towards the 'outside' (i.e., in this case from north-east to south-west), they fall into eight tectonic and palaeogeographic zones (Fig. 16.8). These are as follows: Serbo-Macedonian Massif, Vardar Zone, Golija Zone, Serbian Zone, Bosnian Zone, High Karst Zone, Budva Zone, and Dalmatian Zone.

Serbo-Macedonian Massif

So far as the Dinarides are concerned this is a small area of metamorphic rocks along the west bank of the Morava River, which flows into the Danube below Belgrade and which separates the Dinarides from the southern Carpathians. It consists of a little northern mass and a larger southern one (that of Jastrebac) separated by the young sediments in the vicinity of Kruševac, near the Yugoslav–Bulgarian border. This continues south as a much larger massif in Macedonia and eastern Greece which will be considered under the Hellenides. It is bare, rather forbidding country, rather like the Massif Central, but locally industrialized (e.g., at Kosovska Mitrovica) due to local ore deposits.

The metamorphic rocks of the Serbo-Macedonian Massif stood up as a positive feature through most of Mesozoic time and perhaps Palaeozoic time also. What we see today can only be a small fragment of the foreland which provided not only the clastic sediments of the Dinaride troughs to the south-west, but also those of the southern Carpathians to the east. However, it must be borne in mind that the majority of the Dinaride sediments, apart from the flysch, are of calcium carbonate. In the south, like the other internal zones of the Dinarides, it is cut by a large boss of Miocene grandiorite near Priština. This belongs to a loop of such rocks all round the Adriatic.

Apart from the Kuršumliya flysch (which belongs to the topmost Cretaceous) the only later sediments are Neogene post-orogenic deposits which extend along the River Morava from the Pannonian Basin to the north. The Serbo-Macedonian Massif gives us a glimpse of the ancient massif which underlies the whole of that vast sedimentary accumulation.

The massif is a simple compressional horst. Its south-west margin is a high-angle reversed fault, locally passing upwards into a low-angled thrust, where it is pushed over

---

* Not to be confused with Florence Nightingale's headquarters of the same name on the Bosphorus.

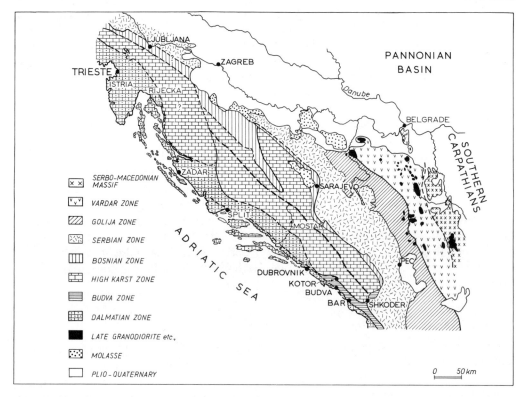

Fig. 16.8   Sketch-map of the main tectonic zones in the Dinarides (after Aubouin et al., 1970, by kind permission of Prof. Aubouin).

the volcanic rocks of the Vardar Zone. To the north-east it has a similar relationship (in the opposite direction) to the southern Carpathians.

The massif in general, therefore, represents a pinched-out fragment of continental crust between outwardly-facing orogenic zones. Presumably it can only be interpreted, in modern terms, as the southern corner or spur of a Pannonian–Transylvanian microplate. However, the sediments of the Pannonian Basin overstep far beyond the crystalline basement on to various zones of the Dinarides as far as the High Karst Zone in Croatia, for example, near Karlovac.

Vardar Zone

This is probably the most complex part of the Dinaric belt. It extends from the isolated massif of Fruška Gora to the north-west of Belgrade, south and west of the Yugoslav capital, down into Macedonia.

Most of the zone is dominated by Mesozoic volcanic rocks, but in the north-west, around Valjevo, there is a large area of metamorphosed Palaeozoic argillaceous sediments. This seems to represent an earlier, pre-Variscan, Dinaric trough that was metamorphosed before the beginning of the Alpine story. In fact the Vardar Zone was probably a trough during the greater part of its Phanerozoic history. It is separated from

494

similar Palaeozoic rocks in the Golija Zone to the south-west by a narrow strip of Mesozoics.

Resting unconformably on the Palaeozoic in the south-west are thin early and mid Triassic pelagic limestones and volcanics. But generally the Mesozoic succession starts with the so-called 'Diabase–radiolarite' Formation of Jurassic age. This includes great ophiolitic masses, especially in the west (e.g., in the Maljen Massif and along the valley of the Ibar). These rocks are extremely confused tectonically and there is still argument about their relationship to the underlying Triassic and Palaeozoic. They may be mainly autochthonous or they may be wholly allochthonous, but certainly there is evidence of an early (Kimmerian) phase of the Alpine orogeny. Whether or not it represents a sub-duction zone is a matter of taste, but the close association of 'basement' rocks must not be forgotten. There is now evidence of major lateral movements along the Vardar Zone.

The 'Diabase–radiolarite' Formation is older here than it is farther to the south-west. It is overlain by white Tithonian carbonates, both shallow-water reef limestones and deep-water *Calpionella* limestones. This relationship is frequently exposed along the valley of the Vardar, for example near Titov Veles. The later Jurassic beds are in turn overlain unconformably by Cretaceous (mostly late Cretaceous) shallow-water rudist limestones to the south-west and by pelitic flysch to the north-east. There is therefore evidence of two early phases of the Alpine movements in the inner Dinarides—probably mid to late Triassic and late early Cretaceous.

By the end of Cretaceous times, flysch sedimentation became general and spread into the Golija Zone to the south-west, but the earlier shallowing in that direction is significant in view of the general palaeogeographical picture. The outer edge of the Vardar Zone overrides the Golija Zone in a series of tectonic slices. Generally the Vardar ophiolites are seen overriding the late Cretaceous flysch of the Golija Zone towards the south-west. The zone was finally cooked and contorted by the emplacement of late Tertiary grandiorites, especially in the region of Novi Pazar, accompanied by volcanism of intermediate and basic composition. Such intrusives and extrusives also cut the Golija Zone and can be dated as post-orogenic, although it is possible that some intrusions were earlier.

Golija Zone

This is a comparatively small zone which extends from the region east of Péc in the south to the region of Zvornic in the north, where it disappears under the molasse basin of Tuzla and the main Pannonian Basin. In the south it abuts the crystalline massif east of Albania and in the north it divides into basement to the east and cover to the west. Basically it consists of a great anticline of Palaeozoic sediments which form the axis (usually hidden under hard-wood forests) and a fringing cover of Mesozoic sediments. It was persistently a 'high' in Dinaric geography.

The Trias starts with red beds which pass up into thick late Triassic and early Jurassic shallow-water carbonates, as can be seen along the main road south-west of Titovo Užice. These are followed by the usual Toarcian *rosso ammonitico* and then by radiolarites, breccias, and basic volcanics. This seems to represent a deepening succession like that of the northern Apennines. But it was its tendency to rise that made this zone distinctive and it may have become an island arc in Cretaceous times. The outstanding feature of the Golija Zone is a late Cretaceous transgression (generally Santonian, which is much later than usual). This cuts right across the Jurassic and Triassic down to the Palaeozoic basement, so this may well have been the axis of the early Dinarides. It seems that the Golija anticlinal structure rose during late Cretaceous times with erosion and was then swamped by shallow-water rudist limestones before renewed subsidence as a flysch-accumulating trough lasting from Maastrichtian into earliest Tertiary times.

Like its predecessor, the Golija Zone may have overridden its neighbour to the south-west. It is sometimes difficult to distinguish here between tectonic thrusting and sedimentary transgression, although in places, for example in the escarpment of carbonates that dominates Titovo Užice, the overthrusting is fairly obvious.

Serbian Zone

This is a large and complex zone extending from Banja Luka in the north (where it appears from beneath the Pannonian Basin) to the Neogene basin of Metchija, near Péc, in the south, where it passes into the vast ophiolitic massif of Mirita which cuts across the external zones and occupies much of Albania. These ophiolites form the black mountains that give Montenegro (Crnagora) its name (although the greater part of that brave little country is paradoxically composed of mountains of dazzling white limestone). So much of this zone consists of ophiolites, both in Montenegro and Serbia, that it is sometimes called the Serbian Ophiolite Zone. Inevitably it becomes involved in any discussion of Mesozoic plate margins. The ophiolites developed at the end of the Jurassic and on into earliest Cretaceous times. The volcanics and ultra-basic intrusives are accompanied by radiolarites together with shales, sandstones, and even conglomerates, but it is the serpentinites that are most obvious, for example north-west of Višegrad, where they form rolling country of fir forests.

Within this zone there is also clear evidence of pre-ophiolite continental crust. In southern Bosnia, in Serbia, in Montenegro, and in south-west Macedonia, the Palaeozoic basement is seen in many places, overlain by early Triassic red sandstones passing up into *rosso ammonitico* associated with acid volcanics. The Mesozoic succession suggests a ridge to the south-west, notable for its Triassic and Jurassic reef limestones and bauxites, and a trough to the north-east with pelagic sediments. By the end of mid Jurassic times, the facies for a while became more uniform with widespread deposition of radiolarites and similar deposits. What is called the Durmitor ridge in the south-west of this zone separated a trough to the north-east from the Bosnian furrow, occupying the next zone to the south-west. These features become less marked towards the north-west. In northern Bosnia, the Serbian Zone seems to be represented only by a great submarine slide coming off the Golija ridge to the east and moving down into the Bosnian flysch furrow to the west.

In Bosnia the ophiolite sequence is overlain conformably, without break, by flysch which spans the Jurassic–Cretaceous boundary and corresponds with the flysch of the Bosnian Zone to the south-west. This is one of the rare places in Europe where one can see the direct relationships of ophiolite and flysch. Farther to the south-east, however, there is a clear break above the ophiolites, which are covered by transgressive late Cretaceous sediments. This transgression apparently came from the west, whereas that in the more internal zones came from the east. This adds support to the idea of an earlier central ridge keeping the two seas apart. There is also evidence in all three internal zones of orogenic movements at the beginning of Cretaceous times forming what have been called the 'Palaeodinarides'. Further tectonic movements occurred at the end of Cretaceous times in the thick molasse deposits of Palaeogene age north-west of Banja Luka.

The most important feature of the Serbian Zone is the allochthonous nature of most of its constituents. All the way from Banja Luka in Bosnia to the Albanian frontier, a great frontal thrust carries these rocks over the flysch deposits of the zone that follows, clearly seen along the main road from Bijelo Polje to Titograd, where Mesozoic limestones of the Serbian cover rest on Bosnian flysch. The ophiolites, in particular, seem to be completely allochthonous. In the south is the remarkable Pešter Nappe of Triassic rocks which was probably emplaced before late Cretaceous times and which left a scatter of klippen on a great variety of geological floors. This zone constitutes one of the most important, if not *the* most important thrust masses of the Dinarides.

Bosnian Zone

The overthrust front of the Serbian Zone appears from beneath the ophiolites and molasse near Banja Luka and passes just east of historic Sarajevo. That city of bloody memory, where Gavrilo Princip fired the shots that started the First World War, stands on a constricted neck in a narrow strip of flysch which extends almost the whole length of the Bosnian Zone. In fact, flysch constitutes the main part of this narrow zone, between two great thrusts, and represents a trough that persisted at least from the beginning of Jurassic times until the late Cretaceous. Characteristically the flysch is poorly exposed except for road-cuttings, for example in the long descent to the Morača River on the road south from Bijelo Polje. The greater part of the Jurassic succession consists of pelagic limestones with chert passing up into true radiolarites and then, right at the end of the Jurassic, into the thick Bosnian flysch. Much of this zone and the one just discussed are hidden under the rolling, unexposed country of post-orogenic Oligocene–Miocene molasse, but wherever seen it consists essentially of deep trench deposits.

In the north-west of the main flysch belt, there are also extensive outcrops of shattered dolomites (e.g., between Sanski Most and Bosanska Kupa), presumably Triassic in age, which seem to belong stratigraphically below the flysch assemblage, although forming a separate and lower nappe. In other words there are three separate structural units in the northern part of this zone: the Palaeozoic dome, east of Sanski Most; the basal dolomitic nappe (only seen north of Sarajevo); and the overlying flysch nappe.

Southwards, only the top nappe is seen, caught between the two thrust planes, and even these come together to cut out the zone altogether for a distance along the Piva Valley, west of the Durmitor Massif. Farther south again the zone reappears before finally terminating at the Scutari–Peć Line.

This is the main frontal allochthonous mass of the Dinarides and can be traced up into the 'Slovene Zone' of the Southern Alps in the extreme north of Yugoslavia. Mention should be made of the lignites in the molasse of this belt, notably near Sarajevo, which indicate an early termination of the tangential movements. West of here is the white limestone country of the travel posters and the partisan films.

High Karst Zone

I prefer to call this the 'High Karst Zone' rather than just the 'Karst Zone' of earlier authors, to distinguish it from the almost equally karstic Dalmatian Zone along the Adriatic coast. It is the region of Yugoslavia most familiar to foreigners, with its dazzling white limestone mountains, eroded and dissolved into deep valleys and caves. Most of the surface water has disappeared underground, leaving ankle-twisting surfaces, beloved by physical geographers, who have taken the word 'karst' all over the world. Among the more spectacular gorges are those of the Neretva River north of Mostar and the Morača River north of Titograd. The karstic plateaux include that of Dinara, inland from Zadar, which gives the whole range its name, and the wonderful lakes and falls of Plitvice, more spectacular in their way than Niagara itself and certainly more dynamic with their constantly breaking and reforming travertine barriers.

In Montenegro, notably around the old capital of Cetinje, karstic limestones provide very little in the way of cultivatable soil. 'A hard land and a hard people' the Montegene-grans boast, and their land is chiefly famous for those who have resisted a bitter succession of occupying armies and carried out generations of vendettas. Now the deeper valleys are dammed and, paradoxically, dry Montenegro produces more hydroelectric power than anywhere else in south-east Europe.

The limestones range from mid Triassic to late Cretaceous in age. They are all shallow-water deposits, often highly fossiliferous, sometimes forming reefs and in places inter-calated with bauxites, notably in the Upper Jurassic and in the Upper Cretaceous, indicating emergence of this ridge. They rest on basal Triassic red beds which rest in turn on a Palaeozoic floor that shows up here and there, notably in the large massif of Travnik, west of Sarajevo. Sedimentologically this is a direct continuation of the Dalma-tian Zone, which has the same geomorphological characters. The whole could be regarded as divisible geographically into three subzones: (1) the 'High Karst' in the strict sense, extending from just north of Postojna in the north to Shkoder in Albania; (2) the 'Prekarst' inland from the above; and (3) the 'Dalmatian', extending along almost the whole of the Yugoslav Dalmatian coast.

Structurally, however, they are different. In the extreme south, for example in the mountains behind Bar, the High Karst Zone can be seen to be overthrust on to the very different rocks of the Budva Zone, which is further thrust on to the Dalmatian rocks. Farther north (as in Provence) it is not so easy to see where one white limestone has been thrust over another, but several parallel thrusts have been recognized both within the High Karst Zone and between it and the Dalmatian Zone in Hercegovina (inland from Split). The limestone area around Knin (north of Split) appears to be a klippe, and the range of Velabit (farther north-west) may be the same. Similar thrusting can be recognized in the north, where the Dinarides pass into the Julian Alps west of Ljubljana. The high limestone plateaux extend the whole length of Yugoslavia, but the two main zones cannot be separated everywhere and a lot of geological detail remains to be filled in. The chief distinguishing feature between the High Karst and the Dalamatian Zone is the beginning of flysch sedimentation, since it is said to be slightly younger in the latter (i.e., mid as distinct from early Eocene).

As already mentioned, it is possible to recognize what is called the 'Prekarstic Subzone' on the north-east of the bleak modern Montenegran capital of Titograd, crossing the main road from Mostar to Sarajevo at the long lake of Ostrozac, up to Bihac in Bosnia, where several thrusts seem to run together. It is also seen as the 'Prerifoulian Subzone' of the southern (Julian) Alps west of Ljubljana, paralleling the 'Rifoulian Zone' which corresponds with the High Karst plateaux. Stratigraphically, the Prekarstic subzone is controlled by its intermediate position between the High Karst ridge and the Bosnian trough and probably represents the slope between the two, characterized by variable sediments with breccias at many levels, the fragments in which diminish in size towards the north-east. Flysch deposits intercalate with limestones in the same direction, while south-westwards towards the ridge, breaks and bauxites appear in the succession. One is frequently undecided whether to use 'flysch' for these rocks, and this uncertainty is perhaps in itself evidence of their intermediate nature. Structurally the 'Prekarst' is much broken up into slices below the great Bosnian overthrust.

Budva Zone

This is the narrow zone that intervenes between the High Karst Zone and the Dalmatian Zone, south of delightful Dubrovnik. But for the Budva Zone, those two zones would probably never have been separated, and perhaps they still should not be for this is a tectonic intruder. It reaches the coast between Budva and Bar, providing the only geological variety along this sedimentologically monotonous, but scenically glorious, carbonate coastline. It is evidence of yet another trough, although a small one, starting off with the usual Lower Triassic red beds but then filling up with flysch-like, pelagic deposits and finally real flysch up into the Eocene, associated with volcanics. The flysch and thin-bedded red limestones are often fantastically contorted, for example along the Adriatic highway, south of Bar. Presumably this trough-full of rocks has been moved bodily some distance (it is impossible to estimate how much) from the north-east. Both sides of the narrow zone are thrusts, the one to the east providing the high limestone wall to the west of Skardarsko Jezero (the great lake of Shkoder) and west of the old Montenegran capital of Cetinje, where the High Karst Zone is thrust over this topographically subdued belt of rocks seen along the sides of the deep inlet of Kotor. The thrust to the west can be traced equally easily in the coast sections and consists of a whole series of thin scales. This thrust continues up parallel to the coast to beyond Split, but for the greater part of its length is within the Dalmatian Zone, coming closest to the coast on the so-called Makarska Riviera, where the mountains rise steeply from the sea. At its southern end, scattered exposures of flysch and flysch-like rocks show the extension of this zone as far as the forbidden Albanian frontier. The tectonic instability of this zone was tragically exemplified by the disastrous earthquakes of 1979.

Dalmatian Zone

From the peninsula of Istria, on the Italian border, all the way down to Albania, extends one of the most magnificent coasts in Europe—the Adriatic shore of Yugoslavia.

With its almost ridiculously elongated offshore islands with unlikely names (to western ears) such as Krk, Pag, Dugi Otok, Uglia, and Hvar, even the largest scale map leaves one in no doubt about the general north-westerly strike of the rocks, although it becomes almost north–south in Istria and almost east–west near Split. Many of the islands, like the equally elongated peninsula of Pelješac, are demonstrably anticlinal and the 'Kanals' between them and the mainland synclinal, so they may be compared with the 'typical' anticlinal ridges of the Jura, although more deeply eroded. Compared with the inland zones, the structure of the Dalamatian Zone is simple. It forms the autochthon, or at least the parautochthon, of the southwesterly thrusting Dinaride orogen, although there may be further zones hidden under the Adriatic. There are suggestions of this in the vicinity of Split, where breccias imply a further external trench to the south-west. There are also some thrusts within the zone, forming a continuation of the Budva structure. Deep borings in Montenegro have proved evaporites punching up through the limestones as high as the Cretaceous, similar to those seen in the westernmost zones of the Hellenides. Generally all that can be seen is a series of open folds along the coast, and where the zone is the widest, in Istria, there is virtually a synclinorium along the same trend continuing up to Trieste.

The evaporites mentioned above, mainly gypsum, presumably come from the Trias, although that system is rarely seen at the surface and then only inland (e.g., in the mountain of Biokovo, behind the seaside resort of Makarska). Where the older rocks can be seen, one cannot be sure if they should be included in the Dalmatian or the High Karst Zone.

On the coast, the scenery is dominated by Upper Cretaceous limestones, both in the scarp that looks down on most of the length of the Adriatic Highway and in the many offshore islands. The succession starts at the surface with the Middle to Upper Triassic (e.g., above the Makarska Riviera) or with the Upper Jurassic (e.g., in Istria where the outcrop is widest), and shallow-water limestones persist from that level to as high as the Middle Eocene. As previously mentioned, this also often produces a karstic topography, notably in the otherwise fertile country around the lovely walled city of Dubrovnik. In this zone in the north, inland from Istria, are the vast cave systems of Postojna and Škocjanska, said to be the finest in Europe. The only obvious interruption in the usually dazzling white limestones is a calcareous shale formation, worked in many places for cement, notably around Zadar. So dreary grey concrete is becoming the standard building material of modern Yugoslavia, replacing the clean lines of limestone blocks and the fascinating shapes and colours of the local bricks.

Stratigraphically the only important break is at the Cretaceous–Tertiary boundary, with evidence of emergence which is elsewhere represented by the important bauxites of Kosina. Above the limestones come thick mid and late Eocene flysch, seen faulted down in places on the coast but usually inland behind the towering battlements of the Dalmatian scarp. Between Split and Zadar there is some indication of deeper water deposits. A second bauxite comes above this and then molasse-type deposits.

Finally, outwards from the coast in the furthest islands—notably Vis and its neighbours—and constituting the whole of the farthest and loneliest island (Jabuka), basic igneous rocks appear again and suggest a further natural zone, not named, but perhaps the equivalent of the Ionian Zone in the Hellenides.

16(f) Hellenides

The Hellenides may be defined as those Alpine ranges that constitute virtually the whole of the birthplace of European civilization in Greece, together with the greater part of the least-known country in our continent—Albania—and the south-eastern corner of Yugoslavia. They are a direct continuation of the Dinarides, but a clear dividing line may be taken (as indicated in the previous section) at the Scutari–Péc line roughly along the northern frontier of Albania. This line, although important, is not a complete break and several of the tectonic zones continue from the Dinarides into the Hellenides, although all are shifted laterally (Fig. 16.9).

The following tectonic zones are recognized, starting from the 'inside' of the range and proceeding in the direction of major thrusting, i.e., from east-north-east to west-south-west; the equivalents in the main part of Yugoslavia are given on the right:

Hellenides	*Dinarides*
Serbo-Macedonian Massif	Serbo-Macedonian Massif
Vardar Zone	Vardar Zone
Pelagonian Zone	Golija Zone
Sub-pelagonian Zone	Serbian Zone
Beotian Zone	Bosnian Zone
Parnassus Zone	High Karst Zone
Pindus Zone	Budva Zone
Gavrovo Zone	Dalmatian Zone
Ionian Zone	Probably under the Adriatic
Pre-Apulian Zone	Probably under the Adriatic

This is, of course, an oversimplification, both in terms of tectonic correlation and in terms of grouping together diverse sub-zones that should, perhaps, be separated, but it serves our present purpose.

Serbo-Macedonian Massif

This is a direct continuation of the zone with the same name in the Dinarides, but is much better known than in that chain. It extends along the border between Montenegro and Bulgaria and then into Greece as what used to be thought of as the western part of the Rhodope Massif. It is separated from that massif, as now understood, by the River Struma (or Strymon)* and it ranges down to terminate in the two eastern spikes of the three-pronged Chalkidiki peninsula, east of Thessaloniki (Salonika) which points out into the Aegean. As in Yugoslavia, the involvement of these ranges in the Alpine structures is said to distinguish them from the Rhodope Massif proper, and the trend of the Chalkidiki 'prongs' alone is sufficient to exemplify this point. Now that the degree of Alpine metamorphism in the Rhodope Massif is better known, the distinction is less obvious.

The Serbo-Macedonian Massif consists of metamorphic rocks, usually assumed to have been affected by Variscan and/or earlier movements, but clearly affected several times up to and including the Alpine orogeny, when it was thrust westwards over the Gavrovo Zone. It appears, like the Rhodope Massif itself, to have been a positive, emergent area during the greater part of its history. It is mostly rather bare, rugged country, often dark and forbidding, characterized by mica schists and mineralization.

* There are many variations in the transliteration of Greek names, and even the Greeks themselves are not consistent.

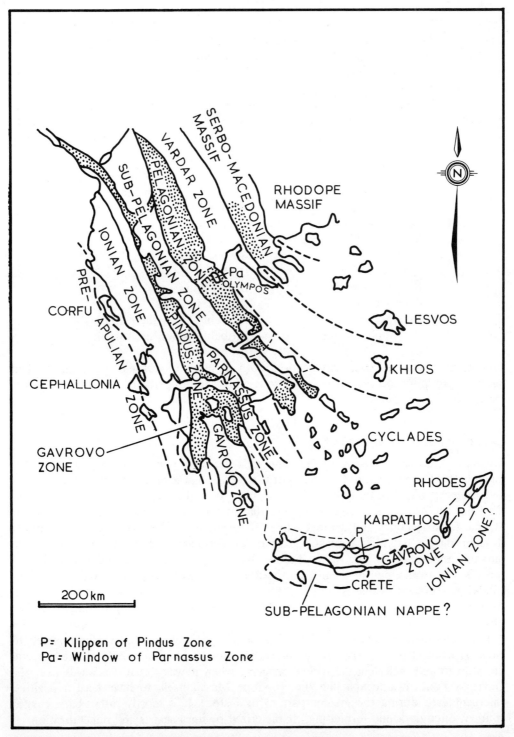

Fig. 16.9 *Sketch-map of the main tectonic zones in the Hellenides (after Aubouin et al., 1963, by kind permission of Prof. Aubouin).*

The easternmost prong of the Chalkidiki trident is the stronghold of the Greek Orthodox Church, culminating in the naked pyramid of Mount Athos, a sort of semi-independent theocracy, packed with monasteries and Byzantine art, that has kept out women for more than nine hundred years. Ironically this belt seems to continue across the Aegean via the tiny island of Agios Efstratios to Lesvos (Lesbos), perhaps the birthplace of 'women's lib.' and personified by that 'burning' poetress Sappho. This is one of the largest of the Aegean islands and is tucked in close to the Turkish coastline. However, a major trough on the sea-floor (perhaps the North Anatolian Fault) seems to divide them.

The metamorphics of this innermost belt are thought to be mainly of Precambrian age, whereas those of the centre prong of the trident, that of Longos (or Sithonia), is mainly Palaeozoic. Both belts are intruded by Variscan granites. Generally speaking the characters of the Serbo-Macedonian Massif are as already described in the Dinarides and, as there, a major structural break separates it from the Vardar Zone to the south-west.

Vardar Zone

This takes its name from the Vardar River (called the Axios River in Greece) which flows from south-east Yugoslavia into the sea west of Thessaloniki and which was named in turn after *vardari*, the icy north wind, which gives this part of Greece (Alexander the Great's Macedonia) a more continental climate than the rest of the country. There is a splendid series of exposures along that river in south-east Yugoslavia, between Katlanovo and the Greek frontier, relieving the monotony of what must be the most wearisome road in Europe.

The Vardar Zone is thought to form the western spike of the Chalkidiki peninsula and embraces the wide bay of Thessaloniki. The Vardar Zone is divided into three parts, themselves often nowadays known as 'zones', but better called 'sub-zones' here.

The most easterly of these sub-zones—that of Peonia—is essentially an inner trough which became distinct early in Jurassic times with the development of an ophiolitic suite, as in the Dinarides. There was then emergence, followed by a transgression very late in the Jurassic (with Tithonian coral limestones) and then the re-establishment of a trench with boulder flysch. A further emergence early in the Cretaceous was followed by a molasse trough before the end of that period. Again there was emergence right at the end of the Cretaceous, and again a molasse or flysch trough in the late Eocene. Thus this belt showed a repeated 'sinking feeling' and might be regarded as a destructive plate margin.

West of this spasmodic trench was a persistent submarine ridge called the 'Veles Axis' in Yugoslavia and the 'Paikon Zone' in Greece. The record there begins with carbonates of Triassic and Jurassic age associated with volcanics, including rhyolites and a spilite–keratophyre sequence. Transgressions during the later Mesozoic correspond with those of the inner trench, but the positive, uplifted aspect of this belt became dominant in Oligocene times. This palaeo-ridge is exemplified by the repeated calcareous breccias and conglomerates of the westernmost prong of Chalkidiki—the peaceful pine-covered promontory of Kassandra.*

The western or outermost of the three belts within the Vardar Zone is that of Almopias. This was another trench, which may have been established in late Jurassic times and

---

* Named after Alexander's general/brother-in-law, not the Trojan prophetess of doom.

also received considerable quantities of late Cretaceous limestone and flysch before the emergence with the central ridge during Oligocene times.

As in the Dinarides a whole series of thrust slices pushed to the west with probable considerable lateral movement. The two sub-zones which were trenches in Mesozoic times are still trenches today, forming the deep embayments on either side of the Kassandra Peninsula. These run into fertile agricultural valleys, cut off by high mountains from the battling city-states of Greece proper. In the north, the ophiolite belt dominates in the black mountains of Montenegro, and the sedimentary cover is largely cut out south of Novi Pazar, but it comes in again in Greece to sag under the great flat, almost tree-less Quaternary basin that lies to the west of the humming city of Thessaloniki and plunges down under its great bay.

The Vardar Zone was clearly thrust westwards in a whole series of slices, with the westernmost nappe pushed right on top of the Pelagonian Zone, for example in the mountains of Vermion, south of Edessa, the ancient capital of Macedonia. Much of it is in the nature of a crush zone comparable to (and perhaps continuous with) the Ankara Melange of Turkey.

Apart from the full ophiolite suite (including pillow lavas, radiolarites, serpentinites, and peridotites) there was considerable magmatic activity in the Vardar Zone. There are so many granodioritic or tonalitic intrusions that it has been called a *cicatrice tonalitique*; these are later than the presumably Jurassic ophiolites and may be Eocene in age. They are clearly related to those of the Southern Alps. There are also considerable masses of Miocene eruptives, mainly dacites and tuffs, especially along the lower limit of the zone. These all post-date the main tectonic movements, which seem to have occurred at the end of the Cretaceous or early in Eocene times.

It is important to remember that these inner zones moved earlier than the outer zones. There is also strong evidence of major lateral movements, perhaps of the order of 300 km, with the zones to the west travelling northwards along this line relative to the zones to the east. This is probably one of the major sutures of Europe and may well be the direct continuation of the Insubric Line of the Alps. One has only to see kilometre after kilometre of pillow lavas along the valley of the Vardar in Macedonia to appreciate that one is seeing something much more oceanic than say the little squirts of pillow lavas in the Variscan belts of Europe.

As in the Dinarides, the greater part of the Vardar Zone in the Hellenides is occupied by Mesozoic and Cainozoic rocks, but just as at the north-west end of the Dinarides, around Valjevo, there are Palaeozoic metamorphics, so there are at the south-east end of the Hellenides. What seems to be the continuation of the Vardar Zone on the far side of the Aegean reveals a much longer history. This is in the island of Khios (Chios or Hios), which is the most likely of seven traditional birthplaces of Homer and of less lyrical Greek shipowners, close to the coast of Turkey. Here there seems to be evidence of mid-Carboniferous and end Palaeozoic movements and metamorphism.

Pelagonian Zone

Whereas the Vardar Zone passes directly down Yugoslavia into Greece without serious complication, the Pelagonian and Sub-pelagonian Zones are not clearly correlated with structures to the north. The Scutari–Péc Line abruptly terminates the Golija, Serbian,

Bosnian and High Karst Zones of the Dinarides; beyond that line the carbonates of Yugoslavia are generally replaced by volcanic and metamorphic rocks.

In Albania, the exact equivalent of the Pelagonian Zone of Greece is the 'Korab Zone' which outcrops along most of the eastern frontier of that country, but for our purposes the one name is sufficient. For the greater part of its length, the Pelagonian Zone consists of 'basement' rocks. These show through their sedimentary cover in three broad areas. The first of these, in the north, is the 'Western Macedonian Massif' where the Palaeozoic rocks are well exposed in the reservoir-filled valleys north of Lake Ohrid (Okhrida). A great variety of cleaved Palaeozoic sediments rest on a metamorphic basement. The massif of Thessaly in the centre, around the tectonic window of Mount Olympos (Olimbos), displays a great area of high-grade metamorphic rocks including marbles (well, if dustily, seen along the bumpy road that runs round the west side of the home of the gods, which is so much more interesting than the dull, fast coast road). In the south is the barren massif of Attica, which somehow supported classical Athens (Athinai), and which continues on into the islands of the Cyclades. Here too are metamorphic rocks, including the famous marbles of Mount Pentelicon, which were quarried extensively for building Parthenons.

The Pelagonian Zone seems to have remained a ridge—either actually emergent or a *haut-fond*—right through from Triassic to Eocene times, but its earlier history is not clear. The basement generally consist of granites and gneisses overlain by a more or less metamorphosed Palaeozoic succession. Devonian fossils have been found and some of the rocks look familiar, such as *griotte*-like red limestones on the east shore of pellucid Lake Ohrid. Massive dark limestones and carbonaceous-looking rocks north-east of Debar in Macedonia make one think of the Carboniferous, but the palaeontological evidence is very inadequate. The whole sequence is cut by younger, presumably Variscan, granites. It has been suggested that these massifs are comparable with the Tauern Window in the Eastern Alps and include significant propostions of Mesozoic rocks in a metamorphosed condition. This does not seem acceptable, although locally (e.g., in western Macedonia) metamorphic rocks have been dated as Triassic and Jurassic. Such later metamorphism took place in early Cretaceous times, with the production of mica schists and marbles.

Between the massifs, the Pelagonian Zone sags as two great 'saddles' in which the sedimentary sequence is most fully preserved. The first is around the dusty little town of Kozani, the centre of western Macedonia, north-west of Mount Olympos. The second forms the karst country that cuts across the peninsula that leads to Athens and forms the main central part of the large island of Euboea. Here, for example, are the Mesozoic carbonate mountains that Byron noted looking down on Marathon and which now provide the Athens water supply.

The break below the Mesozoic is difficult to see (which has caused much of the argument), but this can be equally an argument against an unconformity or against tectonic superimposition. However, there are local conglomerates and red beds, attributed to the Permian. The Mesozoic begins with thick white limestones, more than 1000 m thick, resting on serpentinites near Kozani; the former are notably lacking in fossils due to recrystallization, although Middle Triassic algae have been found north-west of that town. Early Jurassic fossils are known near Lake Ohrid in Albania and late Jurassic corals south-west of Kozani. The whole succession seems to represent fairly shallow-water sedimentation, which makes the immediate superposition of another ophiolite suite surprising to those with fixed ideas about such things.

These ophiolites seem to be later Jurassic in age and include peridotites, radiolarites, and basic lava flows which have flowed across the carbonates, rather than cut through them. They appear to thicken both ways, as if they poured into this limy trough both from the Vardar Zone to the north-east and from the Sub-pelagonian Zone to the south-west. Nevertheless the flows were thick enough for the gravity settling of olivines. The top of the suite is characterized by deeply eroded and reddened serpentinites, sometimes with the development of iron-ores, signifying general emergence of this zone in early Cretaceous times.

A later Cretaceous transgression began with conglomerates and later breccias of local material, but a more extensive transgression near the end of the period cut right down to the basement in places. Splendid rudist limestones are developed forming the Acropolis, the Areopagus, the Pnyx, and the other hills of Athens, where nearly everything worth-while began. There was then a deepening passage into flysch at the end of the era. All that is to be seen of the Tertiary here are local Neogene lake deposits, but they are important because they include valuable lignite deposits, mined on a big scale around Ptolemeus, north of Kozani, and used to provide Greece with much of her electricity.

Structurally, the Pelagonian Zone has been affected by several phases of movement, but the last folding probably predated that to the south-west, in accordance with the general pattern of this chain. Sliding of the cover occurred, although much of it is evidently in place and there were obviously very late vertical movements. The 'basement' itself can in places be shown to have been pushed westwards on to the Sub-pelagonian Zone or, as in Albania, acted as a battering-ram pushing before it an ophiolite nappe (that of Mirdita). It has been suggested recently, in studies of the Mount Olympos 'window' (where the Parnassus Zone appears beneath this unit), that structural evidence indicates movement in the opposite direction, more in keeping with plate tectonic theorizing. At the moment I prefer to accept the classic view of generations of geologists who have spent years working in these mountains (Fig. 16.10). The alternative would seem to imply a contradiction of all that has gone before, and although it must not be rejected on that account it needs very strong supporting evidence.

Sub-pelagonian Zone

The Sub-pelagonian Zone is here defined as including the Mirdita Zone of Albania. It is the great ophiolite belt of the Hellenides and, perhaps, one of the major sutures of Europe. It begins abruptly at the dislocation of the Scutari–Péc Line and forms a large part of northern Albania; it then extends down through the northern Pindus mountains to form the isthmus between the main part of Greece and the Peloponnese, and so on into the Aegean. It is the direct continuation, albeit displaced, of the Serbian Zone of the Dinarides and shares most of its characters. Tectonically, it is wholly allochthonous and rests everywhere on the external Pindus Zone in the north and the Parnassus Zone in the south.

The most important feature about the ophiolites is that this was evidently the line (before displacement) along which they were actually pushed up from below. The suture was probably close to the boundary with the previous zone. The ophiolites are best

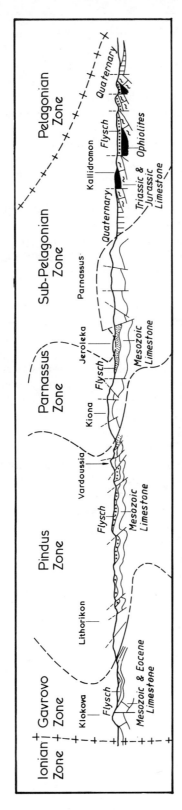

Fig. 16.10 Cross-section of the Hellenides (after Aubouin et al., 1963, by kind permission of Prof. Aubouin).

displayed (although most difficult for most of us to see) in Albania, where they form the great black massif of Mirdita, north of the capital Tirane (Tirana). Here they appear to be late Jurassic in age, since they rest on earlier Jurassic *rosso ammonitico*, and the radiolarites at the bottom of the sequence are intercalated with fossiliferous pelagic limestones. They are, however, much easier for most of us to see in Greece, notably around the Furka Pass* north of Lamia, where slice after slice of pillow lavas, radiolarites, and the others, are exposed by the roadside, or on the Katara Pass, east of Ioannina, where there is mile after mile of gleaming serpentinites. The ophiolite suite may reach several kilometres in thickness. The submarine lavas evidently flowed both ways, back into the spasmodically subsiding Pelagonian trough and forward (in a tectonic sense) into the Pindus trough to the south-west.

The known sedimentary succession begins with the Upper Trias, best known in the mountains of Othrys, north-east of Lamia, where several hundred metres of carbonates yield Ladinian ammonites near their base, but pass up imperceptibly into the Lower Jurassic. They are also magnificently exposed in the cliffs above the coast road farther south, notably at Thermopile, where Leonidas and his three hundred died defending the 'pass' (actually a raised beach) against the Persian host. Later limestones yield Jurassic micro-fossils and occasional ammonitcs, suggesting a deep-water facies that passes up naturally into the radiolarites of the ophiolite suite, but with local pockets of bauxite, suggesting emergence. There is a condensed Mesozoic continental margin sequence to the north-east.

After the emplacement of the ophiolites there was emergence, as in the Pelagonian Zone, followed by a late Cretaceous transgression that was slightly later than in the zone to the north-east. Again rudist reefs were developed and the Upper Cretaceous succession is a shallow-water one until, again as in the previous zone, a development of flysch at the very end of the period.

One big difference in the Sub-pelagonian Zone was the formation of a deep trough here in Oligocene and Miocene times. This 'Central Hellenic Furrow' extended from central Albania to Othrys and acquired no less than 5000 m of molasse-type sediments. These form the fantastic scenery at Meteora, north-west of Trikala, where a famous cluster of pinnacle-perching monasteries was the ascetic haunt of St. Athanasius. The name comes from the mediaeval idea that these towers of conglomerate were extraterrestrial in origin. They are remarkably similar geologically, scenically, and monastically, to Montserrat in north-east Spain. They have been dated in the area of Voion (Vojon) west of Kozani, where thick conglomerates alternate with beds packed with Miocene molluscs. They are followed by river and lake deposits of Pliocene and Quaternary age, which are scattered in a series of little basins.

The whole mass of ophiolites and the associated sediments, forming a belt some 40 km wide and 600 km long on the mainland alone, was pushed in a south-westerly direction after the end of the Cretaceous but before the formation of the Central Hellenic Furrow. The bright green serpentinites of the Katara Pass, for example, are thrust on top of the Pindus Zone. The movement is dated as happening at the end of the Eocene. This was the first nappe recognized in Greece and is taken as marking the limit of the internal zones and the junction either between Europe proper and an Adriatic microplate or

* Not to be confused with the equally geological Furka Pass near Andermath in Switzerland.

508

between Europe and the Adriatic prow of the African continent. It is thought that in the south, notably on the south coast of Crete, the Sub-pelagonian nappe slid right over the Pindus nappe and plunged down towards Africa.

The Central Hellenic Trough of Oligocene–Miocene sediments was itself disturbed by late orogenic movements and its south-western margin coincides with an earlier tectonic melange containing blocks up to several kilometres across. This may have been the result of a major lateral disturbance like that of the Vardar Zone, which shuddered again in Neogene times. The later movements are represented by broad open folds, after which, as in the Hellenides generally, there was simply tensional faulting on north-west and north-east lines which delimited some of the Plio-Pleistocene basins.

Beotian Zone

This zone is not usually separated in the Greek literature and is not shown in Fig. 16.9. It is only included here to conform with the previous chapter on the Dinarides. It would include the Grammas Zone of Albania. Its equivalent in the Dinarides is the narrow Bosnian Zone, between the main mass of ophiolites (the Serbian Zone) and the white limestone country of the High Karst. In the Hellenides, therefore, one would expect to find its structural counterpart between the 'Ophiolite Nappe' and the carbonate-dominated Parnassus Zone to the west. All that can be put into this category in the Hellenides are the lower slices below the ophiolites.

In Albania and northern Greece the Parnassus Zone is also cut out completely and the Mirdita ophiolites are thrust directly on to the equivalent of the Pindus Zone. It may be that the equivalent of the Bosnian Zone is similarly hidden at the surface but there are distinctive units which appear from beneath the ophiolites, notably a series of Triassic volcanic rocks in the section at Lisën, west of Mirdita.

In Greece, the possible equivalent of the Serbian Zone has only been recognized in Beotia on the north side of the Gulf of Corinth. Here there is a flysch unit, comparable with that which makes up the greater part of the Bosnian Zone in the Dinarides.

Parnassus Zone

The Parnassus Zone is only recognized in the southern part of the Hellenides, around Parnassus itself and on the opposite side of the Gulf of Corinth, through the eastern Peloponnese down to the bare island of Hydra. It also emerges as a tectonic window through the Pelagonian Zone as the great Mount Olympos itself. So the two most famous mountains of Greece are linked geologically if not topographically—Olympos, the home of the gods, and Parnassus with Delphi, the 'navel of the earth' and the most sacred place in ancient Greece. Both are spectacular mountain masses and one understands how they impressed the ancients with their remoteness.

The Parnassus Zone is basically a heap of shallow-water carbonates, ranging from Triassic to Paleocene in age. It was essentially a *haut-fond*, with many breaks in deposition and the local development of bauxites, especially near the top of the Jurassic and in the middle of the Cretaceous. The margins of the ridge are shown by such features as rudist debris. Altogether there are some 1500 m of Mesozoic carbonates, passing upwards into a similar thickness of flysch, although at a slightly higher level (in the

Eocene) than in the zones previously discussed. The Delphic Oracle performed right on the Cretaceous–Tertiary boundary. No doubt if she had been asked about the Danian she would have given her usual ambiguous answer, although she might have pointed out that here at least there is evidence of a hiatus above the Maastrichtian. The flysch ends with conglomerates, presumably late Eocene in age, which give notice of the beginning of the orogeny.

Since it is formed, for the most part, of massive limestones, the Parnassus Zone contrasts markedly with the ophiolites of the Pelagonian Zone to the east and with the flysch of the Pindus Zone to the west. As a result it has behaved in a quite different way in response to tectonism. Apart from some *décollement* in Cretaceous red beds, the faults are often at a high angle and very different from the repeated scaly thrusts of the other zones. The main movement is still to the south-west, as is displayed along the coast of the Gulf of Corinth, where the shallow-water carbonates have ridden a long way over the deeper water deposits of the Pindus Zone. Similar heavy-handed tectonics are seen where a Venetian castle perches on the front of the equivalent zone above Nafplion (Nauplia) in the Peloponnese. There are also compressional faults oriented in the opposite direction, as though this massive submarine ridge had been pinched outwards and upwards between the less competent sediments of the troughs on either side. This may be part of the explanation of the anomalous structures recently recorded in the Olympos 'window'.

Very late faulting, cutting across the earlier structures, as in the previous zone, has also much affected the Parnassus rocks, delimiting them to the north (along the Sperchios valley through Lamia) and along the two sides of the Gulf of Corinth which so nearly cuts Greece in two. The Recent nature of this graben formation is seen in many places where the coarse cemented scree is cut by slickensided faults sliding material down into the Gulf of Corinth and its complementary Saronic Gulf on the other side of the Corinthian isthmus.

Pindus Zone

The narrow Budva Zone of the southern Yugoslav coast can be traced as a similarly slender belt through Albania from Shkoder in the north to Leskovic near the Greek frontier. It is known there as the Krasta Zone and is contained between two major, parallel thrusts. In central Albania, however, it also extends eastwards from the town of Shengjerg to the Yugoslav frontier, appearing in a culmination from beneath the more easterly zones. A comparable unit, the Cukali Zone, appears as a tectonic window along the Scutari–Péc Line, between the carbonates of the High Karst and the volcanics of the Mirdita Massif.

For convenience, these Albanian zones are here included in the Pindus Zone of Greece, which has a broader outcrop incorporating the main part of the great barrier of the Pindus mountains and broadens southwards to occupy the greater part of the Peloponnese. Here it splits around a 'window' of the Gavrovo Zone and continues, with nappes and klippen, round through Crete (Kriti) and Karpathos to Rhodes (Rodhos) at the end of Europe. A minor belt in the Dinarides therefore becomes a major one in the Hellenides and one of the most impressive mountain chains in Europe.

The Pindus Zone therefore underlies a great deal of the visible Hellenides and overrode a great deal more. By its very nature this zone is extremely complex structurally. Its incompetent sediments have provided a plane of *décollement* like the Triassic evaporites of the Alps, but on a much bigger scale. Driving through it one sees seemingly endless sections in fantastically contorted flysch, radiolarites, and thin-bedded pelagic limestones.

The whole Mesozoic only amounts to about a thousand metres of sediment and this seems to have been completely squeezed out of its original depositional trough. Some signs of the margins of the trough are preserved in the form of intercalated micro-breccias of shallow-water material, but the rest is of a deep-water facies. Here one really feels in a trough, although one looks in vain for ophiolites in most of the weary traverses.

The Trias (not seen in Albania) consists of thin-bedded siliceous limestones and shales followed by multicoloured radiolarites, often with mangenese, providing spectacularly photogenic mountains. The latter seem to represent the whole of the Jurassic and earliest Cretaceous. Then flysch deposition interceded for a while, followed by more pelagic limestones in the later Cretaceous and a main flysch episode beginning before the end of the Cretaceous and lasting until the mid Eocene. It should be contrasted with the later flysch to the south-west. Presumably the variations in these trough deposits relate partly to the supply of detritus from rising ridges and partly to variations in the calcium carbonate compensation depth in the Mesozoic sea. The flysch dominates the rugged scenery and provides some of the most difficult passes in Europe.

Tectonically it is all obviously allochthonous, but its consistent position between the shallow-water carbonates of the Parnassus/High Karst Zones on the one side and the similar rocks of the Gavrovo/Dalmatian Zones on the other makes it a real and distinct palaeogeographical entity. The Cukali 'window' and the Shengjerg culmination in Albania show that its original situation must have been at least 50 km to the north-east. Its appearance in tiny windows under Parnassus Zone limestones in the islands of Karpathos and Rhodes may mean even greater displacement, but by here the structures have swung round, via an east–west orientiation, to north-east and most of the evidence is hidden under the sparkling waters of the Aegean. From the one great window and two smaller windows of Gavrovo Zone in the Peloponnese, the nappe or nappes must have travelled more than 100 km. In Crete, where the Hellenide structures run east–west, the Pindus Nappe impinges on the north coast of that island at two places; it is seen again as inland klippen and then appears again on the south coast plunging into the sea.

Gavrovo Zone

This includes the Kruja Zone of Albania and is the direct equivalent of the Dalmatian Zone of the Dinarides. As in the latter chain, we have here reached the autochthon and the stability of the now sunken Adriatic. The sedimentary story for the Mesozoic is one of thick, shallow-water carbonates, but the dazzling white hills which dominate the Yugoslav coast soon strike inland in Albania, past the capital and on into western Greece. The zone continues down to the Gulf of Corinth just east of Byron's Messolongi (Mesolongion) and into the western Peloponnese where it is cut out by the overriding Pindus Zone. For most of the Greek outcrop, however, the Mesozoic carbonates are buried beneath thick Tertiary flysch.

The known sedimentary record begins with the late Jurassic, in the form of massive algal limestones that pass up into the early Cretaceous. The Upper Cretaceous is extremely thick (2000 m for this part of the column alone in the mountains of Tymphi in northern Greece). It consists of reef limestones with masses of *in situ* rudists and other horizons with nerineid gastropods suggesting back-reef environments. This gives rise to karst scenery as in Yugoslavia, for example west of Ioannina. The massive carbonates pass up into the Lower and Middle Eocene without significant change in facies, apart from the disappearance of the now extinct molluscs. Many of the beds are now packed with giant forams.

The change to flysch sedimentation came in late Eocene times, significantly later than in the more internal zones. Evidently the trough was moving with time as the inner ridges rose. The flysch is thick and again dominates the scenery of this zone in Greece, in so far as normally unexposed flysch can be said to 'dominate'. It is also like the flysch of the Ionian Zone to the south-west, although it can be distinguished from it by the presence of lenses of striking conglomerates full of pebbles of white pelagic limestone and radiolarite (derived from the rocks of the Pindus Zone) in a black matrix. The slope is now towards the Ionian Sea.

The autochthonous Gavrovo Zone is characterized by broad, simple folds and by steep faults, often of considerable throw (up to 4000 m has been estimated on one in the Tymphi mountains). They trend north-east and north-west, like those in the Parnassus limestones to the east and it is assumed that they are rooted in an unseen basement. The Gavrovo ridge seems to have stopped the advance of the Pindus allochthon. Only at one point in the Pindus mountains, south of Ioannina, and in the extreme south have the Pindus nappes moved right over this zone. Also in the extreme south, a tectonic window attributable to this zone (although usually distinguished as the 'Tripolitza Zone') is seen beneath the Pindus allochthon. It occupies the central part of the southern Peloponnese and only differs from the main outcrop in that it also displays thick dolomitic limestones of the Triassic and early Jurassic. This is a countryside of spectacular limestone scenery such as the Nedon Gorge leading to still spartan Sparta and the huge caves near Areopolis on the rocky headland that runs down to Cape Taenaron (Matapan), the southernmost mainland point in eastern Europe.

It goes on to form the rugged core of Crete—the precipitous 'White Mountains'—with features such as the Gorge of Samaria, south of Chania, which has been called the longest, deepest, and most dramatic gorge in Europe. One of the huge caves here, on Mount Dictaion (Dicte) or Mount Ida, is the legendary birthplace of Zeus who later came back to Crete in the form of a bull to seduce Europa and beget King Minos and the oldest civilization in our continent. East again this zone forms the autochthonous base of the islands of Karpathos and Rhodes.

Ionian Zone

The Ionian Zone first appears on land, going south, near the mouth of the Ishmi River, north-west of the Albanian capital. It is separated from the Gavrovo Zone by a basin of Pliocene and Quaternary deposits such as occupy a great part of the coastline of central Albania. It is west of anything known onshore in Yugoslavia. The zone becomes much broader in southern Albania and crosses the Greek frontier to form the greater part of Epirus, including the whole of Levkas, with its folklore, and Odysseus's home ground of Ithaca. It goes on to underlie the western edge of the Peloponnese, where it is largely covered by Neogene and Quaternary deposits (including the shelly limestones used to build ancient sportive Olympia).

Since we have passed the autochthon at Gavrovo (and Dalmatia) we are really in the Adriatic realm and the Ionian Zone should be included in the Po–Adriatic Basin, but this is by definition so much a part of the Hellenides that it is, for convenience if nothing else, included here. Unlike the rocks of the Gargano Peninsula and Apulia, which are divorced by a long Quaternary trough from the Apennines, these are all part of the same mountain belt.

Again we are in a trough, this time filled mainly with Mesozoic limestones. They are usually said to be 'pelagic', but those at the base are without fossils (although attributed to the Trias). Above are massive limestones ranging up to the Middle Lias, with unextractable corals, algae, and a particularly interesting suite of brachiopods. These deposits may represent the continental slope, leading to the deposits of the Toarcian onwards which are characterized (as so often) by *rosso ammonitico* and siliceous limestones, especially along the axis of the trough. The same story continues into the Upper Jurassic and Cretaceous, with thin-bedded radiolarian and aptychus limestones together with intercalated jaspers in the axis. Calcareous flysch with rudist debris, but no terrigenous material, reminds one in the uppermost Cretaceous that the flanks of this trough were wholly carbonate. More and more breccias come in from the sides until in late Eocene times normal sandy flysch appeared, which is seen along the coast road near Arta. This facies persisted through to the Miocene.

Structurally there is little to say about the Ionian Zone. After the savage excesses of the Pindus, it looks calm and civilized, with gentle dips or none at all. There is still some minor thrusting to the south-west and much vertical faulting, which went on to define Plio-Pleistocene sedimentary basins. The fact that this zone appears to be more disturbed tectonically on the grand scale than the Gavrovo Zone, may relate to its less competent nature. Another factor may be the presence of gypsum, not previously noted in the Hellenides. This was long attributed to the Neogene, but is now known to be almost certainly Triassic in age. In central Albania around Belsch, 40 km south of Tirana, there is even a large salt dome punching up through the Ionian Zone.

Pre-Apulian Zone

If the Ionian Zone might have been included in the Po–Adriatic Basin, how much more so might that be argued for the Pre-Apulian Zone. But the same arguments also apply in the opposite direction. It must be included here to complete the Hellenide story.

This zone is just seen in south-west Albania in the Karaburun Peninsula and in the nearby island of Sazani, which gives its name to the zone in that country. It then barely ventures into Greek territorial waters to occupy the western part of the earthquake-afflicted islands of Cephallonia (Kephallinia) and Zakynthos (Zante) and just touches the south-west corner of Levkas.

We are now far from the ancient mountains of the Hellenides (although the modern ones on Cephallonia reach 1700 m) and the outstanding characteristic of the Pre-Apulian Zone is the complete absence of flysch. It has this in common with the 'Apulian' across the Adriatic. Besides this negative evidence, there is the positive evidence of the debris of rudist reefs (which begin the succession in the Upper Cretaceous) and which may have come from the flourishing colonies of Apulia. The Tertiary succession, up to Lower Miocene, is also like that of the Italian 'heel' with shallow-water limestones and micro-breccias intercalated with pelagic limestones like those of the Ionian Zone.

Structurally there is nothing to say except that there are large faults, perhaps connected with the foundering of the Adriatic and certainly connected with the earthquakes that have so often devasted these islands.

The Neogene and after

One of the standard works on Greek stratigraphy is entitled *Die vorneogen Stratigraphie* ... ('The pre-Neogene stratigraphy ...'), which emphasizes the important point that with the Miocene everything is changed. The Neogene and Quarternary deposits of Greece provided most of her fertile lowlands. Some of them (such as the conglomerates at Meteora) have already been mentioned, and in certain cases (as in other Alpine belts) they were involved in late tectonic movements. But for the most part they ignore all previous structures.

Special mention must be made of the arc of late Cainozoic volcanicity in the Aegean. In the centre is the most famous of the volcanic islands, Santorini (Thera), which from the air shows as the almost perfect arc of a collapse caldera. From sea-level, the walls of the crater rise sheer and straight with the little town perched precariously on the top, unperturbed by either its geography or its violent history. Hydrothermal activity is still in fact going on and sulphides are still being deposited in sheltered embayments.

Selected references to Chapter 16

Section 16(a)   Maghreb

Ager, D. V. (1974), 'The western High Atlas of Morocco and their significance in the history of the North Atlantic', *Proc. Geol. Ass.*, **85**, 23–41.

Bishop, W. F. (1975), 'Geology of Tunisia and adjacent parts of Algeria and Libya', *Bull. Amer. Ass. Petrol. Geol.*, **59**, 415–450.

Choubert, G. and J. Marcais (1952), 'Géologie du Maroc. Monogr. région', *19th Congr. Géol. Internat.*, *Alger*, No. 6, 194 pp.

Glangeaud, L. (1952), 'Histoire géologique de la Province d'Alger. Monogr. région.', *19th Congr. Géol. Internat.*, *Alger*, No. 25, 141 pp.

Kieken, M. (1962), 'Les traits essentiels de la géologie algérienne', *Liv. Mém. P. Fallot*, **1**, 545–614.

Martin, L. ed. (1967), *Guidebook to the Geology and History of Tunisia*, Petrol. Explor. Soc. Libya, 293 pp.

Michard, A. (1976), *Elements de Géologie Marocaine*, Notes Mem. Serv. Géol. Maroc., No. 252, 408 pp.

Roch, E. (1950), *Historie Straigraphique du Maroc*, Notes Mem. Serv. Géol. Maroc, No. 80, 435 pp.

Section 16(b)   Sicily

Alvarez, W. and K. H. A. Gohrbant, eds (1970), *Geology and History of Sicily*, Petrol. Explor. Soc. Libya, 291 pp.

Beneo, E. (1964), 'Présentation de la carte géologique de la Sicile au 500,000', *Geol. Rundschau*, **53**, 17–24.

Caire, A. (1961), 'Remarques sur l'évolution tectonique de la Sicile', *Bull. Soc. Géol. Fr.*, 3(7), 545–558.

Castany, G. (1956), 'Essai de synthese du territoire Tunisie-Sicile', *Ann. Mines Géol.*, **16**, 1–101.

Ogniben, L. (1963), 'Stratigraphie tectono-sédimentaire de la Sicile', *Liv. Mém. P. Fallot*, **2**, 203–216.

Phillips, R. W. (1970), 'Road log for Sicily field trip', Petrol. Explor. Soc. Libya, 14 pp.

Squyres, C. H., ed. (1975), *Geology of Italy*, 2 vols, Earth Sci. Soc. Libyan Arab Repub. 402 and 392 pp.

Section 16(c)   Apennines

Abbate, E. *et al.* (1970), 'Introduction to the geology of the northern Apennines', *Sediment Geol.*, **4**, 207–249 (and subsequent papers in same vol.).

Ager, D. V. (1955), 'Summer field meeting in Italy', *Proc. Geol. Ass.*, **66**, 329–352.

Desio, A., ed. (1973), *Geologia dell'Italia*, Union. Tipogr.-Edit.-Torinese, Turin, 1081 pp.

Kligfield, R. (1979), The Northern Apennines as a collisional orogen. *Amer. J. Sci.*, **279**, 676–91.

Migliorini, C. I. (1952), 'Composite wedges and orogenic landslips in the Apennines', 18th Internat. Geol. Congr., Lond., pp. 186–198.

Squyres, C. H., ed. (1975), *Geology of Italy*, 2 vols, Earth Sci. Soc. Libyan Arab Repub. 402 and 392 pp.

Section 16(d)   Southern Alps

Aubouin, J. (1964), 'Essai sur la paléogéographie post-triassique et l'évolution sécondaire et tertiare du versant sud des Alpes orientales', *Bull. Soc. Géol. Fr.*, **5**, 730–766.

Dal Piaz, G. V., J. von Raumer, F. P. Sassi, B. Zanettin and A. Zanferrari (1975), 'Geological outline of the Italian Alps', in C. H. Squyres (ed.), *Geology of Italy*, Earth Sci. Soc. Libyan Arab Repub., pp. 229–375.

Gwinner, M. P. (1971), *Geologie der Alpen*, Schweizerbart Verlag., Stuttgart, 477 pp.

Leonardi, P. (1968), *Le Dolomiti. Geologie dei monti tra Isarco e Piave*, 2 vols + atlas, Manfrini, Rovereto, 1019 pp.

Trumpy, R. (1976), 'Du Pèlerin aux Pyrénées', *Eclog. Geol. Helvet.*, **69**, 249–264.

Section 16(e)   Dinarides

Aubouin, J. (1960), 'Essai sur l'ensemble italo-dinarique et ses rapports avec l'arc alpin', *Bull. Soc. Géol. Fr.*, **2**, 487–526.

Aubouin, J. (1973), 'Des tectoniques superposées et de leur signification par rapport aux modèles géophysiques: l'exemple des Dinarides; paléotcctonique, tectonique, tarditectonique, néotectonique', *Bull. Soc. Géol. Fr.*, **15**, 426–460.

Aubouin, J., R. Blanchet, J. C. Cadet, P. Celet, J. Charvet, J. Chorowicz, M. Cousin and J. P. Rampnoux (1970), 'Essai sur la géologie des Dinarides', *Bull. Soc. Géol. Fr.*, **12**, 1060–1095.

Celet, P. (1977), 'The Dinaric and Aegean Arcs: the geology of the Adriatic', in A. E. M. Nairn *et al.* (eds), *The Ocean Basins and Margins*, vol. 4A, Plenum Press, New York, pp. 215–261.

Ćirić, B. (1963), 'Le developpement des Dinarides yougoslaves pendant le cycle alpin', in *Mém. h.s. Soc. Géol. Fr., Liv. Mém. P. Fallot*, **2**, 565–582.

Lowell, J. D. (1962), 'Tectonic framework of Yugoslavia', Petrol. Explor. Soc. Libya, Ann. Field Conf., pp. 27–33.

Rampnoux, J. P. (1970), 'Regard sur les Dinarides internes yougoslaves (Serbia Meridionale et Monténégro oriental): stratigraphie, evolution paléogéographique et magmatique', *Bull. Soc. Géol. Fr.*, **12**(7), 948–966.

Roksandíc, M. M. (1966), 'Structures profondes et superficielles des Dinarides externes et de l'Adriatique', *Vesnik Zav. Geol. Geofiz, Istraživanja, Beograd, Ser. C*, 7.

Section 16(f) Hellenides

Aubouin, J., M. Bonneau and 15 other authors (1970), 'Contribution à la géologie des Hellénides: le Gavrovo, le Pinde et la zone ophiolitique subpélagonienne', *Ann. Soc. Géol. Nord*, **90**, 277–306.

Aubouin, J., M. Bonneau *et al.* (1976), 'Esquisse struturale de l'arc Égéen externe: des Dinarides aux Taurides', *Bull. Géol. Soc. Fr.*, **18**, 327–336.

Aubouin, J., J. H. Brunn, P. Celet, J. Dercourt, I. Godfriaux and J. Mercier (1963), 'Esquisse de la géologie de la Grèce', in M. Durand-Delga (ed.), *Liv. Mém. P. Fallot*, vol. 2, pp. 583–610.

Aubouin, J. and I. Ndojaj (1964), 'Regard sur la géologie de l'Albanie et sa place dans la géologie des Dinarides', *Bull. Soc. Géol. Fr.*, Ser. 7, **6**, 393–625.

Brunn, J. H. (1960), 'Les zones helléniques internes et leur extension. Réflexions sur l'orogenèse alpine', *Bull. Soc. Géol. France*, Ser. 7, **2**, 470–486.

Brunn, J. H. and J. Mercier (1971), 'Esquisse de la structure et de l'évolution de la Grèce', in *Tectonique de l'Afrique, Sciences de la terre*, vol. 6, UNESCO, pp. 103–111.

Celet, P. (1977), 'The Dinaric and Aegean arcs: the geology of the Adriatic', in A. E. Nairn *et al.* (eds), *The Ocean Basins and Margins*, vol. 4A, Plenum Press, New York, pp. 215–261.

Dercourt, J. (1962), 'Contribution à l'étude geologique du Péloponese. Terminaison paléogéographique du haut-fond du Parnasse', *Bull. Soc. Géol. France*, Ser. 7, **4**, 340–356.

Norton, P., ed. (1975), *Guide to the Geology and Culture of Greece*, Petrol. Explor. Soc. Libya, 146 pp.

Renz, C. (1955), *Die vorneogene Stratigraphie der normalsedimentaren Formation, Griechenlands*, Inst. Geol. Subsurf. Res., Athens, 637 pp.

Smith, A. G. and E. M. Moores (1974), 'Hellenides', in A. M. Spencer (ed.), *Mesozoic and Cenozoic Orogenic Belts*. Spec. Publ. Geol. Soc. Lond., vol. 4, pp. 159–185.

Chapter Seventeen

General conclusions on Neo-Europa

The fact that Neo-Europa seems to be so much more complicated than all that has gone before arises partly because there is so much more of it in the more familiar (and more spectacular) areas of our continent and partly because its main events are closer to us in time.

So far as the early history of Neo-Europa is concerned, there is really little about which it is reasonable to generalize. We have hints of things happening here right back in Precambrian times. Thus there seems to have been a deep trough which acquired thick sediments in the West Carpathian area during the Proterozoic. This was evidently a continuation of the one that is so much better known at the surface in the Bohemian Massif. There was a similar Proterozoic trough in the Greater Caucasus. There is the possibility of a Cadomian orogeny in various parts of Neo-Europa, for example in the external massifs of the Western Alps, but there is a strong subjective element here. If geologists go around looking for a Cadomian orogeny (or any other orogeny for that matter) then assuredly they will find it. As Sir Edward Bailey once said: 'to see a thing you have to believe it to be possible'.

We are not on much firmer ground in the early Palaeozoic, although few have claimed a Caledonian orogeny in the Alpine ranges. Perhaps the best evidence is in the Pyrenees, where there is a marked contrast in sediment type and metamorphic grade between the Lower and Upper Palaeozoic—Silurian black slates are succeeded abruptly by Devonian carbonates. More convincing (without the confusion of metamorphism) is the situation in the High Atlas of Morocco, where a Lower Palaeozoic trough, at least, is obvious. Climb wearily up the Tizi n Tichka (*tizi* = pass) south of Marrakech, and you cannot but be impressed by the great thickness of Lower Palaeozoic argillaceous sediments. These contrast markedly with the thin, shelly, contemporaneous deposits of the Moroccan Meseta to the north. Here there was a definite, long Palaeozoic preamble to the Mesozoic trough of the High Atlas and to the Cainozoic crumpling that followed. However, these two examples are no sort of general truth about the Alpine ranges.

Moving up into the Upper Palaeozoic, things are much clearer and almost every Alpine range has evidence of a similarly oriented sedimentary trough meeting an orogenic fate in late Palaeozoic times. In a few cases the so-called 'Alpine' chain is directly superimposed on a Variscan massif and the gentle Tertiary folds parallel those of the Variscan orogeny. The obvious example from this part of the book is the Middle Atlas of Morocco, which are exactly comparable with the Celtiberics of the Iberian Massif. In the High Atlas, on the other hand, the Variscan structures of the Tichka Massif (mentioned above) are almost at right angles to the Alpine folding. This may merely reflect the proximity and continuing influence of the Atlantic line. On the other hand, there is clear evidence from the sedimentary record on the Moroccan Meseta that something was happening to the south during late Palaeozoic times.

In the Jura, which are here regarded as comparable in many respects with the High Atlas, the Variscan structures connecting the east side of the Massif Central with the Vosges are very nearly parallel with the folds that arose here in the Tertiary. We also know from boreholes that there was a deep trough full of Upper Palaeozoic sediment right under the centre of the range.

I am influenced by the Pyrenees, because this Tertiary mountain chain can be traced directly into the Palaeozoic mountain chain of Cantabria to the west and because of the line of Variscan-metamorphosed massifs along its axial zone. But I am told that this is no more than a coincidence because the two were only brought in line by the rotation of the Iberian Massif out of the Bay of Biscay. I must say that I prefer the observed fact to the imaginative theory, although this does not mean that I reject some form of independent movement of an Iberian microplate.

So far as the main Alpine ranges are concerned, to cite those that definitely had Palaeozoic antecedents would amount to making an almost complete list. It cannot be a coincidence for all of them. There seems to be very good evidence of late Palaeozoic troughs and orogenies preceding the Mesozoic and Cainozoic events in the Betic Cordillera, the Western Alps, the Eastern Alps, the Carpathians, the Balkan Mountains, the Dinarides, the Hellenides, and the Greater Caucasus. The record of places such as the Aar Massif in the Western Alps, the Vardar Zone in the Dinarides, and the island of Khios in the Hellenides leaves little room for doubt. I am struck particularly by the contrast in the late Palaeozoic record of the Tauern Window in the Eastern Alps with that of the Carnic Alps not very far away to the south, although one has to be careful here because of the possibility of considerable lateral movement along the Insubric Line in between. As a general rule one seems to pass out of a Variscan orogenic belt as one moves southwards in the Alps and the Carpathians.

The exact age of the Variscan movements in Neo-Europa is often difficult to determine, but there seems to have been a widespread mid-Westphalian Asturian phase, with the subsequent formation of intermontane limnic basins, filled with late Westphalian and thick Stephanian sediments. The later (Saalian) phase affected these in mid to late Permian times, but not with the same intensity.

Before leaving the Palaeozoic, I must re-emphasize the close affinities of the various parts of Neo-Europa in terms of stratigraphy and palaeontology. The contrasts mentioned earlier, using terms such as 'Hercynian' and 'Rhenish', are differences of facies rather than of any wide geographical separation. I would particularly emphasize the close similarities in sediments, faunas, and floras between the Maghreb in north-west Africa and what is conventionally thought of as Europe. This is true whether one is talking about Ordovician trilobites, Devonian limestones, or Carboniferous floras. The resemblances in the Mesozoic are even more striking. The essential point is that this part of Africa, whether or not it was attached to the rest of the African plate, was probably never very far from the Iberian peninsula and that in turn was probably never very far from the rest of Europe.

I have no objection to a Tethys Ocean opening eastwards as a wide, wet 'sphenochasm' back in Palaeozoic times, but I cannot accept the cruel dismemberment of my beloved continent and the scattering of its parts to the far corners of the earth, as postulated by some geophysicists. We must never forget the sober observations of field geology when sampling the intoxicating brew of semi-quantified science.

I cannot resist making the same point about the Mesozoic and Cainozoic history of Neo-Europa, where the theories sometimes seem to get almost out of hand. Clever men have related the whole complex evolution of the Alpine fold belts and the more stable masses between them to the opening of the Atlantic and the coming together of the European and African plates. I have no intention of disputing their main conclusions, but see little point in repeating here all the conflicting ideas about splittings and clashings. I do think, however, that sometimes they have allowed their enthusiasm for plate tectonic theory to divert their attention from the simple story of the rocks. I have heard perfectly ordinary spheroidally-weathering terrestrial basalts transformed into submarine pillow lavas; commonplace red sun-cracked mudstones have become deep-sea manganese deposits, and oceans have been postulated where dinosaurs could have wandered without getting their knees wet. My most important criticism is of the tendency to treat every outcrop of ancient rocks (i.e., pre-Mesozoic) as a separate microplate and to ignore the many 'inversions' we know to have occurred in geologically recent times.

Of the general pattern there seems to be no doubt. The tensional effects of Triassic times are obvious throughout western Europe and north-west Africa with graben controlling continental sedimentation and volcanicity. No doubt the North Atlantic was already appearing, if only as a line of weakness down which it would later split. At the same time the Tethyan wedge seems to have been opening at its eastern end as Africa rotated clockwise away from Europe. Fragments of Triassic ocean floor are sometimes claimed in the Caspian and southern Caucasus.

The Triassic Tethys is rather an elusive ocean. There is no doubt that there was a major seaway down in southern Europe in late Paleozoic times, with the Upper Carboniferous becoming marine as one moves south (e.g., in southern Portugal) and fragments of marine Permian scattered around the Mediterranean (e.g., in Sicily). Indeed a 'Palaeotethys' may have gone right back to the archaeocyathid limestones of the Cambrian (e.g., in Sardinia). But marine Trias is not particularly easy to find away from the great belt of shelf carbonates around the Adriatic. Usually all we see are the monotonous red beds and gypsum, with—at the most—just a smell of the peculiar 'Muschelkalk' sea. Recently, marine Trias has been recorded (but not described) in boreholes in northern Egypt. I would love to know what truly African marine Trias looks like, for it is vital to our interpretation of the Adriatic region.

Before the end of the Triassic Period, compression had already started at the eastern end of the European Tethys (Fig. 17.1). This produced the early Kimmerian folding as the first phase of the Alpine orogeny. Evidence is seen, for example, in the Crimea from which it takes its name. As a general rule, this phase is much more obvious in the Caucasus, in the Crimea and perhaps in the Balkan Mountains than farther west, although I have seen it well displayed in Hungary.

It was only a fleeting phase, since the main ophiolite belts of Neo-Europa are Jurassic

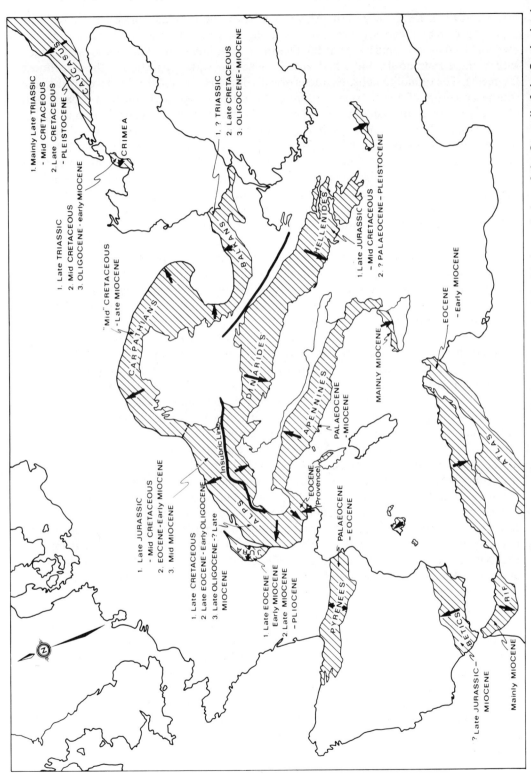

Fig. 17.1 Direction and age of the main Alpine movements in Europe (from Ager, 1975, by kind permission of the Council of the Geologists' Association).

in age and the general story in the Alps is of a 'revolution' in late Jurassic times with the beginning of major convergence. The ophiolite belts are often called 'oceans' in their own right; thus one finds a 'Vardar Ocean' in the literature. That these were major sutures there is no doubt, but I find little evidence for wide separation of the constituent fragments. The ophiolite belts, characteristically in pairs, are most fully developed in the south-east corner of our continent, running down from Yugoslavia through Albania into Greece and then on into Asiatic Turkey. There is also a major development in the Caucasus. It is my, perhaps naive, assumption that ocean-floor material is most obvious here simply because this region had the greatest amount of Mesozoic Tethys to be consumed as Africa and Europe converged. The allochthonous nature of most, if not all, of the ophiolites and accompanying trench sediments makes it difficult to reconstruct the jigsaw puzzle as it once was. Most of the published reconstructions are content to keep Greece, for example, as a single entity rather than split it along its sutures.

Farther west there is less doubt. The serpentinites and associated exotic rocks of the Apennines clearly came from west of the present peninsula, while those in the Pennine Zone of the Alps clearly came from the south and from the gap between Europe proper and a separate mini-continent which I will call the Adriatic Microplate. No fewer than twenty-one such microplates have been postulated for the Mediterranean area, with one for every place where Palaeozoic rocks happen to reach the present surface. I find this excessive and at variance with all the borehole and geophysical evidence of geologically recent inversions. Thus I see no justification for regarding the Middle Atlas as some kind of suture between the Moroccan and Oran mesetas, or for separating the Grande and Petite Kabylie in the Algerian Rif. It does not seem necessary to me to postulate more than four microplates in southern Europe. These are the Iberian Microplate, the Tyrrhenian Microplate, the Adriatic Microplate, and the Pannonian Microplate. Their main movements are shown in Fig. 17.2. It will be noted that the second is today largely under water and the last two are now essentially basins (which is why I prefer the term 'Adriatic' to the previously used 'Apulian'). This emphasizes my point that one must not be too much influenced by the bare patches in the carpet (like the Carnic Alps) when the trap-doors hidden under the carpet (like the Pannonian Basin) are far more important. It is also necessary to emphasize that, in my opinion, none of the movements, even that of Africa itself, was very great. Probably the most important was that of the Adriatic Microplate which sidled sideways along a suture now represented by (or paralleled by) parts of the Insubric Line and the Vardar Zone of Yugoslavia and Greece. It may be necessary to postulate a further Maghreb Microplate in north-west Africa, with a suture along the Agadir Line. One also has to account for the Crimean and Caucasian fold belts, presumably by a northerly or north-easterly movement of Turkey, but this must have happened earlier than the rest, prior to the spreading of the Black Sea.

The Apennines and associated ranges are easy to account for by the anticlockwise rotation of a Tyrrhenian microplate, of which Corsica and Sardinia are obvious remnants. The 'nut-crackers effect' at Gibraltar may be blamed on the direct confrontation of the two continents or on Africa (or a fragment thereof) meeting the Iberian Microplate. This latter is a very believable entity. Spain always seems to have gone its own way (in human as well as geological history) and the evidence for its anticlockwise rotation, and/or sideways slide, out of the Bay of Biscay is convincing. That this motion itself did not produce the Pyrenees is shown by the fact that the anomalies out in the Bay are

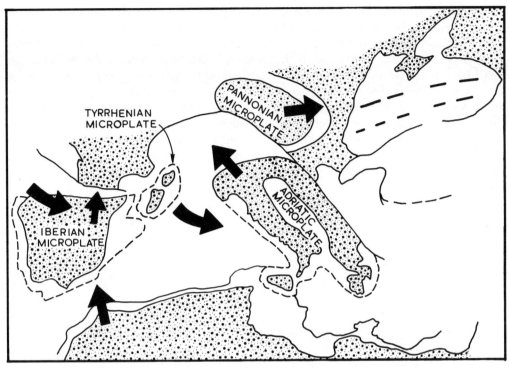

Fig. 17.2 *The main microplates of Neo-Europa, showing their principal directions of relative movement.*

earlier than late Cretaceous, while the main Pyrenean (and Provençal) folding was late Eocene. So the block rotated and *then* the gap closed as Africa advanced on a Europe that was itself turning in the same anticlockwise gyration. It is important to remember that late Eocene orogenesis is not peculiar to the Pyrenean belt. It was the main phase of the Alpine orogeny in the internal troughs of the northern Alps. It was also the main phase in the High Atlas mountains which are the counterpart of the Pyrenees on the opposite side of the western Tethys and could be the southern margin of a Maghreb Microplate. There are no signs of anything oceanic in the Mesozoic or Tertiary here, but the moment you cross the Agadir Line (e.g., south of Ouazazate) you are in a country of pillow lavas and suchlike, albeit much more ancient.

Important movements had happened long before this in the main Alpine ranges and these mostly seem to be related to the Adriatic Microplate. This is by far the most important of these elements. It interests me particularly as a Mesozoic palaeontologist because of the distinctiveness of its Triassic and Jurassic faunas. These were obvious long before the words 'plate tectonics' had passed anyone's lips, especially from the sessile benthos which are much more limited geographically than pelagic organisms such as the ammonites.

All round the Adriatic and particularly in carbonate facies there are shallow-water, benthonic faunas quite different from those of the rest of Europe. These are seen most clearly in the Apennines, the Southern Alps, the Dinarides, and the Hellenides, but they

523

also occur allochthonously in the Northern Calcareous Alps of Austria and in the central Mesozoic hills of Hungary. I am more impressed by this stratigraphical and palaeontological evidence than by any amount of structural evidence. Apart from distinctive formations such as the *Dachsteinkalk* and the *Hauptdolomit*, there are unmistakable fossils which leave their mark on this southern shelf. Lest it be thought that I am dominated by brachiopods, let me mention the giant megalodontid bivalves of the Upper Trias. These are very distinctive. They look superficially like hoofprints in the limestones,* and are a sure indication that we are standing on the Adriatic Microplate. Turkey only has the Triassic representatives of this distinctive fauna, which may be evidence of an earlier collision between a Turkish microplate and the southern edge of Eo-Europa. Farther west, the main collision seems to have started in mid Cretaceous times.

Some would have this great slab of southern facies as part of the African plate—a sort of battering-ram or prow of the ship of Africa as it sailed north and collided with Europe. I find this difficult to accept because none of these things—either the facies or the faunas—are known anywhere that can indisputably be called 'Africa', although there are 'Apulian' elements in the Betics and Rif. There *are* distinctive 'African' faunas, particularly in the Mesozoic seaway down the east side of that continent, but those fossils are not here and these fossils are not there!

The exact junction between the Adriatic Microplate and the main continent is not clear. One looks at the ophiolite zones of the Dinarides and Hellenides, but even today these are being subjected to fundamental reinterpretation. Thus recently it was suggested that the main suture in Greece was west and not east of Mount Olympos, and that the thrusting went in both directions from there. It is also clear that there was considerable lateral movement, for example along the Vardar Zone, which would fit in with the picture of the Adriatic Microplate sliding in a north-westerly direction to crumple up the Alps.

In the main part of the Alps there is no doubt that the Insubric Line, under various names, was the major suture between the north-facing and the south-facing structures. Carbonates of the southern type can be seen literally right up to the line in northern Italy. But the Northern Calcareous Alps are a great slab of shelf, not ocean floor material, carried far to the north. On geophysical and structural grounds the main closing is thought to have begun in the Cretaceous and I am pleased about this, because the distinctiveness of the Adriatic facies and faunas ends at that time. Thus the rudist limestones in the karst country of Yugoslavia are exactly like those in Sardinia and Spain. The ophiolites of the Piémont Zone and their continuation in Austria, together with the *schistes lustrés*, were already being folded in early Cretaceous times. Folding and thrusting continued to the end of that period. From 'mid' Cretaceous times onwards the troughs of flysch-type sedimentation moved progressively outwards from the intruding carbonate slab. The internal troughs of the central Alps suffered most at the end of Eocene times, when the Iberian Microplate was also converging on Europe.

Uplift then began and with it the initiation of molasse-type sedimentation. Compression at lower levels led to gravity-sliding by the higher units. The sliding, the folding, and

---

* They call them 'cow's footprints' (*Kuhspüren*) in Austria, while in the Italian Alps near Annunciata one is attributed to St. Martin's horse leaping a canyon in response to a challenge from the devil.

the sedimentation moved progressively outwards until, in mid to late Miocene times, the frontal ranges of the Alps and the Jura were pushed out over the molasse. In the Pliocene began the main process of uplift and erosion.

A special feature of the Adriatic Microplate is the so-called 'Peri-Adriatic Suite' of late acidic intrusions, such as that at Adamello in the Italian Alps. These turn up all round this separate and distinctive unit.

Exactly contemporaneous with the events in the Alps were those in the Carpathians. Geologists have always been fascinated by the splendid sweeping arc of the Carpathians and have sought to explain it in various ways. With the coming of plate tectonics it was inevitable that these new ideas would soon be applied to the range, but there have been considerable differences of opinion as to how it could be done.

The most popular explanation of the arc revolves around the idea of a Pannonian Microplate, as suggested in Fig. 17.2. This is seen in the northern Apuseni Mountains of Romania and is thought to have converged with the East European Platform in the north and the Moesian Platform in the south. Whether these last two were formerly joined is not clear and there may have been lateral movement of the smaller elements as within the Adriatic Microplate itself.

One can think of the Balkan Mountains of Bulgaria as the least disturbed part of the Alpine chain as a whole, still preserving a 'primitive' east–west orientation, while the Pannonian Microplate was jostled on by the Adriatic Microplate to produce the tremendous buckle of the Carpathians. However, the main ophiolites are on the south side of the Apuseni Mountains in Romania, which implies some relative movement in a north–south direction. At the same time it must be borne in mind that the convergence that produced the Carpathians was only the reversal of a comparatively recent opening between the main continent and a couple of broken-off fragments.

Once more it is the evocative word 'ocean' that causes the trouble. It immediately conjures up a picture of a vast, deep, watery realm of a sort that may not come into the picture at all. There is no evidence of oceanic crust in the Trias, and what appeared in the Jurassic was gone again in the convulsions of the 'mid' Cretaceous. During that fleeting oceanic episode there were probably two troughs (as in south-east Europe) separated by a slice of continent represented by the autochthonous rocks of the Eastern Carpathians.

The eastern trough closed first in mid Cretaceous times and the western trough was closed by the early Tertiary. It has been suggested that the considerably easterly and southerly sliding of the Carpathian nappes was the result of mantle diapirism on a massive scale in Transylvania, at the crossing point of major deep fractures. The idea of a fiery underworld pushing upwards towards the surface in the country of Count Dracula rather appeals to me, although it is rather difficult to associate it with the peaceful, lush pastures of Transylvania today.

Such uplift would fit in with the considerable evidence of gravity tectonics and huge olistostromes all round the Carpathians from Czechoslovakia to Yugoslavia. The movements finally ended by the mid Miocene, although Pleistocene sediments are folded in the area of the Ploeşti oilfields and seismic activity continues.

An important part of the story is the volcanic activity in the Carpathian and Pannonian Basin region. Apart from the basic, submarine volcanism of the troughs, there was a major episode of andesitic activity in the Apuseni Mountains and Southern Carpathians at the end of the Cretaceous and beginning of the Tertiary, following the main movements. This was clearly a 'hot spot' and fits into plate tectonic theory as does the later Tertiary volcanism in the same region, related to block-faulting.

What is not so easy to explain are the allochthonous masses in the centre of Hungary and the olistostrome of southern material in the eastern part of the Balkan Mountains. The former presumably came from the jostling of the microplates. The latter may be connected with the activities of the Rhodope Massif and perhaps of the massif that foundered under the Thracian Depression. There is no obvious source of 'southern' material here, however, and the early Jurassic faunas of the eastern Balkans are different from those of Turkey, which had already adopted a thoroughly 'European' appearance.

It is a curious feature of the geology of Neo-Europa that so many of the obvious basins were, until geologically recently, upstanding massifs. The Pannonian Basin is the outstanding example, but Thrace, the Adriatic, the Tyrrhenian Sea, and the Ebro Basin, are others and could have been added to the excessive number of microplates already postulated.

Finally there were the effects of the main opening of the Atlantic in Tertiary times and the continuing events in the eastern Mediterranean. The tensions and the volcanicity connected with the former have been referred to many times and I am struck by the fact that the influence of these seems to diminish as one moves eastwards across the continent. Also the east–west 'Mediterranean' fold belts terminate as one approaches the great ocean to the west. One can see this in the little anticlines of lowland Portugal and (most convincingly) in the elongated domes of the western High Atlas of Morocco. These turn to a more northerly trend within a short distance of the coast and on the narrow shelf. Most striking of all is the main Alpine fold belt itself, with the sudden reversal at Gibraltar between the Betic Cordillera and the Rif, emphasizing the point that this was a Mediterranean affair involving the coming together of Europe and Africa (which had never been far apart) and nothing to do with the upstart ocean to the west.

The young volcanicity at this end of Neo-Europa is often forgotten, but it is there along the Atlantic coast of Portugal and in western Morocco. It is also present on the extreme south coast of Spain (well do I remember that awful road up to the lighthouse, east of Almeria) and offshore in the island of Alboran (where yet another microplate has been postulated). The other young volcanicity is all associated with Atlantic tensions, as in the Variscan massifs discussed under Meso-Europa, or with the foundering of such massifs, as in the Pannonian Basin and the Tyrrhenian Sea. Although the Insubric Line became a mere dip-slip fault and then ceased altogether, it is interesting to note that this other edge of the Adriatic Microplate is still one of the most active lines in our continent.

Finally there is the volcanicity of the Aegean. This is a quite different matter, being a perfect volcanic arc within the Hellenic trench and Cretan island arc. This is where events are still happening in Europe—where the orogeny is continuing and where we must expect the next great events in the lively history of our continent. Santorini, in the centre of this volcanic arc, is a suitable place to end my book with a bang—for the explosive eruption here about 1450 B.C., which may have destroyed the first European civilization on Crete (some 60 km away), may also have been the loudest noise ever heard by man.

Selected references to Chapter 17

Ager, D. V. (1975), 'The geological evolution of Europe', *Proc. Geol. Assoc.*, **86**, 127–154.

Aubouin, J. (1976), 'Alpine tectonics and plate tectonics: thoughts about the eastern Mediterranean', in D. V. Ager and M. Brooks (eds.), *Europe from Crust to Core*, Wiley, London, pp. 143–158.

Biju-Duval, B., J. Dercourt and X. Le Pichon (1977), 'From the Tethys ocean to the Mediterranean seas: a plate tectonic model of the evolution of the western Alp system', in Biju-Duval, B. and L. Montadert (eds.), *Structural History of the Mediterranean Basins*, Editions Technip, Paris, pp. 143–164.

Bleahu, M. *et al.* (1973), 'Neogene Carpathian arc: a continental arc displaying the features of an "island arc"', *J. Geophys. Res.*, **78**, 5025–5032.

Bourbon, M. *et al.* (1977), 'Mesozoic evolution of the Western Alps: birth and development of the spreading oceanic Tethys and of its European continental margin', in B. Biju-Duval and L. Montadert (eds.), *Structural History of the Mediterranean Basins*, Editions Technip, Paris, pp. 19–34.

Channell, J. E. T., B. D'Argenio and F. Horváth (1979), 'Adria, the African promontory, in Mesozoic Mediterranean palaeogeography', *Earth Sci. Rev.*, **15**, 213–292.

Closs, H., D. Roeder and K. Schmidt (1978), 'Alps, Apennines, Hellenides: geodynamic investigations along geotraverses by an international group of geoscientists', *Inter-Union Commis. Geodynamics Sci. Rept No. 38*, Schweizerbart., 620 pp.

Contescu, L. R. (1974), 'Geologic history and paleogeography of eastern Carpathians: example of Alpine geosynclinal evolution', *Bull. Amer. Ass. Petrol Geol.*, **58**, 2436–2476.

Dewey, J. F. *et al.* (1973), 'Plate tectonics and the evolution of the alpine system', *Bull. Geol. Soc. Amer.*, **84**, 3137–3180.

Herz, N. and H. Savu (1974), 'Plate tectonics history of Romania', *Bull. Geol. Soc. Amer.*, **85**, 1429–1440.

Hsu, K. J. (1972), 'Alpine flysch in a Mediterranean setting', *24th Internat. Geol. Congr., Montreal*, sec. 6, pp. 67–64.

Lemoine, M., ed. (1978), *Geological Atlas of Alpine Europe and Adjacent Alpine Areas*, Elsevier, Amsterdam, 584 pp.

Rădulescu, D. P. and M. Săndulescu (1973), 'The plate-tectonics concept and the geological structure of the Carpathians', *Tectonophys.*, **16**, 155–161.

Trumpy, R. (1975), 'On crustal subduction in the Alps', in Mahel, M. (ed.), *Tectonic Problems of the Alpine System*, Veda, Bratislava, pp. 121–130.

Index

Author's note: Since this book concentrates on the geological history of the European continent, but omits most structural units, formation names and authors, this index only includes formal stratigraphical units, orogenic phases and major geographical regions (including those where comparisons are made with other continents). Some major categories (such as 'Palaeozoic') are used far too often to be usefully indexed.